Water Treatment
Plant Design

Other McGraw-Hill Reference Books of Interest

American Water Works Association • WATER QUALITY AND TREATMENT

Baumeister and Marks • MARKS' STANDARD HANDBOOK FOR MECHANICAL ENGINEERS

Brater and King • HANDBOOK OF HYDRAULICS

Considine • PROCESS INSTRUMENTS AND CONTROLS HANDBOOK

Corbitt • STANDARD HANDBOOK OF ENVIRONMENTAL ENGINEERING

Freeman • STANDARD HANDBOOK OF HAZARDOUS WASTE TREATMENT AND DISPOSAL

Gaylord and Gaylord • STRUCTURAL ENGINEERING HANDBOOK

Grigg • WATER RESOURCES PLANNING

Harris • HANDBOOK OF NOISE CONTROL

Hicks • STANDARD HANDBOOK OF ENGINEERING CALCULATIONS

Karassik, et al. • PUMP HANDBOOK

Merritt • BUILDING DESIGN AND CONSTRUCTION HANDBOOK

Merritt • STANDARD HANDBOOK FOR CIVIL ENGINEERS

Miller • FLOW MEASUREMENT ENGINEERING HANDBOOK

Nalco • THE NALCO WATER HANDBOOK

Perry and Green • PERRY'S CHEMICAL ENGINEERS' HANDBOOK

Rosa • WATER TREATMENT SPECIFICATION MANUAL

Rosaler and Rice • STANDARD HANDBOOK OF PLANT ENGINEERING

Schweitzer • HANDBOOK OF SEPARATION TECHNIQUES FOR CHEMICAL ENGINEERS

Shinskey • PROCESS CONTROL SYSTEMS

Shugar and Dean • THE CHEMIST'S READY REFERENCE HANDBOOK

For more information about other McGraw-Hill materials, call 1-800-2-MCGRAW in the United States. In other countries, call your nearest McGraw-Hill office.

Water Treatment Plant Design

Second Edition

American Society of Civil Engineers

American Water Works Association

McGraw-Hill Publishing Company

New York St. Louis San Francisco Auckland Bogotá
Caracas Hamburg Lisbon London Madrid Mexico
Milan Montreal New Delhi Oklahoma City
Paris San Juan São Paulo Singapore
Sydney Tokyo Toronto

Library of Congress Cataloging-in-Publication Data

Water treatment plant design / American Society of Civil Engineers,
 American Water Works Association.—2nd ed.
     p. cm.
   Includes bibliographical references.
   ISBN 0-07-001542-2
   1. Water treatment plants—Design and construction. I. American
Society of Civil Engineers. II. American Water Works Association.
TD434.W38 1990
628.1′62—dc20
                                                        89-14538
                                                          CIP

The first edition was published in 1969 by The American Water Works
Association, Inc.

  34567890 DOC/DOC   943210

ISBN 0-07-001542-2

The editors for this book were Harold B. Crawford and Gretlyn Cline,
the designer was Naomi Auerbach, and the production supervisor was
Richard A. Ausburn. It was set in Century Schoolbook. It was composed by the McGraw-Hill Publishing Company Professional and Reference Division composition unit.

Printed and bound by R. R. Donnelley & Sons Company.

For more information about other McGraw-Hill materials,
call 1-800-2-MCGRAW in the United States. In other
countries, call your nearest McGraw-Hill office.

Contents

Preface

Water Treatment Plant Design, originally published as a manual of engineering practice for the American Society of Civil Engineers (ASCE) in 1939, has been the authoritative reference on treatment plant design for engineers throughout the world. In 1969, the manual was changed to book form, and was updated to include a discussion of developments in pretreatment and filtration processes. That 1969 update was the result of a joint effort between ASCE, the American Water Works Association (AWWA), and the Conference of State Sanitary Engineers (CSSE).

Today the production of high-quality water is the common goal of all treatment plant operators. The emergence of strict new federal and state drinking-water regulations will further stress water treatment facilities to produce higher quality water. In order to assist engineers and others who are responsible for the design and construction of today's treatment plants and to keep up-to-date information available, the 1969 edition was updated to produce this edition of *Water Treatment Plant Design.*

This work is the result of a joint effort between AWWA and ASCE. The material for each chapter, which was prepared by one or more authors, was reviewed carefully by a joint committee of AWWA and ASCE members. Quite frequently, the final format was a compromise between the original author's concept of the subject and the reviewers' expertise. A distinct effort was made to present proven design concepts. Emphasis has been given to new developments in water treatment plant design to enable the reader to investigate these concepts.

The data presented in this book have been prepared as a guide to the qualified engineer and represent a consensus of opinion of recognized authorities in the field regarding the essential components of today's water treatment plants.

The original steering committee was responsible for developing the format, chapter content, author selection, and the details of coordinating the development of chapter drafts and reviews. This committee included representatives from the three sponsoring associations as follows:

AWWA   Carl L. Hamann, Chairman (CH2M Hill)
ASCE   J. David Griffith (John Carollo Engineers)
CSSE   Robert S. McCall (Kelley, Gidley, Blair & Wolfe)

Richard Panesi (technical editor) and George L. Craft (AWWA Engineering and Construction Division liaison) participated in steering committee meetings and decisions. Special thanks are due to this group for initiating and completing the first phase of the book revision project.

Because the preparation of this book was a group effort, the authors of individual chapters are not identified. Those who contibuted to the preparation of the text as authors, editors, or reviewers are:

Glen H. Abplanalp   *Havens & Emerson, Inc., Saddle Brook, N.J.*
E. Marco Aieta   *J. M. Montgomery Engineers, Pasadena, Calif.*
Bevin Beaudet   *Palm Beach County Water Utilities Department, West Palm Beach, Fla.*
Henry H. Benjes   *Black & Veatch Consulting Engineers, Kansas City, Mo.*
Henry H. Benjes, Jr.   *HDR, Inc., Dallas, Tex.*
Charles A. Buescher   *St. Louis County Water Company, St. Louis, Mo.*
Noel S. Chamberlin (deceased)
Holly A. Cornell   *CH2M Hill, Corvallis, Oreg.*
Michael D. Cummins   *U.S. Environmental Protection Agency, Cincinnati, Ohio*
David W. Ferguson   *Metropolitan Water District of Southern California, La Verne, Calif.*
Harold D. Gilman   *Greeley & Hanson Engineers, Philadelphia, Pa.*
J. David Griffith   *John Carollo Engineers, Phoenix, Ariz.*
Carl L. Hamann   *CH2M Hill, Denver, Colo.*
Paul D. Haney   *Black & Veatch Engineers, Kansas City, Mo.*
Gordon L. Johnson   *J. M. Montgomery Engineers, Pasadena, Calif.*
Stuart W. Krasner   *Metropolitan Water District of Southern California, La Verne, Calif.*
Harold Lacey   *City of Winnipeg, Manitoba, Canada*
John Leak   *Greeley & Hanson Engineers, Philadelphia, Pa.*
O. Thomas Love   *U.S. Environmental Protection Agency, Dallas, Tex.*
Richard Panesi (retired)
Paul W. Prendiville   *Camp, Dresser & McKee, Boston, Mass.*
Margaret Reh   *Greeley & Hanson Engineers, Philadelphia, Pa.*
John H. Robinson   *Black & Veatch Engineers, Kansas City, Mo.*
J. Edward Singley   *J. M. Montgomery Engineers, Gainesville, Fla.*
John E. Spitko, Jr.   *PSC Environmental Services, Maple Glen, Pa.*
Brian G. Stone   *J. M. Montgomery Engineers, Pasadena, Calif.*

L. Gene Suhr   *CH2M Hill, Corvallis, Oreg.*
Cliff Thompson   *CH2M Hill, Montgomery, Ala.*
R. Rhodes Trussell   *J. M. Montgomery Engineers, Pasadena, Calif.*
J. D. Walker (deceased)
William Wheeler   *Clinton Bogert Associates, Ft. Lee, N.J.*

Special thanks are extended to Paul D. Haney who served as technical editor during the time the original draft chapters were being reviewed and revised.

To complete the book update, a joint task force was formed by AWWA and ASCE. The co-chairs were Carl L. Hamann (AWWA) and Harold T. Glaser (ASCE), J. M. Montgomery Engineers, Pasadena, Calif. The task-force effort to complete the book was a joint effort of three firms working closely to finish the revision process. The three firms were CH2M Hill, J. M. Montgomery Engineers, and Black & Veatch Consulting Engineers. The efforts of all of the team from the three firms are appreciated. The principal contributors from these firms were:

CH2M Hill
    Donald Calkins
    Robert L. Chapman
    Donald P. Gallo
    Carl L. Hamann
    Anthony G. Myers
J. M. Montgomery Engineers
    E. Marco Aieta
    Bruce Chow
    Harold T. Glaser
    Susumu Kawamura
    Donald L. Speigel
    Carol H. Tate
    R. Rhodes Trussell
Black & Veatch Consulting Engineers
    Leland L. Harms
    Douglas Kobrick
    John Stukenberg

Mary Kay Kozyra and George L. Craft deserve special thanks from the AWWA staff for their efforts on behalf of the committee and the joint task force.

Water Quality Standards and Treatment Objectives

Introduction

Records of people's desire to improve water quality date back to as early as 2000 B.C.[1] Since that time, advances in water treatment have continuously been made. Water quality standards have been developed and revised based on changing water supply conditions, and on advancing technology in treatment and chemical analysis.

Three basic objectives of water treatment are:

Production of water that is safe for human consumption

Production of water that is appealing to the consumer

Production of water using facilities which can be constructed and operated at a reasonable cost

The production of biologically and chemically safe water is the primary goal in the design of water treatment plants; anything less is unacceptable. A properly designed plant is not a guarantee of safety, however. Skillful and alert plant operation and attention to the sanitary requirements of the source of supply and the distribution system are equally important.

The second basic objective of water treatment is the production of water that is appealing to the consumer. Ideally, an appealing water is one that is clear and colorless, pleasant to the taste, odorless, and cool. It is nonstaining, neither corrosive nor scale forming, and reasonably soft. These characteristics are defined in more specific water quality terms later in this chapter.

The consumer is principally interested in the quality of water delivered to the tap, not the quality at the treatment plant. Therefore, water utility operations should be such that quality is not impaired as water flows from the treatment plant through the distribution system to the consumer. Storage and distribution systems should be designed and operated to prevent biological growths, corrosion, and contamination by cross-connections. In the design and operation of both treatment plant and distribution system, the control point for the determination of water quality should be the consumer's tap.

The third basic objective of water treatment is that it be accomplished using facilities with reasonable capital and operating costs. Various alternatives in plant design should be evaluated for cost-effectiveness and water quality produced. Alternatives developed should be based upon sound engineering principles and under consideration of flexibility for changing future conditions, emergency situations, operating personnel capabilities, and future expansion.

EPA Drinking-Water Standards

In the design and operation of water treatment facilities, it is necessary to express water treatment objectives in more precise terms of water quality standards. One source of water quality standards is the U.S. Environmental Protection Agency (EPA) as a result of the Safe Drinking Water Act of 1974 and subsequent amendments.

The Safe Drinking Water Act charged the EPA with the responsibility for developing drinking-water regulations to protect the public health.[2] In 1975, the EPA published the Interim Primary Drinking Water Regulations,[3] which were made effective June 24, 1977. The primary regulations have since been amended, with changes published November 29, 1979;[4] March 5, 1982;[5] and June 19, 1986.[10] In addition, Secondary Drinking Water Regulations[6] concerning contaminants not covered in the primary regulations were promulgated in July 1979. The secondary regulations became effective January 19, 1981.

The primary regulations are concerned with contaminants which have a direct effect on the public health. They are federally enforceable. The secondary regulations are concerned with those contaminants which affect the aesthetic qualities of drinking water. They are intended as guidelines, and are not federally enforceable.

Significant changes were outlined in the 1986 Amendments to the Safe Drinking Water Act. Major aspects of these amendments include:

The EPA is to set maximum contaminant level goals (MCLGs) and maximum contaminant levels (MCLs) for 83 specific contaminants and for any other contaminant in drinking water which may have any adverse effect upon the health of persons and which is known or anticipated to occur in public water systems.

The 83 contaminants are shown in Table 1.1 (seven substitutes are allowed).

Best available technology (BAT) and monitoring requirements are to be set for the 83 contaminants. Granular activated carbon is identified as BAT for synthetic organic chemicals (SOCs).

There is a filtration requirement for surface-water supplies, with certain exceptions.

Disinfection of all water supplies is required.

Regulation of disinfection by-products is provided.

The use of lead products in all conveyances for drinking water is prohibited.

Groundwater source protection through wellhead protection regulations is required.

The EPA has a phased approach for regulating contaminants. MCLs and MCLGs for organic substances [volatile organic chemicals (VOCs and SOCs)] are to be established first, followed by those for inorganic and microbial contaminants, radionuclides, and disinfection by-products.

Other Water Quality Criteria

World Health Organization

The International Standards were first published by the World Health Organization (WHO) in 1958; a second edition was published in 1963. The current edition was issued in 1984.[11] These standards are intended to supersede both the European Standards for Drinking Water[12] and the International Standards for Drinking Water.[13] In addition to establishing bacteriological, chemical, physical, biological, and radiological requirements for drinking water, the WHO Standards also include standards of quality for water sources and approved methods for examination of water. The criteria for these standards appear to be somewhat more lenient than those for current U.S. standards. The World Health Organization standards are shown in Table 1.2.

European standards

In December 1978, the European Community reached a general agreement on a directive for drinking-water standards.[7] The objective of these standards is to establish limits for physicochemical factors,

TABLE 1.1   Contaminants Required to Be Regulated under the SDWA Amendments of 1986

Volatile Organic Chemicals	
Trichloroethylene	Benzene
Tetrachloroethylene	Chlorobenzene
Carbon tetrachloride	Dichlorobenzene
1,1,1-Trichloroethane	Trichlorobenzene
1,2-Dichloroethane	1,1-Dichloroethylene
Vinyl chloride	*trans*-1,2-Dichloroethylene
Methylene chloride	*cis*-1,2-Dichloroethylene

Microbiology and Turbidity	
Total coliforms	Viruses
Turbidity	Standard plate count
Giardia lamblia	*Legionella*

Inorganics	
Arsenic	Molybdenum
Barium	Asbestos
Cadmium	Sulfate
Chromium	Copper
Lead	Vanadium
Mercury	Sodium
Nitrate	Nickel
Selenium	Zinc
Silver	Thallium
Fluoride	Beryllium
Aluminum	Cyanide
Antimony	

Organics	
Endrin	1,1,2-Trichloroethane
Lindane	Vydate
Methoxychlor	Simazine
Toxaphene	PAHs
2,4-D	PCBs
2,4,5-TP	Atrazine
Aldicarb	Phthalates
Chlordane	Acrylamide
Dalapon	Dibromochloropropane (DBCP)
Diquat	1,2-Dichloropropane
Endothall	Pentachlorophenol
Glyphosate	Pichloram
Carbofuran	Dinoseb
Alachlor	Ethylene dibromide (EDB)
Epichlorohydrin	Dibromomethane
Toluene	Xylene
Adipates	Hexachlorocyclopentadiene
2,3,7,8-TCDD (Dioxin)	

Radionuclides	
Radium 226 and 228	Gross alpha-particle activity
Beta-particle and photon radioactivity	Radon
Uranium	

TABLE 1.2 WHO Standards

Organism, constituent, or characteristic	Unit	Guideline value	Remarks
Microbiological and Biological Quality			
I. Microbiological quality			
A. Piped water supplies			
A.1 Treated water entering the distribution system			
Fecal coliforms	Number/100 mL	0	Turbidity <1 NTU; for disinfection with chlorine, pH preferably <8.0; free chlorine residual 0.2 to 0.5 mg/L following 30 min (minimum) contact
Coliform organisms	Number/100 mL	0	
A.2 Untreated water entering the distribution system			
Fecal coliforms	Number/100 mL	0	In 98 percent of samples examined throughout the year—in the case of large supplies when sufficient samples are examined
Coliform organisms	Number/100 mL	0	
Coliform organisms	Number/100 mL	3	In an occasional sample, but not in consecutive samples
A.3 Water in the distribution system			
Fecal coliforms	Number/100 mL	0	In 95 percent of samples examined throughout the year—in the case of large supplies when sufficient samples are examined
Coliform organisms	Number/100 mL	0	
Coliform organisms	Number/100 mL	3	In an occasional sample, but not in consecutive samples
B. Unpiped water supplies			
Fecal coliforms	Number/100 mL	0	

TABLE 1.2 WHO Standards (Continued)

Organism, constituent, or characteristic	Unit	Guideline value	Remarks
Microbiological and Biological Quality			
Coliform organisms	Number/100 mL	10	Should not occur repeatedly; if occurrence is frequent and sanitary protection cannot be improved, an alternative source must be found if possible
C. Bottled drinking water			
Fecal coliforms	Number/100 mL	0	Source should be free from fecal contamination
D. Emergency water supplies			
Fecal coliforms	Number/100 mL	0	Advise public to boil water in case of failure to meet guideline values
Coliform organisms	Number/100 mL	0	
Enteroviruses	—	No guideline value set	
II. Biological Quality			
Protozoa (pathogenic)	—	No guideline value set	
Helminths (pathogenic)	—	No guideline value set	
Free-living organisms (algae, others)	—	No guideline value set	
Inorganic Constituents of Health Significance			
Arsenic	mg/L	0.05	
Asbestos	—	No guideline value set	
Barium	—	No guideline value set	
Beryllium	—	No guideline value set	

Substance	Unit	Guideline value	Remarks
Cadmium	mg/L	0.005	
Chromium	mg/L	0.05	
Cyanide	mg/L	0.1	
Fluoride	mg/L	1.5	Natural or deliberately added; local or climatic conditions may necessitate adaptation
Hardness	—	No health-related guideline value set	
Lead	mg/L	0.05	
Mercury	mg/L	0.001	
Nickel	—	No guideline value set	
Nitrate	mg/L (N)	10	
Nitrite	—	No guideline value set	
Selenium	mg/L	0.01	
Silver	—	No guideline value set	
Sodium	—	No guideline value set	
Aldrin and dieldrin	µg/L	0.03	
Benzene	µg/L	10*	
Benzo(a)pyrene	µg/L	0.01*	
Carbon tetrachloride	µg/L	3*	Tentative guideline value[†]
Chlordane	µg/L	0.3	
Chlorobenzenes	µg/L	No health-related guideline value set	Odor threshold concentration between 0.1 and 3 µg/L
Chloroform	µg/L	30*	Disinfection efficiency must not be compromised when controlling chloroform content

TABLE 1.2 WHO Standards (Continued)

Organism, constituent, or characteristic	Unit	Guideline value	Remarks
Inorganic Constituents of Health Significance			
Chlorophenols	µg/L	No health-related guideline value set	Odor threshold concentration 0.1 µg/L
2,4-D	µg/L	100*	
DDT	µg/L	1	
1,2-Dichloroethane	µg/L	10*	
1,1-Dichloroethane§	µg/L		
Heptachlor and heptachlor epoxide	µg/L	0.1	
Hexachlorobenzene	µg/L	0.01*	
Gamma-HCH (Lindane)	µg/L	3	
Methoxychlor	µg/L	30	
Pentachlorophenol	µg/L	10	
Tetrachloroethene§	µg/L	10*	Tentative guideline value†
Trichloroethene§	µg/L	30*	Tentative guideline value†
2,4,6-Trichlorophenol	µg/L	10*,‡	Odor threshold concentration, 0.1 µg/L
Trihalomethanes		No guideline value set	See chloroform
Esthetic Quality			
Aluminum	mg/L	0.2	
Chloride	mg/L	250	
Chlorobenzenes and chlorophenols	—	No guideline value set	These compounds may affect taste and odor
Color	True color units (TCU)	15	
Copper	mg/L	1.0	
Detergents	—	No guideline value set	There should not be any foaming or taste and odor problems
Hardness	mg/L (as CaCO3)	500	

	Unit	Guideline value	Remarks
Esthetic Quality			
Hydrogen sulfide	—	Not detectable by consumers	
Iron	mg/L	0.3	
Manganese	mg/L	0.1	
Oxygen—dissolved	—		
pH	—	6.5–8.5	
Sodium	mg/L	200	
Solids—total dissolved	mg/L	1000	
Sulfate	mg/L	400	
Taste and odor	—	Inoffensive to most consumers	
Temperature	—	No guideline value set	
Turbidity	Nephelometric turbidity units (NTU)	5	Preferably <1 for disinfection efficiency
Zinc	mg/L	5.0	
Radioactive Constituents			
Gross alpha activity	Bq/L	0.1	
Gross beta activity	Bq/L	1	(a) If the levels are exceeded, more detailed radionuclide analysis may be necessary. (b) Higher levels do not necessarily imply that the water is unsuitable for human consumption.

*These guideline values were computed from a conservative hypothetical mathematical model which cannot be experimentally verified and values should therefore be interpreted differently. Uncertainties involved may amount to two orders of magnitude (i.e., from 0.1 to 10 times the number).

†When the available carcinogenicity data did not support a guideline value, but the compounds were judged to be of importance in drinking water and guidance was considered essential, a tentative guideline value was set on the basis of the available health-related data.

‡May be detectable by taste and odor at lower concentrations.

§These compounds were previously known as 1,1-dichloroethylene, tetrachloroethylene, and trichloroethylene, respectively.

organoleptic factors, undesirable factors, toxic factors, and microbiological factors.

AWWA water quality goals

AWWA adopted a Policy Statement on Quality Goals for Potable Water on January 28, 1968.[8] These goals were established to enable water utilities to evaluate their own finished water. They were substantially more exacting than the then-current Public Health Service Standards[9] with respect to aesthetic qualities but were generally considered to be attainable by correct application of known treatment processes and methods. These goals are currently under review and revision.

The AWWA water quality goals should be considered as water quality characteristics worthy of achievement in plant design and operation.

Design Philosophy

Water treatment plants should be designed so that water quality objectives can be met with reasonable ease and cost. Pilot-plant tests are valuable for new plants, and full-scale tests may be performed on existing plants. The design of water plants should incorporate flexibility for dealing with seasonal changes in water quality and with future drinking-water regulations.

Water quality should be evaluated at the point of consumer use, and maintenance of quality should be considered in the design and operation of both treatment plant and distribution system.

The engineer should consider federal requirements concerning protection of the environment, with regard to discharges from the treatment plant into streams in determining what preliminary studies and reports are needed.

Water quality criteria based on current mandatory standards, and professional guides are presented here to assist in the establishment of performance goals for any treatment plant. These criteria may change the current and future design practices, and new public health hazards associated with drinking water may be disclosed. The trend is toward production of water of higher quality, as evidenced by both federal primary and secondary regulations and AWWA quality goals for potable water. The quality of some water sources can be expected to improve as pollution control measures now in effect are fully implemented. However, it is certain that other sources will be degraded as population and industrialization increase. This will require more source water quality monitoring and more complex processes for water treatment. Proper water treatment plant design and operation is essential to the production of water of the highest quality.

References

1. M. N. Baker, *The Quest for Pure Water,* American Water Works Association, Inc., New York, 1949.
2. *The Safe Drinking Water Act of 1974,* Public Law No. 523, 93rd Congress, Dec. 16, 1974.
3. U.S. Environmental Protection Agency, "National Interim Primary Drinking Water Regulations," *Federal Register,* vol. 40, Dec. 14, 1975.
4. U.S. Environmental Protection Agency, "Amendments to National Interim Primary Drinking Water Regulations: Control of Trihalomethanes in Drinking Water," *Federal Register,* vol. 44, Nov. 29, 1979.
5. U.S. Environmental Protection Agency, "Proposed Amendments to the National Interim Primary Drinking Water Regulations: Trihalomethanes," *Federal Register,* vol. 47, March 5, 1982.
6. U.S. Environmental Protection Agency, "National Secondary Drinking Water Regulations," *Federal Register,* vol. 42, March 31, 1977.
7. P. L. Knoppert, "European Communities' Drinking Water Standards: Corporation, Implementation and Comments," *Proc. 1980 Annual AWWA Conf.,* Atlanta, Ga., June 1980.
8. Policy Statement by the AWWA (adopted by the Board of Directors Jan. 28, 1968).
9. *Drinking Water Standards,* U.S. Public Health Service Pub. no. 956, U.S. Government Printing Office, Washington, D.C., 1962.
10. U.S. Environmental Protection Agency, "Safe Drinking Water Act Amendments of 1986," *Federal Register,* vol. 42, June 19, 1986.
11. *Guidelines for Drinking Water Quality,* vol. 1, World Health Organization, Geneva, 1984.
12. *European Standards for Drinking Water,* 2d ed., World Health Organization, Geneva, 1970.
13. *International Standards for Drinking Water,* 3d ed., World Health Organization, Geneva, 1971.

2

Design of Treatment Facilities

Introduction

This chapter is devoted to the general considerations involved in the design of new treatment facilities and the upgrading of existing facilities. Existing facilities may be upgraded for capacity, water quality, or both. Discussions center on design standards, plant siting and layout, water quality parameters, operational concepts, and constructibility.

The upgrading of an existing plant is a challenge to the designer. Many times existing process basins can be used to house updated treatment technology; for example, trays, tubes, and/or plates can be installed in existing sedimentation basins to increase the efficiency of sedimentation and allow for increased capacity. At the same time, filter media can be replaced with dual media or granular activated carbon, both allowing more flow to be put through the filters and providing improved water quality.

In new installations it is important to provide hydraulic capacity for future capacity increases and to provide both room on the site and hydraulic head for future processes.

Design Standards

Drinking-water standards are discussed in Chap. 1. There are, in addition to quality standards, design standards published by state and federal government, and these must be adhered to when designing water treatment facilities. Traditionally, states have published design standards for the different processes, such as mixing, flocculation, sedimentation, and filtration. These standards, in many cases, have come down from traditional conservative practice and must be recognized. Many states, however, are willing to listen to arguments for, and to accept, less conservative and more cost-effective treatment design parameters, if one can show results from pilot tests or from full-scale treatment. It is important that recommended criteria be discussed with approving agencies early in the design period.

Other standards, such as building, electrical, fire, and plumbing codes and applicable ordinances, as well as OSHA safety standards, must be adhered to. In addition, large municipalities, districts, and private agencies have developed design standards over the years, and these must also be taken into account. Like state standards, many of these can be discussed in the beginning, and with experience and back-up, a consultant can convince an authority to modify some standards. However, more often than not, the standards and criteria arrived at by large authorities are the result of years of experience, and a consultant can do well to pay attention to such experience.

Plant Siting

The selection of the purest drinking-water source available should be the first priority. A clear upland supply is preferable to a river that receives discharges from industry, agriculture, and municipalities. The source, the treatment plant, and the distribution system should be thought of as a system. The better the source, the less stress will be put on the rest of the system. And once the supply is chosen, its protection should be a priority.

Availability of land, cost of the land, and taxes that will be incurred on land and plant often dictate where a plant will be located once the supply is identified. In many cases, a treatment facility can be at the point of supply, and where possible raw water can gravitate to the plant from the reservoir or the river. More often, however, low-lift pumping is required to lift the raw water to the treatment site.

A treatment plant site close to power and sewerage is ideal. If two independent sources of public power are available, standby power facilities at the plant can be kept to a minimum. If a large intercepting sewer is close by, waste solids from the processes can be sent to the wastewater treatment plant. Needless to say, the impact on the environment should be of utmost concern in the siting of the facility.

Vehicular access to the site is important. One must consider two types of traffic: automobiles driven by staff and visitors, and trailer trucks that deliver chemicals and utilities. It used to be popular to locate treatment plants beside railroads, but with the increased popularity of trucking, this is not generally a priority.

Where a treatment plant can be located so that the raw water can gravitate to the treatment plant, this is ideal. Usually up to 15 ft energy head is required to push the water through traditional treatment processes (pretreatment and filtration). Where ozone contact chambers and granular activated carbon are to be provided, additional head is required; 20 ft is probably not unusual. The finished water is then gravitated to distribution storage or, where the topography requires it, lifted to that storage.

The treatment process should be located above high groundwater, but when this is not practical, the structures must be prevented from floating by providing extra concrete, or by providing positive underdrainage of the structures. In addition, the ground floor of all buildings must be located above high flood levels, and equipment and drives must be protected from flooding.

The geologic condition of the site should be established by a geotechnical investigation. Borings and test pits are driven and opened to establish the underground soil and rock strata. This information is vital to the establishment of the bearing capacity of the soils, to the establishment of rock elevations, and to the monitoring of groundwater levels.

Climatic conditions at the site are established for the purpose of locating structures, plantings, and process units. Wind patterns help in locating facilities such as sludge drying beds.

Water Quality Parameters

A study of records determines long-term historical water quality trends. Some parameters of concern are:

1. Inorganic chemicals of public health concern, for example, aluminum and asbestos. The corrosivity of the water is important.
2. Inorganic chemicals of esthetic concern, for example, iron and manganese.
3. Organic chemicals—trihalomethanes, other volatile organic compounds, and synthetic organic compounds, important to the public's health. However, just as important to us are organics that can cause tastes and odors which make the waters not suitable for drinking and bathing.
4. Microbiological—bacteria, virus, protozoa.
5. Radiological.
6. Turbidity and particle counts—an indicator of impurities in the water which serve as protective shelters for organic matter, heavy metals, and microbes.

After examination of the water quality data, a discussion with operators, and a plot of the seasonal and yearly variations, the concentrations of the parameters of concern can be determined. Personal computer software is employed for graphing the historical water quality trends. The plots can be analyzed, and statistical studies of the trends are used to project future water quality. In addition, it is often desirable to incorporate a new quality monitoring program to augment existing records and to provide a complete picture of the parameters of importance, including organics and microbiological constituents.

One should then set the water quality objectives with the owner, in concert with all regulating authorities. It is desirable to put the objectives on paper so that all parties can agree on both public health issues and esthetic parameters, for the initial design period and for future planning.

One should then, together with the owner and regulating authorities, determine the need for bench and pilot-scale studies. If the raw water is similar to others that one has treated, and if traditional treatment devices are being used, then testing may not be needed. More often, however, with the need to pay more attention to organics and with the desirability of using cost-effective treatment procedures like ozone/direct filtration and granular activated carbon, testing is not only desirable but necessary.

Bench and pilot-scale tests are conducted to:

1. Determine the suitability of certain treatment processes
2. Determine basic design criteria for the full-scale water purification plant, that is, chemical reagent dosages and mixing and flocculation needs as well as appropriate filter rates and contact times

The bench- and pilot-test programs are usually conducted for three periods during a calendar year in order to capture seasonal changes in water quality, such as the temperature of the water, the presence of organic matter and algae, and changes in color, turbidity, tastes and odors, and total organic matter.

In addition to bench and pilot-scale studies, visits to installations and brainstorming sessions will assist in the selection of treatment processes. The results of the bench and pilot-scale tests, experience with similar water, and the brainstorming sessions help in selecting a cost-effective process train that will meet the finished water quality objectives.

The processes available for forming the process train are discussed in detail in other chapters of this text. Suffice it to say here that the treatment of ground and surface water takes many forms. For groundwater contaminated with volatile organics, one should consider air stripping and/or granular activated carbon adsorption. For water with a minimum of contamination, but requiring disinfection, coagulation, and filtration for removal and deactivation of bacteria, virus, and protozoa, one should consider in-line or direct filtration with chemical disinfection. For water high in turbidity and color, consider conventional treatment with chemical disinfection (for hard water, softening processes would be added). And finally, for water that is heavily burdened with organic matter, complete treatment is needed (for heavily mineralized water, demineralization processes would be added).

Alternative pretreatment oxidants can be used to replace chlorine. Ozone and chlorine dioxide are more powerful disinfectants than chlorine, and they do not form trihalomethanes. Following pretreatment and the removal of as much organic matter as possible in the water purification plant, chlorine or chloramines are added for residual disinfection of the water mains.

Even though complete treatment may not be required in many cases at the time of design, the site should be planned for future upgrading. For example, for any new direct or conventional treatment plant, it is wise to provide for the future addition of granular activated carbon reactors. Additionally, site planning can include space for facilities needed for future process expansions.

Plant Capacity

Present and future water consumption is dependent on (1) the population served by the system, (2) water use by residents, and (3) water use by commercial and industrial establishments. We first plot historical population and water use trends, noting restrictions imposed on water use during droughts, so that the real demand on the system can be established.

We then plot water use trends for average 24 h, maximum 24 h, and peak hour demands. The peak hourly demands are met from distribution storage and therefore do not have to be passed through the treatment facility. The treatment facility is normally designed for maximum 24-h demand, so that an adequate amount of water will be treated and transmitted to the distribution storage system throughout the year, including days when usage is maximum. In some cases where plants are operated for less than a full day for various reasons (one being to avoid peak power demand periods), the capacity is set for something other than maximum 24-h demand.

Trends in both total and per capita residential and commercial water use are looked at. The projections will show either a leveling off or an increase in per capita use. If the community is modern, many households will have already installed dishwashers, air conditioners, and other high-water-use appliances; in fact, there is a trend toward the installation of water conservation devices, so that residential per capita usage in large metropolitan areas will probably be leveling off over the design period. Commercial and industrial usages are obtained from the records of the water utility or, in the case of large users, by visits to the facility to discuss past trends and future projections.

The design period for processes and equipment is often 15 to 20 years. Processes do become outmoded, and equipment wears out. Structures, however, are normally planned for longer periods, so the planning of a site and of buildings and civil structures often involves a 40- to 50-year planning period. Room is provided at the site for either replacing or adding equipment, and for adding additional process units.

It is advantageous to consider staging the construction of a facility in order to optimize the economics. This can be done by conducting a present-worth or life-cycle costing analysis. Processes can be staged, while support facilities are sized to serve the future expansion. Figure 2.1 is an example of a treatment facility staging process. The original process units are sized for 40-mgd maximum 24-h demand with room on the site for ready expansion to 50 mgd. Additional expansion beyond that point is considered in siting the plant.

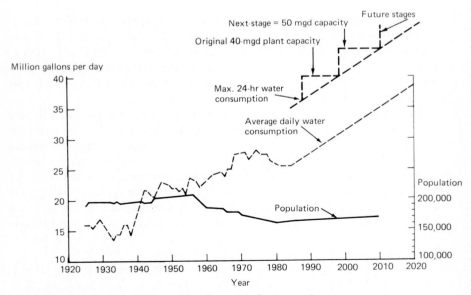

Figure 2.1 Population, water consumption, and plant capacity.

It is also necessary to analyze daily and annual fluctuations in demand for the purpose of sizing process units, such as chemical feed facilities, sludge treatment, and disposal units.

Plant Layout

The process, along with its control and monitoring, is represented by a process and instrumentation (P&I) diagram. Together with a table of detailed design criteria and a hydraulic profile, this diagram forms the basis for design, and the package of documents should be thoroughly thought out and reviewed by all concerned parties before one proceeds to the preliminary design of the treatment plant.

The P&I diagram and the detailed design criteria are developed by establishing (1) the major process units and their size and place in the scheme of design, (2) the kind, amount, and application points of chemical reagents, and (3) the monitoring and control of the processes and chemicals. The design criteria are developed in the detail necessary to establish the dimensions of the process tanks and pump and equipment specifications; the hydraulic profile can then be established for pumpage and for gravitation.

As an example of the information contained in a table of design criteria, the following criteria for a certain set of rapid mix units are offered:

Number of units	2 in series
Flocculation of each unit (ML/day)	250
Velocity gradient at design capacity and 85°F water temperature, G sec+	1000
Size of basin	
Width × length × average water depth, m³	3.0 × 3.0 × 3.2
Total net volume, m³	58
Detention time at design flow capacity, s	12.5
Detention time at hydraulic capacity, s	10
Mixer motor size	30 kW
Type drive (electric)	Variable speed
Speed, rpm	1000–750
Mixer type	Vertical axial-flow turbine

Similar criteria are specified for each process in the train. Note in the example above that the unit design is based on a normal maximum 24-h capacity, but that hydraulically the units can pass 25 percent more flow. It is normal to allow this amount of excess capacity in hydraulic structures.

The hydraulic gradeline ties down the elevations of the water surfaces in process structures. Some of the critical hydraulic considerations are:

1. The suction and discharge total dynamic head for lifting the raw water to the headworks of the treatment plant

2. The losses through trash racks and fine screens

3. The loss and recovery of energy through the raw-water flow measurement device

4. The built-in entrance losses to parallel flow trains to equalize the flow of water through the basins

5. The influent or effluent rate of flow device losses for filters

6. The losses through connecting open channels and closed conduits and fittings

7. The set loss through filters and contactors, allowing the buildup of impurities in the filter/contactor media

8. The suction and discharge total dynamic head to lift the finished water from the filtered-water reservoir to the distribution chamber system storage reservoirs

The profile should be drawn for average, maximum, and peak hydraulic conditions, in order to set adequate freeboard in basins and channels, and thereby allow establishment of critical elevations for process units and support facilities. It is important to satisfy the hydraulic needs of the processes as well as to acknowledge the topography of the site.

When this package of material has been reviewed and agreed to, the preliminary design phase can be started. The preliminary design outlines architectural, structural, process, and electrical plans, and specifies equipment. This package, when approved and agreed to, becomes the basis for the preparation of detailed construction documents.

The preliminary design phase centers around siting the pumping and treatment facilities and laying out the processes and support facilities. The flow of water through the units should be kept as direct as possible. Likewise, chemical lines should be kept as short as possible; therefore chemical storage and feed facilities should be located adjacent to the point of application. At the same time, we should make the plant a pleasant place to work in. It can be a compact plant that allows the operating staff to be always close to the process units as well as to their support facilities. Off-loading of chemicals and vehicular maintenance areas can be kept separate from people facilities.

The preliminary site plans are drawn to a reasonable scale so that the location of process tanks, buildings, and roads can be tied down; in addition, the plans show the drainage and landscape patterns and the location of large pipelines. The structural and architectural drawings replicate the shape and size of structures; decisions on building materials are shown, and the process/mechanical drawings represent decisions on types and size of equipment. The structural dimensions of major walls and beams are determined.

The site plans represent several decisions, including:

1. The location of access roads and the placement of buildings for the convenience of staff, public visitors, chemical deliveries, and vehicular maintenance
2. Solids handling
3. Buffer zones, neighbors
4. Future expansion
5. Architecture
6. Geotechnical/structural elevations
7. Compactness of the layout

The site should be planned to encourage separation of staff and visitor traffic from heavy truck movement. Signs are posted, where necessary, so that administrative staff and visitors take one route to their parking slots outside administrative areas, while chemical delivery and maintenance vehicles and operating staff go via another route for delivery of chemicals and for maintenance and parking.

Solids drying areas are often located remote from the immediate plant site. Prevailing wind patterns, along with the need to separate drying areas from the plant proper, force the beds away.

It is nice to buffer sites by natural or formed earth mounding and landscaping. The locations of heavy pipelines and existing pump stations guide the plant siting. Water views are taken advantage of for office frontage, and native landscaping is maintained.

The expansion of plant processes is paid attention to. Space is made available for adding capacity and for the addition of processes such as ozone and granular activated carbon.

The locations of processes are set at an elevation convenient for reducing earth work and rock blasting. This is the case when water is pumped from the raw-water source up to the plant, where the structures can be located above groundwater and ledge. At other sites, where the flow into the plant is by gravity, the process elevations are restricted by hydraulic requirements; where groundwater is present, precautions must be taken to prevent flotation of structures and seepage through concrete walls. This can be accomplished by providing enough weight in the structures to hold them down when process water is removed, or by positive underdrainage of the groundwater by gravity to a local water course. In addition, where earthquakes are prevalent, the location of faults and appropriate design for the protection of structures and people become an important part of the process.

Architectural treatment and the compactness of facility layout go together. The pretreatment units, the filters and supporting processes, and the administration facilities can be designed as a rectangular block, with operators able to observe process units from the control room. Maintenance facilities are provided for the level of maintenance to be conducted at the plant site. Some plants can serve as regional maintenance headquarters, while others remove their equipment to a remote site for major repairs.

Operational Concepts

Enclosed offices are provided for plant managers and engineers. The control room houses a desk and cubicles, and amenities are provided on operating floors and in maintenance areas. Meeting rooms and lunchrooms should be adequate for serving both plant personnel and visitors. It is not uncommon for larger installations to become a popular site for professional meetings.

The plant laboratory is designed for conducting the routine testing and analyses necessary for controlling and monitoring the plant, including organic and microbiological tests. Major testing programs that require sophisticated equipment can often be performed at the state water laboratories or at private regional facilities. However, this is not always the case. At some larger treatment plants, the laboratory is sized to handle microbiological, physical, chemical, and sophisticated organic chemical testing for a region.

Special care is given to the design of counter and floor materials in the laboratories, as well as to heating, ventilating, and air conditioning (HVAC), including exhausts. Laboratory storage is provided.

Modern instrumentation and control of treatment processes can be by remote process controllers at filters, pumps, and chemical feed stations; the remote controllers are connected by data highway to a central process controller at the operations center of the plant. Monitoring and control of the process loops can be central or remote. This is an appropriate approach for a sophisticated operation. In other cases, a simplistic approach can be taken, where instrumentation is kept to a minimum.

Figures 2.2 and 2.3 are examples of treatment plant floor plans and sections through process tanks and support facilities, respectively.

Constructibility

When upgrading an existing facility, it is important to schedule construction so that operation is not impaired. Close attention must be paid to constructibility and sequence of operation in the contract documents. For example, if outdated control hardware and wiring are being replaced with modern hardware and software, the plant must be kept in operation and the integrity of the finished water quality must be preserved throughout construction.

It is during the detailed design process that we begin to involve construction specialists so that the small and large problems experienced during construction can be kept to a minimum. Some of the items to be given proper attention are:

1. The design of process structures and building foundations to allow for simplicity of excavation and foundation engineering

2. Temporary operation of an existing plant throughout the construction period

3. A complete detailed check of the construction documents to cut down on major and minor conflicts in the field

4. The contractor's requirements for temporary utilities and storage of equipment

5. Training of the plant staff by the engineer and manufacturers

6. An adequate start-up period

These items are always important, but they are especially important when existing facilities are to be upgraded.

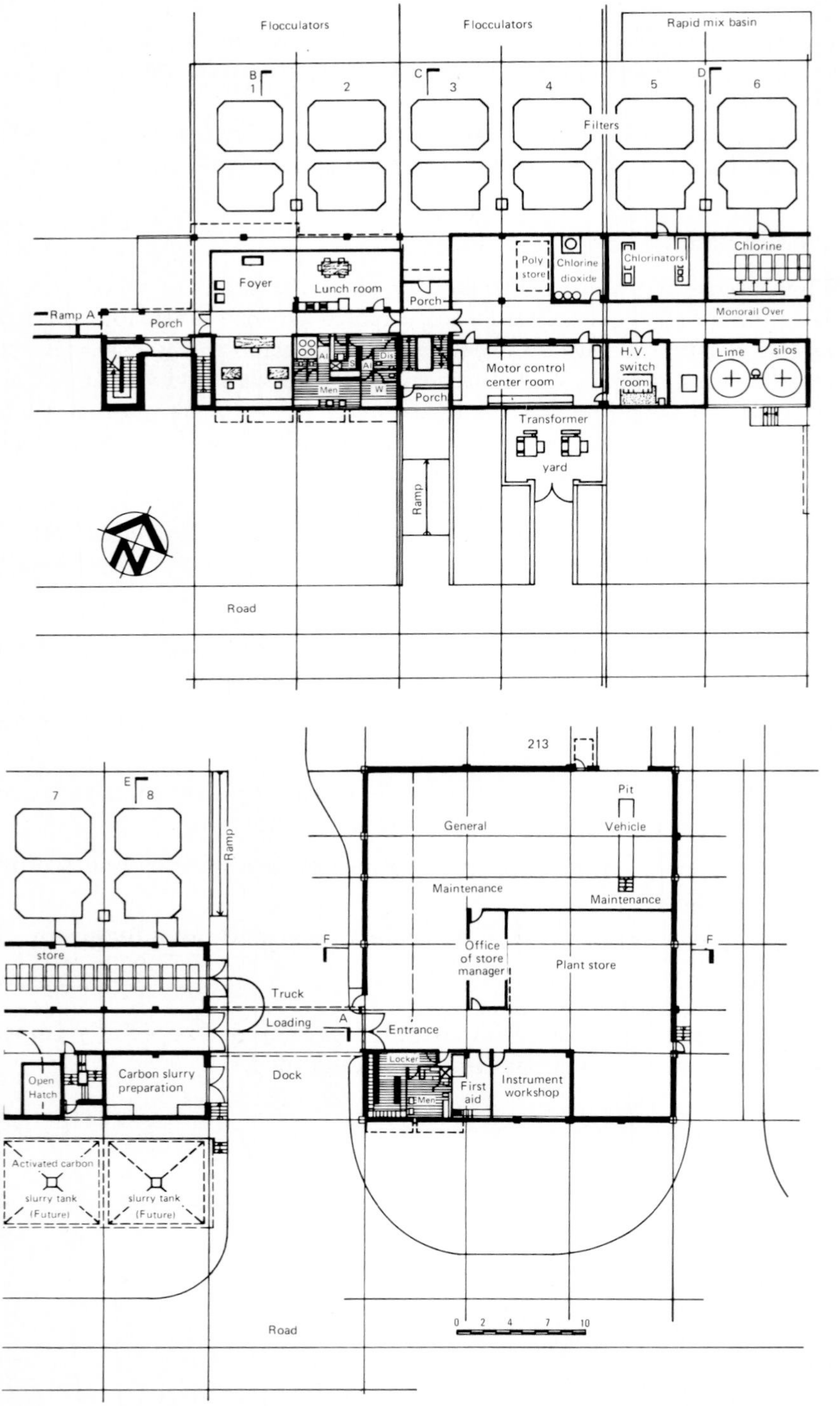

Flocculators   Flocculators   Rapid mix basin

B
1   2   C   3   4   5   D   6

Filters

Poly store   Chlorine dioxide   Chlorinators   Chlorine

Foyer   Lunch room   Porch   Monorail Over

Ramp A   Porch   Porch

Men   W   Dis   Motor control center room   H.V. switch room   Lime   silos

Ramp   Porch   Transformer   yard

Road

7   E   8   213

Ramp   Pit   Vehicle

General

Maintenance   Maintenance

store   F   Office of store manager   Plant store   F

Truck Loading   A   Entrance

Open Hatch   Carbon slurry preparation   Dock   Locker   First aid   Instrument workshop   Men

Activated carbon   slurry tank (Future)   slurry tank (Future)

Road   0 2 4 7 10

Figure 2.2   Example of a treatment plant floor plan. (*Courtesy of Camp Scott Furphy & Pty. Ltd., Australia.*)

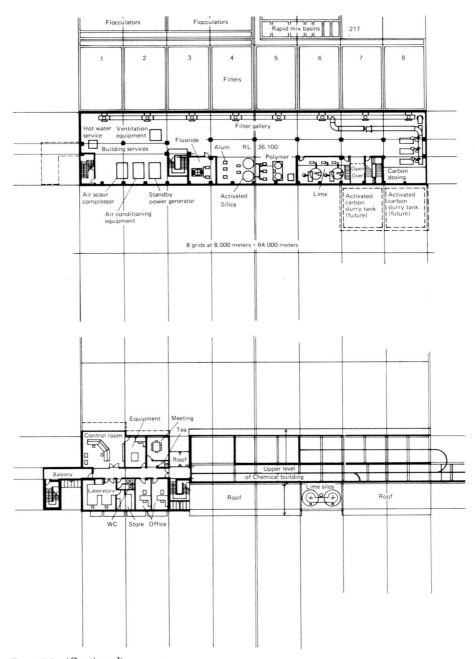

Figure 2.2 (*Continued*)

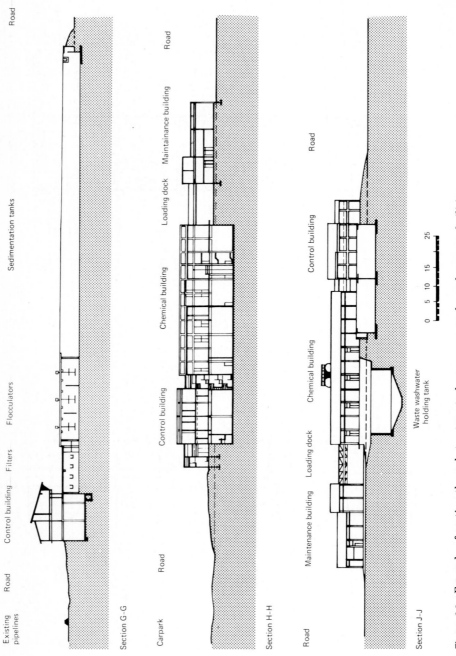

Existing
pipelines

Road

Control building

Filters

Flocculators

Sedimentation tanks

Road

Section G–G

Carpark

Road

Control building

Chemical building

Loading dock

Maintainance building

Road

Section H–H

Road

Maintenance building

Loading dock

Chemical building

Control building

Road

Waste washwater
holding tank

Section J–J

0   5   10   15   25

Figure 2.3 Example of section through treatment plant process tanks and support facilities. (*Courtesy of Camp Scott Furphy Pty. Ltd., Australia.*)

Chapter

3

Intakes

Introduction

Definitions and scope

Intakes are structures built into a body of water for the purpose of drawing water for use.[1] Reliability and adequate quality and quantity are the key components of an intake's function. As discussed in this chapter, intake systems include the works required to divert and transport water from a supply source, such as a river, lake, or reservoir, to a pumping station, pipeline, or treatment plant. For small water supplies, the intake system may be relatively simple, consisting of little more than a submerged pipe protected by a rack or screen. In contrast, for major supplies, intake systems are often quite elaborate, with diversion accomplished by large towerlike structures or submerged inlet works. Such systems may include, in addition to the diversion works, submerged transmission conduits, screens, pumping stations, and, in some instances, chemical storage and feeding facilities. For intakes located on rivers, jetties or low-head dams may be required to assure adequate submergence during low-flow periods.

For any type of intake system, the close relationship between intake works and raw-water pumping should receive careful consideration. Hydraulic design of the system, in addition to assuring adequate capacity, must provide suitable conditions for raw-water pump operation. Intake works and raw-water pumping stations are often combined in a single structure; however, the design of pumping stations is beyond the scope of this chapter.

The design of infiltration galleries and other facilities to receive water from underground sources is not included in this chapter. A good discussion of the design principles involved in these facilities can be found in a recent text by Driscoll.[27]

Importance of intakes

The purpose of an intake system is to furnish, under all conditions, an adequate supply of water of the best quality available. An intake system must, therefore, possess a high degree of reliability.

Intakes are subject to many hazards, but even under the most adverse conditions, the intake system must be able to meet the demand for water. Reliability is essential, especially for those waterworks that are dependent on a single intake system. Although redundancy is common in waterworks engineering, it is the exception rather than the rule that duplicate intakes are provided. For systems served by a single intake, failure of the intake works means failure of the supply, an emergency condition that if not promptly corrected will become a water supply disaster.

Intakes are exposed to numerous natural and artificial perils, and it is important that the designer anticipate and make provision for them. Hazards include those associated with pollution, storms, ice, navigation, waves, floods, low water, unstable river channels, silt, and bed load. For intake works, conservative structural and hydraulic design and careful consideration of intake location should be the rule. Reliable intake systems are costly and may represent as much as 20 percent of the total water treatment plant investment. Pipeline construction associated with intakes may involve extensive underwater work and the use of specialized marine equipment. As a result of these and other factors, the cost of such work will be 2.5 to 4 times that of a generally similar land project.[2] The achievement of economy, along with the required capacity and reliability, poses a challenge to the designer.

Essential features of intakes

The location and design of intake works are influenced by a multiplicity of factors, and therefore the designer has considerable latitude for the exercise of ingenuity and independent judgment. Factors affecting design and location include characteristics of the water source, required present and future capacity, water quality variations, climatic conditions, existing and potential pollution sources, protection of aquatic life, water-level variations, navigation, foundation conditions, sediment and bed loads, required reliability, and economic considerations. While each intake system presents unique problems, certain features of intake design may be generalized: (1) provision against failure to supply water because of fluctuations in water level or channel instability; (2) provision for water withdrawal at various depths where desirable and feasible; (3) protection against surges, ice, floods, floating debris, boats, and barges; (4) location of the intake to provide water of the best available quality, to avoid pollution, and to provide structural stability; (5) provision of racks (gratings) and screens as required to protect pumps and treatment facilities; (6) provision of adequate space for routine equipment cleaning and maintenance; (7) provision of facilities for removal of pumps and other equipment when major repairs are necessary; (8) location and design to minimize damage to aquatic life;[3] and (9) if chemical treatment is to be practiced at the intake works, provision of space and facilities for receiving, storing, and feeding the chemicals.

A shore intake that serves the Washington, D.C., water system is shown in Fig. 3.1. The intake and raw-water pumping station, housed in a single structure, are located at Little Falls on the Potomac River just upstream of the District line. The intake system and pumping station were designed for an ultimate capacity of 600 mil gal (2270 ML) daily to be provided by six 100-mgd (380-ML/day) vertical, centrifugal pumping units. The currently installed pumping capacity is approximately 450 mil gal (1703 ML) daily. Raw water enters the intake through six rectangular ports. A mechanically cleaned bar rack and a hydraulically cleaned traveling screen are provided ahead of each pumping unit. A pool maintained by the Little Falls dam provides submergence for the intake. Pumping power is obtained from

Figure 3.1 Washington, D.C., intake. Serves metro area, including Washington, D.C., Arlington County, Va., and part of Fairfax County, Va. (*Source: Washington Aqueduct Division, U.S. Army Corps of Engineers.*)

two high-voltage feeders, which terminate at enclosed substations located at the shore end of the prestressed concrete access bridge. The gantry crane shown in the photograph is available for handling screening equipment. An additional gantry crane is located inside the pumping station. The discharge conduit, which terminates at the Dalecarlia raw-water reservoir, is a concrete-lined tunnel, 10 ft in diameter.

Principal types of intake systems

A variety of intake systems have been successfully employed. Broad classifications of the principal types are intake towers, shore intakes, submerged intakes, and siphon-well intakes. Many variations of these principal types have been used. Unusual intake systems include suspended intakes, movable intakes, and floating intakes.

Intake towers are commonly employed at reservoirs and are usually located in the deepest part of a lake or reservoir. They may be incorporated into the dam that creates the reservoir. Inlet ports should be placed at various elevations to permit water quality selection. Towers have also been employed as part of a river intake system.[4] The intake tower is located in the river channel, and water is conducted from it by gravity pipe or tunnel to the intake pumping station, located on the shore. Tower accessibility can be a problem during adverse river conditions. Intake towers offer permanence, reliability, and flexibility in depth of draft, but their cost is substantial. While intake towers are often installed at reservoirs, other less costly systems are likely to be used in large lakes and rivers.

A shore intake system is frequently employed for large installations on rivers; it usually consists of a large concrete structure equipped with gated ports protected by coarse bar racks. Mechanical screens are usually placed in a well behind the ports. Such intake structures generally include space for raw-water pumping equipment. An alternative arrangement consists of screened inlet pipes located in the river channel and a wet-type shore tower equipped with vertical pumps. Caisson construction is employed for the shore tower.

Submerged intakes may be constructed as "cribs" surrounding an upturned, bell-mouth inlet connected to an intake conduit. The crib is often constructed as a timber polygon, weighted and protected by crushed rock. The intake conduit conveys water to the shore shaft, which serves as a pump suction well. It is designed to dissipate surges, and contains either fixed or traveling screens. Submerged intake systems employing the wood-crib arrangement have proven generally reliable in the Great Lakes region when properly located. Other inlet configurations have also been successfully employed.[2]

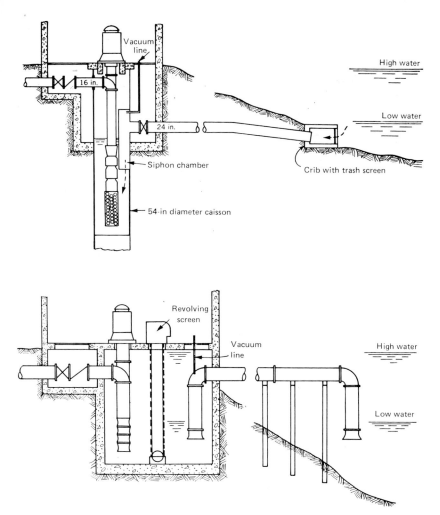

Figure 3.2 Siphon-well intakes. (*Source: V. C. Lischer and H. O. Hartung, "Intakes on Variable Streams," Journal AWWA, vol. 44, no. 10, 1952, p. 873.*)

Siphon-well intakes are employed in rivers and may consist of a shore structure which receives water from the river via a siphon pipe (Fig. 3.2). The siphon-pipe inlet may be a submerged crib equipped with a trash rack or simply a screen section attached to the open pipe. Siphon-well intakes have a record of satisfactory service and are generally less costly than other types of shore intakes.

Suspended, movable, and floating intakes (Figs. 3.3, 3.4, and 3.5) have been employed on rivers and reservoirs; they are described in waterworks literature.[4,5,6]

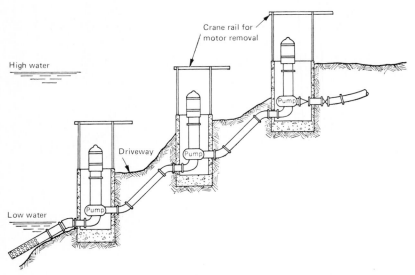

Figure 3.3 Intake pumps with removable motors in series. (*Source: V. C. Lischer and H. O. Hartung, "Intakes on Variable Streams," Journal AWWA, vol. 44, no. 10, 1952, p. 873.*)

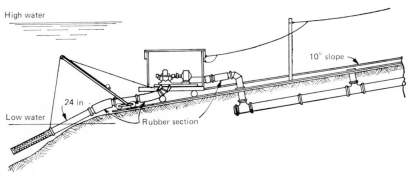

Figure 3.4 Intake pump on movable carriage. (*Source: V. C. Lischer and H. O. Hartung, "Intakes on Variable Streams," Journal AWWA, vol. 44, no. 10, 1952, p. 873.*)

Elements of Design

Capacity

Once built, intakes are extremely difficult and costly to enlarge. While many elements of a water system, such as pumping stations, basins, and filters, can be arranged for easy expansion, the basic intake system usually cannot be readily expanded to provide additional capacity. Therefore, long-range, as well as present and near-future, water supply needs must be carefully considered before the intake de-

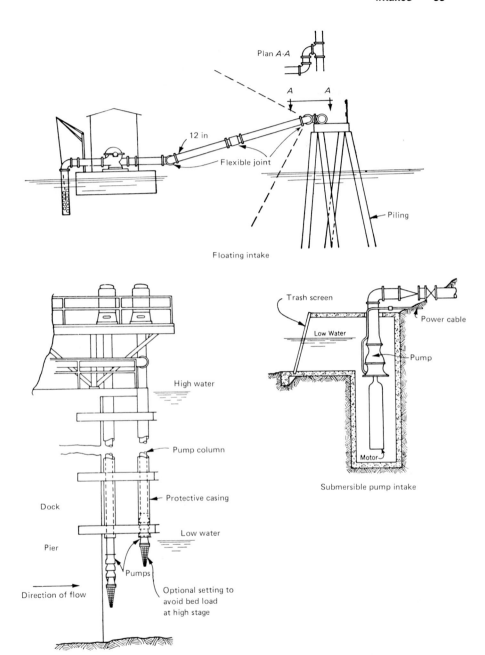

Plan A-A

A   A

12 in

Flexible joint

Piling

Floating intake

Trash screen

Low Water

Power cable

Pump

High water

Pump column

Protective casing

Dock

Low water

Pier

Motor

Direction of flow

Pumps

Optional setting to
avoid bed load
at high stage

Submersible pump intake

Suspended intake

Figure 3.5 Various intake arrangements. (*Source: V. C. Lischer and H. O. Hartung,
"Intakes on Variable Streams," Journal AWWA, vol. 44, no. 10, 1952, p. 873.*)

sign is fixed. In general, intake-system sizes that will meet water needs 20 to 40 years in the future should be investigated. Although intake-system construction which involves underwater work and the assembly and use of specialized equipment is costly, the incremental cost of providing substantially greater capacity may be relatively small. In 1969, Richardson[2] cited a bid price of $600,000 for an intake conduit with a capacity of 39 mgd and a bid price of $700,000 for an alternative conduit providing 69-mgd capability. Thus, in this instance, a cost increase of less than 20 percent provided a capacity gain of more than 75 percent.

Submergence

Intake capacity is directly related to inlet submergence, and the designer should be aware of the substantial variations in water levels that are encountered in many lakes, reservoirs, and rivers. The intake system must have the capacity to meet the maximum water demand during its projected service life, and intake capacity equal to this demand must be available during the period of minimum water level in the source of supply.

Location

Important factors influencing the location of intake-system inlet works are water quality; water pollution; protection of aquatic life; adequate submergence; ice, silt, and sand problems; wind; waves; floods; channel characteristics; navigation; accessibility; foundation conditions; economy; and others. Some intakes have had to be abandoned because of increased water pollution; however, with strengthened state and federal water pollution control programs, this should be less of a problem in the future. Nevertheless, in considering alternative intake sites, pollution potentials should be carefully reviewed and a thorough study made of available water quality data. Where such data are not available or are inadequate, a substantial water sampling and testing program may be warranted, particularly if a high-capacity, costly intake is under consideration. Extensive water quality investigations were conducted in connection with the location of the Wayne County intake in the Detroit River, for example.[7]

Ice

Various forms of ice, especially frazil, have caused serious intake difficulties. In regions where ice is likely to be a problem, careful attention must be given to intake location, submergence, port velocity, materials of construction, and hydraulic design. Ice problems are considered in detail in a subsequent section of this chapter.

River Intakes

For large water systems using rivers as a supply source, a shore intake that combines inlet works and raw-water pumping facilities is commonly provided. A shore intake system that serves the city of Kansas City, Mo., is shown in Fig. 3.6. This combined intake and raw-water pumping station is located on the Missouri River and supplies raw water to the city's nearby treatment plant. This facility, developed as part of a long-range water supply program, was designed for an ultimate capacity of 480 mil gal daily. Space was provided for six vertical, mixed-flow, wet-pit pumps, each located in an individual cell and each protected by a removable bar rack and traveling screen. Raw water enters through six rectangular ports located about 1 ft above the bed of the river. Sluice gates were provided so that each cell can be isolated for inspection, cleaning, or maintenance. The gantry crane is used for the removal of pumping equipment. Access to the intake and pumping station is provided by a 10-ft-wide bridge.

However, alternative intake systems should be considered because under some circumstances they may offer equally reliable service at lower cost. Alternatives include an exposed or submerged river inlet tower and shore pumping station, siphon intakes, suspended intakes,

Figure 3.6 Kansas City, Mo., intake. (*Photograph courtesy of Kansas City, Mo., Water Pollution and Control.*)

floating intakes, and movable intakes. The latter types may prove useful in overcoming low-water and flood difficulties and bed-load problems.

Figure 3.7 shows, in abbreviated form, a plan and section of part of the Ohio River submerged intake system which serves Cincinnati, Ohio. The inlet structure is 38 ft in diameter and contains rectangu-

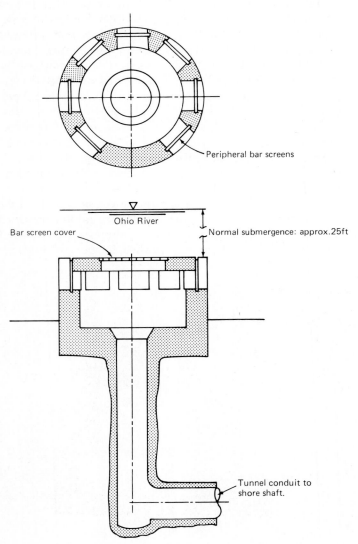

Figure 3.7   Cincinnati, Ohio, river intake. (*Source: Cincinnati Water Works, Cincinnati, Ohio.*)

lar, vertical bar screens and a circular bar screen cover. The intake conduit is a concrete-lined tunnel 10 ft in diameter. Traveling screens are provided at the shore shaft. The pumping station and screen chamber, constructed concentrically with the shore shaft, are approximately 110 ft in diameter and 110 ft deep. The station is divided into two compartments, each of which provides space for three 70-mgd centrifugal pumps. Figure 3.8 shows a section through one of the cells of a shore intake system constructed for the city of Topeka, Kan. Located on the Kansas River near the city's treatment works, the intake's design capacity is 60 mgd. The structure, which includes a raw-water pumping station, is divided into three interconnected cells, each of which contains two inlet ports equipped with bar racks and controlled by sluice gates. The initial installation includes two traveling screens

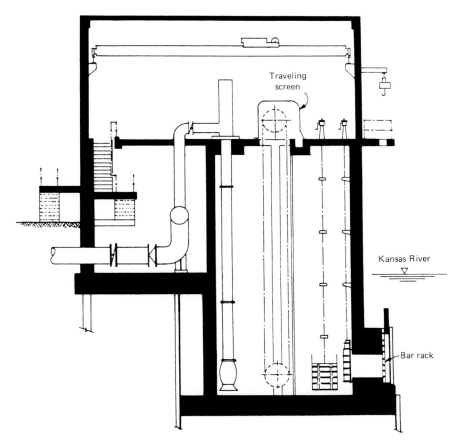

Figure 3.8 Topeka, Kan., river intake. (*Source: City of Topeka Water Division, Topeka, Kan.*)

and four vertical wet-pit pumps. Space is provided for a future screen and two additional pumps.

The groundwater potential of the river valley is also worthy of consideration. Gravel-packed wells or horizontal groundwater collection systems may offer an economical alternative to difficult, costly intake construction and associated operating problems.

Location

The preferred location for a shore intake system is one that provides deep water, a stable channel, and water of good quality. In general, the outside bank of an established bend offers the best channel condition. The inside bank is likely to be troublesome because of shallow water and sandbar formation. The location should be well upstream of the local sources of pollution. Considerable lateral variation in water quality can result from the entrance of point-source pollution and tributary streams above the proposed intake location. Thus, water quality near one bank may be inferior to that near midstream or the opposite shore.

Submergence

A conservative approach should be used in establishing the lowest water level for which the intake system is designed. Lack of adequate submergence during periods of extreme low water will result in greatly reduced capacity. Above-normal submergence should be made available for rivers that are subject to floating and slush ice.[4] Extreme low water may occur during the winter season as a consequence of ice jams.

On some rivers it may be impossible to obtain adequate submergence. For such situations, a low, self-scouring channel dam is required to provide a reliable intake system.

Floods

Ample protection against flood damage should be provided. The intake structure must be designed against flotation and the thrust of ice jams. Careful consideration should be given to flood stages at the intake site, and a substantial margin of safety provided. Because of watershed and channel alterations, future flood stages may exceed those of the past, and the designer should consider the possibility that the intake will be exposed to flood stages in excess of those of record.

Silt and bed load

Many streams carry heavy loads of suspended silt at times; in addition, there is movement of heavy material along the bed of the stream.

The intake must be designed so that it will not be clogged by silt and bed-load deposits. In addition to intake clogging, silt, sand, and gravel can cause abrasion of pumps and other mechanical equipment, and can lead to severe problems at the treatment plant. To help prevent such deposits, jetties have been built to deflect the principal flow of the river past the face of the intake.

Entrance ports

For intakes located on deep rivers, gated inlet ports may be provided at several depths for selective withdrawal of water. In most rivers, submergence governs, and ports must be placed at as low an elevation as possible. The lowest ports of an intake should be about 1 or 2 ft above the bottom of the channel in order to avoid clogging by silt, sand, and gravel deposits. Port inlet velocities should be selected to minimize entrainment of frazil ice, river debris, and fish. In general, the velocity through the gross area of the ports should not exceed 1.0 ft/s. When there is no ice hazard, somewhat higher velocities may be satisfactory, but for situations where ice is known to be a severe problem, velocities of 0.5 ft/s or even less may be desirable. Ice clogging has caused numerous intake failures.

Racks and screens

Racks and screens are essential for the protection of pumps and treatment works from river debris.[8] Racks (also termed bar racks or bar screens), preferably removable, are commonly located at the ports to prevent entrance of large floating objects. Racks are constructed of ½- to ¾-in metal bars spaced to provide 1- to 3-in openings. Velocity through the net open area of the racks should not exceed 2.0 ft/s. Screens remove material that is too small to be deflected by the coarse racks. Screens may be of various types—for example, the basket or panel types, which can be raised for cleaning, or the mechanical, traveling types, which are cleaned by water jets. The latter are generally employed at large intakes. Clear openings in the screens should be approximately ⅜ in. The velocity of the water in the net screen openings should be less than 2.0 ft/s at maximum design flow and minimum screen submergence.

Hydraulically cleaned (backwashed) stationary screens (Fig. 3.9) have been used successfully at reservoir and river intakes.[9,10] An early installation at a reservoir intake resulted from operator complaints about difficulties in cleaning panel screens. For several reasons a traveling screen was impractical, and stationary screens, which could be cleaned quickly and easily by backwashing, were provided. Numerous variations in design involving the use of backwashed, fixed

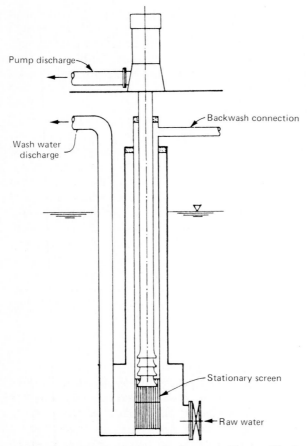

Figure 3.9 Stationary, backwashed screen. (*Source: Black & Veatch, Engineers-Architects.*)

screens have been employed. Figure 3.9 shows a schematic diagram of an installation of a stationary screen arranged for backwashing. Numerous variations in design have been employed. An advantage of the arrangement shown is that the pumping equipment can be installed or removed from the surface. Where the screened water is conveyed to a treatment plant, ³⁄₁₅- to ³⁄₈-in screen openings are commonly used. Whitlock and Mitchell[9] recommend that the velocity through stationary screen openings not exceed about 0.6 ft/s.

Part of the Wichita, Kan., water supply is obtained from Cheney Reservoir, located west of the city on the Ninnescah River. At this installation, fine screening is accomplished ahead of the raw-water pumps by two 30-in, self-cleaning basket strainers (see Fig. 3.10). The dam which forms this multipurpose reservoir was designed by the

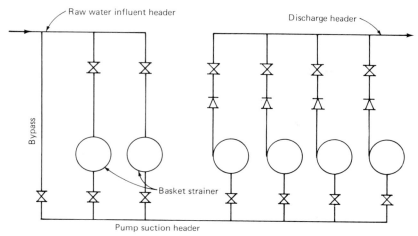

Figure 3.10 Wichita, Kan., basket strainers. (*Source: City of Wichita, Wichita, Kan.*)

U.S. Bureau of Reclamation and built under the bureau's supervision. A municipal water supply intake and outlet works, constructed as a part of the project, includes an intake structure provided with gated inlet ports at various levels. These inlets are equipped with bar racks. A 96-in intake conduit carries water under the dam to an access structure. The city's raw-water pumping station is located approximately 2100 ft downstream from the access structure and is connected to the intake conduit by a 72-in pipeline. Inasmuch as the water level in the reservoir is normally considerably above the elevation of the city's raw-water pumping station, head was conserved by the use of strainers, which operate under full pipeline pressure. The strainer baskets revolve either continuously or intermittently, depending on the amount of debris, principally leaves and twigs, anticipated in the pumping station influent. During intermittent operation, strainers revolve only during backwashing. Backwash normally is governed by a pressure switch that controls motor-operated plug valves on the strainer—backwash outlets—but a time clock was also provided to ensure periodic backwashing. Backwash water is obtained from the raw-water pump discharge header. The straining medium consists of slotted bronze cones. Small twigs and other debris caught in the cones are sheared between them and the knife-edge surfaces on the strainer body, and are readily removed by backwashing. A schematic diagram of the strainer arrangement is shown in Fig. 3.10.

Cellular design

Cellular design of large shore-intake systems is advisable. Cellular design divides the intake into two or more independent cells. This arrangement enhances reliability, provides flexibility, and simplifies any necessary maintenance. Individual cells can be taken out of service as required for cleaning or repair. Cellular design is also used for intake systems constructed in lakes and reservoirs.

Lake and Reservoir Intakes

Both tower intakes and submerged intakes are employed for water supplies derived from lakes and reservoirs. A tower intake often includes a pumping station and may be a part of the dam that creates the impoundment. Alternatively, the tower may be designed as an independent structure located some distance from shore in the deepest part of a reservoir. For such towers, access is provided by bridge, causeway, or boat. Towers must be designed to cope with flotation, wind, wave, and ice forces.

Submerged intakes do not obstruct navigation and are usually less costly than exposed towers (Fig. 3.11). If properly located and designed, submerged intakes experience a minimum of ice difficulties;

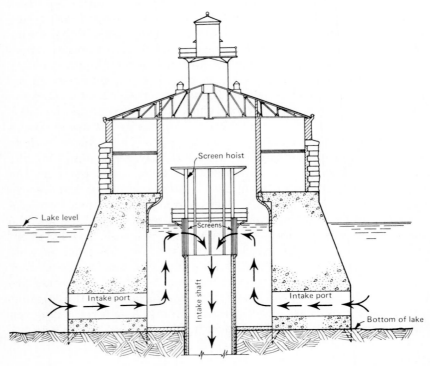

Figure 3.11   Chicago intake tower. (*Source: C. B. Burdick, "Water Works Intakes," Journal AWWA, vol. 38, no. 3., 1946, p. 315.*)

they have been used extensively for supplies obtained from the Great Lakes. They consist of a submerged inlet structure, an intake conduit, and a shore shaft or suction well. Shore intakes have been employed, but ice and sand problems reduce their effectiveness part of the time.[2,11]

Location

The intake location should be selected with a view to obtaining an adequate supply of water of the best possible quality, consistent with reliability, economical construction, and minimum effect on aquatic life (Fig. 3.12). To avoid sediment, sand, and ice problems, a submerged intake's inlet works should be located, if practicable, where the water is 50 ft or more deep. To achieve this depth in lakes where shallow water extends for a long distance from shore will require a long intake conduit.

The Indianapolis Water Company's tower intake and raw-water pumping station, shown in Fig. 3.12, are located in Eagle Creek Reservoir near Indianapolis. This installation serves the company's Eagle Creek water treatment plant. The structure includes two cells, each served by three inlet ports located at three elevations. Pumps are the vertical, wet-pit type and are protected by removable bar racks and traveling screens. Firm pumping capacity is 26 mil gal daily. Gantry

Figure 3.12 Indianapolis Water Company intake. (*Source: Indianapolis Water Company, Indianapolis, Ind.*)

cranes for equipment handling are located inside the structure. Access is provided by the concrete bridge. Eagle Creek Reservoir is located in a parklike setting; its appearance was a major design consideration.

In the past, pollution has forced the abandonment of some lake intakes; therefore, the pollution potential at candidate intake-inlet sites should be evaluated. In this connection, prevailing winds and currents are significant. Assembly and analysis of seasonal water quality data will provide further guidance in site selection. Special water quality surveys over a period of several years may be required to define the optimum location.

Submergence

As with river intakes, a conservative approach should be used in establishing the lowest water level for which a tower or a submerged intake system is designed. Substantial variations in water levels are inevitable, and the hydraulic performance of the overall intake system must be evaluated under the most adverse lake or reservoir levels. Maximum capacity should be available at extreme low-water levels.

Inlet works

Intake towers, located in deep lakes or reservoirs, should provide gated inlet ports at several levels in order to permit selection of water of the best available quality. In general, the lowest ports should be approximately 2 to 6 ft above the lake or reservoir bottom to avoid sediment accumulations. Ports are usually provided at three or more levels with a vertical interval of 10 to 15 ft. Studies[12,13,14] have shown a marked variation of water quality with depth in stratified lakes. These and other studies confirm the value of intake tower designs that include multilevel inlet ports. Occasional adjustment of the depth of draft will often provide substantial improvement in chemical, physical, and biological quality parameters, and thus simplify treatment and reduce its cost. As with river intakes, the velocity through the gross area of the ports should not exceed 1.0 ft/s, and lower velocities are advisable where ice is a severe problem. Racks and screens, as previously described, are essential for the protection of pumping equipment and treatment works.

The intake tower shown in Fig. 3.13 is located in Monroe Reservoir, the water supply source for Bloomington, Ind. Two intake cells, each equipped with three intake ports, are provided. Bar and traveling screens protect four vertical, wet-pit pumps. Design capacity of the intake system is 48 mil gal daily.

Various inlet designs have been employed for submerged intakes.

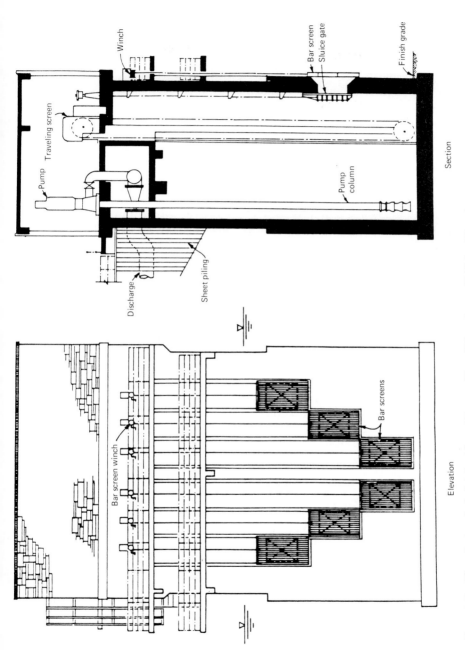

Figure 3.13 Bloomington, Ind., intake tower. (*Source: City of Bloomington Utilities, Bloomington, Ind.*)

45

To avoid sediment, sand, and ice problems, it is desirable that the inlet works be located in deep water and that inlet velocities be less than 0.5 ft/s, preferably about 0.2 to 0.3 ft/s. Inlet structures are often constructed of wood or other nonferrous material, which is less susceptible to ice deposits because of its low heat conductivity. Several authors have described wood-crib design and construction.[2,11,15,16] Such cribs are usually polygonal and are built of heavy timbers, bolted together, weighted with concrete and crushed stone, and bedded on a crushed stone mat. The crib surrounds a bell-mouth pipe which is connected to the intake conduit. Crib ports are sized to provide a maximum velocity of about 0.25 ft/s. Riprap fill is placed on all sides of the crib. Wooden inlet cribs have provided many years of reliable service in the Great Lakes.

Figure 3.14 shows a section of the 315-mgd Milwaukee, Wis., intake crib located in Lake Michigan. The crib is an octagonal, coated steel structure 11 ft high and 52 ft wide between parallel sides. It was floated into position and sunk by filling the air tanks with water, which was then displaced by pumped concrete for permanent anchorage. The horizontal baffle ensures relatively uniform flow through all parts of the intake screen. At the design flow rate, average velocity through the screen openings is 0.31 ft/s. Mean water depth at the intake location is approximately 50 ft. The 108-in intake conduit extends 7600 ft to the Texas Avenue pumping station on the west shore of the lake. Figure 3.15 shows the Saginaw-Midland intake crib. The 60-ft submerged inlet structure was built of 12-in by 12-in timbers. It was floated into position, sunk by weighting with concrete and stone, and bedded on a crushed rock mat on the lake bottom.[2]

Other configurations for submerged intakes include hydraulically

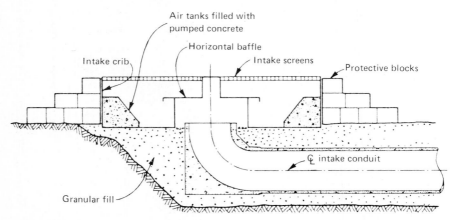

Figure 3.14   Milwaukee, Wis., intake crib. (*Source: City of Milwaukee, Milwaukee, Wis.*)

Figure 3.15   Launching of the Saginaw-Midland intake crib.

balanced inlet cones;[2] screened, baffled steel cribs;[17] and inlet drums.
Hydraulically balanced inlet cones have been used at several Great
Lakes intakes. The structure in Fig. 3.16 consists of three groups of
three equally spaced inlet cones connected to a cross at the inlet end of
the intake conduit. This configuration provides essentially identical
entrance velocities through all cones. The lower photograph shows a
group of three inlet cones prior to placement in Lake Michigan. The
intake serves Evanston, Ill.[2] Figure 3.17 illustrates part of the
Wyoming, Mich., intake system, located 4500 ft offshore in Lake
Michigan. Minimum water depth at the site is approximately 40 ft.
The 15-ft-diameter intake drums were fabricated of steel and then
coated with coal tar. The intake conduit, a 66-in concrete pipeline,
connects to a shore pumping station, which has a firm capacity of 83
mgd.

Regardless of the configuration, it is essential that the inlet velocity
be low (e.g., 0.25 ft/s) and practically uniform in all parts of the inlet
structure. Unbalanced inlet conditions have been responsible for ice
problems in some of the older intakes on the Great Lakes.[2]

Intake conduit

The intake conduit, which connects the submerged inlet works with
the shore shaft, may be a pipeline or a tunnel. Tunnels have a high
degree of reliability, but are usually too costly for small water systems. On the other hand, when the intake will serve a large system, a
tunnel may be an economical choice. Velocities in the conduit should

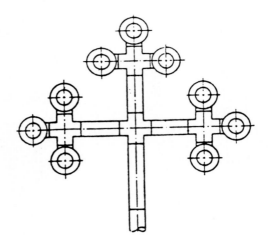

Figure 3.16 Hydraulically balanced inlet cones.

be sufficient to prevent deposition, usually from 3 to 4 ft/s. Biological growths on the interior surface of the conduit may reduce its capacity; therefore, conservative hydraulic design is advisable.

Where the intake conduit is constructed of pipe, subaqueous concrete pipe is generally employed, laid in a trench on the lake or reservoir bottom. Approximately 3 to 4 ft of cover over the top of the pipe

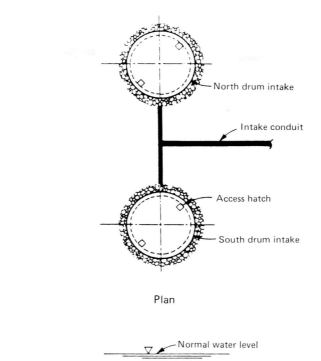

Plan

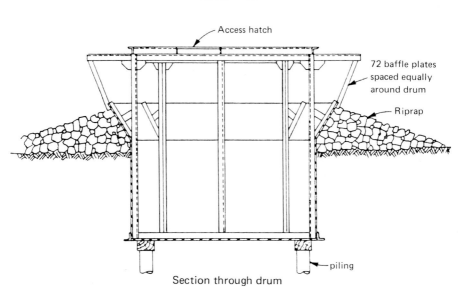

Section through drum

Figure 3.17 Wyoming, Mich., intake. (*Source: City of Wyoming Wastewater Treatment Plant, Grandville, Mich.*)

plus an additional protective top layer of crushed rock are provided. Richardson[2] suggests about 1 yd^3 of rock over the entire width of the trench for each linear foot of pipe. The allowable drawdown in the shore shaft is a critical factor in the hydraulic design of the intake conduit. The drawdown is the result of friction loss in the conduit and is equal to the difference between the lake or reservoir level and the level of water in the shore shaft. It is desirable to limit drawdown to avoid excessive excavation for the shore shaft, and a maximum drawdown allowance of approximately 15 ft has been used in the design of several Great Lakes intake systems.

The conduit should be laid on a continuously rising or falling grade to avoid reduction in conduit capacity as a result of air accumulation at the high points. When an undulating conduit cannot be avoided because of the profile of the lake bottom, air release provisions may be required at the high points.

Shore shaft

The shore shaft, which is a part of the intake system and is connected to the submerged inlet works by the intake conduit, serves as a screen chamber and a raw-water pump-suction well. The depth of the shore shaft must be adequate for the drawdown that will be encountered when the intake is operating at design capacity and the source-water elevation is at its minimum design value. In addition, the shaft must provide an ample submergence allowance for the raw-water pumps. The shaft must also be capable of resisting and dissipating the surges that will occur when a power failure stops the raw-water pumps. An outlet in the shaft large enough to readily discharge the surge back to the supply source will accomplish this.

The shore shaft should be equipped with screens for pump protection. Fixed and traveling screens have been used successfully. In general, traveling screens are preferable for all except small systems. Cellular construction of the shore shaft is advisable, and inlet control gates should be provided so that all or part of the shore shaft can be taken out of service for inspection and repair.

Design Principles and Practices

Ice problems

Introduction.   Intake systems located in regions with long, severe winters are subject to a variety of problems associated with ice in its various forms. Ice may be encountered as surface ice, anchor ice, frazil ice, or slush ice. All forms can cause problems, but most difficulties are the result of the formation of frazil and anchor ice, and these forms are considered in more detail in subsequent paragraphs.[18]

Surface ice and ice floes resulting from the breakup of surface ice create a structural hazard to exposed intakes. On lakes, an accumulation of wind-driven floes near a shore intake can produce a deep, nearly solid layer of ice that will restrict or completely block intake ports. Under such conditions, reliable intake operation is virtually impossible, and water supplies obtained from lakes and reservoirs that are subject to severe ice problems are usually served by offshore intakes. Ice jams can cause partial or complete blockage of river intakes. Ice jams below a river intake can also cause extremely high river stages, while an upstream jam can produce low water levels at the intake location, reducing its capacity.

Frazil and anchor ice.   Ice starts to form when the temperature of the water is reduced to 32°F (0°C) and the water continues to lose heat to the atmosphere.[19] For pure water, supercooling to temperatures well below the freezing point (0°C) is necessary to start ice formation. In the case of natural water, however, the required supercooling is much less. Two types of ice formation are recognized: static ice formation on the quiet waters of small lakes and stagnant river pools; and dynamic ice formation in turbulent areas of rivers, where the greatest flow often is, and in lakes mixed by wind action.[20] Frazil ice, the type formed under dynamic conditions, adversely affects the hydraulic characteristics of intakes.

When natural water loses heat to the atmosphere and a condition of turbulence exists, the result will be uniform cooling of a large fraction of the water body. If the initial water temperature is slightly above the freezing point and cooling is rapid, the small amount (0.05°C) of supercooling required will occur, and small, disc-shaped frazil ice crystals will form and be distributed throughout the turbulent mass. These small crystals are the initial stage of ice production; other ice forms can develop from them in sizable quantities.

Where there is little or no mixing, supercooled water and existing surface ice crystals are not carried to a significant depth, and the result is the formation of a layer of surface ice rather than a mass of frazil. Surface ice formation reduces heat loss from the water and usually prevents the formation of frazil ice.

Two kinds of frazil ice have been identified: active and inactive, or passive. Freshly formed frazil crystals dispersed in supercooled water and growing in size are in an active state. When in this condition, they will readily adhere to underwater objects such as intake screens or rocks. The production and adhesiveness of active frazil ice are associated with the degree of supercooling, which is related to the rate of cooling of the water mass.[21] Frazil ice particles will remain in an active, adhesive state for only a short time after their formation. The production of active frazil is considered a transient occurrence, which, as it persists, eliminates the conditions necessary for its continuance.[21] With the reduction of supercooling and the return of the water to 32°F (0°C), the frazil crystals cease to grow and change to an inactive, or passive, state.[19] Passive frazil has lost its adhesive properties and is therefore less troublesome.[19,21]

Frazil ice has been aptly termed "the invisible strangler."[21] When conditions favor its formation, the rate of buildup on underwater objects can be rapid; frazil accumulations can reduce an intake's capacity substantially or clog it completely in a few hours. Conditions favoring the production of frazil are:[21]

Clear skies at night (high heat loss by radiation)

Air temperature 19.4°F (−7°C) or less

Daytime high-water temperatures not above 32.4°F (0.2°C)

Winds greater than 10 mi/h (16 km/h) at the water surface

There is some confusion concerning the relationship between frazil ice and anchor ice. It has been suggested that anchor ice occurs rarely, and consists of sheetlike crystals which adhere to and grow on submerged objects.[22] Accumulations of frazil ice may closely resemble anchor ice. Some investigators[23] designate all ice attached to the bottom as anchor ice regardless of how it is formed. Anchor ice may form in situ on the bottom and grow by the attachment of frazil crystals. According to Giffen,[24] on the other hand, ice crystallizing and growing directly on the surface of a shallowly placed intake structure in open water is commonly termed anchor ice. Such ice is usually formed at night in clear, cold weather or on cold, cloudy days. It normally does not form at depths greater than 40 to 45 ft, although the depth associated with anchor ice formation is dependent on the turbidity of the water.

Frazil crystals can agglomerate into large, spongy masses generally termed slush ice. Slush ice may clog vulnerable parts of the intake system.

Predicting frazil ice formation. The nature and quantity of frazil ice production correlates well with the cooling rate.[24] When this rate is greater than 0.01°F (0.01°C) per hour over a narrow temperature range extending from slightly above 32°F (0°C) to a supercooled condition, frazil ice will form. As the extent of supercooling increases, the quantity and stickiness of the frazil also increase. When the cooling rate is less than 0.01°C/h, surface ice will form. Low cooling rates normally occur during calm weather.

The climatological conditions that encourage formation of frazil ice have been summarized previously. Even at extremely low air temperatures [−22°F (−30°C)], if there is no wind, frazil may not form because of the insulating layer of water vapor at the surface. In a discussion of ice difficulties at the Chicago waterworks, it was reported[25] that studies of weather data from the periods previous to and during each problem period indicated that frazil ice formed under variable conditions of wind velocity and direction and air temperature. Frazil ice consistently accumulated in the late evening or early morning hours and seldom lasted until noon. A further significant finding was that ice problems caused by frazil ice in water drifting past a shore intake were encountered despite ice cover on the forebay. Apparently conditions favorable to frazil ice formation can vary considerably from site to site, making it difficult to use weather data alone as a forecasting tool.

Precise temperature measurements have been used to indicate cooling rates and thus to detect conditions that are favorable to frazil ice formation.[24] At one power plant, such data provide a guide for the use of intake screen heaters. At Chicago, a tell-tale chain suspended in the intake basins was used to provide forewarning of ice problems. If ice adhered to the chain, ice clogging and consequent loss of raw-water capacity were expected.[25]

Overcoming ice problems

Design considerations. Research and experience on the Great Lakes and elsewhere indicate that location and design features of submerged intakes can mitigate intake ice problems, although, as other data show,[24] the problem may occur despite these precautions. Conditions peculiar to each site appear to play a prominent role in ice formation. Apparently the best that judicious design can accomplish is the reduction of the frequency and intensity of ice problems.

Submerging lake intakes in deep water and sizing the inlet ports for a velocity of 0.3 ft/s or less will minimize the amount of frazil ice transported downward to the structure. However, during winter storms, strong wind and wave action can carry ice crystals and supercooled water to considerable depths, making accumulation of ice on and around the intake likely. Foulds and Wigle[20] suggest various procedures to alleviate frazil ice problems at submerged intakes. These include:

1. Location of the intake where it will be protected by an ice cover

2. Intake openings sufficiently large that ice adhering to the edges cannot readily bridge across (i.e., 24 in minimum dimension)

3. Enough heat supplied around the openings to prevent an adherence of frazil

4. Provision of enough heat around the openings to raise the temperature about 0.1°C, thus eliminating supercooling with resultant formation of slush ice rather than frazil

Creation of a quiet body of water at the intake location will promote surface ice formation. At the Billings, Mont., waterworks, frazil ice was a severe winter problem in the turbulent Yellowstone River. In this case, the solution was the enlargement of an off-river intake channel into an earthen forebay with a detention time of approximately 1 h. Surface ice formed on the nearly quiescent forebay. This insulating ice cover prevented the formation of additional frazil ice and provided the opportunity for river frazil carried into the forebay to combine with the surface ice and revert to a passive condition. This or any other method that will create a quiet body of water at and near the intake will be helpful.

To prevent, or at least minimize, ice clogging, the structure can be built of low-heat-transfer materials with smooth surfaces that are not conducive to the accumulation of ice crystals. Metals such as steel are less suitable because they have a high heat conductivity and act as a sink for the latent heat released when ice begins to form. This encourages ice buildup. In contrast, ice will not readily crystallize or grow rapidly on wood or plastic. Fiberglass-reinforced plastic with a low thermal conductivity and a smooth surface was employed for screen construction at a new submerged intake serving Hamilton, Ont.[26] Giffen[24] recommends that any exposed metal surfaces be coated with some inert material such as black epoxy paint to effect better thermal properties and increase radiation heat gain. Use of special materials doubtlessly will help reduce ice problems, but will not provide absolute protection. Under prolonged conditions favorable to frazil ice formation, even the use of special materials will not ensure freedom from intake blockage.

Heated intake screens have been used successfully at power plant installations and may have application at waterworks intakes where severe frazil ice problems develop quickly and do not endure for long periods. Frazil ice will not adhere to objects whose temperature is slightly above the freezing point. Logan[21] concludes that heating trash racks at power plant intakes is of value when frazil ice is in the active (adherent) state. A wide range of trash-rack heating values appear in the literature. For typical intakes, these range from about 250 to 500 W/ft^2 of trash-rack frontal area. Giffen[24] cites an example of a power-plant intake installation located on Lake Ontario where heater elements were installed in each bar of the intake screen to maintain a metal surface temperature about 2°F (1°C) above that of the bulk water. In addition, a black, coal-tar epoxy coating was applied to increase radiant heat gain. The system, which is located in 31 ft of water and was designed for an inlet velocity of 0.8 ft/s, has operated without icing problems since 1968. Heating probably would not be completely effective for situations where large masses of packed ice or slush ice are drawn into the structure. Heating facilities will add significantly to the operating costs of an intake installation. For larger installations in cold climates, a prohibitive amount of energy may be required for heating.

Control methods.   In the 1940s, frazil ice formation in low-lift pumps in Chicago's south district filtration plant threatened the raw-water supply from Lake Michigan. Of the several remedies applied,[25] steam injection into pump suctions was the most satisfactory. The temperature rise required to prevent clogging was approximately 0.1°F. Ice clogging also occurred at two intake structures, and this problem was solved by exploding light charges of dynamite opposite the openings. Other control methods involved backflushing with settled water and compressed air discharge in front of a gate opening.

An indicator of icing problems at an intake is abnormal drawdown in the intake well.[24] In one instance, severe clogging and resultant drawdown caused rupturing of the intake screen. Fixed screens are difficult to clean, and remedies include compressed air or steam injected in back of the screen, hand and mechanical scraping, and removal of the screen when ice troubles start. Backflushing of the intake by pumping or use of water stored in elevated tanks or reservoirs is a frequently used procedure, but it is not consistently successful. If backflushing is to be routinely practiced, provision must be made for it when the intake is designed. It has sometimes been possible to clear partially clogged intake ports by a method termed "control drawdown,"[24] which involves throttling the intake-well pumps and maintaining reduced intake flow. Under some conditions this flow may be sufficient to erode ice bridges at the ports and restore intake capacity. Giffen[24] considers this method preferable to backflushing,which wastes water and is not generally successful at installations that experience severe ice problems of long duration.

References

1. Thaddeus Merriman and Thomas H. Wiggin, "Collection of Water Intakes," in *American Civil Engineers' Handbook,* 5th ed., Wiley, New York, 1930.
2. William H. Richardson, "Intake Construction for Large Lakes and Rivers," *Journal AWWA,* vol. 61, no. 8, 1969, p. 365.
3. Victor J. Schuler and Lory E. Larson, "Improved Fish Protection at Intake Systems," *Journal Envir. Engr. Div. (ASCE),* vol. 101, no. EE6, 1975, p. 897.
4. Vance C. Lischer and H. O. Hartung, "Intakes on Variable Streams," *Journal AWWA,* vol. 44, no. 10, 1952, p. 873.
5. Ralph Tone and E. T. Conrad, "Centrifugal Pumps Ride the Rails of Unique Water Intake," *Public Works,* vol. 100, no. 12, 1969, p. 64.
6. Anonymous, "Rise and Fall of a Pumping Station," *Water Works Engineering,* vol. 112, no. 3, 1959, p. 208.
7. Francis P. Coughlan, Jr. "Locating the New Intake," *Journal AWWA,* vol. 50, no. 5, 1958, p. 668.
8. John W. Cunningham,"Waterworks Intakes and the Screening of Water," *Journal AWWA,* vol. 23, no. 2, 1931, p. 258.
9. Ernest W. Whitlock and Robert D. Mitchell, "Hydraulically Backwashed Stationary Screens for Surface Water," *Journal AWWA,* vol. 50, no. 10, 1958, p. 1337.
10. Leo F. Peters, "Hydraulically Backwashed Well Screens Used as Intakes," *Water & Wastes Engineering,* vol. 6, no. 3, 1969, p. 52.
11. Charles B. Burdick, "Water Works Intakes," *Journal AWWA,* vol. 38, no. 3, 1946, p. 315.
12. Charles M. Weiss and Ray T. Oglesby, "Limnology and Quality of Raw Water in Impoundments," *Public Works,* vol. 91, no. 8, 1960, p. 97.
13. G. Fred Lee and C. C. Harlin, Jr., "Effects of Intake Location on Water Quality," *Industrial Water Engineering,* vol. 2, no. 3, 1965, p. 36.
14. Lloyd R. Heinzel, "Storm Effects on Turbidity in Trinity Project Waters," *Journal AWWA,* vol. 59, no. 7, 1967, p. 835.
15. Louis Howson and Gerald Remus, "Best Features of Four Existing Plants Highlighted in New Detroit Water Facility," *Water and Wastes Engineering,* vol. 7, no. 12, 1970, p. 50.
16. Louis R. Howson, "Saginaw-Midland Supply Project Begins Operations," *Water Works Engineering,* vol. 102, no. 5, 1949, p. 415.
17. H. M. Ihling and D. P. Proudfit, "New Facilities Add 100 mgd to Milwaukee's Water Supply," *Civil Engineering,* vol. 33, no. 9, 1963, p. 31.
18. Abel Wolman, "Ice Engineering," *Journal AWWA,* vol. 21, no. 1, 1929, p. 133.
19. George D. Ashton, "River Ice," *American Scientists,* vol. 67, no. 1, 1979, p. 38.
20. D. M. Foulds and T. E. Wigle, "Frazil—The Invisible Strangler," *Journal AWWA,* vol. 69, no. 4, 1977, p. 196.
21. T. H. Logan, *Prevention of Frazil Ice Clogging of Water Intakes by Application of Heat,* REC-ERC-74-15, U.S. Dept. of Interior, Bureau of Reclamation, Denver, Colo., September 1974. (Distributed by National Technical Information Service, U.S. Dept. of Commerce, Springfield, VA 22161.)
22. Vincent J. Shaefer, "The Formation of Frazil and Anchor Ice in Cold Water," *Trans. Am. Geophys. Union,* vol. 31, no. 6, 1950, p. 885.
23. H. T. Barnes, *Ice Engineering,* Renouf Publishing Co., Montreal, 1928.
24. A. V. Giffen, *The Occurrence and Prevention of Frazil Ice Blockage at Water Supply Intakes,* Research Branch Publication No. W 43, Ministry of the Environment, Toronto, 1973.
25. John R. Baylis and H. H. Gerstein, "Fighting Frazil Ice at a Waterworks," *Engineering News-Record,* vol. 140, no. 16, 1948, p. 562.
26. R. G. Tredgett and D. R. Fisher, "New Waterworks Intake for Hamilton, Ontario," *Water & Wastes Engineering,* vol. 7, no. 2, 1970, p. 32.
27. F. G. Driscoll, *Groundwater and Wells,* 2d ed., Johnson Division, St. Paul, Minn., 1986.

4

Aeration

Introduction

As applied to water treatment, "aeration" may be defined as the process by which a gaseous phase, usually air, and water are brought into intimate contact with each other for the purpose of transferring volatile substances to or from the water. These volatile substances may include oxygen, carbon dioxide, nitrogen, hydrogen sulfide, methane, and various unidentified organic compounds responsible for taste and odor. Oxygen, nitrogen, and carbon dioxide are universally present in air, and all substances named may be encountered in natural water.

Use of aeration in water treatment

Aeration may be used to reduce the concentration of taste- and odor-producing substances, such as hydrogen sulfide and, to a limited extent, certain volatile organic compounds. It may also be used to partially remove those substances that may in some way interfere with or add to the cost of subsequent water treatment. This would include, for example, the removal of hydrogen sulfide before chlorination and the removal of carbon dioxide prior to lime softening. Aeration is used exclusively as a means of adding oxygen to water for oxidation of iron, manganese, hydrogen sulfide, and, to a limited extent, organic matter. Addition of carbon dioxide for recarbonation of excess lime in softened waters and for assistance in hydrogen sulfide removal is often accomplished by methods that are essentially the same as those employed in aeration.

Aerator types

Structures or equipment for aeration may be classified as waterfall aerators, which may be spray nozzles, cascades, or multiple trays; diffusion or bubble aerators, which bubble compressed air through the water; and mechanical aerators. The waterfall type accomplishes aeration by causing the water to break into drops or thin films, thereby increasing the area of water exposed per unit of volume. The diffusion type produces a similar effect by discharging bubbles of air into water by means of air-injection devices. Mechanical aerators employ motor-driven impellers alone or in combination with air-injection devices. They find their greatest application in treatment of wastewater.

Theoretical Principles

The transfer, by aeration, of a volatile material to or from water is dependent upon a number of factors. These include the characteristics of the volatile material to be removed or added, temperature, gas transfer resistance, partial pressure of the gases in the aerator atmosphere, turbulence in gaseous and liquid phases, area-volume ratio, and time of exposure.

Equilibrium conditions

Applied to gases dissolved in water, the term "equilibrium" signifies a steady state in the concentration of these dissolved substances. The aeration process promotes the establishment of equilibrium between dissolved, volatile constituents in the water and these constituents in the air or other gaseous phase to which the water is exposed. For example, when water is exposed to air, oxygen and nitrogen will dissolve in the water until a state of equilibrium is reached. The function of aeration is to speed up this natural process. True equilibrium may not be attained by aeration unless the air-water exposure period is long; however, from a practical standpoint, it is generally unnecessary to achieve absolute equilibrium.

The concentration of a gas dissolved in a liquid at equilibrium is known as its "saturation value." This value is an important characteristic of a dissolved gas. The saturation value is principally dependent upon the temperature of the water, the partial pressure of the gas in the atmosphere in contact with the water, and the presence of dissolved solids. The higher the partial pressure, the greater the dissolved gas concentration (Henry's law). At a fixed partial pressure, the higher the temperature, the lower the solubility or saturation value of a gas. Gas solubility is also reduced by dissolved solids.

The saturation value has considerable practical and theoretical significance. It is the difference between the saturation value of a gas and its actual concentration in the water that provides the driving force for the interchange of gas between air and water. Water that is deficient in oxygen will absorb it when brought into contact with air, and the air-water equilibrium will be approached from the direction of oxygen deficiency. Prolonged aeration will produce oxygen saturation. On the other hand, if the water contained more oxygen or, as is more frequently encountered, more carbon dioxide than the saturation amount, aeration would bring about release of the gas. In this instance, equilibrium is approached from the direction of supersaturation. The final result of prolonged aeration, however, would be the same—saturation.

Equilibrium conditions are important to the aeration process, but of equal or greater significance to the designer is the rate of achievement of equilibrium. Equilibrium and rate of approach to it are not independent of one another, for under similar conditions, the further the air-water system is from equilibrium, the more rapid will be the interchange of gas in the direction of attainment of equilibrium.

Films at the air-water interface appear to have an important bearing on the rate of gas transfer. Both liquid and gas films can retard the rate of exchange of volatile material, but the former are considered more important in the case of gases of fairly low solubility, such as oxygen and carbon dioxide. Film resistance is influenced by numerous factors, notably turbulence and temperature. High temperature and turbulence promote gas transfer by reducing film thickness. A temperature rise also increases the rate of molecular diffusion.

Diffusion

The rate of molecular diffusion of a dissolved gas in a liquid is dependent on the characteristics of the gas and the liquid, the temperature, the concentration gradient, and the cross-sectional area through which diffusion occurs. The diffusional process is defined by Fick's first law:

$$\frac{\delta m}{\delta t} = -D_L A \frac{\delta c}{\delta y} \qquad (4.1)$$

where $\dfrac{\delta m}{\delta t}$ = time rate of mass (m) transfer by diffusion

D_L = diffusion coefficient of the gas in the liquid

A = cross-sectional area through which diffusion occurs

$\dfrac{\delta c}{\delta y}$ = concentration gradient (change in concentration per unit length)

y = length through which diffusion occurs

Aeration equations

Mass transfer occurs through films at the gas and liquid interfaces and through the turbulent body of fluid. This transfer from the atmosphere to a body of turbulent fluid may be described by the Lewis and Whitman[1] two-film concept, expressed in differential form similar to Fick's law of hydrodiffusion. This leads to the equation

$$\frac{\delta M}{\delta t} = -D_g A\left[\frac{\delta c}{\delta y}\right]_1 = -D_L A\left[\frac{\delta c}{\delta y}\right]_2 = -D_e A\left[\frac{\delta c}{\delta y}\right]_3 \qquad (4.2)$$

where $\left[\dfrac{\delta c}{\delta y}\right]_1$ = the concentration gradient through the gas film

$\left[\dfrac{\delta c}{\delta y}\right]_2$ = the concentration gradient through the liquid film

$\left[\dfrac{\delta c}{\delta y}\right]_3$ = the concentration gradient in the body of the liquid

D_g = the diffusion coefficient of the gas through the gas film

D_L = the diffusion coefficient of the gas through the liquid film

D_e = the eddy diffusion coefficient of the gas in the body of the liquid

In addition to the molecular diffusion through the gas and liquid films, Eq. (4.2) also includes the eddy diffusion through the body of the liquid. In the vast majority of cases of aeration, turbulent flow prevails. The value of the eddy diffusion coefficient is of the same order of magnitude as that of the eddy viscosity of the fluid, and depends upon the physical and hydraulic characteristics of the system. Because the eddy diffusivity is so great compared with the diffusivity through the liquid film, it follows from Eq. (4.2) that the concentration gradient does not vary much with the depth of the liquid in comparison with its variation across a liquid film. In most practical cases, then, the concentration of the dissolved gas throughout the liquid body may be taken as uniform. The diffusivity in the gas phase is many orders of magnitude greater than that in the liquid phase. It may be concluded from these considerations that in the transfer of a sparingly soluble gas such as oxygen or carbon dioxide, the controlling resistance is in the liquid film.

Because the concentration of the dissolved gas may be taken as uniform at all depths, the entire gradient may be assumed to exist at the interface of the two phases, and Eq. (4.2) may be reexpressed as follows:

$$\frac{\delta m}{\delta t} = \frac{D_L}{Y_L} A(C_s - C) = K_L A(C_s - C) \qquad (4.3)$$

Here, the liquid film coefficient K_L is defined as the diffusivity (diffusion coefficient) divided by the hypothetical liquid film thickness, Y_L. C_s is the saturation concentration of the gas in the water, and C is the concentration of the gas in the water after any time t.

Equation (4.3) may be expressed in concentration units by introducing the volume of the liquid V:

$$\left(\frac{I}{V}\right)\left(\frac{\delta m}{\delta t}\right)\left(\frac{\delta C}{\delta t}\right) = K_L \frac{A}{V}(C_s - C) \tag{4.4}$$

Equation (4.4) shows that the rate of transfer at any time t is proportional to the difference between the saturation concentration C_s and the actual concentration C at that time. In the case of gas absorption, the term $(C_s - C)$ will always be positive but will approach zero as the system approaches equilibrium. For gas release, the term $(C_s - C)$ will always be negative, reaching zero when equilibrium is achieved.

Equation (4.4) also shows that for a given saturation deficit or surplus $(C_s - C)$, the rate of gas transfer is proportional to the ratio of interfacial area to the liquid volume and the transfer coefficient K_L. Because of the difficulty of measuring interfacial areas in some systems, an overall transfer coefficient $K_L a$ is usually employed. This yields the following:

$$\frac{\delta C}{\delta t} = K_L a(C_s - C) \tag{4.5}$$

in which $a = AV$. $K_L a$ is a function of the interfacial area, the volume of liquid, and other physical and chemical variables of the system. Equation (4.5) integrates to

$$C_s - C = (C_s - C_o)e^{-K_L at} \quad \text{or} \quad C_s - C = (C_s - C_o)10^{-K(A/V)t} \tag{4.6}$$

in which C_o is initial concentration. The eddy diffusivity through the body of the fluid is usually so great that the concentration of the gas may be taken as uniform in most practical cases.

The Lewis and Whitman[1] model indicates a linear relation between the transfer coefficient K_L and the diffusivity D_L. Both the Higbie[2] and Danckwerts[3] models predict that the transfer is proportional to the square root of the diffusivity. By contrast, Kishinevski[4] developed a relationship indicating that K_L is independent of D_L and depends only on the intensity of turbulence at the interface. Dobbins[5,6] has presented a development leading to the following relationship:

$$K_L = [D_L r]^{1/2} \coth\left[\frac{r Y_L^2}{D_L}\right]^{1/2} \tag{4.7}$$

Equation (4.7) was developed employing the concept of Lewis and Whitman[1] and the random renewal concept of Danckwerts.[3] Equation (4.7) has the property that K_L approaches D_L/Y_L as r approaches zero and approaches $(D_L r)^{1/2}$ as r approaches infinity. The practical difficulty in Eq. (4.7) is the evaluation and definition of both r and Y_L. The previously developed relationships by Lewis and Whitman[1] and by Danckwerts[3] require the evaluation of one parameter, either Y_L or r. It is only in the case of natural streams that an approximation has been made of the rate of surface renewal, in terms of the velocity of depth of flow.[7] It is necessary to relate the various parameters of aeration equipment and devices to the film thickness and surface renewal.

Area-volume and time relationships

Langelier[8] has called attention to the reciprocal relationship between area exposed per unit volume A/V, and time t. This relationship is evident from Eq. (4.6), based on the Lewis-Whitman model. For a given situation, as long as the product of A/V and t is constant, the aerator performance will remain constant. Therefore, t may be increased at the expense of A/V and vice versa without efficiency loss. This reciprocal relationship is applied in various types of aerators. An important theoretical advantage of waterfall aerators in general is the high area-volume ratio obtained through the production of drops or thin films of water. The maximum surface area can be obtained by drop-producing spray nozzles, but exposure time will be short unless there is considerable expenditure of head to force the water high into the air. Tray and cascade aerators, on the other hand, generally produce less surface area, but the exposure time may be longer.

Diffusion-type aerators generally provide a longer contact period. For example, the water in the jet of a waterfall aerator rising 10 ft vertically and then falling back travels at an average rate of approximately 13 fps, and hence has somewhat less than a 2-s exposure. On the other hand, a bubble of air of the size often employed in diffusion aerators has a rising velocity of about 1 fps and, therefore, a contact period of approximately 10 s in a basin of 10-ft water depth.

The factor A/V representing exposed water area per unit of volume of water is of obvious importance in the aeration process. Consideration of the relationship between the area and volume of spherical drops or bubbles is, therefore, of theoretical and practical interest. From the geometry of spheres, it is evident that their area-volume ratio is $6/D$, where D is the sphere diameter. Small drop diameters are associated with large area-volume ratios and hence increased aeration efficiency. Theoretical considerations, cited by Maier,[9] also emphasize the value of obtaining as much uniformity as possible in bubble or drop diameters. The volume of a spherical drop or bubble increases as the cube of the diameter; therefore, a small percentage of large bubbles or drops can substantially reduce the surface area exposed and, hence, aeration efficiency.

Ventilation

Inasmuch as the saturation value of a gas is influenced by its partial pressure in the air in contact with the water, it is evident that ventilation is an important consideration in aerator design. An increase in the partial pressure of the gas in the air will produce a proportional increase in the saturation value. This would be advantageous in the case of gas absorption but a distinct disadvantage in the case of gas release. For gas release, the saturation value of the gas to be removed should be kept as low as possible. The minimum practical partial pressure in the air surrounding the water can be achieved by thorough ventilation.

Aeration theory leads to the prediction that aeration under pressure in a closed tank should be quite efficient as an oxygen absorption method but inefficient for carbon dioxide removal, even though the carbon dioxide removed and the excess air are periodically vented to the atmosphere. Under such conditions, the oxygen partial pressure would be high and its absorption favored. On the other hand, the partial pressure of carbon dioxide in the gas pocket in the tank would increase as removal continued, slowing the rate of release. For gas release in a closed tank, reduction in partial pressure can be accomplished by reducing the total air pressure. Large vacuum deaerating systems have been described by Powell and Bacon[10] and by Speller.[11]

Thorough ventilation is also important from a safety standpoint when gases such as carbon dioxide, methane, and hydrogen sulfide are being removed. Carbon dioxide is an asphyxiant, methane may create an explosion hazard, and hydrogen sulfide is highly poisonous.

Taste and odor removal

Certain theoretical aspects of aerator performance indicate that the efficiency of this process as a means of taste and odor reduction is limited. Compared with oxygen and other similar gases, the volatility of most taste- and odor-producing compounds is low. Vapor pressure is a measure of volatility, and the vapor pressure of a substance is the pressure at which the liquid substance and its vapor are in equilibrium at a given temperature. Vapor pressure increases with increasing temperature, and the temperature corresponding to a vapor pressure of 1 atm is the boiling point of the substance. The vapor pressure of a gas may be high even at extremely low temperatures. Carbon dioxide, for example, has a boiling point of $-78°C$. Consequently, this substance is extremely volatile at ordinary temperatures, and is susceptible to removal by aeration. Phenol, on the other hand, has a fairly high boiling point and a comparatively low vapor pressure at ordinary temperatures. Because of its low vapor pressure, it would not be at all practical to attempt phenol removal by conventional aeration processes. Within the usual water temperature range, 0 to 30°C, compounds that boil at much more than 0°C probably cannot be removed by aeration.

If the taste- and odor-producing compounds could be identified and their solubility and vapor pressure determined, an estimate of the extent to which they could be removed by aeration could be made. In general, such estimates would probably indicate that few taste- and odor-producing substances (hydrogen sulfide excepted) could be effectively removed by conventional aeration processes.

Hydrogen sulfide removal

Hydrogen sulfide can be removed by aeration, but if the concentration is high, special provisions may be required. An important property of hydrogen sulfide is its high solubility in relation to that of carbon dioxide. Also of importance is the way hydrogen sulfide ionizes in water. It is a weak acid and its ionization equations are as follows:

$$H_2S \leftrightarrows H^+ + HS^-$$

$$HS^- \leftrightarrows H^+ + + S^{2-}$$

When water containing both carbon dioxide and hydrogen sulfide is aerated, the less soluble carbon dioxide is readily removed. It also ionizes to a weak acid in water, and its removal reduces the hydrogen ion concentration (pH increase) of the water, shifting the hydrogen sulfide ionization equilibria in the direction of higher concentrations of HS^- and S^{2-}, which cannot be removed by aeration. Another complicating factor is that aeration invariably introduces oxygen, which reacts with hydrogen sulfide to form water and free sulfur. The latter reaction reduces the hydrogen sulfide concentration, but by a chemical reaction rather than by gas transfer, and unless the free sulfur is removed, it may create further water treatment problems.

The efficiency of hydrogen sulfide removal by aeration (actually gaseous transfer) can be enhanced by conducting the initial aeration process in an atmosphere containing a higher than normal concentration of carbon dioxide. Such an atmosphere can be obtained by use of flue gases. Aeration of the water in an atmosphere containing 10 percent carbon dioxide will increase or at least maintain the carbon dioxide concentration in the water, producing pH conditions favorable to the H_2S form of the sulfide and promoting its transfer from the water to the gaseous phase. Carbon dioxide can then be removed subsequently by a standard aeration process.

Design Principles and Practice

From the aeration theory presented in the preceding section of this chapter, it is evident that the transfer, by aeration, of a volatile material to or from water is dependent upon a number of factors, many of which are interrelated. The designer has little or no control over some of them, but he or she has considerable opportunity to exercise ingenuity and originality in connection with turbulence, area-volume ratio, and time of exposure. Within limits, some control also may be maintained over the composition of the aerator atmosphere.

In designing an aeration system, one factor may be favored at the expense of another. Economic considerations are likely to be as important as those of hydraulics; the final decision as to the type of aeration process to be installed—or whether aeration will be used at all—may be determined as much by economic as by physical laws. Still another factor, largely intangible in nature but quite important in some situations, is the public relations value of an ornamental or spectacular aerator that is pleasing in its architecture.

Aerator types

Spray aerators.   Spray aerators direct the water upward, vertically or at an inclined angle, in such a manner that the water is broken into small drops. Installations commonly consist of fixed nozzles on a pipe grid. Spray aerators are usually quite efficient with respect to gas transfer (carbon dioxide removal or oxygen addition) and have esthetic value. However, they require a large area, cannot be housed readily, and pose an operating problem during freezing weather.

The time of exposure of each drop is dependent on its initial velocity and trajectory. Drop size, and hence area-volume ratio, is a function of the dispersing action of the nozzle. The initial velocity of a drop emerging from an orifice or nozzle is given by

$$V = C_v\sqrt{2gh} \tag{4.8}$$

and the discharge, by the equation

$$Q = C_d A \sqrt{2gh} \qquad (4.9)$$

where h = total head on the nozzle
  g = acceleration due to gravity
  A = area of the opening
  C_v = coefficient of velocity
  C_d = coefficient of discharge ($C_d = C_v C_c$, where C_c is the coefficient of contraction)

The coefficients of velocity, contraction, and discharge will vary with the shape and other characteristics of the orifice or nozzle.

The trajectory of the spray may be vertical or inclined. If θ represents the angle between the initial velocity vector and the horizontal, the theoretical exposure time of the water drops is given by

$$t = 2C_v \sin \theta \sqrt{\frac{2h}{g}} \qquad (4.10)$$

Inasmuch as the sine of an angle of less than 90° is less than 1.0, the vertical jet gives the longest exposure time for a given value of h. The inclined jet, however, has the advantage of a longer path and less interference between falling drops. Wind will influence the path of the rising and falling drops, and an allowance must be made for its action.

Nozzle design is important in achieving optimum dispersion of water. Among the special designs are the rifled nozzle, the centrifugal (West Palm Beach) nozzle, Sacramento floating cones, impinging devices, and rotating reaction nozzles.

The size, number, and spacing of spray nozzles depend upon the head to be expended, area allocated to aeration, and interference between adjacent sprays. Theoretically, numerous small nozzles capable of producing atomized water could be used. Practically, however, extremely small nozzles are to be avoided because of clogging and consequent excessive maintenance. The nozzles in existing aerators are generally 1.0 to 1.5 in in diameter and have discharge ratings of about 75 to 150 gpm at approximately 10 psi. Nozzle spacing generally varies from 2 to 12 ft.

The area allocated to spray aeration generally varies from approximately 50 to 150 ft^2 per daily million gallons of capacity, although much larger areas have been utilized at some plants. Corrosion may be a serious problem in aerator piping, both inside and out. Corrosion-resistant materials are desirable for aerator installations.

Spray aerators are spectacular, have esthetic value, and provide a high area-volume ratio. Because spray aerators are rarely housed, ventilation presents no problem. Gas transfer between the water drops and air proceeds rapidly, and spray-type aerators usually exhibit fairly high efficiencies. In general, spray aerators will remove more than 70 percent of dissolved carbon dioxide, and removals as high as 90 percent have been experienced. Disadvantages of spray aerators are principally those associated with space requirements, cold-weather operating difficulties, short exposure time, and fairly high head requirements. Table 4.1 presents data on a number of typical spray aerator installations.

Multiple-tray aerators. Multiple-tray aerators consist of a series of trays equipped with slatted, perforated, or wire-mesh bottoms over which water is distributed and allowed to fall to a collection basin at the base. Securing good distribution of the water over the entire tray area is important for good efficiency. In many tray aerators, coarse media such as coke, stone, or ceramic balls ranging from 2 to 6 in in size are placed in the trays to improve the efficiency of gas exchange and distribution, and to take advantage of catalytic effects of deposited manganese oxides.

From three to nine trays are generally used; spacing between trays may vary from 12 to 30 in. The area required usually ranges from approximately 25 to 75 ft^2 per daily million gallons of plant capacity, but approximately 50 ft^2 per daily million gallons is the upper limit for most installations. Water application rates are roughly 20 to 30 gpm/ft^2.

Multiple-tray aerators are frequently housed. Ventilation is important and must be carefully considered in connection with location and design. Pilot-plant and design studies have emphasized the importance of ventilation as well as of water distribution. The Allen substation aerator at Memphis, Tenn., is enclosed, but ventilation was carefully considered in connection with design.[12] Aluminum scroll panels are used to promote good cross-ventilation, and the roof is open except directly over the distributing trays. This aerator has consistently produced a 90 percent or greater reduction in dissolved carbon dioxide. The carbon dioxide concentration in the raw water exceeds 90 ppm.

Tray aerators are analogous to cooling towers in many respects, and the problems encountered in the design of each are similar. If either tray aerators or cooling towers are placed in a poorly ventilated building, performance is certain to be impaired. Artificial ventilation is a requirement under these conditions. For certain types of enclosed tray aerators, good artificial ventilation is provided by a forced draft. Such aerators generally employ the counterflow principle. The air is supplied at the bottom of the aerator and travels counter to the downward flow of the water. The counterflow of air and water is advantageous, and such aerators exhibit excellent oxygen absorption and carbon dioxide removal capabilities.

TABLE 4.1 Typical Spray Aerators

Installation	Design capacity, mgd	Number of nozzles	Spacing, ft	Type	Pressure, psi	Space per mgd capacity, ft²	Operating results		
							Flow, mgd	CO$_2$, ppm	
								Raw	Aerated
Contra Costa, Calif.	12	42	4	Sacramento	1.64	138			
Denver, Colo., North Side Filter Plant*	64	600	3	Special	11.27	85	64	Trace	
Jacksonville, Fla.†									
Main St.	12.95	200	2.5	Floating cone	0.98	97	7	10	4
Hendricks Ave.	7.30	26	6	Adjustable cone	1.19	129	2	8	4
West Palm Beach, Fla.‡	20	202	2&3	West Palm Beach	10	78	Variable		
Bangor, Me.§	8	80	2 to 2.5	Spraco	3	50	4.25	7.5	
Lawrence, Mass.¶	10	70	10	Sacramento	1.73	700			
Springfield, Mo.¶	5.6	39	12	Spraco #13A	17	1000			
Appleton, Wis.††	8	72	3.5 × 4	Spraco #13A	2.3	128			

*Surface supply essentially free of carbon dioxide.

†Supply from deep wells, all containing hydrogen sulfide in concentrations from 1.5 to 2.0 ppm. Aeration removes from 25 to 40 percent and supplies oxygen for oxidation of remainder.

‡Supply from shallow lakes; aeration for reduction of algal odors and carbon dioxide reduction.

§Surface supply; aeration for reduction of carbon dioxide and nitrogen trichloride. Aerated water contains about 15 ppm free chlorine.

¶Surface supply; aeration for reduction of algal odors.

††Surface supply; aeration for reduction of algal odors; reports average reduction of threshold odors from 24 to 51 percent; alum added prior to aeration.

Avoidance of corrosion, of slime, and of algal growths are important considerations in the design of tray aerators. Stainless steel, aluminum, rot-resistant wood, and concrete are examples of durable, corrosion-resistant materials that have been used effectively in existing aerator installations. Slime and algal growths may be controlled by chlorination and copper sulfate treatment of the raw water. Information on a number of multiple-tray aerators is given in Table 4.2.

Carbon dioxide removal by multiple-tray aerators can be approximated by the following empirical equation developed by Scott:[13]

$$C_n = C_c 10^{-kn} \qquad (4.11)$$

where C_n and C_c are the concentrations of carbon dioxide in parts per million after passing through n trays and as determined originally in the distribution tray, n is the number of trays including the distribution tray, and k, which ranges from approximately 0.12 to 0.16, is a coefficient dependent on ventilation, temperature, turbulence, and other characteristics of the installation. Attention is directed to the fact that this equation is similar to that previously presented in the discussion on gas transfer theory, Eq. (4.6). The empirical equation does not contain the factor C_s found in the theoretical equation, but for carbon dioxide this is only about 0.5 ppm and its omission is not significant, especially if the raw water contains a high concentration of carbon dioxide. The value k is equivalent to A/V in the theoretical equation, and the value n is approximately directly proportional to t.

Cascade aerators.   In cascade aerators, increases in the exposure time and area-volume ratio are obtained by allowing the water to flow downward over a series of steps or baffles. The simplest cascade aerator is a concrete step structure which causes the water to fall in fairly thin layers from one level to another. Exposure time can be increased by increasing the number of steps, and the area-volume ratio can be improved by adding baffles to produce turbulence. Head requirements vary from 3 to 10 ft. A cascade aerator at Champaign-Urbana, Ill., reduces the dissolved carbon dioxide concentration from 44–55 to 27–34 ppm. A similar aerator at Ames, Iowa, results in a reduction from about 19 to 10 ppm. Carbon dioxide reduction by cascade aerators often ranges from 20 to 45 percent. Space requirements are of the order of 40 to 50 ft^2 per daily million gallons. In cold climates these aerators must be housed, and adequate provisions must be made for ventilation. As with tray aerators, corrosion, slime, and algal problems may be encountered.

Diffusion aerators.   Diffusion aerators consist of rectangular concrete tanks in which perforated pipes, porous diffuser tubes, or various pat-

TABLE 4.2 Typical Multiple-Tray Aerators

Installation	Design capacity, mgd	Area of trays, ft²	Type and size of media	No. of trays including distribution plan	Vertical distance between pans, in	Housing	Space per million gallons per day capacity, ft²	Operating results		
								Flow, mgd	CO₂, ppm	
									Raw	Aerated
Naples, Fla.*	1.1	81	2-in coke	4	18	Outside	74	0.67	28	4
Wichita, Kan.†	48	986	2-in coke	5	18	Inside	21	30	21	7.9
Owensboro, Ky.‡	10	280	Coke	6	14	Outside	28	5.4	34	8
Columbia, Mo.§	3	160	None	5	18	§	53			
Marshall, Mo.¶	2	80	None	6	18	Inside	40	1.03	28	10
Memphis, Tenn.†† Allen Sta.	30	896	3-in–6-in coke	10	15½	Inside	30	10.5	96	3.2
Sheehan Sta.	30	690	Coke	6	16	Inside	23	22.6	38	10

*Removal of hydrogen sulfide and carbon dioxide.
†Removal of carbon dioxide; has forced-draft ventilation at rate of 29,500 cfm.
‡Removal of carbon dioxide.
§Removal of hydrogen sulfide; outdoors with roof and screen sides.
¶Removal of carbon dioxide; has forced-draft ventilation at rate of 2000 cfm.
††Removal of carbon dioxide; natural ventilation through open walls.

ented impingement or sparger devices are inserted near the bottom of the aeration basin. Compressed air is injected through the system to produce bubbles. On rising through the water, these cause turbulence and provide opportunity for the exchange of volatile materials between the bubbles and the water and between the air and the water at the latter's surface.

An aerator of the diffused-air type generally provides a longer aeration time than one of the waterfall type. This is advantageous, but other factors, including turbulence, air-volume ratio, and gas transfer resistance, also influence aerator performance, so that comparison with the waterfall type cannot be made solely on the basis of aeration time.

Tanks for employing the diffused-air process are commonly 9 to 15 ft deep and 10 to 30 ft wide. Ratios of width to depth should not exceed 2 if effective mixing is to be obtained. Tank length is governed by the desired detention period, which usually varies from 10 to 30 min. Air diffusers (perforated pipes, porous plates, or tubes) are generally placed along one side of the tank to impart a spiral flow to the water. A spiral flow pattern is desirable because it produces higher water surface velocities, which promote gas transfer. In addition, a substantial number of bubbles do not escape immediately but are carried across the aeration basin and held in a more or less fixed position by the descending water.

Porous tubes or plates are generally located at about middepth in the tank to reduce air compression head. The amount of air required ranges from 0.01 to 0.15 ft^3 per gallon of water treated. Sufficient diffuse capacity must be provided to supply air at the required rate without excessive pressure loss. Lateral baffles are used in some cases to prevent short circuiting.

Air pressure requirements will depend upon the submergence of the air diffusers and the friction loss through the air distribution system. Power requirements vary from 0.5 to 2.0 kW per daily million gallons of plant capacity. The average is about 1.0 kW per million gallons per day. When porous plate or tube or other types of diffusers producing relatively small bubbles are used, the air supply should be filtered to avoid rapid diffuser clogging.

Diffuser-type aerators require less space than spray aerators and generally more than tray aerators. Practically no head is lost through diffusion units, and this is frequently an important aspect in overall plant design. Furthermore, few or no cold-weather operating problems are encountered, and there is no need for housing. In some instances, diffusion aerators have been used for chemical mixing as well as for aeration. Data relating to several diffused-air installations are given in Table 4.3.

TABLE 4.3   Typical Diffused-Air-Type Aerators

Installation	Capacity, mgd	Period of aeration, min	Objective	Air supply, ft^3/gal	Power requirement per million gallons per day capacity, kW
Petersburg, Ind.*	1.0	30	Odor removal and mixing	0.10	1.46
Huntingburg, Ind.*	0.4	8.5	Odor removal	0.15	0.75
St. Paul, Minn.†	48	0.16	Odor removal and mixing	0.01	
Brownsville, Texas*	4	14	Gas removal and mixing	0.07	0.48
Ft. Atkinson, Wis.*	0.75	18	Iron and odor removal	0.16	1.87
Kenosha, Wis.†	11.6	0.21	Odor removal	0.01	
Milwaukee, Wis.†	104	1.76	Rapid mixing	0.035	0.90
Salt Lake City, Utah†	100	15	Odor removal	0.16	1.49

*From data given in *Water Quality and Treatment,* 2d ed., American Water Works Assn., New York, 1950, p. 127.
†Activated carbon also used for odor removal.

Patented types.   In addition to the general types of aerators previously discussed, there are a number of patented types available. Operating and design data relating to patented aeration devices may be obtained from the manufacturers of such units.

Limitations of aeration

Aeration finds its greatest application in the absorption and release of gases, principally oxygen, carbon dioxide, and hydrogen sulfide. Whenever water is aerated, its dissolved-oxygen content is increased. This may render some waters appreciably more corrosive. A few plants have abandoned aeration because of increased corrosiveness caused by a higher dissolved-oxygen level. On the other hand, many water treatment plants have made effective use of aeration for oxygen addition and carbon dioxide reduction without any reported corrosion difficulties.

The use of aeration processes after filtration, or as the sole treatment for well water, has the disadvantage of subjecting the water to airborne contamination just prior to its introduction into the distribution system. Such applications are of doubtful value. Excessive aeration may adversely affect iron and manganese removal when these elements occur in combination with organic matter. In such instances, it may be better to design a less vigorous aeration system.

Taste and odor removal

Most water supply taste and odor problems are caused by minute amounts of organic matter, and many of these organic compounds do not have sufficient volatility to respond to conventional aeration processes. Some plants equipped for aeration have discontinued the process because of its inability to remove tastes and odors. In general, conventional aeration processes are not particularly effective as a means of taste and odor reduction. Experiences at Appleton, Wis.,[14] and Nitro, W. Va.,[15] are in some respects exceptions to this generalization. At the Appleton plant, during the warm months of August and September, spray aeration has reduced the threshold odor number approximately 25 units (44 percent reduction). During colder periods, when volatility of the taste- and odor-producing materials was much lower, aeration was less efficient and of questionable value economically. At Nitro, raw water from the Kanawha River has exhibited threshold odor numbers of 5000 to 6000 caused by industrial wastes. High-pressure aeration into the atmosphere has been reported to be a good means of reducing these odors. Odor-number reductions as high as 98 percent were achieved by an experimental, single-stage spray aerator operating at a pressure of 110 psi at the nozzle.

The full-scale aerator installation at Nitro normally operates at a nozzle pressure of 55 psi and consists of 30 nozzles arranged along a pipe which decreases in diameter stepwise from 18 to 8 in. The aerator pump delivers 4000 gpm through the aerator at 55 psi. When the raw-water pumps are off, a check valve in the aeration basin effluent line opens to permit the recirculation of aerated water. Thus, some of the water receives additional aeration. Haynes and Grant,[15] who conducted the aeration investigations at Nitro, while pointing out the value of high-pressure aeration, caution against assuming that the same results can be obtained with odors of other types. They call attention to the fact that the Nitro aerator could not be operated during very cold weather because of ice difficulties. Another problem encountered in the practical application of high-pressure aeration was the abrasion of the diffusion vanes, or turbine centers, of the nozzles. High abrasion rates were associated with high raw-water turbidity.

Carbon dioxide removal

Approximately 10 ft of head are required for many of the waterfall aerators, and air compression requirements are roughly the same for the air diffusion process. Energy requirements for the two types will not differ materially, and for the purpose of the following discussion are taken at 39 kWh/mil gal. This is the energy requirement for pumping based on 80 percent overall efficiency. To remove the carbon dioxide chemically, 5.9 lb lime (90 percent CaO) per million gallons is required for each part per million of carbon dioxide. If the neutralization is complete (calcium carbonate), the lime requirement is doubled. If electric energy costs 1 cent per kilowatthour, the operating cost for power to lift water through the aerator, based on the preceding assumptions, will be approximately 39 cents per million gallons. If lime costs 1 cent per pound, the cost per million gallons of removing 1 ppm of carbon dioxide by complete neutralization will be 12 cents. (Partial neutralization costs half as much but results in an increase in water hardness.) Evidently, if carbon dioxide reduction will be no more than about 4 to 7 ppm, it may be more economical from an operating standpoint to dispense with aeration unless there are other benefits associated with its use. Baylis[16] has expressed the opinion that when the carbon dioxide concentration in the raw water is approximately 10 ppm or less, it is generally more economical to remove carbon dioxide by chemical neutralization than by aeration.

Application criteria

In deciding when to use aeration for the treatment of water, particular attention must be paid to the source of the water, that is, whether it comes from ground or surface resources.

Groundwater. Aeration processes are most useful in connection with the removal of carbon dioxide from groundwater, along with the simultaneous addition of oxygen. Removal of the former, to the extent possible by aeration, is often advantageous, especially if the water is to be softened by the lime–soda ash method. If the raw water, however, contains no more than approximately 10 ppm of carbon dioxide, aeration solely for carbon dioxide reduction probably cannot be justified from the standpoint of operating economics. Lime neutralization would in general be cheaper in such cases. Exceptions might be encountered in locations where chemical costs are unusually high or where electric energy costs are low.

Oxygen addition is generally desirable, especially if iron and manganese removal is a treatment requirement. Aeration processes are an effective means of adding oxygen to groundwater, which usually has an oxygen deficiency.

Aeration is also useful for the removal of hydrogen sulfide from groundwater. Concentrations of the order of 1.0 or 2.0 ppm can be handled satisfactorily by conventional aeration processes. High concentrations may require special provisions, such as prolonged aeration or an initial aeration period in the presence of an atmosphere with a high partial pressure of carbon dioxide. In general, aeration should receive careful consideration in connection with the treatment of groundwater supplies, and its use for their treatment is probably justified in many cases.

Surface water.   Surface water is usually very low in carbon dioxide, free of sulfide, and fairly high in dissolved oxygen. Furthermore, conventional aeration processes are of questionable value as a means of taste and odor removal. In view of these facts, aeration does not appear to have general applicability to the treatment of surface water. Certainly, it is not axiomatic that all surface water should be aerated. The use of aeration with surface water should be examined critically and determinations made of what it will accomplish and what its cost will be. This cost should be compared with the costs of alternative methods of achieving similar results.

Pilot-plant studies are often desirable in connection with an engineering analysis of the applicability of aeration processes to water treatment problems. Results of a few pilot-plant runs, using relatively simple equipment, may, if properly analyzed, provide useful aerator design criteria.

References

1. W. K. Lewis and W. G. Whitman, "Principles of Gas Absorption," *Indus. and Eng. Chem.*, vol. 16, 1924, p. 1215. H. G. Becker, "Discussion," *ibid.*, vol. 16, 1924, p. 1220.
2. R. Higbie, "The Rate of Absorption of a Pure Gas into a Still Liquid during Short Periods of Exposure," *Trans. AICHE*, 1934–1935.
3. P. V. Danckwerts, "Significance of Liquid Film Coefficients in Gas Absorption," *Indus. and Eng. Chem.*, vol. 43, 1951, p. 1460.
4. M. Kishinevski, "Two Approaches to the Theoretical Aspects of Gas Absorption," *USSR Journal Appl. Chem.*, September 1955, p. 881.
5. W. E. Dobbins, "The Nature of the Oxygen Transfer Coefficient in Aeration Systems," *Proc. Manhattan College Conf. on Biolog. Waste Treat.*, April 1965.
6. W. E. Dobbins, "BOD and Oxygen Relationships in Streams," *Journal San. Eng. Div. ASCE*, vol. 90, no. SA3, June 1964, p. 53.
7. D. J. O'Connor and W. E. Dobbins, "Mechanism of Reaeration in Natural Streams," *Trans ASCE*, vol. 123, 1958, p. 641.
8. W. F. Langelier, "The Theory and Practice of Aeration," *Journal AWWA*, vol. 24, no. 1, 1932, p. 62.
9. C. G. Maier, "The Ferric Sulfate-Sulfuric Acid Process," *Bull. 260*, Bureau of Mines, U.S. Dept. of Interior, Washington, D.C., 1927.
10. S. T. Powell and H. E. Bacon, "Corrosion Control by Aeration," *Water and Sew. Works*, vol. 84, 1937, p. 109.
11. F. N. Speller, *Corrosion Causes and Prevention*, 3d ed., McGraw-Hill, New York, 1951.

12. R. L. Brown, "Aeration Experiments at Memphis, Tenn.," *Journal AWWA,* vol. 44, no. 4, 1952, p. 336.
13. G. R. Scott, "Committee Report: Aeration of Water," *Journal AWWA,* vol. 46, no. 9, 1955, p. 873.
14. W. U. Gallagher, "Control of Algae at Appleton, Wis.," *Journal AWWA,* vol. 32, no. 7, 1940, p. 1165.
15. L. Haynes and W. Grant, "Reduction of Chemical Odors at Nitro, W. Va.," *Journal AWWA,* vol. 37, no. 10, 1945, p. 1013.
16. J. R. Baylis, *Elimination of Taste and Odor,* McGraw-Hill, New York, 1935.

5

Coagulation and Flocculation

Definitions

Coagulation and flocculation may be broadly described as a chemical/physical process of blending or mixing a coagulating chemical into a stream and then gently stirring the blended mixture. The overall purpose is to improve the particulate and colloid reduction efficiency of the subsequent settling and/or filtration processes. The function and definition of each stage of the process are summarized as follows:

1. *Mixing* (frequently referred to as flash mixing, rapid mixing, or initial mixing) is the physical process of blending or dispersing a chemical additive into an unblended stream. Mixing is used where an additive needs to be dispersed rapidly (within a period of 1 to 10 s).

2. *Backmixing* is the dispersion of an additive into a previously blended or partially blended stream or batch. In most cases, backmixing results in less efficient use of chemicals. Backmixing frequently occurs when the volume of the mixing basin or reactor section of a process is too large or the flow rate is low. Backmixing or solids contact may be advantageous to some processes (see the section, "Proprietary Designs").

3. *Coagulation* is the process of destabilization of the charge (predominantly negative) on suspended particulates and colloids. The purpose of destabilization is to lessen the repelling character of the particles and allow them to become attached to other particles so that they may be removed in subsequent processes. The particulates in raw waters (which contribute to color and turbidity) are mainly clays, silts, viruses, bacteria, fulvic and humic acids, min-

erals (including asbestos, silicates, silica, and radioactive particles), and organic particulates. At pH levels above pH 4.0, such particles or molecules are generally negatively charged.

4. *Coagulant chemicals* are inorganic and/or organic chemicals that, when added to water at an optimum dose (normally in the range of 1 to 100 mg/L), will cause destabilization. Most coagulants are cationic in water and include such common water treatment chemicals as alum, ferric sulfate, lime (CaO), and cationic organic polymers.

5. *Flocculation* is the agglomeration of destabilized particles and colloids toward settleable (or filterable) particles (flocs). Flocculated particles may be small (less than 0.1 mm diameter) micro flocs or large, visible flocs (0.1 to 3.0 mm diameter). Flocculation begins immediately after destabilization in the zone of decaying mixing energy (downstream from the mixer) or as a result of the turbulence of transporting flow. Such incidental flocculation may be an adequate flocculation process in some instances. Normally flocculation involves an intentional and defined process of gentle stirring to enhance contact of destabilized particles and to build floc particles of optimum size, density, and strength to be subsequently removed by settling or filtration.

6. *Direct filtration* may be defined as a treatment process that includes mixing, coagulation, flocculation, and filtration, but intentionally excludes a clarification process. With direct filtration, *all* suspended solids are removed during the filtration stage.

7. *In-line filtration* is a treatment process that includes mixing, coagulation, and filtration, but excludes flocculation and clarification. It is not possible to exclude flocculation completely from any process that includes the addition of a coagulant chemical, because, as a result of turbulence, incidental flocculation takes place in the conduit between the mixing stage and the filter, in the volume above the filter media, and within the filter media (see the section, "Incidental Flocculation").

   In some instances, it may be possible to exclude coagulant addition (and mixing) and simply run water through a filter. Such a process may not significantly change turbidity, but it may remove gross particulates [particles larger than 20 μm (0.02 mm)].

Criteria Considerations

Particulates and colloids in raw water are diverse and variable. Raw-water sources may display significant seasonal, and in some cases frequent daily variations. The designer may have limited control over variations in source quality and may be required to design a facility to

treat the least favorable combinations of flow and quality characteristics. Extremes with respect to particulate loads, as may be indicated
by turbidity data, may not be critical. Highly turbid water may respond efficiently to coagulation but usually requires higher coagulant
doses and produces more sludge. Provided there is provision in the design for the disposal of removed solids, the critical raw-water quality
characteristics may not coincide with maximum particulate load. Difficult water may be water with relatively low turbidity or low total
dissolved solids (TDS). Low temperature may also reduce the process
efficiency (see the section, "Temperature"). Critical raw-water quality
conditions are those that are liable to occur at maximum demand periods.

Water drawn from major impoundments and groundwater may
have predictable characteristics, and thus design criteria may be less
conservative. The most unpredictable water is generally that drawn
from live rivers or surface sources subject to variations in quality.
Treatment plants for such water may require frequent technical adjustment. If full-time technical supervision is not available, conservative design criteria would be appropriate.

Where there are existing plants treating a given source of water,
full-scale testing, including modification of an existing plant for testing purposes, provides more reliable data than pilot testing. Pilot
plants for the testing of mixing and flocculation processes require
careful design, scale adjustments, and statistical analysis of developed
data. If selection of coagulant chemicals is the goal, jar testing may
provide adequate information for conventional processes. On the other
hand, for design of major plants, especially in the absence of existing
treatment plant data from the same source, pilot-plant testing may
yield significant capital cost savings.

On all treatment plant designs, provision for adjustment and flexibility should be incorporated even when processes and criteria have been
confirmed by pilot or full-scale tests. The provision of adjustable features
(such as alternative chemical feeding locations, adjustable mixing energy input, spare chemical feeding equipment, adjustable weir plates,
compartmentalization baffles, and provision for monitoring facilities)
usually involves only incremental additional costs but may add significantly to plant efficiency and the investment value.

Process Objectives

Particulate or turbidity reduction

For almost all plants that treat surface water (for potable use), a major objective is to lower turbidity (or particulates) to a predetermined
standard. The mixing and coagulation process does not reduce the volume of particulates but changes their characteristics so that they may

be efficiently removed in subsequent stages (clarification and/or filtration).

Particulates include all suspended material such as clays, and other materials listed in the definition of coagulation. Their collective presence may be indicated by turbidity measurements. [Particle counts provide an insight into the size and distribution of suspended particulates greater than 2.0 μm (0.002 mm) diameter.] Particulates less than 2.0 μm diameter, however, normally contribute most of the turbidity.

Normally the plant objective is to consistently reach an effluent turbidity goal. Related objectives, such as color reduction, particulate number goals, or removal of specific pathogenic organisms, may also be incidentally achieved. The ultimate goal for turbidity may be in the range of 0.1 to 1.0 TU, depending on the standard to be achieved. If the standard or turbidity goal is less than 0.5 TU, an additional adjustment, such as the feeding of filter aids prior to the filtration stage, may be required. (Radioactivity due to nonionized radionuclides may also be reduced by coagulation and subsequent processes.)

Color reduction

Natural color in raw water (often described as peat stain) is usually due to humic and fulvic acids. Humic and fulvic acids are present in water as hydrophilic colloids. They are strongly negatively charged and will pass through conventional sand or anthracite filters unless destabilized.

Color in water that is due to industrial discharges should be investigated thoroughly and where possible should be corrected prior to the water treatment process.

Color removal objectives vary over a wide range depending upon the criteria and standards adopted. The USEPA (1984) recommended limit for color is 15 mg Pt (platinum)/L. The WHO International (1971) recommended limit is 5 mg Pt/L. With certain naturally colored water, it may be very difficult to consistently lower color to 5 units by conventional processes (which include coagulation). Large doses of coagulants may be required, and for highly colored soft raw water, a limit of 15 units may be a more achievable objective.

In other cases, however, color reduction may be an incidental effect of turbidity reduction.

Organics reduction

Coagulation (and subsequent processes) may be an efficient means of meeting objectives for organics reduction. Organics such as total organic carbon (TOC), color, trihalomethane (THM) precursors, or specific organic compounds listed in drinking-water standards may be incidentally reduced to acceptable levels in meeting turbidity goals or may be specifically reduced by higher coagulant doses or by selected coagulants or treatment sequences. Normally the addition of oxidants (especially ozone, but also chlorine in some instances) prior to coagulants improves the efficiency of the coagulation process. In other cases it may be necessary to defer addition of certain oxidation chemicals until after the removal of most of the suspended solids and colloids.

Microbial reduction

Coagulation and associated processes are an effective means of reduction of specific or indicator organisms.[1] There is a strong correlation between turbidity reduction and microbiological reduction (bacteria and viruses). The designer should be aware of the correlation and should also be aware that filtration is not necessarily a barrier to pathogenic cysts. Coagulation of water prior to filtration (in instances where raw water conforms to standards for turbidity and color) should be practiced in order to reduce passage of all particulates less than 100 μm diameter through the filtration process.

Relationship of Coagulation to Subsequent Processes

Clarification

For turbid raw water (turbidity which exceeds 10 TU, as a guide), clarification is normally an essential process subsequent to coagulation and flocculation. It may be feasible to directly filter water with 20 TU, but such applications should be preceded by pilot-plant testing. The efficiency of the clarification process is highly dependent upon:

Optimum coagulant dose

Selection of appropriate coagulant(s)

Mixing

Flocculation

Clarification, however, may not need to be a highly efficient process, provided that the suspended load is reduced sufficiently to permit efficient operation of the filtration process (see Chap. 6).

Filtration

The efficiency of the filtration process is highly dependent on the preceding coagulation (conditioning) process. Filtration is not a straining process, and its efficiency, as measured by turbidity (or particulate) reduction, can vary over a range of 50 percent to 99 percent or higher, depending upon the adequacy of the preceding destabilization process.

Typically, a raw water with a turbidity of, say, 10 TU applied to a well-designed filter will provide an effluent of approximately 5 TU if no coagulation chemicals are added. With the addition of appropriate coagulants, plus optimum mixing and flocculation, the filter effluent quality could drop to, say, less than 0.2 TU.

Factors Affecting Coagulation

Raw-water source

The source of raw water is of particular interest to the designer. Groundwater sources may be of constant temperature and quality and thus provide more assurance of predictable conditions. Water drawn from major impoundments normally shows seasonal changes in temperature, turbidity, and other parameters, but may be of predictable quality.

Water sources from unregulated rivers or live streams or from relatively small impoundments (less than 2 days storage based on projected maximum river flow rate) may be more difficult to treat than more constant quality sources. Changes in stream flow rates are usually accompanied by changes in quality which require adjustment of coagulant chemicals and feed rates. Live streams may also be more vulnerable to toxic or adverse discharges and spills. Off-river storage (2 to 10 days detention) is often practiced to improve the reliability of plant effluent quality and to reduce coagulant and disinfectant chemical costs.

Temperature

Low temperatures have an adverse effect on the efficiency of all treatment processes. There is generally adequate flexibility in mixer design to take care of temperature effects, but the detention time in flocculation facilities should be adjusted, as noted in the following guidelines:

Guidelines for Flocculator Detention Time
Temperature Adjustment

Temperature, °C	Detention time factor (20°C = 100)
0	135
5	125
10	115
15	107
20	100
25	95
30	90

Anaerobic water

Anaerobic water may be more difficult to treat than surface water as a result of interference of unoxidized organics with the coagulant process. Water drawn from impoundments of more than 10 m depth should be investigated for seasonal stratification effects. The costs of destratification may be less than the cost of the additional coagulants required. Other adverse water quality parameters, such as iron, manganese, and taste and odors, may also be reduced by reservoir management techniques.

Suspended solids

The nature of suspended solids in raw water is a design consideration. Although highly turbid water may be relatively easy to treat, turbid water normally requires higher coagulant doses and results in greater volumes of sludge. Exceptionally high levels of suspended solids should be evaluated. Off-river storage should be investigated.

Coagulant Chemical Selection

Appropriate testing, prior to design, should be the basis for coagulant selection; however, all designs should be flexible enough to permit changes if conditions and new technology indicate. If possible, predesign tests should cover critical seasonal conditions. For small plants—less than 10 ML/day—provision for one coagulant may be appropriate, if tests indicate. Provision for feeding two coagulants is justified on live rivers. For large plants, provision for feeding three or even four coagulant chemicals is common (see the section, "Adjustment of pH").

The selection of coagulant chemicals that can meet quality goals is generally made on economic considerations along with reliability, safety, and chemical storage considerations (see Chap. 13).

Sludge production and disposal is a consideration. Metal ion coagulants do produce larger volumes of sludge than polymers. Also, pretreatment (ozonation, for example) may reduce coagulant demands and thus sludge production.

Generally, liquid coagulant chemicals have advantages. Most solid (powder or granular form) coagulant chemicals need to be converted to a soluble form for feeding. The most commonly used coagulants are shown in Table 5.1. Chemical evaluation data obtained from pilot-plant tests or extensive jar tests can be evaluated by several methods. A combination of a metal ion coagulant and an organic coagulant may provide the most effective and economical destabilizing option. Metal

TABLE 5.1   Common Coagulation Chemicals

Common name		
Aluminum sulfate	$Al_2(SO_4)_3 14(H_2O)$	Most common coagulant in the U.S. Often used with cationic polymers
Ferric chloride	$FeCl_3$	May be more effective than alum in some applications
Ferric sulfate	$Fe_2(SO_4)_3$	
Aluminum polymers	—	Includes polyaluminum chloride
Cationic polymers	—	Synthetic polyelectrolytes. Large molecules

ion coagulants lend themselves to quality control and standard specifications. Organic polymers, on the other hand, are not standardized and may be difficult to evaluate and to ensure consistent characteristics. Manufacturers and suppliers of polymers can provide valuable assistance during the test period, design, and operations. Simple descriptions of polymers should be used for design purposes. In general, the selected polymer can be defined by such factors as (1) cationic, anionic, or nonionic, (2) specific gravity, (3) viscosity or granular characteristics, and (4) standardized tests as well as trade names. Designs should be flexible enough to ensure that alternative organic coagulants could be used.

The coagulation process may be improved by preozonation. Ozone may significantly reduce coagulant requirements to the point where low residual solids (or filtration efficiency) make direct filtration feasible.

Oxidation with air and chemical oxidants such as chlorine and potassium permanganate may also aid coagulation by oxidizing iron and manganese, which can aid floc formation.

Lime is also a coagulant and may significantly assist in the reduction of suspended solids and colloids.

Adjustment of pH

Control of pH and alkalinity may be an essential aspect of coagulation. The optimum pH for coagulation varies but is generally within the following ranges:

Alum	pH 5.5 to 7.5	typically pH 7.0
Ferric	pH 5.0 to 8.5	typically pH 7.5

In natural water with low pH or low alkalinity, it is often necessary to add caustic soda or lime to raise the pH and to offset the acidity of metal ion coagulants.

The final effluent from a plant is often adjusted to a pH above 7.5 to provide a less corrosive effluent. The pH adjustment in the plant may be at several stages:

Initial mixing

Prefiltration

Postfiltration

Thus it may be necessary to split the feed of pH-adjusting chemicals to two or three process locations.

For small plants and for plants where the chemical requirements for upward pH adjustment are small, liquid caustic soda is the most commonly used chemical because of the ease of handling. When larger quantities of upward-pH-adjusting chemicals are required, lime is normally the most economical choice. Lime, however, may add turbidity. If lime is used for postfiltration pH adjustment, it may be necessary to use a lime saturator to ensure that no turbidity is added.

In theory, lime or caustic soda may need to be added ahead of the initial mixing (coagulation) stage, but in practice, it is often added with the coagulant chemicals. (If lime or caustic soda is adequately dispersed across the total influent turbulent flow, initial high-energy mixing of the pH-adjusting chemicals may not be required if the chemicals are added more than 10 s upstream. Otherwise they may be added with coagulant chemicals, if jar tests indicate no adversities.)

Mixing

General

All chemical additions to a flow require mixing to ensure dispersion across the total flow. In cases where mixing time and energy are not factors, such as fluoride chemicals and postfiltration chlorination, the turbulence due to friction in a pipe or channel may be adequate for mixing. Normally a minimum distance of 30 pipe diameters or channel widths is necessary to ensure dispersion.

When mixing time is a consideration, as is the case with most coagulant chemicals, additional energy is required to ensure mixing within a period of 1 to 3 s. As a guide to mixing, the G value is used to calculate energy requirements (see the section, "Mixing Energy"). The G value is an indication of medium shears and turbulence in an assumed volume of liquid. Energy within the mixing zone may vary significantly, and judgment is necessary to determine the volume of the zone where the energy is dissipated. It may be necessary to provide stators or baffles to ensure that energy is transferred from rotating mixers.

For alum and polymer mixing, the required G value is in the range of 600 to 1000 s^{-1} or a Gt of 1000 or 2000, where t is effective mixing time in seconds. (Older texts may quote G values of 300 s^{-1}. Such references often referred to mixing times of 15 to 30 s, and the actual total power input may have been greater than in higher-intensity and lower-volume applications.)

For mechanical flash mixers, fixed-speed applications are common, and the maximum tip speed of propeller mixers should be approximately 5 m/s so as to limit shear on long-chain-molecule polymers.

For mixing in large conduits or pipes (diameters or width greater than 750 mm), it is usually necessary to provide multiple nozzles for chemical addition to ensure that the coagulant is dispersed across the total zone of turbulence. Pump mixers overcome the problems of initial dispersion. Where mixing takes place in a pipe or conduit with a defined velocity of more than 0.5 m/s, the volume V for computing G may be assumed to be equivalent to the volume of 2 s of maximum flow. In mixing basins, where there is a lower velocity or the possibility of backflow eddies, the total volume of the basin should be used to determine V.

Types of Mixers

Introduction

Mixing of coagulant chemicals can be achieved by a number of methods. The method selected depends on plant size, range of flow, available head, and type of coagulant. Typical methods include:

Method	Comment
Mechanical mixing	Common application. See the sections, "Proprietary Designs" and "Sludge Recirculation and Solids Contact"
Air	Simple, advantageous if aeration required. Not common. May cause scum and floatables
Hydraulic mixing	Simple, effective, nonmechanical. Energy may vary with flow
In-line blender (mechanical)	Efficient. Effective at all flows
In-line blender (static)	Simple. Energy varies with flow
Pump mixer	Effective, efficient. Not affected by flow rate
Grid mixer	Effective. Maintenance problems
Throttle valve	Simple. May result in excessive energy. Can shear polymers. Not common

Mechanical mixers

Mechanical mixers are generally propeller- or paddle-type devices. More than one set of propeller or paddle blades may be provided on a shaft. Stators (baffles near the blades of the mixer or on the wall of the basin) may be provided to maximize energy transfer to the fluid and to minimize residual velocities at the outlet. Mechanical mixers often include a vertical shaft with a speed reducer and electric motor. Propeller-type mixers can be arranged so that flow is directed in any direction (Fig. 5.1). With propeller-type blades, the coagulant chemical is generally directed to the eye of the propeller on the suction (upstream) side. Mechanical mixers often provide reliable service and satisfactory results. However, unless carefully designed within a small-volume basin or conduit (2- to 5-s detention time), they may incorporate backmixing characteristics and may not utilize chemicals efficiently. In some cases, backmixing may be advantageous. Solids contact is a feature of some circular proprietary-design mixer-clarifiers (see the section, "Proprietary Designs").

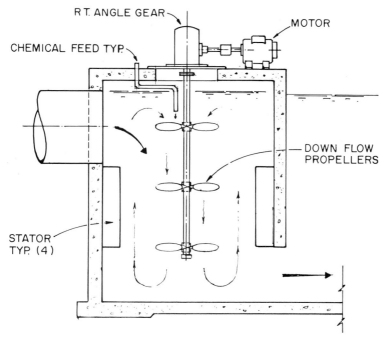

Figure 5.1   Propeller-type mechanical flash mixer.

Normally, mechanical mixers are not provided with variable-speed drives. (Note that energy, kW, input for a propeller or paddle mixer varies as speed, rpm^3. G varies as speed, $rpm^{1.5}$.) If adjustments to energy input are necessary, they may often be achieved by changing propellers or paddle blades or by adjusting shaft speed by changing pullies or using other mechanical methods.

Air mixing

Air mixing may be a simple and reliable method and has advantages where aeration is required. It is easy to incorporate into existing structures where installation of other mechanical equipment may not be convenient. It is especially applicable to deep conduits or vertical sections of piping. The energy applied in adding air may be computed as the volume of water displaced per unit time, multiplied by the depth below the free surface. The energy applied may be varied directly by adjusting air flow.

Air mixing is not widely used, and before it is incorporated into a design, a check should be made to determine whether scum and floatable material would be a problem. Limited quantities of floating scum (or sludge) may be accepted onto filters. Certain coagulants and/ or algae may increase floatables.

Energy input, US units:

$$hp = \frac{Qh}{528} \tag{5.1}$$

where Q = free air discharge, ft^3/min
$\qquad h$ = depth of air inlet nozzle below water surface, ft
$\qquad$ hp = horsepower input

Energy input, SI units:

$$kW = \frac{qh}{100} \tag{5.2}$$

where q = free air discharge, L/s
$\qquad h$ = depth of air inlet nozzle, m
$\qquad$ kW = energy input

Hydraulic mixing

Hydraulic mixing can be achieved by use of weirs, V-notch weirs, Parshall flumes, orifices, throttled valves, swirl chambers, and simple turbulence due to velocity in a pipe, fitting, or conduit. Hydraulic mixing is widely used and reliable. It is a nonbackmix method and can be highly efficient. The principal problem is that energy input varies with the flow. Under conditions where flows are relatively constant, energy variations may not be a concern. The problem of flow variations on a seasonal basis can sometimes be overcome by varying the number of plant modules in operation and thus maintaining more or less constant flows on those modules in operation.

The total head loss across a throttled valve used for mixing coagulant chemicals should not exceed 1.2 m (4 ft). Excessive confined energy may shear polymers. If head loss exceeds 1.2 m, coagulants should be added to the flow downstream of the valve in the zone of decaying energy.

The energy (G value) provided by a weir with an effective fall of 1 ft (300 mm) provides a G of 1000 s^{-1} at 20°C. Such a weir mixer with a downstream baffle will develop the following relative G values under the range of flows shown. If the volume where the turbulence dissipates is assumed to be constant, G may vary significantly, but if the volume of turbulence is assumed to be proportional to Q, then there is a lesser G variation.

Q (% of Max.)	G Relative (V constant)	G Relative (VQ)
1.0	1.0	1.0
0.9	0.92	0.97
0.8	0.83	0.93
0.7	0.74	0.88
0.6	0.65	0.84
0.5	0.56	0.84
0.4	0.47	0.73
0.35	0.42	0.71

Weir mixers require that coagulant chemicals be fed equally across the length of the weir (at multiple points spaced at not more than the head of the weir). Because of maintenance problems with multiple-orifice chemical feed manifolds and other practical considerations, weir mixers tend to be used on plants of capacity less than approximately 40 U.S. mgd (150 ML/day). If approach velocity to weirs and end contractions are ignored, the quantity of water that may be mixed per unit length of weir (G = 1000 s^{-1} at 20°C) is as follows:

300 mm head loss is equivalent to 300 L/s (26.1 ML/day) per meter.

12 in head loss is equivalent to 1495 U.S. gpm (2.1 U.S. mgd) per foot of weir length.

On applications where the head loss varies as Q^2 (fixed-orifice devices) G varies more rapidly (in respect to Q) than for weirs.

Automatic variable-orifice devices, such as a constant-head-loss valve, cause G to remain constant for applications within a conduit.

In-line blenders

In-line blenders include a mechanical mixer that provides constant G values over a broad range of flow. They are normally proprietary items of equipment and can be specified to provide any required G value (see Fig. 5.2).

In-line blenders that are static (nonmechanical) are essentially hydraulic devices. The zone of turbulence is defined as $GQ^{1.5}$.

Pump mixers

Pump mixers may be regarded as a combination mechanical-hydraulic device. They provide a constant mixing energy over a range of flows. Energy G can be varied by throttling the pump. They permit the addition of the coagulant to the carrying water. Pump mixers may require more energy than direct mechanical devices. Efficiency losses in the pump do not contribute to mixing energy. Only the velocity head of the flow from the blending nozzle may be applied toward computing the G value. They are reliable, flexible, nonproprietary devices that may be used on a broad range of plants. They are more appropriate on plants larger than 20 U.S. mgd (75 ML/day) (see Fig. 5.3).

The energy input of a pump mixer can be computed from the velocity head of the water leaving the nozzle of the mixer and the quantity of water pumped. The effective mixing volume may be assumed to be equivalent to 2 s of mainstream flow. High dilution of alum solution may result in clogging of injection nozzles. The pH of alum solution should be maintained below pH 3.3. Typically the pumped volume of

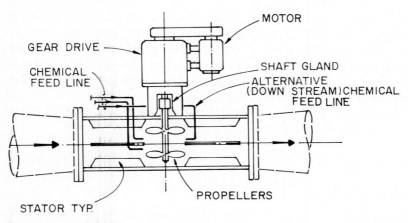

Figure 5.2 Typical in-line blender (mixer).

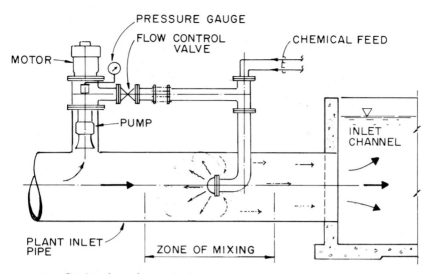

Figure 5.3 Section through pump mixer.

water should not exceed 100 times the volume of alum solution to be fed. A more precise approach to computing pump mixer requirements has been created.

Grid mixers

Grid mixers are not common and may be utilized on major plants. They are essentially hydraulic devices that may be installed at the inlet to an existing mixing basin. They eliminate backmixing. Essentially they include a baffle or grid designed to create a head loss of 50 to 150 mm (2 to 6 in) under maximum flow conditions. A pipe system with orifices is incorporated in the grid, and the coagulant (normally diluted to a 2 percent solution in the case of alum) is distributed to the pipe system and uniformly fed to the total cross section of the flow. High, relatively intense turbulence and shears may be a feature of grid mixers. They are efficient even though the zone of mixing V is small and time t is limited. Supplemental energy (tapered energy devices) may be utilized downstream. The large number of small orifices that is necessary to distribute the coagulant can cause maintenance problems. Grid mixers are not recommended if there is any debris in the raw water. They should not be used except for groundwater, screened water, and pilot plants.

Mixing Energy

The energy required for mixing and for flocculation is expressed as G. G is a term which is used to compare "velocity gradients" or "the relative number of contacts per unit volume per second" made by suspended particles during the stirring (flocculation) process. It is conveniently applied and widely accepted as a means of computing mixing energy requirements (although theoretical particle contacts are not a factor in mixing). Velocity gradients G may be calculated from the following equation:

$$G = \frac{550P}{\mu V} \qquad (5.3)$$

where G = velocity gradient/second, s^{-1}
   P = applied horsepower, hp
   V = effective volume, ft
   μ = viscosity, lb · s/ft^2

Note that the unit G is applicable to both U.S. and SI units. The equation in SI units is

$$G = \frac{kW \times 10}{\mu V} \qquad (5.4)$$

where G = velocity gradient/second, s^{-1}
   kW = applied energy, kW
   V = volume, m^3
   μ = viscosity, cP

The viscosity of water μ varies with the temperature in accordance with the following table:

Temperature, °C	Temperature, °F	μ, cP	μ, lb · s/ft^2
0	32	1.792	3.75×10^{-5}
5	41	1.520	3.17×10^{-5}
10	50	1.310	2.74×10^{-5}
15	59	1.145	2.39×10^{-5}
20	68	1.009	2.10×10^{-5}
25	77	0.895	1.87×10^{-5}
30	86	0.800	1.67×10^{-5}

Incidental Flocculation

After mixing, coagulated water needs to be transferred to the flocculators (see Fig. 5.4). In small plants there may be no significant distance or time involved, and thus incidental flocculation is negligible. In large plants, transfer may involve distances of more than 40 m (130 ft) through low-velocity conduits, weirs, or other means of distributing water equally to each flocculation basin or compartment. Travel

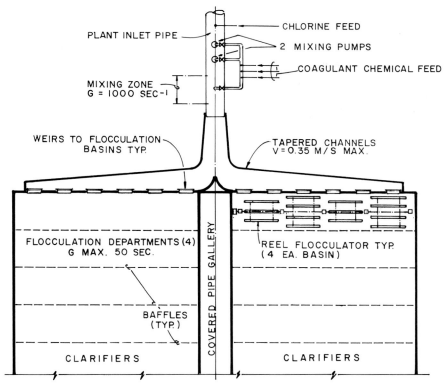

PLANT INLET PIPE

CHLORINE FEED

2 MIXING PUMPS

COAGULANT CHEMICAL FEED

MIXING ZONE
G = 1000 SEC⁻¹

WEIRS TO FLOCCULATION
BASINS TYP.

TAPERED CHANNELS
V = 0.35 M / S MAX.

FLOCCULATION DEPARTMENTS (4)
G MAX. 50 SEC.

COVERED PIPE GALLERY

REEL FLOCCULATOR TYP.
(4 EA. BASIN)

BAFFLES
(TYP.)

CLARIFIERS

CLARIFIERS

SEE DESIGN CRITERIA TABLE 5.2
HORIZONTAL PADDLE (REEL) FLOCCULATORS
TWO BASIN DESIGN, FOUR COMPARTMENTS
EA. BASIN BAFFLED DESIGN.

SCALE 0 2 4 6 8 10   20 METERS

0   10   20 30   40 50 FEET

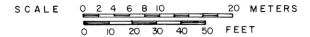

Figure 5.4 Partial plan for mixing and flocculation facilities [368 ML/day (97 mgd)].

involves turbulence and thus flocculation. Flow splitting is normally
by weirs or orifices. Weirs at the postmixing stage of the process
should be low-velocity submerged weirs. Because the transfer distance
in large plants is significant and because turbulence cannot be
avoided, incidental flocculation takes place and floc is formed. If velocities or levels between the conduits and the flocculation basin are
not limited, the floc may be fragmented and there will be a loss in
plant efficiency. Higher coagulant feed rates may be required to overcome fragile floc problems.

TABLE 5.2   Typical Design Criteria, Mixing and Flocculation*

	U.S. units		SI units	
Description	Units	Quantity	Units	Quantity
Plant capacity	cfs	150	L/s	4261
Design flow	mgd	97	ML/day	368
Plant inlet pipe diameter	in	84	mm	2150
Initial mixer				
Pump blender	No.	2	No.	2
Pump rating ea.	hp	10	kW	7.5
Energy input (20°C)	s^{-1}	1000	s^{-1}	1000
Mixing zone (2 pipe diameters)	ft^3	538	m^3	15.3
Mixing zone (detention time)	s	3.6	s	3.6
Distribution channel				
Depth	ft	10	m	3.0
Width	ft	6.5–1.5	m	2.0–0.4
Maximum velocity	ft/s	1.2	m/s	0.35
Flocculation				
Number of basins	No.	2	No.	2
Compartments (each basin)	No.	4	No.	4
Depth (average)	ft	16	m	4.9
Compartment width × length	ft	15 × 80	m	4.57 × 24.4
Volume total (per basin)	ft^3	76,800	kL	2180
Flocculation time (total detention)	s^{-1}	1080	s	1080
Horizontal shaft paddles (per basin)	No.	4	No.	4
Maximum energy input (per compartment)	s^{-1}	50	s^{-1}	50
Maximum power (per compartment)	hp	2.0	kW	1.5
Chemical dosages (partial data)				
Chlorine (mixer, prefilt. post) (maximum)	mg/L	5	mg/L	5
Alum (liquid) to mixer (maximum)	mg/L	20	mg/L	20
Cationic polymer to mixer (maximum)	mg/L	2	mg/L	2
Nonionic polymer to second-stage flocculator (maximum)	mg/L	0.5	mg/L	0.5
Potassium permanganate 2% to mixer (maximum)	mg/L	2.0	mg/L	2.0
Nonionic polymer filter aid (maximum)	mg/L	1.0	mg/L	1.0

*Criteria for mixing and flocculation prior to clarification and filtration.

Typical velocities in conduits from the mixer to flocculation basins are 1.5 to 3.0 ft/s (0.45 to 0.9 m/s). Distribution channels between the mixer and flocculation basins are often tapered, either in width or depth, so as to maintain constant velocity.

Tapered Energy

Once mixing is achieved, the coagulated water should be subjected to a decreasing level of energy. Floc begins to form within 2 s of coagulant addition and mixing. If high turbulence or shear is subsequently applied to the water, the formed flocs may be fragmented. Broken floc may not readily settle or reform.

Optimum floc that can be efficiently settled or filtered is usually formed under conditions of gradually reducing energy. In large plants, it may be difficult to distribute water to flocculation basins or filters without quiescent stages and high-energy stages such as weirs. Conduits handling mixed water should minimize head losses, but may on the other hand include water jets or air mixing to maintain G at values of 100 to 150 s^{-1} before the water is transferred to the flocculation stage.

Certain proprietary flocculator and clarifier designs may include variable energy or pulsing features. Such features appear to contradict the principle of tapered energy. These proprietary designs have been developed from full-scale tests. Deviations from the principle of tapering flocculation energy should not be made without full-scale testing.

Flocculation

General

The building of optimum-size flocs (0.1 to 2.0 mm effective size) requires gentle mixing in the energy gradient range of 20 to 70 s^{-1} for a total period of approximately 20 min. For direct filtration, a small, dense floc is required; this is usually formed at the higher end of the energy range. For settling, a larger, visible floc is normally required, and lower energy levels are applied.

The gentle mixing process of flocculation is designed to maximize contact of destabilized particles and build settleable or filterable floc particles. It is desirable to maintain shear forces as constant as possible within the process. Thus flocculator mechanisms tend to be slow and to cover the maximum possible cross-sectional area of floc basins.

It is desirable to "compartmentalize" the flocculation process by dividing the process into two or more defined stages or compartments

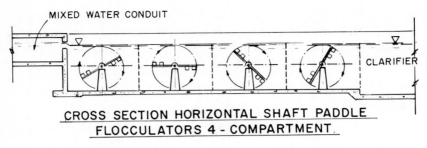

CROSS SECTION HORIZONTAL SHAFT PADDLE
FLOCCULATORS 4 - COMPARTMENT

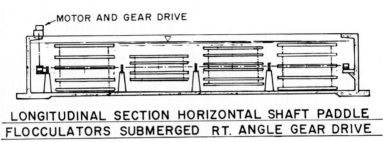

LONGITUDINAL SECTION HORIZONTAL SHAFT PADDLE
FLOCCULATORS SUBMERGED RT. ANGLE GEAR DRIVE

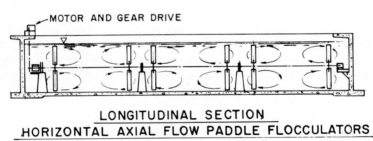

LONGITUDINAL SECTION
HORIZONTAL AXIAL FLOW PADDLE FLOCCULATORS

Figure 5.5 Sections through horizontal shaft paddle flocculator.

(see Figs. 5.5 and 5.6). The purpose of the compartments is to prevent short-circuiting and to permit defined zones of reduced energy input or tapered energy. In order to ensure that short-circuiting does not occur, baffles are typically placed between each stage of flocculation. For mechanical (nonhydraulic) flocculation basins, the baffles are designed to provide an orifice ratio of approximately 3 to 6 percent or a velocity of 0.3 m/s (0.9 fps) under maximum flow conditions. On plants smaller than 5 U.S. mgd (20 ML/day) and on proprietary designs, the flocculation compartmentalization may be omitted so as to simplify the design.

Flocculation time

Most modern plants provide approximately 20 min of flocculation time (at 20°C) under maximum plant flows. Some older references may rec-

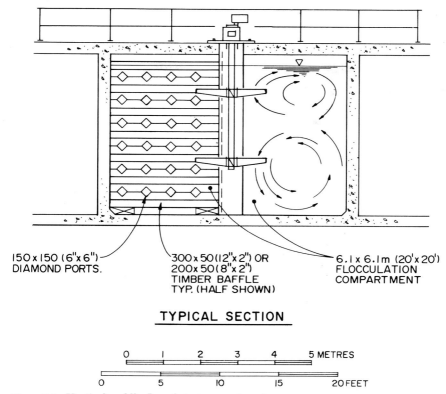

150 x 150 (6"x 6")
DIAMOND PORTS.

300 x 50 (12"x 2") OR
200 x 50 (8"x 2")
TIMBER BAFFLE
TYP. (HALF SHOWN)

6.1 x 6.1m (20'x 20')
FLOCCULATION
COMPARTMENT

TYPICAL SECTION

```
0      1      2      3      4      5 METRES
```

```
0        5        10        15        20 FEET
```

Figure 5.6 Vertical paddle flocculator compartment.

ommend flocculation times of 30 min or longer. Older references (including the previous edition of this book) do not define "nominal flows," and it appears that earlier texts based detention times on mean, or nominal, flows rather than maximum plant capacity. Also, note the temperature adjustment in the section, "Temperature." The applicable water temperature is the temperature liable to be encountered under maximum flows. For direct-filtration plants, high-energy flocculation is typically in the range of 15 to 20 min detention. When clarification is required, lower energy input and detention times of 18 to 25 min are a guide. If compartmentalization is not provided, increased detention times should be provided in addition to adjustments for water temperature. In all cases, pilot-plant or full-scale tests and economic evaluation offer the most reliable indication.

Typical major plant data are as follows:

Flocculation Times, Contemporary Plants

Plant	Flocculation time at maximum plant flow	Comments
Los Angeles (Calif.) Plant, 1987	15.0 min	Direct filtration, preozonation
Happy Valley, South Australia, 1987	20.0 min	Large plant conventional process (750 ML/day)
Ozuka Plant, Tokyo, 1970	18.5 min	Large plant, limited site

Energy requirements

Energy input for flocculation on plants using metal ion and organic coagulant chemicals ranges from 20 to 70 s^{-1}. Other considerations and time factors are indicated in the following table:

Flocculation Criteria (20°C)

Process	Energy G, s^{-1}	Detention time t, s	Gt
Distribution channels. Mixer to flocculator	100–150	Varies	—
High-energy flocculation (for direct filtration)	20–75	900–1500	40,000–75,000
Conventional flocculation (presettling)	10–60	1000–1500	30,000–60,000

The size and density of floc should be matched to subsequent settling and filtration stages. Large flocs may be applicable to settling but may result in poor direct filtration performance and frequent backwashing of filters. A small, dense (high-energy) floc is generally appropriate for coarse deep filter beds.

Types of Flocculators

General

Flocculation can be achieved by hydraulic methods or mechanical devices. Normally hydraulic flocculation is used on small plants. Mechanical flocculators cover a broad range of configurations.

Hydraulic flocculation

Hydraulic methods are simple and effective, especially if flows are relatively constant. In the case of flocculation, the assumed flocculation volume is the total volume of each compartment, even though in some cases there may be reduced turbulence in portions of the compartments. If V is assumed to be constant, then G varies as Q^5.

Energy may be applied to the water by means of maze-type baffles or cross-flow baffles (Fig. 5.7). For maze-type baffles, optimum plug-flow conditions prevail, and excellent results can be obtained. At ve-

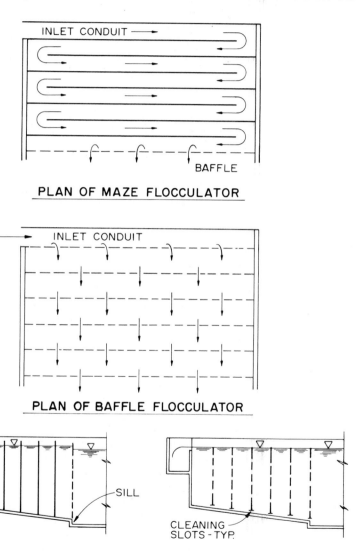

Figure 5.7   Plan and section of maze and baffle flocculators.

locities in the range of 0.2 to 0.4 m/s (0.7 to 1.4 f/s), flocculation may be adequate as a result of 180° turn turbulence at each end of the baffle. End head loss may be assumed to be equivalent to $3.2^{VZ/2G}$. For lower channel velocities, it may be necessary to provide an orifice at the end of each channel to induce higher energy input.

For cross-flow baffles, energy may be transmitted to the water in each compartment from the head loss across orifices in the entrance baffle. The G in each compartment can be calculated simply from the estimated head loss across baffles into each compartment.

$$G = \frac{62.5 \, hv}{t\mu} \qquad (5.5)$$

where hv = head loss entering compartment, ft
      t = detention time in compartment, s
      μ = viscosity, lb · s/ft^2

or

$$G = \frac{hv \times 10^7}{t\mu} \qquad (5.6)$$

where hv = head loss entering compartment, m
      t = detention time in compartment, s
      μ = viscosity, cP

The head loss through orifices in timber, concrete, or brick baffles may be computed from the square-edged submerged orifice formula where the discharge coefficient may be assumed to be 0.8. [Many texts may indicate figures of 0.61 for the discharge coefficient for square-edged orifices. In water treatment applications, head losses and velocities are lower than the velocities assumed in textbooks (less than 0.5 m/s), and coefficients are typically 0.8. If in practice, head losses across baffles are greater than assumed, higher head losses and higher G values will result.]

For cross-flow baffle flocculators, slots typically 100 to 150 mm high and 400 to 600 mm long should be provided in the bottom of baffles for cleaning purposes. The slots should be staggered to prevent short-circuiting.

Normally the floors of hydraulic flocculation basins slope toward the clarifier to:

1. Provide ease of cleaning

2. Provide tapered energy

It is general practice to make flocculation basins approximately the same depth as the adjacent clarifier [typically 3 to 5 m (10 to 16 ft)]. In addition to the slope in the flocculator floor, a drop sill is frequently provided at the entrance to the clarifier.

Mechanical flocculators

The shape of compartments is influenced by the type of mechanical flocculator. Vertical flocculators are often associated with square compartments with maximum dimensions of approximately 6 × 6 m (20 × 20 ft) and depths of 3 to 5 m (10 to 16 ft). Horizontal shaft reel or paddle flocculator compartments are often long, 6 to 30 m (20 to 100 ft), and 3 to 5 m (10 to 16 ft) wide. (The smaller dimensions are more common.)

Baffles between each zone or stage of mechanical flocculation should be designed to prevent short-circuiting. Typical orifice areas in compartmentalization baffles should be in a range that will provide a velocity of approximately 0.3 to 0.45 m/s (1.0 to 1.5 fps). Baffles are normally of timber but may also be of concrete or, in nonseismic regions, brick.

Vertical flocculators are often higher-speed devices than horizontal shaft flocculators, and the proportion of the volume of the compartment that receives energy from the vertical flocculators may be less. Thus, with vertical flocculators, a wider range of energy is applied to the flow, and for a portion of the time, some of the flow may be subjected to a higher G.

Vertical flocculators are more applicable to high-energy flocculation applications (and thus direct filtration). Where a uniform floc is required, low-tip-speed flocculators may be more suitable. For large plants that utilize vertical flocculators, the equipment manufacturers should be consulted to ensure that appropriate paddle designs are specified.

Vertical flocculators are often specified because they have no submerged bearings, are usually higher speed (less torque), and usually involve lower investments. High-speed flocculators, however, may not provide floc suitable for high-rate horizontal flow clarifiers. Improved clarification may require increased coagulant doses or flocculant aids.

As a guide, for high-energy flocculators (G = 50 to 75 s^{-1}), maximum tip speed of mixer blades should not exceed 3 m/s (10 fps). For low-energy flocculators and paddle-type flocculators (G = 20 to 45 s^{-1}), blade tip speeds in the range of 0.3 to 0.75 m/s (1.0 to 2.5 fps) are appropriate. Some method of varying speed is normally provided on major plants. Normally only the upper 25 percent of the speed range requires adjustment, and such adjustment will provide a variation of 65 to 100 percent of maximum G. G need not be varied frequently but may require adjustment after installation, or on a seasonal basis. Provision to change pulleys or gears for different shaft speeds is a valuable feature that should be provided on mechanical flocculators.

End baffles

Most flocculator systems require an end baffle between the flocculation zone and the clarifier or some provision to prevent residual energy of the flocculation process from being transferred to the clarification stage. Such baffles also minimize short-circuiting and reduce the effects of water temperature changes. End baffles may be designed on the same basis as compartmentalization baffles, as outlined in the subsection above. End baffles should not provide a barrier to removing sludge (during cleaning of the floc basin), and limited openings in the bottom of the baffle are appropriate. Similarly, a small submerged section at the top of the baffle is often provided to allow scum to pass to the filtration.

Proprietary designs

Many proprietary designs for mixing, flocculation, and clarification are circular in layout. Generally such layouts provide for upflow through the clarification stage, although in large-diameter units the flow may be more accurately described as radial. Often the process may be designed to include intentional backmixing (solids contact) in the flocculation stage, and the clarification stage may be designed for "sludge blanket" conditions. The designs may include a conical section in the mixing and flocculation stage and increasing area in the upflow zone in the clarifier stage. Proprietary equipment may have significant advantages for many applications. For all applications, especially for small plants, constant-flow applications, and conditions where solids contact is known to be advantageous, alternative proprietary designs should be evaluated (see Fig. 5.8). Numerous designs and sizes of combination flocculators ("reactors") and clarifiers are available. They may be constructed of steel or concrete. A typical layout is shown in Fig. 5.4.

Sludge recirculation and solids contact

The intentional introduction of preformed sludge into the mixing and flocculation stage is often a feature of proprietary water treatment equipment. High concentrations of suspended solids in the flocculation process (and in the sludge blanket of the clarifier) can provide improved efficiency in reduction of particulates, colloids, organics, and certain ionized chemicals.

Floc recirculation and the reintroduction of filter wash water into

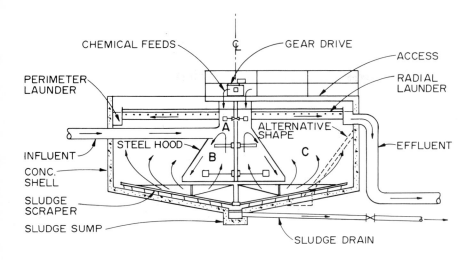

ZONE A – RAPID MIX

ZONE B – FLOCCULATION AND SOLIDS CONTACT

ZONE C – UPFLOW AND SLUDGE BLANKET ZONE

ALTERNATE SHAPE FOR SLUDGE BLANKET DESIGN

Figure 5.8   Typical proprietary design of solids contact reactor unit.

the mixing and flocculation stage may also improve efficiency and reduce chemical requirements. Sludge recirculation may be difficult to
optimize at the pilot-plant stage of investigation. It is relatively simple and inexpensive to provide such features in full-size plants. Provision of such flexibility should be considered at the design stage.

Contact flocculation

The ability of a coarse-media bed to act as a flocculation system is well
demonstrated. Where there is close contact with preformed flocs, the
time required to build optimum size and density of floc may be reduced. The time factor is important for plants treating very cold water
and for portable plants and pressure plants. Contact flocculation may
be applicable for difficult water, such as water containing "glacial
milk" or water with very low total dissolved solids (TDS) that may not
respond readily to metal ion coagulants.

A typical application of the process is to pass coagulated (mixed) water through a coarse-media or gravel bed. Such a bed may be gravity
or pressure (enclosed). The gross detention time may be 3 to 5 min at
5°C. The G should be tapered, and a range of 400 to 50 s^{-1} may be

appropriate. Flow may be either upflow or downflow. The system should have provision for removing excess accumulated floc, usually by means of air scour, similar to air scour of filters.

Pilot-plant investigations should precede design, or the criteria for contact flocculation should be based on proven applications on similar water sources.

Several manufacturers offer equipment or processes that utilize the principles of contact flocculation.

Flocculant Aids

After floc has begun to form, it may be desirable to add a flocculant aid. Such additions may strengthen floc, making the floc larger and less fragile and improving settling and/or filtration efficiency. Typical additives used for floc aids are

1. High-molecular-weight anionic or nonionic polymers

2. Activated silica

Normally such chemicals are added after coagulants at a stage of 5 to 600 s after mixing. If the water to be treated with a flocculant aid is in the flocculation stage, the added chemical will need to be fed in such a manner that it can be spread across the flocculation basin. Such feeding normally involves carrying water, dilution, and pipe headers above the surface.

Reference

J. M. Montgomery Engineers, *Water Treatment Principles and Design,* Wiley, New York, 1985, p. 42.

6

Clarification

Introduction

Importance of clarification

Clarification of water by sedimentation of flocculated particles in a basin or tank following coagulation is one of the most important unit processes employed in water treatment. It takes place during a protracted period of quiescence by continuous flow through a sedimentation basin (also known as a settling basin or clarifier). Fill-and-draw operation is obsolete; essentially all modern continuous-flow sedimentation basins feature continuous sludge removal by mechanical equipment. Efficient clarification preceding filtration permits longer filter runs and helps to reduce filter problems such as cracking and mudball formation.

Sedimentation basins are relatively easy to operate and use very little energy. Over the years, considerable theory has been developed on how sedimentation basins operate, but the application of theory to design has been limited. For the most part, sedimentation basin design criteria have been developed empirically from field operational data. Some sedimentation basin operational problems have been aggravated by improper application of theory and misunderstanding of operational data.

Presedimentation is sometimes employed to reduce heavy sediment loads in surface supplies prior to chemical coagulation. Presedimentation may also be used for removal of color and taste- and odor-causing compounds prior to lime softening. The principal use of sedimentation, however, is following chemical coagulation and flocculation to remove solids that have been made more settleable by chemical treatment. Coagulants are added to remove color and turbidity, and lime and/or

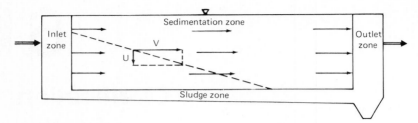

Figure 6.1 Hypothetical zones in a rectangular sedimentation basin.

soda ash is added to remove hardness. (See Chap. 5, Coagulation and Flocculation, and Chap. 10, Softening.)

Zones in sedimentation basins

Sedimentation basins have traditionally been divided into four zones, each with a specific function. These four zones and their individual functions are as follows:

1. The *inlet zone* provides a smooth transition from the influent flow to the uniform steady flow desired in the sedimentation zone.

2. The *sedimentation zone* provides volume and surface area for sedimentation to take place.

3. The *sludge zone* receives the settled floc particles.

4. The *outlet zone* provides a smooth transition from the sedimentation zone to the effluent flow.

These functions are illustrated in Fig. 6.1, which shows the four hypothetical zones, the ideal flow distribution, and the theoretical path of a discrete particle. If the inlet, outlet, and sludge zones performed as well as desired, the efficiency of sedimentation basins would be much higher than is typically experienced, because the sedimentation zone could then permit undisturbed sedimentation. However, in many basins, displacement flow through the sedimentation zone is not regular as a result of short-circuiting. Density currents in the sludge blanket may also create local scour disturbances and carry sludge particles up the far wall and into the effluent launders.

The effectiveness of a sedimentation basin depends on the subsidence rates of the floc particles that are to be removed, and on the geometry and design of the basin.

Types of sedimentation basins

Most sedimentation basins used in water treatment are of the horizontal-flow type. One exception is the upflow solids-contact basin,

which combines chemical mixing, flocculation, and upflow sedimentation in a single unit, and is especially important in cold lime softening. Horizontal-flow basins may be either rectangular (or square) or
circular in plan. Circular basins may have a center feed with radial
flow or peripheral feed with radial flow. The former are the most common (see Fig. 6.2). Both long rectangular basins and circular basins
(generally center-feed type) are used; the choice is based on local

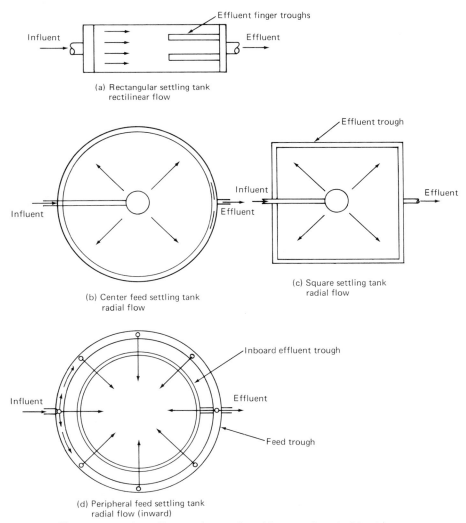

Figure 6.2 Flow patterns in sedimentation tanks with several typical basin arrangements.

conditions, economics, and so on. Most sedimentation basins are continuously cleaned with mechanical equipment, the choice of which has a bearing on the type of basin used. Instead of very large, square basins with circular collectors and corner sweeps, it may be better to employ long rectangular basins. Camp[1] felt that this configuration exhibited more stable flow characteristics and therefore better sedimentation performance.

Long rectangular basins. The influent flow is uniformly distributed across the end of these basins. It displaces water horizontally through the basin; effluent overflows into long "finger" weirs or into cross troughs. The ideal sedimentation basin would have displacement flow vectors that are all parallel, indicating uniform flow toward the effluent end. Actually, the flocculant influent feed, though uniform, disturbs this pattern. The homogenous floc-water mixture, typically heavier than ambient clear water, enters the sedimentation zone and descends to the bottom sludge blanket layer in the forebay (inlet zone), where it moves along the bottom toward the effluent end. Ideal settling cannot be achieved because the vectors do not displace in parallel or uniformly, and a degree of dynamic instability develops. Basins operating on a 3-h detention period (hydraulic filling time) may pass some dye tracer to the effluent in 10 to 25 min.

Circular center-feed basins. Influent flow typically enters the center of the basin through an inverted siphon running under the basin and has its direction changed 180° by a feedwell skirt. The feed may also enter horizontally through a sidewall entry pipe which discharges into the feedwell skirt. The influent is diffused radially as horizontal flow toward a peripheral overflow weir or inboard trough.

As in the long rectangular basin, the denser floc-water mass sinks to the bottom to join the sludge blanket and disperses radially. The displacement vectors the flow to the periphery of the basin, where the peripheral overflow weir or inboard weir trough receives the clarified overflow. Often, more elaborate means of radially diffusing the influent flow are used. These means may include a multiple-biased gate diffusion system, mushroom diffusers, or shutter diffusers to discharge multiple, equal flows through a relatively large feedwell. At the feedwell, which is virtually a point source, radial influent vectors are most apt to be unstable and fall short of displacing in an orderly radial manner, giving rise to short circuiting. Short circuiting increases with larger basins where the point source energy increases, and surface wind stirring becomes more evident.

The time-concentration curve (Fig. 6.3) illustrates what might be

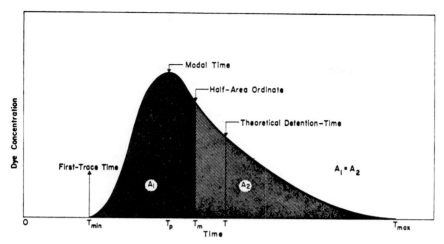

Figure 6.3 Time-concentration curve and its characteristics.

expected from a real basin, rather than a theoretical one. A tracer injected at the inlet is measured at various times at the outlet. The less the difference between t_p, the peak, and the theoretical detention time, the nearer the basin approaches the ideal.

Elements of Design

General considerations

The density and volume of both flocculating particles and precipitating particles change as they become attached to one another through flocculation and chemical precipitation. The settling velocities of the particles change with time and depth as the particles agglomerate and form larger floc. Thus, sedimentation is influenced by flocculation within the sedimentation basin, and as a result, both depth and detention time, along with surface area and overflow rate, become considerations in the design of settling basins.

In addition to depth and detention time, flocculation is dependent on the number of particle contacts per unit time; the size, density, and fragility of the floc; particle surface charge; and pH and other factors. There is no commonly acceptable formulation relating the variables influencing the settling of flocculant particles. The number of particle contacts per unit of time depends on the concentration of material in the water, the relative sizes and velocities of the particles, and the velocity gradients that increase the probability of contact. Settling rates for a flocculant suspension can be determined from batch settling data developed in the laboratory.

In an ideal continuous-flow basin, sedimentation would take place exactly as it would in a quiescent container of equal depth. Every element of water would have a detention time equal to the theoretical detention time. Moreover, for the case of discrete particles, every particle with a settling velocity equal to or greater than the surface loading rate would be removed.

In a real basin, however, wind, thermal and inertial currents, and other phenomena cause short-circuiting and disrupt the flow pattern. Figure 6.3 illustrates a time-concentration curve that might be expected from an actual basin. The time-concentration curve is determined by injecting a tracer (a dye or electrolyte) into the inlet of a sedimentation basin and repeatedly measuring its concentration at the outlet. The concentration at the outlet will be zero for a time equal to t_{min} (Fig. 6.3). It will rise to a peak t_p, then decrease more slowly than it rose until all of the tracer has passed through the basin (t_{max}). The less the difference between t_p and the theoretical detention time, the nearer to the ideal is the basin. The time-concentration curve is, therefore, a useful device for studying the hydraulic performance of a settling basin. If the repeatability of time-concentration curves for a particular basin is poor, then the basin is said to be hydraulically unstable. This hydraulic instability is a result of short-circuiting and jet streaming.

Predicting sedimentation performance

Mathematical relationships developed to predict sedimentation performance have met with little success when applied to real situations because of the many invalid simplifying assumptions made in their formulation. As there are so many factors influencing the performance of settling basins, model studies will probably provide the most satisfactory answers about hydraulic performance. However, geometric scale models may not be practicable when studying clarification of floc-bearing flows, because the laws of hydraulic similitude require that all dimensions be scaled down proportionally—which is impossible for floc.[2] For this reason, the data obtained from the operation of actual full-scale basins will remain the primary source of design criteria for settling basins and, along with pilot-plant research, will serve as the ultimate test of the applicability of new theories of sedimentation.

Another approach is for the engineer to learn as much as possible about the settling properties of the suspended solids in the water to be treated through laboratory tests and investigations. He or she should then attempt to use a sedimentation-unit design that is known to have hydraulic properties best suited to these settling properties. However, there are a multitude of raw-water characteristics, and most of the published design criteria will be quite broad and perhaps unreliable for specific situations. Often the engineer does not have access to samples of the water to be treated and must design on the basis of his or her own best judgment.

The effect of water properties on sedimentation. Several properties of the water and its suspended solids influence sedimentation, including the temperature of the water, the specific gravity of the materials in suspension, and the size and shape of the suspended particles. Water temperature has been found to be a very important design criterion; in fact, it may be even more important than the specific gravity of the particles. The settling velocity of a particle varies inversely with kinematic viscosity, which is related to water temperature. With cold waters, basin overflow rates should be lower than with warmer waters. The engineer is thus required to design for the lowest water temperature of the supply source, unless demand is lower in cold weather.

The settling velocity of a particle varies directly with its specific gravity. Thus, the higher the specific gravity of the particle, the higher will be its settling velocity and the higher the corresponding overflow rate that can be used in the sedimentation-basin design. Camp[3] notes that a turbid surface water may contain suspended matter whose specific gravities range from 2.65, such as for sand, to about 1.03 for flocculated particles of organic matter and mud containing 95 percent water. Floc particles resulting from coagulation with alum or iron oxides may have a specific gravity as low as 1.02 to 1.10. This value may be increased by the presence of clay or silt, or be drastically reduced by the presence of organic matter or entrained or adsorbed water. The specific gravity of particles of calcium carbonate formed during the softening process may be as high as 1.2.

Seasonal water temperature variations of greater than 1°C per hour, such as are encountered in some lake supplies, can cause serious upsets in the clarifier. The influent may override the basin mass in the rare case of higher temperatures, or it may underride the mass in the case of lower temperatures. In the latter case, the eddy currents can scour the sludge blanket to the point where the tank appears to be boiling—a serious disruption of clarification.

Algae-laden surface supplies (primarily from lakes in temperate to warm climates) can cause "sun floc" to rise in the basin, typically during the bright sunlight hours. Sun rays penetrate the clear surface water and activate the algae-infested floc, producing enough entrained gas bubbles to cause large floc particles to rise and overflow at the surface. Such plants will typically produce crystal-clear surface overflow during the dark hours and more turbidity during bright sunlight hours. In many plants this problem has been solved by covering the sedimentation basins to shut out the sun's rays.

Alternative Clarifier Designs

Rectangular basins

Long rectangular sedimentation basins have long been popular with water treatment plant designers. Besides the savings resulting from common-wall construction and reduced area requirements, it seemed easier to distribute the influent laterally across the forebay end than to evenly distribute the point source influent of circular basins. All in all, the long rectangular basins seemed to yield better clarification, particularly with larger units.

The development of sedimentation basins equipped for continuous sludge withdrawal led to some dissatisfaction with iron chain drag equipment, and new interest was aroused in the less troublesome circular mechanisms for moving sludge. The introduction of carriage-mounted scrapers and suction units, along with float-mounted suction desludgers, has made long, rectangular basins more practical with regard to maintenance of desludging equipment.

Density currents—longitudinal vector systems. As floc-bearing displacement settles to the bottom in horizontal flow basins, a downward current is induced near the basin inlet, with a corresponding upwelling near the outlet. The homogenous floc-bearing entry is heavier than the surrounding clear water (assumed to be the same temperature) and starts to settle toward the bottom en masse. The velocity of settling at the inlet zone depends on the homogeneity, the degree of previous flocculation, and the weight of natural or process-added solids.

This sinking homogenous mass enters the sludge blanket at the basin floor near the inlet zone. The kinetic energy in the falling mass acts in the sludge blanket as a density current with vectors longitudinal to the basin floor, so that the sludge blanket slowly flows—much as a river does—along the bottom toward the outlet end. The strength of the density current is somewhat dependent on the amount of suspended solids carried by the influent. In another field, wastewater treatment, the concentration of suspended solids carried to the clarifier may be 3000 or 4000 mg/L, causing a greater density current effect than found in most color- or low-turbidity-removal water treatment plants. In lime-softening plants, as well as in flocculation operations where solids recycling is practiced or floc weighing agents are added, the density current may be strong. Even in clarification of flocculated waters with relatively low suspended solid content, a density and displacement inertia current of some magnitude will exist.

Unfortunately, the vectors of the density current running along the bottom are not parallel and equal, as a result of short circuiting and jet stream tendencies. This can lead to scour in the thickening sludge blanket. Some groups of floc particles may be broken away and be carried to the surface as "thunderheads"—visible large clusters or clouds of otherwise settleable floc milling around at the surface that may partially join the basin overflow.

There have been examples in water utility operation of 100- or 200-ft-long basins in which the surface water was crystal clear until it reached the effluent end, where the surface overflow was joined by an upwelling sludge blanket. The upwelling sludge blanket acted to produce a turbid effluent and short filter runs. This effect was the result of density currents in the blanket that caused it to flow to the far end and literally "climb the wall" to join the clear surface overflow.

Pyramidal "thunderheads" occur when eddy currents, produced by imbalances in the influent feed, cause scour in this moving blanket. Insufficient water depth in the basin or too deep a sludge blanket can also generate these "thunderheads."

A typical flow pattern discloses two general systems of longitudinal vectors: one system shows drift along the floor toward the effluent end, and the other shows backward drift under the surface toward the influent end. As material settles to the inlet bottom, a downward current is induced near the inlet end, with a corresponding upwelling near the outlet, and a countercurrent under the surface. The surface in a typical basin is clear, and this is why finger weirs are designed to extend more or less one-third to one-half of the basin length toward the inlet end (see Fig. 6.4). Also, when high-rate tube modules are placed in a long rectangular basin to enhance clarity, they are typically placed in the last 60 to 70 percent of the basin length—in the clear backflow region.

Besides the density-current effect, the bottom displacement flow occurs primarily in the lower one-half or one-third of the basin depth,

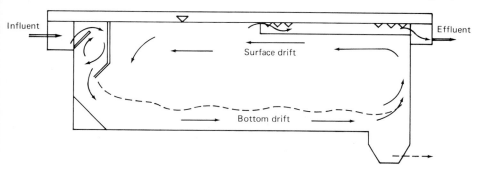

Influent   Effluent

Surface drift

Bottom drift

Figure 6.4   Displacement vectors in a real basin showing the prevailing drifts.

which magnifies this displacement vector of drift. There are also vertical thermal convection currents; these are especially dominant during midday hours in regions of strong sunlight exposure. These currents are capable of carrying masses of floc toward the basin surface.

Wind sometimes acts on the surface of large open basins and causes surface vectors that can accumulate to effect a partial or complete overturn of the basin contents. In windy locations it is often necessary to cover basins to protect them from wind stirring.

As material settles to the inlet bottom, a downward current is induced near the inlet end, with a corresponding upwelling near the outlet and a countercurrent under the surface.

Influent control.   The transverse distribution of feed into the head end of a long rectangular clarifier is very important. Any imbalance in the feed immediately sets up short circuiting, jet streams, and overall lack of hydraulic stability. Some traditional sedimentation basins, which are fed through equally spaced open ports by taking flow from an outside distribution channel, have proven to be unsatisfactory. These systems reflect the manner of flow into the outside channel. Typically, the flow entered the channel in the center, forcing an imbalance of flow through the center ports. No inboard target baffle, either vented or perforated, can ameliorate the imbalance that is created—gross short circuiting is likely to take place.

The balanced energy inlet system consists of a number of equal-sized surface ports distributed transversely at the basin entrance on about 5-ft centers. These ports receive flow from a feed channel across the inlet end of the basin; it is unimportant from what point the channel is fed—either end or the middle. The channel could also be air-agitated without any deleterious influence on the multiple inlets. The flow through each inlet diffuser is controlled by an adjustable (and then locked) biased gate which directs equal streams of influent at a velocity of about 2 to 3 fps into the top of the forebay. The biased gate is clamped between side guides so that the streaming flow from each control unit enters the mass of the forebay and causes it to rotate about a horizontal axis at about 2 fps; an ideal speed for floc aggregation. This causes the surface of the forebay to appear as though a horizontal, reel-type slow paddle mixer were operating in it. The biased gates are adjusted by eye, since it is easy to compare the streaming discharges for equality. The amount of bias of all the gates sets the head loss and consequently the velocity of slow roll in the feedwell.

The rolling energy is confined behind a perforated baffle; this uniformly distributed energy yields equal displacement vectors transversely disposed of along the lip of the baffle turnback. This balanced feed effect can be observed by looking through the clear water just outside the forebay and seeing the floc-laden influent displaced from the turnback lip. A glass-bottomed clam bucket or face mask is required to make this observation.

The gate units are designed to be spaced transversely on about 5-ft centers. This spacing can be altered to suit influent flow conditions. The ports in the concrete headwall are about 12 in wide by 24 in high, and the sill of the port is set at about 12 in below the nominal basin water overflow level.

The nominal design flow velocity through each port is about 1½ fps through the bottom 12 in of the port plus a surcharge of 4 in—a 16-in height in all. The width of the gate may be 12 in for a flux of, say, 2 cfs, but may be widened or narrowed as desired to hold to the 1½-fps nominal velocity through the 16-in-high port. Also, the spacing in the ports could be adjusted, leaving the port size constant. However, port spacing should not exceed 6 ft.

The biased gate proper is clamped between the side guides of the streaming-flow control unit, and adjusted to cause equal flux through each gate and a backup (or head loss) into the cross channel of about 4 in of water column. There is one unit of velocity head $V^2/2g$ loss through each control gate. Water plants are typically designed for one flow rate; if the flow rate is changed, the biased gates can be adjusted accordingly.

A variation in this design, which accommodates diurnal flow variations (more apt to be encountered in wastewater treatment plants), is provision of adjustable means for overflow into the streaming-flow surface pattern between each pair of biased gates. The overflow would take place each time the head loss exceeded, say, 4 in. Then the control of the biased gates would be adjusted to cause a head loss of 4 in at maximum hourly flow; at higher flows the overflow means would come into play and contribute overflow to the multiple-streaming-flow system.

There are other ways of achieving transverse balance of the influent, but most of them are not easily adjustable in response to changes in plant flow rates. One way is to use a brick wall with bricks left out to form a checkered pattern of small ports. This open brickwork system would extend from about middepth to surface. Balanced flow through this system is achieved by leaving a sufficient number of brick openings to maintain about a 3- or 4-in head loss. Later, the head loss through the system can be adjusted by partially blocking some openings with half bricks. This means of balanced feed has been successfully used to upgrade many otherwise poor sedimentation basins.

Overflow weir troughs.   The basin overflow system is very important in helping to keep displacement through a sedimentation basin as uniform as possible. Good placement of overflow weir troughs does not correct the harm done by poor influent diffusion or lack of adequate basin depth, but it will assist in good influent diffusion.

The overflow troughs should be designed to cover at least one-third, and preferably up to one-half, of the basin length. Whether they be cross troughs or finger-weir troughs, they should be evenly distributed to accept flow from the surface of the effluent end of the basin.

Regulatory agencies have stated that the weir overflow rate parameter[4] should not exceed about 20,000 gpd/lin ft of weir. Research[5] has established that overflow rates as high as 100,000 gpd/lin ft will not reach down into the sludge blanket, given reasonable water depth. Density currents, if strong enough, will force the sludge blanket up to the end weir, regardless of how low the overflow rate per linear foot. The regulatory agencies' parameter forces designers to use a greater length and, it is hoped, better distribution of weir troughs. Actually, it is the distribution of the weir troughs that is important in order to avoid a high upwelling rise rate such as could occur with a short or crowded weir system. The extent of weir-trough distribution should not exceed 1 to 1.5 gpm/ft^2 rise rate for the surface area covered by the trough system.

Weir troughs should be spaced on the centerline of the area they serve, about 16 to 20 ft apart. There is a vast empirical background to such a weir spacing, and there is little advantage in setting them any closer. Although wash-water troughs are typically spaced at about half this distance, the overflow conditions are not relevant. In the case of chain drag conveyors, the effluent weir troughs are typically arranged transversely across the basin; in the case of suction or bladed scrapers, the troughs must be arranged longitudinally as parallel finger weirs supported on piers. Both arrangements are equally effective.

In the unusual case in which high-rate tube modules or lamella plate separators are to be added to or designed into the sedimentation basin, the weir troughs should be more closely spaced than is usual in order to ensure equal displacement flows through the modules. Optimal spacing is about 8 to 12 ft. Because of the great length of such a weir system, the spacing of V notches must be greater than usual in order to maintain a flow depth of about one-half the V-notch height.

Bottom slopes.   Except for the possible need to provide a drainage slope for emptying a basin—which is more apt to be necessary if iron chain drag equipment is used—there is little reason to design a longitudinal slope into a long rectangular basin.

Suction pickup equipment generally does not require a longitudinal slope. Basins equipped with this kind of unit should have level floors.

Cross-collector trenches are usually built without floor slope, except for the accumulating hopper, which should have a side slope of at least 60° to the horizontal.

Often large fillets are used at the inlet end to accommodate the desludging equipment. The fillet slope can be as flat as 45° because of the wash effect of the inlet displacement and density current on the surface of the fillet (see Table 6.1).

Rectangular basin equipment

Traditional equipment. Traditional desludging equipment was mostly chain-and-flight drags made up of two strands of 6-in-pitch iron chain with wooden flights attached at 10-ft intervals, operated at about 2 fpm to convey dense sludge to a cross hopper. The flights were usually redwood, either 2 in by 6 in or 3 in by 8 in, and 16 to 20 ft long (which became the practicable working width of the drag unit). Steel flights

TABLE 6.1 Bottom Slopes and Collector Speeds

Type of basin	Bottom slopes	Collector tip speed
Circular	Basins <100 ft dia: 1¼ in/ft Basins 125 ft in dia. use two-slope: Outer half—1 in/ft; inner half—2 in/ft	6–12 fpm; typically, 10 fpm*
		Flight Speed
Long rectangular	Typically flat, or may use drainage slope of, say, 12 in for length of basin	Typically 2 fpm Flight cross collector: 2–4 fpm Screw cross collector: Typically 10 rpm (varies from 5 to 10) 18-in × 9-in pitch screw with 8-in OD shaft
		Tip Speed: (Circular)
Desilting	Use two-slope as above for circular	10 fpm
		Flight Speed: (Rectangular)
	Drainage slope on rectangular basin	1 fpm

*Plow-type equipment moves so slowly near the center of the circular basin that additional bottom slope may be necessary to move the thickened underflow into the center hopper.

were not used for conveying sludge because they presented too much bottom drag resistance and consequently too much overall wear on both drag equipment and drives.

Drags for continuous desludging have been popular with design engineers because they fit the long rectangular basin geometry. The iron chain system, although it desludges efficiently, requires considerable maintenance and basin downtime for chain, sprocket, and bearing repair.

Plastic chain of dimensions similar to No. 730 pintle iron chain links (6-in pitch) has been developed to replace iron chain. Typical operating conditions require no more than 600 to 700 lb of chain pull to propel the sludge, provided that the wooden flights are kept to a reasonable depth of about 6 in and plastic friction-free wearing shoes are used. The plastic chains have about a 2000-lb chain-pull working capacity. Observation of a chain replacement installation (South Milwaukee, Wis.) disclosed satisfactory operation over a 3-year period.[5] The only problem experienced was a slight elongation of the chain due to inundated growth, which was corrected by removing several links. No other operating trouble has developed, even though this chain replacement installation uses the original wooden flights and original iron-on-iron wearing shoes, which contribute to chain pull. Fiberglass flights are available for new plant construction or rehabilitation of existing basins.

Circular collector equipment.   Circular sludge collector units have been used in long rectangular tanks to avoid using chain drag equipment. The circular units were generally installed at the influent end of the basin; a transverse barrier wall was added to stop the density current and drifting of sludge toward the unscraped effluent end. In these cases, the circular mechanism "pushes" sludge to a circumferential hopper at the center pier from which it is automatically discharged as sludge underflow. The remainder of the basin must be periodically cleaned manually.

Many of these units were not effective, particularly where the circular desludging unit was placed only in the first quarter of a long basin with a strong density current. Sludge did not thicken where the unit was placed, which left the circular desludging mechanism with nothing to do, and the majority of the basin had to be manually cleaned. Recent designs have expanded basin coverage with multiple collector mechanisms to improve sludge removal and thus eliminate the need for manual cleaning.

In small rectangular basins, where the corners not swept by the circular collector are relatively small, corner sweeps are generally not specified in order to minimize collector maintenance. When corner sweeps are not used, typical practice is to add steep corner fillets to encourage movement of sludge to the area swept by the collector mechanism. However, in larger basins, where corner areas are large, or when sludge is of organic composition and must be continuously removed, corner sweeps are specified.

Corner sweeps can be subject to mechanical problems, and the larger the basin, the greater the likelihood of problems. The sweep suspension should be a four-bearing cantilever pantograph unit. To reduce bearing loadings, the long cantilevered sweep boom should be filled with closed-cell flotation material to make it of almost neutral density under water. The outer end should be guided by a semi-pneumatic tire about 18 in in diameter. This guide tire runs around a small-radius corner formed by an at least 24-in-high steel curb. The corner is filleted back of the curb, and the height of the curb prevents the guide wheel from running above the curb and binding at the wall intersection. Unfortunately, many corner sweeps have failed or required an inordinate amount of maintenance because of poor mechanical details. The mechanical details of corner sweeps should be specified in great detail to protect against an inferior system winning a low-dollar bid.

In general, circular collector mechanisms are highly reliable because of their simplicity, have low maintenance requirements, and provide positive sludge removal. Disadvantages include the large submerged metal surfaces which must be protected from corrosion, and maintenance requirements of corner sweeps (if provided).

Carriage-type collectors. Oscillating-bridge collectors have become more popular during the past several decades. These top-of-wall running units span the width of one or more long rectangular basins. They clean thick sludge either by means of a single transverse vertical blade (typically 24 to 30 in deep) which conveys dense sludge into a cross hopper, or by means of a transverse suction header which discharges into a longitudinal trough along one side of the basin. The transverse blade has an adjustable angle of attack and slides on flat bottom rails, or sometimes on a heavy neoprene squeegee riding on the floor. The blade automatically adjusts to varying floor slopes, and can be raised above the water level for maintenance. It pushes dense sludge at about 6 fpm toward the cross hopper on the cleaning run, then is hoisted about 3 ft and deadheads at double speed back to the influent end to repeat (see Fig. 6.5).

The carriage units generally run on double-flanged iron wheels, along heavy steel rails mounted on the long walls of the clarifier. Rubber tires running on the top of concrete walls have been used occasionally in western Europe, but their use is discouraged because of prob-

Figure 6.5 Carriage-type collector with a sludge blade. Carriage-type collector with sludge blades desludging turbidity removal (alum coagulation) sedimentation basins. Long, well-distributed finger weirs receive the overflow. Basins are 110 ft long × 50 ft wide × 15 ft 6 in deep, with cross collectors. Bridge-mounted drive pinions engage rack in foreground. (*Source: Walker Process Corporation, Aurora, Ill.*)

lems with snow and ice buildup. The units are traction-driven with automatic compensation to prevent "crabbing" or, preferably, by driven cog rails located adjacent to the steel rails on either side of the basin.

Power for the driving and hoisting motors is typically supplied through a flexible power cable. This cable is reeled in and paid out (as the carriage moves) by a motor-driven cable reel. Simple spring motor reels are unsatisfactory because they overstress (pull) the cable when the carriage is at the far end and frequently do not have enough reserve force to reel in the cable at the near end, so that they sometimes run over and sever the loose, kinked cable. Several cleverly designed power reels have been developed, either using a backstay cable to power the reel in the retrieving attitude, or having the cable reel synchronized to the carriage travel and employing a spring motor slave reel core to compensate for minor variations in cable length.

Feed rails are sometimes used for power feed, but they are vulnerable to vandalism and sometimes burn out or carbonize because of the slow speed of the brushes. Another form of power supply is an overhead power cable festooned and sliding back and forth on a taut steel carrier cable running a few feet above the surface for the length of the basin. Such a system is rather unsightly and suitable only for short basins.

Floating-bridge type. To fill a need for a durable, yet less expensive sludge cleaner, the floating suction-header type of equipment was developed.

The suction unit is mounted on massive floats built of closed-cell Styrofoam encased in fiberglass-reinforced polyester (FRP) and tied together as a rigid structure so that it is free-standing when the basin is dewatered. A header system supported by the floats draws dense sludge from the bottom of the basin, and by means of low-head siphon discharges it into a longitudinal trough attached to the side of the sedimentation basin. The cross header is broken into several subheaders, each carrying flow overhead to a control siphon freely discharging into the sludge trough. The effect of each lateral section can be observed and modulated. The siphon system is started with a portable low-differential suction source. Experience has demonstrated that for water treatment sludges, once started, the siphon can be maintained for months.

The floating-bridge system is towed back and forth either by a single, center-mounted, stainless steel flexible tow cable, or by two cables acting on either end of the rigid floating structure. In either case, the cables are powered by a geared motor drive and idler sheave arrangement, mounted at either end of the basin on top of the wall in an accessible location. Because the floating system eliminates friction and most wind problems, remarkably little power is required to tow the bridges, even in basins 200 ft long or longer. Figure 6.6 shows several floating siphon desludging units. Dense sludge sucked up by the system is siphoned into the longitudinal trough. The amount of siphonage is being controlled by valves, one for each siphon section forming the transverse header sludge pickup system.

The sludge suction pipes are either of light-gage, epoxy-coated aluminum or stainless steel, and are equipped with fluidizing vanes. In operation, the suction system is run up and down the length of the basin at about 6 fpm as often as is required to vacuum up the dense sludge layer (compression zone). Where there is not enough sludge to require continuous suction up and down the basin, the siphon discharge is temporarily arrested by a programmed closing of the longitudinal trough discharge gate so that the water level in the trough

Figure 6.6   Floating siphon sludge collector. (*Photograph courtesy of F. B. Leopold Co., Inc.*)

rises to equal the basin level. When the next programmed desludging cycle begins, the trough valve opens and the siphons continue from where they stopped, again discharging dense sludge into the trough.

Both carriage-type and floating-bridge-type collection mechanisms minimize use of submerged metal, thereby minimizing corrosion problems. However, both can be used only in temperate climates where ice accumulation is not a problem. Some installations have also experienced drive synchronization problems and incomplete sludge removal.

Cross collectors–cross hopper(s).   The cross hopper is a trench, typically 4 ft wide by 3 or 4 ft deep, running the width of one or more longitudinal sections of the sedimentation basin. Dense sludge falls into this cross trench and is scraped at about 2 fpm by chain-driven flights 8 in deep, spaced 5 ft on centers. These scraper flights deposit dense sludge into a 6-ft-deep accumulating hopper at the end of the cross trench, from which the underflow is withdrawn.

Sometimes a helicoid screw is used in the cross trench in place of the chain-driven flights. The screw turns slowly, paced to have a theoretical capacity of 4 times the volume of sludge to be actually moved, to minimize bearing wear. The bottom of the cross trench is filleted to accommodate the outside diameter of the screw. In screw cross-collector applications, instead of propelling dense sludge all the way to one end, the flights of the helicoid screw are opposed so that dense sludge is carried only half the trench length to the center point, where the accumulating hopper is placed.

Some designers like to use the traditional steep-sided (60°) hopper for removal of sludge underflow. For basins greater than 10 ft wide, more than one hopper must be used to keep the hopper depth within reason. Sometimes anchor sludge ("liver") forms even at a 60° slope, since the slope at the corner intersections is far less than 60°, and sludge accumulates by bridging. Multiple hoppers can be more expensive than cross hoppers and not as satisfactory in operation; if they are joined with a manifold to a common pipe, only one hopper will be served.

Underflow control.   The drawoff of underflow must be very carefully controlled. If underflow is removed at too low a rate, dense sludge will accumulate in the basin, creating too deep a sludge blanket. If underflow is removed too quickly for too long an interval, the drawoff will "posthole," i.e., there will be a breakthrough of less viscous liquid, and dense sludge will remain to accumulate in the basin and overload the desludging equipment.

It is best to draw off underflow with a programmed blowdown valve or transfer pump. Such a program can consist of a 24-h timer emitting a signal to a repeating-interval timer, which would cause blowdown (or pumping) to occur for approximately 3 to 5 min (or any predetermined interval), then stop for approximately 30 to 60 min. Such a program must be completely adjustable, and be adjusted by the design engineer during early operation to fit the plant operation. Manual drawoff control by guess and "gut feeling" will often lead to operating troubles.

In a lime-softening plant, the sludge line to the hopper should be purged with clear water after each blowdown cycle for just long enough to remove the lime slurry remaining in the line. Without purging, the lime slurry will accumulate and will soon clog the line.

New facilities should be designed with sludge viewing pits, which permit the operator to observe the consistency of the sludge during blowdown. The ability to observe sludge during blowdown permits optimization of withdrawal rates and reduces excessive loading of sludge-handling facilities.

Circular basins

Circular sedimentation basins became more prevalent in water clarification when periodic manual cleaning of long rectangular basins became unpopular. The top drive circular mechanisms used for sludge cleaning have no bearings under water, resulting in longevity with little maintenance. In reasonable sizes—not exceeding 125-ft diameter—the circular center feed clarifiers evidently perform as well as the long rectangular basins, provided care is taken to obtain a reasonably well-balanced radial flow from the center well and substantial water depth is maintained at the center. Circular basins greater than 50 to 60 ft in diameter are improved by use of an inboard circumferential weir (see Fig. 6.7 and Table 6.2).

The point source at the feedwell makes balanced control of radial feed vectors very difficult and may easily lead to rampant short circuiting. This has encouraged the use of rim-feed clarifiers, where influent flows through a circumferential trough which communicates with the basin through downdraft pipes spaced about every 20 ft. It is difficult to balance feed through these pipes because of the low velocity of the flow through them. Slime and accretionary buildups also contribute to imbalanced flow. Early designs of the rim-feed tanks em-

Figure 6.7 Circular basin with collector. Typical circular sludge collector mechanism. Inlet feed is down through the center feedwell, which is equipped with a distribution section to discharge balanced flow. The overflow is into an inboard annular weir trough. Basins are 130 ft diameter × 15 ft deep. (*Source: Walker Process Corporation, Aurora, Ill.*)

TABLE 6.2   Typical Sedimentation Tank Surface Loading Rates

Application	Long rectangular and circular gpd/ft^2*	Upflow contact gpd/ft^2*
Lime softening:		
Low magnesium	1700	3200
High magnesium	1400	2600
Alum (iron) coagulation:		
Turbidity removal	1000	1200
Color (taste) removal	700	850
High algae content	500	

*The rates shown are guides, applicable at moderate temperatures—not less than about 10°C. For ice-cold supplies, reduce the rate. Note that in winter many plants operate at considerably reduced throughput rates.

ployed a group of closely spaced weir troughs taking surface overflow from the center one-third of the basin (about 10 percent of the basin area). More recently, following experimental work by Krauss of Peoria, Ill., rim-fed basins have been designed with peripheral weir overflow troughs. As with center-feed units, displacement stability and overall efficiency appear to decline when basin diameters exceed 125 ft. Rim-feed units are never square.

Displacement.   The center feed in a circular (or square) basin amounts to a point source, since the feedwell seldom represents more than 3 or 4 percent of the basin area. Therefore, a great deal of flow mass is crowded into a very small space and cannot be expected to efficiently displace itself in an exactly radial pattern. This crowding of the center feed leads to hydraulic imbalance and short circuiting, which is accentuated by the tendency to design oversized basins that are expected to carry an 800- to 1500-gpd/ft^2 surface overflow rate. These basins are too shallow for an efficient center feed.

Density and displacement currents for circular basins are much the same as for long rectangular basins. The vector system is influenced by the well-flocculated influent mass sinking to the bottom adjacent to the feedwell area, typically in the center one-third of the basin (about 10 percent of the total basin area). The vector system shows displacement radially along the bottom in the blanket zone and upwelling adjacent to the peripheral wall. Clarified water generally flows across the surface toward the influent (see the discussion, "Long Rectangular Basin Density Current").

Radial-flow feedwells.   Circular clarifier feedwells are very important in attempting to initiate true radial flow through the circular clarifier from what is essentially a point source to the circumferential sidewall. Unfortunately, true radial flow at the center is never realized, but some feedwell designs come closer than others.

One questionable type of feedwell is the small-diameter circular skirt of about 1 percent of the basin area extending only 3 to 4 ft below the surface. The feed into this well may be by four ports discharging horizontally from a pier riser, or from a horizontal pipeline discharging horizontally into the well from just below the surface. In the four-port design, variation of flow rate is accommodated with a design exit flow of about 2 fps. This does not ensure equal egress from each port, however.

A more controllable feed design includes use of a distribution well inside a large feedwell (about 3 to 4 percent of the basin area). This distribution well has multiple ports hooded with adjustable biased gates, which balance the tangential feed discharges by imposing about a 4-in head loss through the ports. The effect of this type of discharge is to cause the homogenized mass within the large feedwell to rotate about the vertical axis at about 2 fps. The well-distributed, fine-scale turbulence within and below the feedwell encourages floc aggregation, and the overall slow rotation ensures that the flow from the bottom of the skirt into the hindered sludge mass moving radially across the floor has equal displacement vectors.

Overflow weir troughs.   Experience has demonstrated that instead of a V-notch overflow weir mounted on the peripheral wall, a double-sided weir trough mounted inboard at least 15 percent of the tank radius has the advantage of minimizing wall flow disturbances as well as drawing overflow from a more widely distributed region. Inboard weir troughs also have the effect of partially breaking up wind-current stirring.

Some designers prefer orifice troughs to overflow weir troughs, because less floc breakup will occur. Others have pointed out that the velocity gradient in a weir trough is no greater than in an orifice trough. The weir trough is far easier to adjust for equal linear overflow. However, submerged orifice-type troughs reduce passage of floating trash to the filters and permit variation in basin water depths during operation. This capability is useful in balancing differences in plant inflow and discharge rates (as when multiple filter washing occurs).

Regulatory agencies sometimes stipulate weir rates[8] not to exceed around 20,000 gpd per linear foot of weir. Flood[4] found that weir overflow rates several times this value could be used if the weirs were well distributed over a substantial portion of the surface. Placing a double-sided weir trough 1 ft away from the peripheral wall satisfies the regulatory requirements, but still draws overflow from a narrow band of surface immediately in the path of the upwelling peripheral flow.

An advantageous placement of circular weir troughs is at least 15 percent of the basin radius inboard from the periphery. This requires a substantial cantilever bracket, but it has the advantage of avoiding all but the most serious peripheral floc upwelling disturbances. The troughs often are fabricated of steel with adjustable V-notch fiberglass edges, and straight troughs about 18 to 20 ft long are landed on the brackets. Each trough section should have a 2-in hole in the bottom to relieve loadings (when the basin is drained) and prevent buoyancy up-lift during basin filling.

Radial-overflow troughs are typically used on upflow solids-contact basins, but are seldom used on separate circular sedimentation basins. Radial-overflow troughs present a structural problem when used on larger circular basins because of the long unsupported trough span. They are sometimes used on small circular basins, but the advantage is doubtful where the flow system is radial-horizontal.

Sludge hopper and bottom slopes.   A circular sludge hopper surrounding a central pier holds the greatest volume and is therefore preferable over the older-style offset hopper. A pair of heavy stirrups reach down from the arms of the circular scraper, move the dense sludge around the hopper to the outlet, and prevent buildup of anchor sludge and grit. The sludge drawoff pipe should never be less than 6 in in diameter, and should be designed so that a rotor rodder, or "go-devil," can be placed into the line from outside the basin in case of clogging. In lime-softening plants, this line should be given a short purge of clear water to flush out residual slurry after each blowdown cycle. (See the discussion on intermittent sludge drawoff under "Long Rectangular Basins—Underflow Control.")

Bottom slopes are very important, especially with heavy or sticky sludges. The plow blades keep the bottom free of adhesions, literally plowing extremely dense sludge and grit to the center hopper. Otherwise, the thixotropic sludge flows along the bottom to replace the blown-down underflow. As the dense sludge approaches the basin center, there is increased crowding and concurrent reduced tangential speed of the rotating blades.

In large basins, a second set of arms is typically employed to cover the center half (25 percent of the basin area), where blade movement is extremely slow. Deep blades formed into spiral sections bridge the main and auxiliary arms to better push the crowded sludge into the hopper. In basins larger than about 80 ft in diameter, it is advisable to use a double bottom slope. For example, the slope in the outer half of the basin diameter would be 1 in/ft, and that in the inner half 2 in/ft.

The two-slope design gives steeper slopes (greater hydraulic gradient) at the sludge hopper without excessive basin depth. The greater center depth is desirable for dissipation of scouring currents; it is needed because of the concentration of influent energy in this relatively small region. With outsized basins, 125 ft in diameter or larger, the two-slope bottom is a "must" (see Table 6.1).

Turntable drive.   The tried-and-true, relatively trouble-free drive for circular collectors—both bridge-supported and pier-supported—is the sealed turntable drive with the gear and pinion running in oil. Properly lubricated and with automatic condensate overflow, these drives operate for years without any major repair. Typical turntable drives rotate on renewable bearing strips, and the gear is split so that the ball bearings and strips can be replaced without dismantling the remainder of the equipment. These drives are protected by an indicator and overload circuit breaker device actuated by the thrust of the primary worm gear, which drives the pinion and turntable gear.

Square basins

Basins larger than 30 ft square are typically equipped with central sludge feed systems with corner sweeps, always in pairs, to clean sludge frame corners. The corner sweeps eliminate the need for larger corner fillets, which are more or less unacceptable, although smaller basins are equipped with corner fillets built up on a 60° slope. Corner sweeps should be avoided in basins larger than 100 ft square because of structural problems and wear associated with large cantilevered corner sweep units.

Hydraulic problems usually occur with the larger square basins. Radial density and displacement currents impinge on the peripheral walls at various angles, drift toward the corners, meet, and may cause a rising "corner floc" phenomenon that often contributes turbidity locally to the effluent.

Where inboard weir troughs are used in square tanks, they are designed to cut across the corner so as to avoid any rising "corner floc"; where radial troughs are used (as is typical with upflow basins), they are always arranged to straddle the corner for the same reason. It is best not to run a single peripheral weir around the walls of a square basin because of the "corner floc," as well as for other reasons discussed under inboard weir troughs.

High-rate sedimentation

In recent years, there has been an awakening of interest in modular, high-rate floc sedimentation units. A clearer effluent has been

achieved from several unsatisfactorily performing clarifiers by passing the basin's effluent through added clarification devices, such as
short tube-settler modules. In these "retrofit" cases, the tube modules
intercepted and reclarified turbidity-bearing flows. This suggested
that the entire clarification process could be accomplished in the much
smaller tube-settler unit, with considerably shorter detention times
and at higher surface-loading rates. This could be especially practical
in small-flow applications. Where slime-forming or calcite-deposition
propensities are small, the tube or plate modules can do an excellent
job of removing settleable solids. Properly designed clarifier basins
that are not overloaded do produce clear effluent, however, and even
though larger, may be cheaper than high-rate basins equipped with
tube or plate modules.

On the other hand, a very small plant may well be better served by
a system of high-rate tube or plate module clarifier units, in terms of
both construction expense and performance. In their favor, the high-
rate modules are not ordinarily more difficult to operate than a typical
clarifier basin, and the same chemical dosage and floc formation processes are employed.

Many high-rate settler designs are proprietary, and by and large
are variations of either inclined, small-dimension (roughly 2-in) tube
forms or closely spaced inclined lamella plates (approximately 2 in
apart). The feed mode is upflow, on a laminar-flow, very low Reynolds
number basis (typically less than 200). Soon after the flow enters the
inclined narrow space, particles fall only a very short distance to the
lower plate or tube surface, and the sludge rapidly compacts and slides
down the inclined slick plastic surfaces to discharge at the bottom.
The sludge falls into either a raking area or a hopper for blowdown.

The surface loading rate for basins equipped with tube settled modules is about 2 to 3 times the rate used for conventional clarifiers.
Loading rates for basins equipped with plate settlers range up to 5 to
8 times that of conventional basins. For flocculated waters, application rates must be consistent with their different theoretical settling
velocities, as illustrated in the following example. Laboratory settling
analysis of alum floc formed during treatment of water containing
nonorganic turbidity yields a particle settling rate of 2 in/min (about 5
cm/min). Therefore, ideally, such a system should have a calculated
surface overflow rate of 1795 gpd/ft^2. An 80-ft-diameter by 15-ft-wide
center-feed clarifier for this alum floc would be designed with a balanced inlet and inboard weir troughs and a maximum surface overflow rate of about 900 to 1000 gpd/ft^2, thereby allowing a margin for
hydraulic instability. A basin with a poor inlet, or a smaller basin,
might be designed with a surface overflow rate of about 600 to 700
gpd/ft^2. A tube clarifier for this system could be safely designed near

the theoretical subsidence point—in this case about 95 percent, or 1700 gpd/ft^2 of horizontal tube area, assuming a closely spaced weir overflow system above the tube modules.

Herein lies the charm and space-saving benefit of the high-rate settler; for large flows, however, the cost is apt to be prohibitive because of the provisions for mechanical desludging from under the inclined tube modules. For very small plants, hoppers can be used, and these high-rate systems look economically feasible.

Two of the most frequently used high-rate settlers are described herein. Further information is presented in Yao[6] and Culp et al.[7]

Inclined-plate sedimentation. Based on shallow-depth sedimentation theory, the inclined-plate settler consists of a series of plates inclined at 55° from horizontal. Flow enters at the side, near the bottom of each plate, and exits at the top. Plate spacing is typically 2 in. Solids which settle onto the plates slide by gravity to the basin's sludge zone. Effluent is collected by a header system which helps maintain equal flow through the spaces between plates. Laminar flow exists between the plates, so there is improved hydraulic stability, and density currents are eliminated. However, use of inclined-plate equipment typically requires deeper basins (20 to 24 ft), which are more costly to construct. Where subsurface rock is present, the costs of rock removal may offset savings to be gained from using the plate-settler equipment and the reduced basin sizes.

Tube sedimentation. Several possible configurations of tube shapes and sizes are possible, with most designs employing an upflow configuration. A typical commercial design is a system of 2-in by 2-in tubes inclined at 60° from horizontal. For added strength, the tubes are inclined alternately in both directions. The modules are generally constructed of PVC and ABS smooth plastic.

At typical application rates, the laminar flow characteristics and clarification results are quite similar to those for inclined-plate sedimentation. Properly designed tube modules provide excellent clarification. The influent flow moves up through the tubes, and the sludge moves down the tubes.

Because of superior hydraulic stability, application rates in terms of gpd per square foot horizontal tube surface can be expected to be approximately twice and possibly up to 3 times the surface rates applied to standard clarifier basins.

Tube modules are typically installed over 60 to 75 percent of the surface area of the basin. This provides an open area at the basin influent for removal of readily settleable floc particles by conventional sedimentation and for stabilization of flow patterns prior to clarification within the tube modules.

Solids-contact upflow sedimentation systems

The solids-contact unit is a combination rapid mix, floc-aggregation, and upflow sedimentation basin constructed in either a round or a square configuration. Solids recycling acts to nucleate the flocculated turbidity, causing additional floc aggregation by particle contact. In plants where lime-softening is practiced (see Chap. 10), the reactions are driven closer to completion, thereby reducing the hydroxyl alkalinity and much of the need for stabilization acid. Typically a small dose of sodium hexametaphosphate is used for final stabilization.

These units are typically desludged continuously, and sludge blowdown is usually controlled by automatic valves operated by a preset timer (see "Underflow Control under Rectangular Basins"). The amount of recycled slurry carried in the process can be selected by the operator on an empirical basis and must be carefully controlled. Solids-contact units are designed in two typical modes. The first is a blanket contact design, where the displacing flow filters up through a sludge blanket, uniformly expanding to a blanket interface area large enough to allow only clarified flow to pass. Displacement through the fluidized sludge blanket effects particle contact. The second design involves solids recycling into the rapid-mix region under operator control, so that any desired amount of solids admixture for contact can be carried in the mixing and flocculation sections. The solids-recycle-type clarifier is the design most commonly used in current practice.

The solids-contact unit, when conservatively designed with a practical upflow rate, a realistic flocculation period, and controlled slurry recycle and blowdown, is as efficient as any comparable traditional design—and more dependable than many.

Softening unit. The solids-contact system is ideal for lime-softening facilities, where the rise rate in the sedimentation section can be very high as a result of the formation of a dense, readily settleable floc.

The use of recycled high-solids effluent as a catalytic agent is indicated for the greatest stability, and in some plants up to 25 percent solids are carried in the flocculation zone. However, too high a recycle load may cause stratification, in which case the heavier solids remain in the recycle tube, and the lighter fraction passes to the basin overflow. In such a case, the operator stops the recycle operation, blows down all the sludge in the hopper, and starts over. Solids build up with amazing rapidity. Rapid mixing and flocculation periods with recycled solids should generally last at least 15 min—in the case of cold water, at least 30 min.

For lime-softening operations, recycling nucleates the lime-softening reactions, and the recycling of fresh slurry is important because it retards calcite buildup. In a softening plant, rapid buildup of calcite can be an operating nuisance wherever surfaces are exposed to turbulence. When recycling of slurry is practiced, the rotating turbine contacts the slurry first, and, depending on the amount of slurry recirculated, this retards the buildup of hard calcite on the blades. Calcite accumulations reduce or destroy the circulation efficiency of the turbine and must be removed by hand chipping. To slow calcite buildup, the lime should be fed to the discharge of the turbine, not into the raw-water line or suction tube.

Turbidity removal unit. Initially, the solids-contact units were accepted for softening, but regulatory agencies accepted them only grudgingly for alum coagulation. Today, these units are used for turbidity and color removal throughout the United States. Some units are only moderately successful, which is easily understandable when their design is analyzed. Many plants operate very well at about half their design capacity, but experience difficulty in producing clear water at the anticipated design rate. Often, this can be attributed to improper selection of design parameters.

Careful attention must be paid to the mixing of coagulant with the raw water so that the aggregating floc is exposed to previously formed floc particles.[8] Also, alkalinity must be available for coagulation. Feeding coagulant into the mixing section is not enough; it will either result in the use of excessive coagulant or produce poor results, which are too easily blamed on the solids-contact system. Alum (or iron) should be introduced in an instant blending section for mixing with the feed before it enters the recirculation region. Polyelectrolytes should also be specially blended with the supply because of the minuscule feed rates. Clay and other inert additives can be fed directly into the rapid-mix section.

The flocculation period in a solids-contact unit should be calculated using the same parameters as for a separate flocculation basin or based on jar tests. In general, the flocculation period should not be less than about 15 min in temperate waters and 30 min or more in cold waters. Also, the operator has the ability to modulate recirculation rates to provide the desired G values.

Flocculation and sedimentation. In a solids-contact unit, flocculation takes place while the influent displaces through a conical hood. The G value of fine-scale turbulence is dependent on the amount of mass recirculation selected by the operator. Radial displacement vectors egress well out into the annular upflow sedimentation region from under the lip of this large hood. This causes vertical (rather than horizontal) flow through the sedimentation basin, where surface drawoff weir troughs are placed radially, with their outer ends spaced about 20 ft apart. Because the rise through the sedimentation section is vertical, there is little scour or density current in the sludge blanket, and basin stability is better than in most horizontal flow basins. Hydraulic efficiencies of 75 to 85 percent have been measured in upflow basins approximately 80 ft in diameter, with surface loading rates of approximately 1400 gpd/ft^2 and a 2-h detention period.

Solids recycle.   Solids contact for nucleation is a surface-contact phenomenon, and is typically controlled on the basis of volume. The usual test is to settle a grab sample in a cylinder for 5 min and record the volume percentage of settled slurry. A typical softening plant recycle operation carries about 15 to 30 percent solids, and a typical turbidity-removal operation carries about 2 to 5 percent solids, depending on the putrescibility of the turbidity particles. For color and taste removal, and with algae-laden supplies, little or no solids recirculation is practiced.

Mass recirculation.   A slow-speed turbine circulates flow around and through the rapid-mix aggregation to the extent of about 3 times the median plant throughput. The turbine speed is adjustable, so that the operator may select the capacity which yields the best results with the water to be treated.

The turbine is typically either a radial-plate unit with a tip velocity not greater than 3 to 4 fps or a slow-speed axial flow unit which has a velocity of over 60 rpm, a large hub, and a low (35°) blade angle. The principal requirement is that the turbine not cause local turbulence great enough to break up floc.

Sludge scraper and hopper.   It is of great importance that dense sludge be continuously removed from the bottom and systematically drawn from the center hopper. The typical sludge scraper is a two-arm collector operating at a tip speed of about 10 fpm. The floor slope should be about 1.25:12; a two-slope bottom should be used for basins greater than 80 ft in diameter (see Table 6.1). Sufficient torque should be applied to the scraper to ensure continuous operation. For basins greater than 75 ft in diameter (or square), the scraper should have two full arms and two short arms extending to midradius. All arms should have a full complement of overlapping flights set at 30° to the radius.

The hopper should be centered, circular, and not more than 3 ft in depth. In the case of a center pier, the hopper surrounds the pier, and spades carried by the scraper arms keep the dense sludge moving around the hopper. Whenever the plant is shut down, the scrapers and sludge blowdown system should be kept operating long enough to remove all the dense sludge from the bottom.

Sample lines are often provided to determine the sludge blanket level in the clarifier section and to detect solids stratification. Ordinarily, the sludge blanket should not be higher than the bottom of the flocculation skirt, to prevent hydraulic scour within the sludge blanket. In lime-softening applications, sample lines tend to plug rapidly as a result of scale deposition, and therefore are not typically provided.

The advantages of these basins are lower construction cost because of the absence of interconnecting pipe, valves, and so on, and relatively rapid response to any change in coagulants, coagulant aids, and so on, which aids the operator when changes in chemical dosage may be advantageous.

Process Criteria and Design Details

Surface loading rates

The daily overflow rate of the basin divided by the nominal surface area yields the surface loading rate (surface overflow rate) in gpd per square foot. This rate can be calculated on a theoretical basis by measuring the settling velocity of the smallest particle to be removed in a jar test. The value, however, cannot be realized in an actual sedimentation basin because of efficiency-destroying interferences, such as eddy currents from influent distribution, surface currents, vertical thermal convection currents, density currents, and short circuiting as a result of feed imbalance. This causes the designer to lean heavily on empirical criteria based on the type and size of the basin as well as the particle-settling velocity.

Solids loading rate

Solids loading is a common sludge-thickener design parameter and an indicator of the maximum weight of sludge per day that can be thickened on the floor area of a sedimentation basin without experiencing serious blanket scour. The solids loading rate is limiting in basins receiving mixed liquor solids on the order of 3000 to 4000 mg/L, as in activated sludge sedimentation, but it is usually unimportant when dealing with relatively thin suspensions of coagulated particles in water. However, in lime-softening plants, particularly where considerable solids recycling is practiced, the solids loading rate may become a limiting factor.

Ordinarily, circular basins designed for surface loading rates less than 1000 gpd/ft^2 can handle solids loading rates up to about 30 lb/(day)(ft)^2 of floor area; long rectangular basins can be subjected to lb/(day)(ft)^2 loadings of about 40.

Sidewater depth

Water depth in a sedimentation basin is an important factor in avoiding hydraulic instability caused by wind stirring, thermal convection currents, and "sun floc" (described in the section, "Predicting Sedimentation Performance"). Depth also ameliorates scour effects in the blanket, and provides a factor of safety against the "thunderheads" of floc that may rise at random from blanket disturbances and pour solids into the otherwise clear overflow in a too-shallow basin.

For circular center-feed clarifiers, center depth is more important than sidewater depth. The center region is a point source for a large amount of energy charged into the relatively small feedwell, and water depth at this point can act as a buffer against hydraulic imbalance and formation of radial jet streams.

Ideally, basin performance is controlled by the surface loading rate, but in the case of large sedimentation basins, center depth for circular center-feed basins and sidewater depth for long rectangular basins are important parameters. It is far better to design a basin several feet too deep than too shallow. The cost of the additional depth is typically relatively low, and may improve the basin's performance for a long time under a great many variables.

Detention period

Detention period (the basin filling time at the rate specified) is relatively unimportant as a design parameter and typically serves only as an approximate guideline. However, in the past, some regulatory agencies have been adamant in requiring long detention periods. Detention periods not less than 4 h do tend to enforce greater water depths at the surface loading rates most likely to be used, which tend to be conservative.

Length-to-width ratio

The length-to-width ratio of a rectangular basin is usually not considered a reliable parameter. In the case of small basins, higher L/W ratios yield longer rectangular basins, but since there is a reasonable length of basin not to be exceeded, large plants frequently have basins that are wider (in total) than they are long. Efficient basins have been built that were wider than they were long. For example, a basin at Bensonville, Ill., is 150 ft wide and 30 ft long, the horizontal flow being well distributed along the 30-ft dimension. A carriage collector picks up sludge along the 150-ft dimension.

Successful foldback basins have been built in which the first-half and second-half lengths were built side by side, with reverse flow at the far end of the first section. The Manatee River Water Plant (near Sarasota, Fla.) is an example. The long finger-weir troughs were installed toward the end of the second section. A common carriage collector served both sections, scraping sludge with blades to a common hopper.

Hydraulically separate basins can be so wide that they suffer from wind stirring; the length can be so long that it exceeds the limitations of some forms of sludge removal equipment. Basins 300 ft long have utilized two sets of collector mechanisms, usually with a cross hopper positioned about 200 ft down the length of the basin. The length of long rectangular basins should probably not exceed 200 to 250 ft and the width of hydraulically separate basins should not exceed 50 to 75 ft; however, there are many basins that are much longer.

In general, a wider basin with a correspondingly shorter length for the same surface loading rate will require a better inlet control system to ensure lateral feed balance than would a narrow, long tank. Also, equipment for sludge removal, in general, is more expensive for a wider, and therefore shorter, basin.

Narrower basin design, and correspondingly greater length, requires longer finger-weir troughs to produce a clear overflow. Also, if the basin is too long (more than about 300 ft), some types of cleaning equipment become more expensive if two sets of equipment must be used.

Longitudinal velocity

Median longitudinal velocity is a relatively poor design parameter. Many texts have given the design range as about 0.5 to 4 fpm. Based on a 2-h detention period, this range could produce calculated basin lengths of 60 to 480 ft—a considerable difference. Also, the calculated plug-flow cross-sectional velocity does not exist. Because of jet streaming and short circuiting, the displacement velocity at any cross section will typically be greater than the median velocity. At some places flow will even reverse and drift toward the inlet.

The floc-bearing feed tends to sink at the rectangular forebay (or under a circular feedwell) and drift along the bottom one-third or one-half of the basin depth, depending on the water depth. The density current adds to the longitudinal displacement drift along the bottom, with consequent return, or reverse drift, of clarified water under the surface.

The many decisions that are made in the design of a sedimentation basin result in a calculated median displacement velocity; the median displacement velocity is thus not used as a design parameter.

Sludge pumping

Whenever possible, the treatment facility hydraulic profile should be such that clarifier sludge discharges by gravity to the sludge disposal facilities. When this is not practical because of the site constraints, sludge must be pumped to the disposal facilities. The following is general information on selection of pump capacities.

Selection of sludge pump capacity is based on projected sludge production rates and available pump sizes. The pump's ability to successfully handle materials other than clarification sludge which may enter the basin, e.g., leaves, twigs, and branches, must be considered as well. Typically these considerations limit the designer somewhat with respect to available capacity ranges. In general, nonclogging pumps with suction and discharge piping 4 in in diameter are the practical minimum size. Another consideration is the need to limit pump startup to a maximum of 3 to 4 times per hour in order to minimize pump wear and reduce energy demands.

An example calculation for an alum coagulation facility is presented below. Calculation of sludge solids production rates is discussed in Chap. 12, "Solids Handling, Disposal, and Recovery."

Clarifier design capacity	5 mgd
Solids production (dry weight)	200 lb/mil gal
Sludge solids concentration by weight	0.5%

Assuming that because of its low solids content, the sludge density is approximately equal to that of water, daily sludge production is as follows:

$$\frac{(200 \text{ lb/mil gal})(5 \text{ mgd})}{(0.005)(8.34 \text{ lb/gal})} = 23{,}980 \text{ gpd} = 16.7 \text{ gpm}$$

Assuming that the sludge is to be pumped approximately 10 min/h, required pump capacity is $(16.7 \text{ gpm})(60/10) = 100$ gpm. Where sludge concentrations are anticipated to exceed approximately 1 percent, it is recommended that the sludge density utilized in the above calculation be estimated as follows:

$$\text{Density (lb/gal)} = \frac{8.34}{C_p/\text{SG}_s + C_w/\text{SG}_w}$$

where C_p = fractional percent sludge solids by weight
$\quad\text{SG}_s$ = specific gravity of sludge solids
$\quad C_w$ = fractional percent water by weight
$\quad\text{SG}_w$ = specific gravity of water (approximately 1.0)

For example, for a 5 percent sludge composed of solids with a specific gravity of 2.5,

$$\text{Density} = \frac{8.34}{0.05/2.5 + 0.95/1.0} = 8.60 \text{ lb/gal}$$

Process Monitoring and Control

Equal flow to parallel basins

Many groups of basins intended to receive equal flow in parallel are designed on the basis that leveling the V-notch effluent weirs will result in equal flow through each basin. However, experience disproves this assumption and indicates that dependence on the long overflow weirs will result in great variations of flow through parallel basins. One reliable way to control the flow is to use a weir-splitter box as feed control to the several basins. The distribution-control weirs can be somewhat submerged to reduce head loss and floc disturbance. Where flocculation basins are coupled with sedimentation basins, flow splitting should take place ahead of the flocculation basins.

Sludge-blanket depth

The sludge-blanket depth should be monitored daily. A handy device for this purpose is a long, clear plastic tube about 2 in in diameter which is inserted vertically through the water. The tube is equipped so that it captures a core sample. There are also many photocell and electronic devices available for making this measurement.

Sludge density

The density of sludge withdrawn from the basin as underflow should be monitored daily. The density of the sludge on the floor in the compression zone should be monitored biweekly. A comparison of the average terminal density of the compression-zone (bottom-layer) sludge and the density of the underflow discloses whether the mechanics of sludge blowdown are yielding as dense a sludge as possible. A large discrepancy would indicate the need to revise the technique or means of drawing off sludge. Subsequent treatment preceding sludge disposal requires the densest drawoff possible.

Solids recycling

Solids recycling to nucleate flocculation and softening reactions is typically practiced in solids-contact basins by internally recirculating the sludge, and is often applied to separate sedimentation basins by external sludge return. The effect of solids recycling and contact is a surface phenomenon; therefore, the operator sets the recycling level by checking a flocculation basin sample for the volume of sludge settling in a cylinder for 5 min. The volume of recycled slurry for contact that works best is then held constant. In the case of putrescible sludge, the operator has to maintain the percentage of contact slurry at a low level to avoid putrefaction.

Mass recirculation, upflow solids-contact type

Variable-speed impeller recirculation within the mixing section of a solids-contact basin accomplishes three primary objectives: (1) fresh precipitate (that has not yet had time to exude moisture) is withdrawn from the top of the sludge hopper and recycled into the raw-water feed as a controlled admixture, (2) 3 to 5 times the basin throughput is recycled by means of a variable-speed impeller (with or without solids recycling), which vastly increases early turbulence, mixing, and contact during the addition of coagulant and coagulant aids, and (3) this recirculation maintains hydraulic balance within the mixing-flocculation stage, which aids in uniform distribution of floc displacement under the flocculation skirt and, in turn, produces good hydraulic stability through the annular upflow sedimentation section.

Proprietary Clarification Processes

"Pulsator" clarifier

Developed and marketed by Infilco Degremont, the Pulsator is a sludge blanket-type clarifier which utilizes a unique hydraulic pulsating system to maintain a homogenous sludge solids layer within the clarifier. Chemically coagulated water first enters a vacuum chamber adjacent to the clarifier. A vacuum pump draws the water up into the chamber, and an air vent releases the vacuum and allows the water to flow into the clarifier. This creates a hydraulic pulsing action within the clarifier, and flocculation energy imparted is a function of pulse intensity and duration. The coagulated water enters the clarifier through a series of perforated distribution laterals at the clarifier floor. Inverted V-shaped baffles directly above the perforated laterals "still" excessive turbulence and assist in distribution of flow evenly over the bottom of the sludge blanket. Passage of the coagulated water upward through the sludge blanket results in contact of the water with previously formed floc particles, i.e., "contact flocculation," and clarification of the incoming raw-water results. During the introduction of flow into the clarifier, the sludge blanket expands uniformly upward. During the portion of the pulsation cycle when flow is not introduced into the clarifier, the sludge blanket settles. Continuous "pulsing" of the sludge blanket maintains a uniform sludge layer within the clarifier, thereby reducing the potential for short circuiting of flow through the sludge blanket. As a result of intimate contact of the incoming flow with the sludge blanket, high coagulant utilization may be achieved, and high-clarity water is produced. The pulsation cycle typically lasts 40 to 50 s. Sludge-blanket depth is maintained at a preset level through use of a sludge drawoff weir system at one side of the basin (see Fig. 6.8). The Pulsator is particularly useful in the treatment of highly colored, low-turbidity waters, where formation of a readily settleable floc is frequently difficult. Design loading rates for operating installations range from approximately 0.25 to 1.9 gpm/ft^2 of clarifier surface area, with an average loading of approximately 0.5 gpm/ft^2.

"Superpulsator" clarifier

Also developed and marketed by Infilco Degremont, the Superpulsator sludge-blanket clarifier combines the hydraulic pulsation system of the Pulsator clarifier with a series of inclined parallel plates located within the sludge blanket. The inclined plates help maintain high solids concentrations at increased hydraulic upflow rates, thus permitting the Superpulsator to be operated at loading rates two to three times greater than for the Pulsator. Plate inclination is 60° from the horizontal, and plate spacing ranges from 12 to 20 in. Small deflector vanes are attached to the inclined plates transverse to the direction of flow between the plates. These deflectors create vortex currents which assist in the mixing of previously settled sludge particles with the water to be treated.

"Trident" contact adsorption clarifier

Developed and marketed by Microfloc Products, the Trident water treatment system combines coagulation, flocculation, and clarification processes in a single upflow adsorption clarifier which utilizes the con-

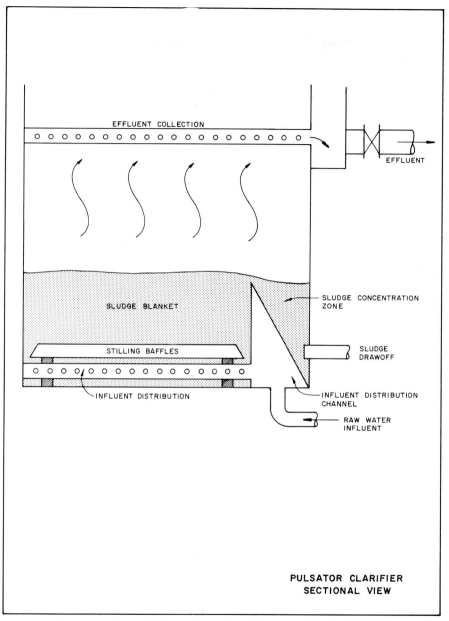

Figure 6.8 Sectional view of Pulsator® clarifier. (*Courtesy of Infilco Degremont, Inc., Richmond, Va.*)

tact flocculation/adsorption phenomenon for removal of turbidity and color. Adsorption media consist of buoyant plastic beads retained within the adsorption clarifier by a screen. Turbidity and color removal are accomplished by adsorption of chemically coagulated and flocculated particles onto the surface of the plastic media and on previously attached particles.

During operation, coagulant is added to the raw water, and the water is introduced at the bottom of the adsorption clarifier (see Fig. 6.9). The water passes upward through the plastic media, and flocculation is accomplished by turbulence imparted as the water passes through the media. The solids formed as a result of flocculation adhere to the media, and subsequently enhance the removal of newly formed floc particles. Required coagulant dosages may be less than for conventional flocculation/sedimentation processes, as formation of a large, rapidly settling floc is not required for efficient operation. Turbidity removal by the adsorption clarifier typically ranges from 75 to 95 percent.

When solids accumulation within the clarifier results in excessive head loss (typically 3 to 4 ft), or when clarifier effluent quality declines to unacceptable levels, the clarifier is cleaned by upflow hydraulic flushing. Air is introduced at the bottom of the clarifier through a series of perforated laterals. The air reduces the buoyancy of the plastic media, which then expand downward. The air also provides vigorous "scrubbing" of media surfaces. The dislodged solids are flushed out of the clarifier and discharged to waste. Influent raw water is used for flushing, and the required flushing time is generally 2 to 5 min. In actual operation, the flushing cycle is typically controlled to permit some floc to remain on the media, as these particles enhance

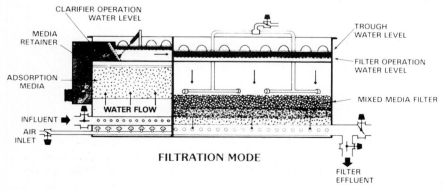

Figure 6.9 Sectional view of Trident® contact adsorption clarifier. (*Courtesy of CPC Engineering Corporation.*)

clarifier performance during initial operation. Contactor operating times vary with the quality of the water being treated, but typically average 4 to 8 h.

Trident clarifiers are typically designed to provide a media loading rate of approximately 10 gpm/ft^2. Effective media size is 4 to 6 mm, and media depth is generally about 4 ft. Trident clarifiers are available in modular form, with capacities ranging from 0.5 to 4 mgd. "Tricon" modular systems are designed for installation in concrete tanks, and are available in sizes ranging from 3 to 6 mgd. Tricon modules combine contact adsorption clarification with mixed-media filtration in a single modular tank insert.

Flotation

Where raw waters contain high levels of low-density particles such as algae, or where chemical coagulation typically produces a light, slowly settling floc (as in treatment of low-turbidity, highly colored waters), dissolved-air flotation (DAF) may represent a viable alternative to conventional sedimentation processes. While DAF processes have not been utilized in the United States for potable water production to any significant extent, flotation is an established technology in the treatment of municipal and industrial wastes.

Flotation is based on the transfer of particles to the surface of a liquid through attachment of bubbles to the particle surfaces. The particles are then removed as a floating sludge, usually by mechanical skimming. Potential advantages of DAF include the following:

Reduced chemical coagulant requirements, as formation of a large, rapidly settling floc is not required

Reduced land requirements as a result of operation at high surface loading rates

High sludge solids concentrations (typically 3 percent or greater)

Rapid stabilization of effluent water quality upon start-up because of the short process detention times

A typical DAF process train consists of chemical coagulation, flocculation, air injection, and flotation. A portion of the flotation tank effluent is recycled, pressurized, and saturated with air. When this recycled water is injected back into the process stream ahead of the flotation tank, fine bubbles form and attach themselves to the previously formed floc particles, then the bubble/floc aggregate rises to the surface.

Flotation tanks are normally designed with surface loading rates ranging from approximately 3 to 5 gpm/ft^2. Baffling is required at the tank influent to direct the incoming flow toward the tank surface while reducing its velocity to minimize disturbance of the floating sludge layer. Methods used to dissolve air under pressure in the recycling stream include sparging of the air into the water in a pressure vessel, passing the water through a packed-bed aeration tower, entraining the air with an ejector, and injecting air into the recycle pump suction line.

References

1. Thomas R. Camp, "Studies of Sedimentation Basin Design," *Sewage and Ind. Wastes,* vol. 25, no.1, 1953, p. 1.
2. Thomas R. Camp, "Camp on Settling Tanks," *Trans. ASCE,* vol. III, 1946, p. 955.
3. Thomas R. Camp, "Sedimentation and Design of Settling Tanks," *Trans. ASCE,* vol. III, 1946, p. 895.
4. F. L. Flood, "Sedimentation Tanks," *Seminar Papers on Wastewater Treatment and Disposal,* Boston Soc. of Civil Engineering, 1961.
5. Jack Quandt, Superintendent, South Shore Treatment Plant (Milwaukee Metro Sewerage District). Private telephone conversation, Aug. 9, 1977, concerning plastic drag chains.
6. Kuan Mi Yao, "Design of High-Rate Settler," *Journal ASCE, Environmental Engineering Division,* vol. 5, paper no. 10051, 1973, p. 621.
7. G. L. Culp, K. Hsiung, and W. R. Conley, "Tube Clarification Process Operating Experiences," *Journal ASCE SA5,* vol. 5, paper no. 6823, 1969, p. 829.
8. J. W. Moffet, "The Chemistry of High Rate Water Treatment," *Journal AWWA,* vol 60, no. 11, 1968, p. 1255.
9. *Recommended Standards for Water Works,* Great Lakes–Upper Mississippi River Board of State Sanitary Engineers, 1982.

Filtration

Introduction

Filtration, as it applies to water treatment, is the passage of water through a porous medium for the removal of suspended solids. According to Baker,[1] the earliest written records of water treatment, dating from about 4000 B.C., mention filtration of water through charcoal or sand and gravel. Although a number of modifications have been made in the manner of application, filtration remains one of the fundamental technologies associated with water treatment.

Water filtration is an adaptation of natural processes. "Purification" of water as a result of passage through granular soil was recognized long ago. Some of the earliest filter designers applied this principle by simply digging a hole near a river and using the soil between the river and the hole as a filtering medium. Filters were subsequently constructed artificially, using sand, gravel, and other materials. Although filtration was originally used only to improve the visual appearance of water, research in the late nineteenth century demonstrated that the filters were also providing excellent removal of bacteria. This indicated that the "improved healthfulness" of the water resulted not only from turbidity removal, but also from bacterial count reduction.

Developments in filtration include enhanced solids removal through the use of coagulants, and improvements in media selection, underdrain design, and backwashing techniques. Currently, filters are most commonly used in plants treating surface water. Filtration of groundwater is generally limited to locations where softening or iron-manganese removal is required. The 1977 National Primary Drinking Water Standards included a monthly average "one turbidity unit (TU)" limit for surface water supplies. This requirement increased the number of surface water supplies that use filtration. Impending regulations may result in further decreases in allowable turbidity levels, which will expand the number of utilities that use filtration processes.

Types of filters

Filtration systems may be classified in several ways. Filters are variously described in terms of driving force, depth of solids penetration, media distribution, direction of water flow, and pretreatment provided.

Driving force

Filters operate under either gravity flow (Fig. 7.1) or pressure (Fig. 7.2). Pressure filters are more suited to operating at higher head loss, which may be advantageous for some applications. Pressure filters also allow pumping through the unit under relatively high pressures, which may eliminate the need for additional pumping facilities. Pressure filters are commonly used in smaller plants because they tend to be more economical. In larger plants, gravity filtration is more common, as pressure filters are limited by available tank sizes. A serious disadvantage of pressure filters is the inability of the operator to observe the filter during filtration and backwash. As a result, in some

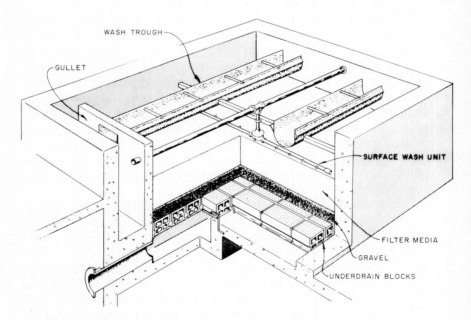

Figure 7.1   Typical gravity filter. (*Source: F. B. Leopold Co.*)

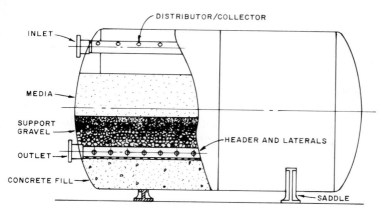

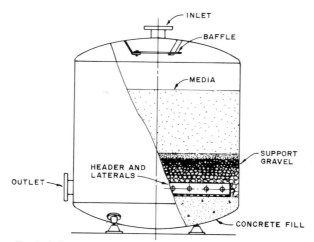

Figure 7.2 Typical horizontal and vertical pressure filters. (*Source: Roberts Filter Manufacturing Co.*)

states the use of pressure filters in potable water applications is restricted.[2]

Characteristics

Depth of solids penetration, media distribution, and direction of water flow are interrelated characteristics of filters. Consequently, the use of descriptive terms related to any one of these characteristics often implies something about a filter in terms of the others. Media distribution may be ungraded, uniformly graded, or graded fine-to-coarse or coarse-to-fine (see Fig. 7.3a). Filters may also be described as downflow, upflow, or biflow units (Fig. 7.3b). As a result of media distribution and flow direction, solids removal will occur primarily at the filter surface or throughout the bed ("in depth").

Backwashing of single-medium filters results in movement of the finest grains to the top of the bed. In downflow operation, the bed is then graded fine-to-coarse, with the smallest pore sizes at the top of the bed. As a result, solids removal occurs primarily at or very near the bed surface. This type of operation is characteristic of rapid sand filters, which for years have been the mainstay of potable water production in the United States. The operation of single-medium anthracite filters is similar, although anthracite's characteristically higher porosity may permit slightly deeper solids penetration. Single-medium anthracite filters are used in relatively few locations.

Slow sand filters are also downflow surface filters. They are not backwashed and thus have randomly distributed (ungraded) media.

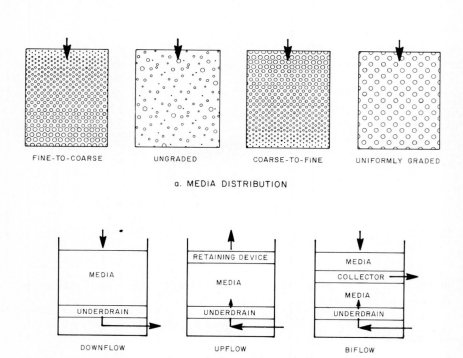

Figure 7.3 Filter configurations: (a) media distribution and (b) direction of flow. (*Source: Black & Veatch, Engineers-Architects.*)

Relatively fine media are used, however, resulting in small pore sizes throughout the unstratified bed. In combination with the low driving head provided, this results in little solids penetration beyond the top few inches of the bed. Slow sand filters are a virtually obsolete means of water treatment, although a few units remain in use.

Current practice is directed toward using a greater volume of the filter bed to maximize run lengths and minimize wash-water usage. European practice has been centered on upflow beds and uniformly graded downflow beds. In the United States, efforts to achieve in-depth filtration have involved downflow coarse-to-fine beds almost exclusively. Downflow coarse-to-fine beds are constructed using two or more materials of varying specific gravities and size distributions. Materials are chosen so that during backwashing, relatively low-density, coarse media remain at the top of the bed and higher-density, fine media at the bottom. Downflow coarse-to-fine beds account for most of the current construction in the U.S. potable water industry.

Upflow beds are single-medium beds stratified by backwashing. Since water to be filtered is fed from the bottom, the coarsest media are encountered first. A variation of the upflow filter is the biflow filter. Water enters from both the top and bottom of the bed and exits through a central collector. If a single-medium bed is used, the top half of the bed operates as a downflow fine-to-coarse filter and the bottom as an upflow coarse-to-fine unit. In a dual-media biflow filter, the top of the bed also approximates a coarse-to-fine filter. Downflow uniformly graded filters utilize deep beds of relatively large media with an unusually narrow distribution of grain sizes. Stratification of such beds during backwash is avoided. Although common in Europe, upflow, biflow, and deep uniformly graded filters have gained little acceptance in municipal practice in the United States. It is expected that the use of deep-bed uniformly graded filters will become more common in U.S. potable water treatment facilities. Full-scale U.S. operating experience is currently limited to one southwestern facility, but other facilities are under design.

Pretreatment

Water plants treating surface water, particularly river supplies, routinely include coagulation, flocculation, and sedimentation to remove some solids prior to the filters. Some surface supplies and many groundwater supplies do not require sedimentation. Water utilities in which filtration is not preceded by sedimentation are commonly referred to as direct-filtration plants to distinguish them from conventional plants. More restrictive definitions of direct filtration have appeared in the literature, but are less widely recognized.

Mechanisms of filtration

The removal of suspended solids by filtration is a complex process involving a number of phenomena. Attempts to develop theories which quantitatively predict solids removal performance with sufficient precision and versatility to be of use in practical filter design have met with relatively little success. Consequently, filter media selection is often an empirical process.

In current granular filtration techniques, solids removal occurs primarily as a two-step process.[3] During the initial transport step, particles are moved to the surfaces of media grains or previously captured floc. Transport is believed to be due largely to hydrodynamic forces, with contact occurring as stream lines converge in pore restrictions. The second step is attachment of the particles to either grain or floc surfaces. Electrokinetic and molecular forces are probably responsible for the adherence of the particles on the surfaces within the bed.[4,5,6] Physical straining may have been a principal filtration mechanism in the "schmutzdecke" of a slow sand filter, but it is generally a minor means of solids removal in modern filters.

Elements of Design

General considerations

Number of filter units.   The number of filter units varies with the plant capacity. A minimum of three filters is desirable even for small plants. One or two filters may be used only if sufficient capacity in the second filter or storage can be provided to ensure water supply during filter outages for backwash and maintenance.

The recommended minimum number of filters in medium- and large-sized plants (roughly 10 mgd and greater) is four. The number is based on the demand exerted on the filters remaining in service when one is shut down for backwashing. The number of filters required depends on the plant capacity and the filter size selected. If more than four filters are used, an even number of filters is usually chosen to simplify the layout.

Filter arrangement.   Filters are normally placed next to each other along one or both sides of a pipe gallery. This approach provides the most compact arrangement and also simplifies filter operation and maintenance. Area for future expansion should be available at one end of the row (or rows) of filters. Piping in the gallery may be installed with blind flanges to make addition of future filters easy.

In larger plants, placement of filters in rows on opposite sides of a pipe gallery is common practice. In smaller plants, a single row of filters may result in simpler construction. Typical filter arrangements are shown in Fig. 7.4. For reasons cited in subsequent paragraphs, the

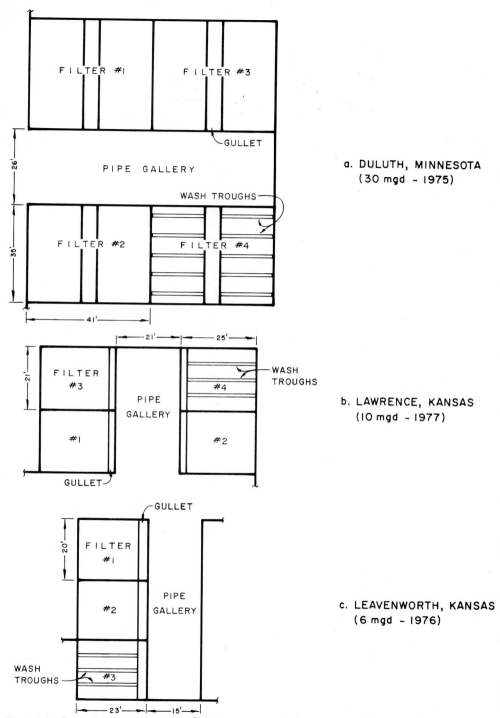

Figure 7.4 Typical filter arrangements (schematics): (a) Duluth, Minn., (b) Lawrence, Kan., and (c) Leavenworth, Kan.

151

practical size of an individual filter is not unlimited. Beyond some point, capacity is increased by using more, rather than larger, filters.

Location of the filtered water clearwell under the pipe gallery, and common walls between filtered and unfiltered water, should be avoided to prevent the possibility that leakage through the walls will contaminate the filtered water. A false floor should be placed in the wash-water gullet to prevent a common wall from existing between unfiltered water in the gullet and filtered water in the underdrainage system. Drainage should be provided for spaces beneath false floors of this type.

Many designers favor construction of conduits connecting filters and flocculation or sedimentation basins in such a manner that turbulence and high velocities which might result in floc destruction are minimized. Drops, bends, elbows, and long runs are avoided. The need to avoid turbulence, however, is not universally accepted.[7] Low velocities may be dictated by head loss between basins and filters.

Filters may be placed outdoors in warm climates. In colder regions, filters are normally housed to prevent icing. Controls are usually enclosed in a building. Ground-level access to the pipe gallery is often provided. Location of the filters near the control room for operating convenience is desirable, although in large plants substantial distances are often unavoidable.

Size of filter units.   The size of individual gravity filters is determined by the plant capacity, the filtration rate, and the number of units desired. Hydraulic considerations and the effect of removing a filter from service limit the maximum filter size. Additional considerations include the maximum area to which backwash water can be evenly distributed, the span length of the wash-water gutters, and available sizes of surface-wash equipment, if used. Single gravity filters up to about 4500 ft^2 have been reported,[8] but units less than half this size are more typical, even in large plants. Large filters may have a center gullet (Fig. 7.4a), permitting half of the unit to be backwashed at a time, although influent and effluent piping are shared.

Pressure filters are limited by steel tank sizes. The largest standard units typically available are 10-ft-diameter tanks, as larger sizes present shipping difficulties. This limits vertical filters to about 78 ft^2 of media. Horizontal units are normally not longer than 40 ft (400 ft^2). Larger units of both types can be specially fabricated.

Generally, the capital cost of filters can be minimized by designing for the minimum number of filters consistent with size limitations. Plant expansions are usually accomplished by adding filters of the same size as the existing units, as installing larger filters may require extensive changes in the backwash system and other piping.

Process alternatives

Direct filtration.   Where applicable, direct filtration can produce water of a quality equal to that obtained through the use of flocculation, sedimentation, and filtration. Because all solids removal in direct filtration takes place in the filter, this process should be employed only for high-quality water. Recommended raw-water quality criteria for the direct-filtration process are presented in the section, "Design Criteria." Pilot filter operations are recommended before a decision is made to use direct filtration.

Cost savings is the principal advantage of direct filtration. Cost savings of up to 30 percent can be realized as a result of the elimination of sedimentation (and possibly flocculation) basins and equipment. A 10 to 30 percent reduction in chemical costs is possible, as generally less coagulant is required to produce a filterable floc than to produce a floc that will settle. Polymer, acting as a filter aid, is often added ahead of the filters. Operation and maintenance costs may be reduced, and the quantity of sludge produced is less than that produced by conventional treatment. The sludge is relatively dense and more easily dewatered than conventional filtration plant sludge.[9]

Disadvantages include shorter filter runs prior to backwash and the inability of the process to handle large variations in suspended solids loadings. Generally, more operator attention is required to maintain a high-quality effluent because the retention time in the plant is substantially shorter, and wash-water requirements may be higher than for conventional filtration facilities.

Filter media designs for direct filtration are generally similar to those for filters preceded by flocculation and sedimentation. However, sand filters generally cannot provide the pore space that is required for storage of solids removed from the water; therefore, dual and mixed-media beds are more frequently used.

Pilot testing and previous experience have indicated that filter rates of 1 to 8 gpm/ft^2 can yield a high-quality effluent.[9] A common design value is 4 to 5 gpm/ft^2, which provides operational flexibility and a margin of safety against variations in raw-water quality. Recent pilot testing indicates that deep-bed uniformly graded anthracite filters, when preceded by ozonation, can operate reliably at rates of 10 to 15 gpm/ft^2. All filter effluent lines should be equipped with a turbidimeter for continuous monitoring of effluent quality, which will permit optimization of coagulant and polymer dosages. Additional information concerning process monitoring is presented in the section, "Control and Monitoring."

While the filtrate quality produced by direct filtration will not exceed that of a conventional filtration plant, the lower cost of direct filtration may permit its implementation in locations where filtration is desirable but is not presently provided.

Automatic backwash control. Automatic control systems are available that can interpret a triggering signal indicating high filter head loss or filter effluent turbidity, remove the filter from service, backwash it, and return the filter to service. The controls normally are designed to permit the plant operator to optimize backwash sequencing and the rate and duration of each sequence.

Continuous backwash. An alternative to the automatic control of standard filters would be the use of continuously backwashing filter beds which eliminate the need to remove the beds from service for washing. The beds are divided into a series of narrow, contiguous cells, each containing its own underdrain system which allows it to be backwashed independently from the remaining cells. Backwashing is accomplished by means of a traveling hood suspended above the bed. As the hood travels across the bed, each cell is isolated, and a small backwash pump draws clean water from the filter effluent and reverses the flow through that particular cell. The water is removed by a second backwash pump located in the traveling hood and discharged to waste. The backwash cycle time is controlled by preset adjustable timers to permit optimization of the automatic operation feature. Media depth will vary with each application, but the depth is typically 30 to 36 in.

In addition to the automatic backwashing features, these filters have the capability of producing relatively constant wash-water flow. In a properly sized system, this constant flow can eliminate the need to provide wash-water equalization facilities and permits direct recycle to the plant headworks.

Granular media alternatives

In potable water filtration applications in the United States, the most commonly used filter media are natural silica sand and crushed anthracite coal. Other materials, less widely used, include garnet, ilmenite, and granular activated carbon. Selection of appropriate media involves a number of design decisions concerning filtration configuration, raw-water quality, pretreatment, and desired filtrate quality. Backwashing requirements and underdrain system options are dependent upon the media chosen.

The media variables over which the designer has control include bed composition, bed depth, grain size distribution, and, to a lesser extent, specific gravity. (The designer has a very limited number of materials with different specific gravities from which to choose.) In addition to media design characteristics, some control can be exercised over media quality through specifications covering, where applicable, hardness or abrasion resistance, grain shapes, and acid solubility, impurities, moisture, adsorptive capacity, manner of shipment, and other such factors. Suggested criteria and a discussion of the applicability of these parameters can be found in the AWWA Standards for Filtering Material (B100-72)[10] and Granular Activated Carbon (B604-74).[11]

Traditionally, in the United States, granular media have been described in terms of effective size and uniformity coefficient. The effective size is that dimension exceeded by all but the finest 10 percent (by weight) of the representative sample; it is also referred to as the "10 percent finer" size. The uniformity coefficient is the ratio of the "60 percent finer" size to the effective size.

Common practice in Europe is to express media sizes as the upper and lower limits of a range. These limits may be expressed either as linear dimensions or as passing and retaining sieve sizes (i.e., 1.0 to 2.0 mm or $-10 + 18$ mesh). Conversions between the standard U.S. sieve series and dimensions in millimeters are presented in Table 7.1.

As indicated previously, filter beds may be classified as upgraded, graded fine-to-coarse, graded coarse-to-fine, or uniformly graded, depending upon the distribution of grain sizes within the bed during filtration. The transition from the upgraded slow sand filter to the fine-to-coarse rapid sand filter resulted from dissatisfaction with the low loading rates and laborious cleaning procedure characteristic of the slow filter. Filters with uniformly graded or coarse-to-fine beds are now being operated at higher loading rates and longer run times than are feasible with the conventional rapid sand filter.

Ungraded media.   The primary example of an ungraded bed is the slow sand filter. Because slow sand filters are not backwashed, no hydraulic grading of the media occurs. Distribution of the various grain sizes in the bed is thus essentially random. Typical slow filter beds contain

TABLE 7.1   U.S. Sieve Series

Sieve designation number*	Size of opening, mm	Sieve designation number*	Size of opening, mm
200	0.075	20	0.850
140	0.106	18	1.00
100	0.150	16	1.18
80	0.180	14	1.40
70	0.212	12	1.70
60	0.250	10	2.00
50	0.300	8	2.36
30	0.600	4	4.75

*Approximately the number of meshes per inch.

2 to 4 ft of sand with an effective size of 0.2 to 0.35 mm and a uniformity coefficient not exceeding 3.0.

Fine-to-coarse media.   Fluidization and expansion of rapid sand filter beds during backwashing results in accumulation of the fine grains at the top of the bed and the coarse grains at the bottom. Consequently, filtration occurs predominantly in the top few inches, and head loss increases relatively rapidly during operation. Rapid sand beds typically have effective sizes of 0.35 to 0.60 mm and uniformity coefficients of 1.3 to 1.8. Smaller effective sizes are seldom practical because of the shortened run times. Grains passing a number 50 sieve (0.3 mm) or captured on a number 16 sieve (1.18 mm) are normally limited by specifications to very small portions of the media. Bed depths are typically 24 to 36 in.

Single-medium anthracite beds have been used in the same basic configuration as rapid sand beds. Because anthracite is more angular than sand, the porosity of an anthracite bed is higher than that of a sand bed containing media with the same effective size. A typical anthracite bed has a porosity of 50 to 55 percent. The porosity of a single-medium sand bed is generally 40 to 45 percent. Consequently, anthracite will not perform in exactly the same manner as sand of equivalent size. Because of the lower specific gravity, anthracite beds are also easier to fluidize and expand than sand beds.

Coarse-to-fine media.   In a coarse-to-fine bed, both small and large grains contribute to the filtering process. The presence of fine media in a filter is desirable because of the relatively large surface area per unit volume they provide for particle adhesion. Fine media are instrumental in achieving high filtrate quality. Coarse media, when placed before fine media in filtering sequence, decrease the rate of head loss buildup and increase the available storage capacity in the bed.

Tests by Oeben, Haines, and Ives[12] and Craft[13] demonstrated that sand media placed in a downflow reverse-graded (coarse-to-fine) alignment exhibit filtering performance superior to that of the same media in the conventional fine-to-coarse alignment. Better utilization of the entire bed, manifested as lower head loss and longer run time, was achieved by the reverse-graded beds without decline in filtrate quality. Reverse grading of the beds used in these studies was accomplished, however, by physically transferring backwashed media to another filter vessel, a method not applicable to full-scale operations. Attempts in the United States to approximate coarse-to-fine filtration have been directed almost entirely toward the use of dual- and mixed-(triple-) media beds.

Dual-media beds normally contain silica sand and anthracite coal. Triple-media beds contain an additional layer of garnet or ilmenite sand. Beds with three or more media types which intermix after backwashing have been patented as "mixed-media" filters and are proprietary technology.[14] Specific gravities of materials used in filtration are roughly as follows: silica sand, 2.55 to 2.65; anthracite coal, 1.5 to 1.75; garnet, 4.0 to 4.3; and ilmenite, 4.5. A typical dual-media bed contains 6 to 12 in of silica sand (effective size 0.4 to 0.55 mm) and 20 to 27 in of anthracite (effective size 0.8 to 1.1 mm). A typical mixed-media filter contains 3 to 4 in of garnet (effective size 0.15 to 0.35 mm), 6 to 9 in of silica sand (effective size 0.35 to 0.5 mm), and 18 to 24 in of anthracite (effective size 0.8 to 1.1 mm). Figure 7.5 displays media grain distribution in a typical mixed-media bed.

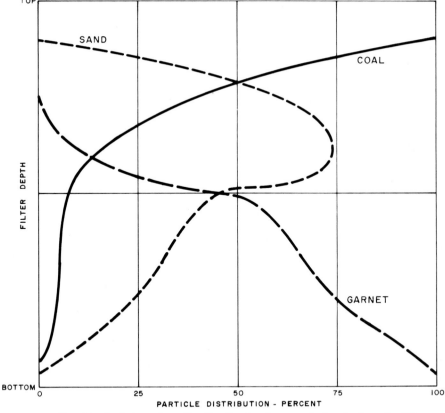

Figure 7.5 Graphic depiction of media distribution in a typical mixed-media filter. (*Courtesy of MicroFloc Products, CPC Engineering Corp.*)

The degree to which media layers are intermixed in the bed depends upon the sizes and shapes of the media used, the nature of the backwashing procedure, the rate of valve closure, and the specific gravities of the different media. There is disagreement over whether distinct layers or intermixed layers are most desirable. If layers mix completely, the purpose of using more than one medium would be defeated. If no mixing occurs, individual fine-to-coarse layers would result, and the possibility of rapid clogging at interfaces is raised. Proponents contend that in a properly designed mixed-media filter, a gradual decline in pore sizes from the top to the bottom of the bed is established after backwashing. The original argument can be traced to Conley[15,16] and Camp[17,18] in the early 1960s. More recently, Brosman and Malina[19] concluded that a slightly mixed bed was superior to a distinctly layered bed in terms of head loss development, filter run time, and effluent turbidity. Cleasby and Sejkora,[20] however, disagree that superior performance can be attributed to interfacial intermixing in and of itself; rather, it is a result of differences in the media sizes required to construct mixed and separated beds. They found that to provide a relatively sharp interface in a dual bed, fairly coarse sand was required. The resulting bed would not provide the same filtrate quality as a bed using finer sand which mixed more readily with the coal. The sizes of sand and coal used by Cleasby and Sejkora to achieve separate and mixed beds are presented in Table 7.2.

Provision of anthracite and silica sand in sizes commonly used in dual-media filters inevitably results in some intermixing of layers. In a triple-media bed, intermixing of silica sand and garnet sand normally occurs more readily than mixing of silica sand and coal. Cleasby and Woods[21] suggest that, as a rule of thumb, the ratio of the average particle size of coarse silica grains to the size of coarse garnet grains should not exceed 1.5 to ensure that some garnet remains at the bottom of the bed. They also suggest that a ratio of coarse coal grain size to the fine silica sand grain size of about 3 will result in a reasonable degree of mixing in dual- or mixed-media beds. Brosman and Malina[19]

TABLE 7.2   Media Sizing for Layered and Intermixed Dual Beds

	Layered bed	Intermixed bed
Effective size (D_{10}), sand	0.85 mm	0.46 mm
Uniformity coefficient, sand	1.29	1.49
Effective size (D_{10}), coal	0.91 mm	0.92 mm
Uniformity coefficient, coal	1.45	1.60
Ratio of bottom coal to top sand, (D_{90} coal/D_{10} sand)	1.93	4.05

found that "anthracite-sand filter media with a size ratio at the interface of less than 3:1 will exhibit little mixing" and that "the zone of mixing increases linearly as the size ratio increases above 3:1."

In a few cases in the United States, taste and odor removal and filtration have been combined in a single filter using granular activated carbon.[22,23,24,25] The granular carbon is sometimes added to existing rapid sand units from which some sand has been removed. Granular carbon depths of 12 to 36 in over silica sand layers of 6 to 18 in have been reported. Typically, 0.5 to 0.65 mm effective size carbon has been used. This technique is applicable only where taste and odor and not turbidity are of primary concern. The use of activated carbon rather than anthracite just to provide a coarse upper layer is not economical. Also, if turbidity levels are high, activated carbon pores will become plugged fairly rapidly, and carbon life will be greatly reduced. If both turbidity and taste and odor are significant problems, activated carbon beds should be preceded by conventional granular filtration. If carbon adsorption is desired for removal of organics, the depth of carbon which can be provided in a converted gravity filter is likely to be too shallow to provide adequate contact time.

In Europe, upflow filters are frequently employed to achieve coarse-to-fine filtration. Hamann and McKinney[26] reported that the upflow filters commonly used in the Soviet Union are relatively deep (6.5 to 8.5 ft of sand) and that recommended media sizes range from 0.5 to 2.0 mm. The primary difficulty associated with upflow filters is breakthrough resulting from bed lifting as head loss increases. Grids are frequently installed above the sand to discourage lifting. An upflow filter tested in the United States contained a 6-ft sand bed.[27] As used in a demonstration program, the bed consisted of 3 ft of 0.95-mm effective size sand with a uniformity coefficient of 1.26 above 3 ft of 1.8-mm effective size sand with a uniformity coefficient of 1.11. Available literature contains no evidence of the use of upflow filtration for potable water production in a permanent installation in the United States. Upflow filters have received greater acceptance in nonpotable than potable water applications in the United States.

An alternative solution is the biflow filter, in which water is introduced at the top and the bottom of the bed simultaneously. Russian biflow filters typically contain 5 to 5.5 ft of sand. Filtrate is withdrawn at an intermediate point 1.5 to 2 ft below the top surface. During filtration, the head on the upper bed aids in preventing expansion of the lower bed. The loadings on the upper and lower portions of the filter are not equivalent. The lower bed is a coarse-to-fine bed, although the finest grains in the upflow filter are as coarse as the coarsest grains in the downflow bed. Variations observed in filtrate quality between the upper and lower portions of the filter are attributable to differences in grain sizes and media depth. Potable water treatment plants using biflow or upflow sand filters are apparently common in Europe and in the Soviet Union.[25]

Uniform media. The uniformly graded deep-bed filters used in Europe utilize relatively coarse media, ranging from 0.5 mm to as much as 6.0 mm. (These extreme sizes would not be found in the same filter.) Media uniformity coefficients are typically 1.2 to 1.3, but values as high as 1.5 may be found. Greater media depth is substituted for the lack of fine media in the bed. Such a substitution requires more vigilant operation and increased chemical usage to avoid breakthrough. Depths of 4 to 6 ft are common, and in some cases media depths reach 8 ft. Filters of this type are not expanded during backwash, and stratification of grain sizes does not occur.

Design criteria. A granular filter designed for potable water production should produce a high-quality filtrate. The National Primary Drinking Water Standards set by the U.S. EPA in 1977 require monthly average turbidities to be less than 1.0 TU for surface supplies, and impending regulations may result in further reductions in allowable turbidity levels.

Additional interrelated criteria, including loading rate, run time, head loss, and applied water quality, are less predetermined. Increased loading rates accelerate head loss and decrease run times. At some point, increased throughput will also result in declining filtrate quality. A low loading rate, however, will not guarantee a high filtrate quality. If coagulation and flocculation are inadequate, a high-quality filtrate cannot be achieved at any loading rate. With proper media selection and pretreatment, low effluent turbidities can be readily achieved at rates much higher than the once-standard 2 gpm/ft^2. Loading rates, type of media, media depth, and backwash design are largely determined by the designer's experience with similar applications. In some cases, pilot-plant testing is needed prior to design. Specialized media are available for some applications, such as iron and manganese removal (see Chap. 11).

The amount of water required to backwash a filter using a given washing technique is relatively constant regardless of run time. Consequently, long runs are desirable. Runs are ended when either the terminal head loss is reached or filtrate quality declines beyond a predetermined level. The maximum head available to operate a gravity filter is dependent upon the depth of the filter box and the hydraulic configuration of the plant. Filter design should preclude the application of sufficient head to produce shear forces which will strip even well-coagulated floc from the bed during filtration. For maximum utilization of bed storage capacity, terminal head loss should ideally occur immediately before filter breakthrough. The quality of the water to be filtered naturally affects the rates at which head loss develops, and thus, the length of runs between washes. The desired filtration rate is that which, for a given applied water quality, results in the maximum net production of water meeting filtrate quality requirements.

Filtration rate

Slow sand filters, designed for loadings of 3 to 6 million gallons per acre per day (0.05 to 0.10 gpm/ft^2), were replaced by rapid sand filters loaded at 1 to 2 gpm/ft^2. The 2-gpm/ft^2 rate became widely accepted as an upper limit in U.S. water supply practice. Subsequent investigations have demonstrated that dual-media and mixed-media, as well as single-medium, filters can be successfully operated at higher rates. The overall performance of multi-media units is, however, superior to that of single-medium filters. Table 7.3 presents operating experience with plant-scale rapid sand and multi-media filters. Laughlin and Duvall[28] conclude that mixed-media beds can be successfully operated at an average rate of 5 gpm/ft^2 and a maximum rate of 8 gpm/ft^2. In side-by-side comparison with single-medium filters, mixed-media beds achieved longer runs with the same head loss, required less backwash water per unit of water filtered, and produced higher filtrate quality. Tuepker and Buescher[29] concluded that a dual-media bed, while operating at a higher hydraulic loading (3.5 vs. 2.0 gpm/ft^2), could yield longer runs and lower percent usage for backwash than a sand filter, without reducing the quality of the product water. Westerhoff[32] found the performance of a mixed-media bed operating at 5 to 6 gpm/ft^2 superior to that of a sand bed at 2 gpm/ft^2 in terms of run length, percent usage for backwash, and filtrate quality. Additional sources, cited in Table 7.3, found dual- and mixed-media filters to operate successfully at rates from 3 to over 6 gpm/ft^2 in a variety of locations. Similar results regarding the feasibility of high-rate filtration have been reported as a result of pilot studies by Conley[16,35] Robeck et al.,[36] Dostal and Robeck,[37] Kirchman and Jones,[38] and Rimer.[39] The quantity of evidence of the practicality of high-rate filtration is such that in 1972 the AWWA Committee on Filtration Problems concluded, "It has been amply demonstrated that filters can be designed and operated to produce water of acceptable quality at flows substantially higher than the rate of 2 gpm/ft^2 once considered the maximum."[40]

Average filtration rates of roughly 2 to 7 gpm/ft^2 are reported for the upflow, biflow, and deep-bed filters discussed previously, but data are limited.[26,41] Pilot testing conducted in the southwestern United

TABLE 7.3 Plant-Scale Performance Results

Reference	Media	Water source	Pretreatment*	Average rate, gpm/ft²	Average raw turbidity, TU	Average applied turbidity, TU	Average filtered turbidity, TU	Average run length, h	Terminal head loss, ft	Percent backwash
28	Single	River	C(A), F, S	2	nr	4.9	0.28	45	8	2.11
	Mixed	River	C(A), F, S	2	nr	4.9	0.24	63	8	1.62
	Single	River	C(A), F, S	4	nr	6.3	0.35	19	8	3.15
	Mixed	River	C(A), F, S	4	nr	6.3	0.29	24	8	2.11
	Single	River	C(A), F, S	6	nr	4.5	0.45	10	6.8	2.93
	Mixed	River	C(A), F, S	6	nr	4.5	0.3	15	6.8	2.07
29	Single	River	LS, C(FE, P), CL, S	2	nr	2	0.1	42	3.0	2.1
	Dual	River	LS, C(FE, P), CL, S	3.5	nr	2	0.1	60	2.2	1.6
30	Dual	River	C, F, S	6.87	25–300	2	0.06	51	nr	0.58
31	Mixed (16 plants)	nr	nr	3–6	nr	0.5–10	0.1–0.5	15–80	nr	1–3
32	Single	Lake	AE, C(A), F, S	2	5	1	0.06	40	8	2.5
	Mixed	Lake	AE, C(A), F, S	5–6	5	1	0.05	23	8	1.8
33	Mixed	River	C (A, P)	5	2–15	nr	0.3	8–12	nr	nr
34	Dual	Reservoir	CL, C (A, P)	3.3	0.5	1–3	0.07	80	nr	nr

nr = not reported.
*C (A, FE, P) = Coagulation (alum, ferrous sulfate, polymer); F = flocculation; S = sedimentation; LS = lime softening; AE = aeration; CL = chlorination.

States has shown that deep-bed uniformly graded anthracite filters, when preceded by ozonation, can operate reliably at rates of 10 to 15 gpm/ft^2.

Applied water quality

The nature as well as the quantity of suspended material in the applied water is critical to the performance of the filter. Unflocculated water can be very difficult to filter regardless of the type of media in use.[7,42] However, the work of Robeck et al. with dual-media filters showed that if the applied water is properly coagulated, filtration at 4 or 6 gpm/ft^2 will produce essentially the same filtrate quality as filtration at 2 gpm/ft^2. Subsequent investigations have shown similar results for mixed-media filters.[28,31,32]

The use of chemicals in conjunction with filtration is limited primarily to metal salts used as coagulants and to polymers. Coagulants are ideally fed into mechanical mixing basins preceding flocculation. Whether sedimentation is also required depends on the quantity of suspended solids in the influent water. Coagulants are intended to produce agglomerations of natural and chemical solids. Polymers added with coagulants aid in the strengthening and growth of these agglomerations during flocculation. Cationic polymers are sometimes used as primary coagulants, eliminating the need for two chemical feed systems. Anionic and nonionic polymers are used as coagulant or filter aids. Filter-aid polymers are used to increase the strength of adhesion between media grains and floc in coarse-to-fine filters.

The use of a filter-aid polymer can result in improved floc capture, better filtrate quality, and longer filter runs and higher head loss prior to turbidity breakthrough. Filter-aid polymers are not generally used with fine-to-coarse filters because they promote rapid surface clogging. Filter aids are often fed in dilute liquid form to allow dispersion without mechanical agitation just prior to filtration. Filter-aid polymer doses to gravity filters are usually low (0.03 to 0.05 mg/L). Doses required for pressure filters may be higher if a higher operating head loss is employed. Because the viscosity of water increases with decreasing temperature, breakthrough as a result of floc shearing is more likely at lower water temperatures. Consequently, increased polymer doses may be required in cold weather. A longer contact time prior to filtration may also be necessary in cold weather.

Assuming that adequate coagulation is feasible, the designer must decide whether sedimentation is desirable. In the past, settling has been provided prior to rapid sand filtration if turbidities exceeded roughly 10 TU.[43] The increased storage capacities of dual- and mixed-media filters have made filtration of water with higher turbidities practicable. The primary advantage of providing direct filtration is the elimination of the capital and operating costs associated with sedimentation. The higher solids load on the filter will, however, shorten run times and increase the portion of the product water required for backwashing. Although the point at which advantages outweigh disadvantages will vary with local conditions, a number of investigators have suggested conditions which would justify consideration of direct filtration. Culp[9] lists the following as alternative conditions under which direct filtration is likely to be feasible: turbidity and color both less than 25 units; low color and maximum turbidity less than 200 units; and low turbidity and maximum color less than 100 units. He adds an additional general qualification that diatom levels in excess of 500 to 1000 areal standard units (asu)/mL can make direct filtration impracticable and that lesser levels will affect media selection. Based on experience in the Great Lakes region, Hutchison[44] states as conditions for direct filtration that diatoms be less than 1000 asu/mL and that the alum dose required for coagulation be less than 15 mg/L. Conley[35] indicates that sedimentation is probably required if raw-water turbidities often exceed 100 units. Robeck et al.[36] concluded that direct filtration using dual-media beds is probably feasible if turbidity is less than 25 units. The variations among these recommendations reflect the fact that they are intended only as guidelines. Differences in local conditions at each site under consideration require that pilot studies be conducted to determine the feasibility of using direct filtration.

Head loss

Terminal head loss through rapid sand, dual-media, or mixed-media gravity beds is typically 4 to 10 ft. Because of coarse top grains, however, the rate at which head loss increases in a well-designed multimedia bed will be much less than in a sand bed under the same loading conditions. Terminal head losses in pressure filters in potable water applications are usually in the same range as in gravity beds, but may be as high as 25 ft. Outlet pressures are sometimes determined by the needs of the distribution system. Rated tank pressures can be as high as 150 psi (roughly 350 ft), but 50 psi is more common.

If the head loss at any level in the filter bed exceeds the static head, a vacuum can result. This situation is referred to as negative head and can result in air binding of the filter. When the pressure in the filter bed drops below atmospheric levels, dissolved gases will be released from the water being filtered. Gas bubbles trapped in the bed will further increase the head loss and aggravate the problem. They may also result in displacement of media during backwashing. This problem is particularly acute when filtering with insufficient water depth over the media or when surface waters are saturated with atmospheric gases because of rising temperatures in the spring. Remedies for air binding in gravity filters include increased frequency of backwashing, maintenance of adequate static head above the media surface, or a clearwell water level above the surface to keep the filter media submerged. Pressure filters normally discharge well above atmospheric pressure and are not subject to air binding.

Filter run length

Rapid sand filters are generally operated with run lengths between 12 and 72 h, with 24-h runs being typical. Plant-scale tests of dual- and mixed-media filters listed in Table 7.3 reveal run lengths of 8 to 80 h. The 17 direct-filtration plants surveyed by Culp[9] had similar average run lengths. Pressure filters may have somewhat longer run lengths than gravity filters if they can be operated at higher head losses without breakthrough.

Long run lengths are desirable in that they result in a reduction of the portion of total water production used for backwashing. Run lengths may, however, be influenced by the need to maintain reasonable operating shifts. Control of biological growth in the filter may also be a factor in determining run times in some locations if prechlorination is not provided.

Design Details

In addition to selection of media and loading rate, a number of factors contribute to the success or failure of filter design. The filter box (or tank) must be constructed to permit effective and reliable filter performance over the ranges of loading rate and head loss desired. Features which must be considered include piping and valving, and placement of underdrains and media within the filter.

Influent

Raw or flocculated water is usually delivered to a gravity filter through the wash-water gullet. Influent to a pressure filter is generally distributed by a tapped pipe serving as a manifold, or by a baffle plate. Influent conduits should be designed to deliver water to the filters with as little disturbance as possible. Free fall or turbulence which can disturb the media surface is undesirable. Delivery of influent beneath the water surface in the filter or baffling of the incoming stream may be employed to prevent bed disturbance. Necessary measures will depend upon the control strategy used.

Piping and valves

Typical piping serving a gravity filter is shown in Fig. 7.6. Influent piping is often sized to limit velocities to about 2 ft/s. This may result in the use of an influent flume rather than a pipe in large plants. Hydraulic considerations generally result in velocities of 3 to 6 ft/s in wash-water and effluent piping. At higher velocities, head losses often become excessive, and undesirable effects such as water hammer are more likely to occur. Flanged and cement-lined cast iron, ductile iron, or steel pipe is commonly used for filter piping. Where flexibility or removability for maintenance is required, harnessed mechanical joints or couplings are often used.

A typical filter is equipped with five valves: influent, effluent, wash-water supply, wash-water drain, and surface wash or air wash supply. A filter-to-waste valve may also be included; however, waste lines con-

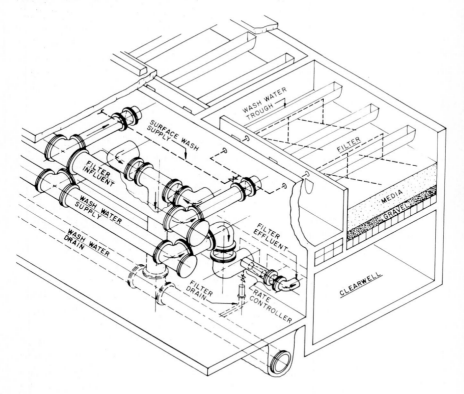

Figure 7.6 Typical filter piping. (*Source: Black & Veatch, Engineers-Architects.*)

stitute a potential cross-connection and must be equipped with air-gap protection against backflow from the drain to the filter. The filter effluent line configuration should provide positive pressure on the downstream side of the effluent rate controllers. Rubber-seated butterfly valves are most common in filter valving.

Placement of piping and valves should permit easy access for maintenance. Valves should be equipped with easily distinguishable position indicators.

Wash-water troughs

In U.S. practice, wash-water troughs are suspended at even spacings above gravity filter beds to provide uniform removal of wash water during backwashing. This limits the horizontal travel required and equalizes the static head on the underdrainage system. In contrast, European designs often feature narrow beds with wash-water conduits on one or both sides, but not suspended over the media. In the European designs, tilting side weirs, horizontal water jets, and a procedure allowing influent water to enter the filter on the side opposite the wash-water trough at the end of the wash cycle are sometimes used to aid the movement of scoured solids to waste. Spacing of troughs in U.S. practice is usually at 5- to 7-ft centers to limit horizontal travel disturbances to 2.5 to 3.5 ft. Media loss may result if troughs are placed too close to the surface of the unexpanded filter bed. The design elevation of the weir edge of the troughs may be determined by adding the depth required for maximum bed expansion (usually 50 percent) and the overall depth of the trough, plus a small margin of safety. If air scour is installed, additional care must be taken in locating the troughs. Simultaneous use of backwash water at 6.2 gpm/ft^2 and air at 4 scfm/ft^2 can toss 1- to 2-mm sand grains 15 to 16 in. If anthracite is placed above sand, the danger of media loss is increased because of the lower density of the coal.

The flow in a rectangular trough with free discharge can be determined by an equation of the form

$$Q = Cbh^{3/2}$$

where Q = rate of flow, cfs
  C = a constant
  b = trough width, ft
  h = maximum water depth in the trough, ft

For horizontal, rectangular channels of such length that friction losses are negligible, the theoretical value of C is 2.49. Values of C as low as 1.72 are used in practice. Capacities of nonrectangular channels may be approximated by using the dimensions of a rectangular section of equivalent area in the formula. A more rigorous result can be obtained by referring to derivations provided by Fair, Geyer, and Okun[46] and Brater and King.[47]

Troughs are usually made of reinforced concrete or fiberglass-reinforced plastic (FRP). Concrete troughs usually have V-shaped bottoms and FRP troughs semicircular bottoms. Typical cross sections are shown in Fig. 7.7.

After troughs are installed in a filter, the weir edges should be smoothed and leveled to uniformly match a still water surface at the desired overflow elevation.

Media placement

Careful placement of media is critical to subsequent filter operation. AWWA publication B-100-72[10] describes procedures for placing, washing, scraping, and disinfecting media prior to filter operation.

If the underdrains and media are not uniformly laid, uneven flow patterns which may affect filtrate quality will develop. Uneven solids deposition in the bed and unequal distribution of backwash water may be aggravated with each successive filter cycle until serious disruption of the bed occurs.

Washing and scraping of the filter media after placement are required to remove excessively fine material. In order to match design media elevations after fines are removed, excess material must be

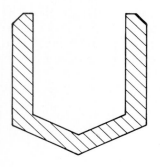
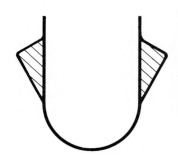

a. REINFORCED CONCRETE   b. FIBERGLASS REINFORCED
                                            PLASTIC

Figure 7.7 Typical wash trough cross sections: (a) reinforced concrete and (b) fiberglass-reinforced plastic. (*Source: Black & Veatch, Engineers-Architects.*)

placed in the bed initially. If too much material is removed, however, the resulting media will have a higher effective size than desired.

Underdrain systems

Underdrain systems are provided to support and retain filtering media, distribute backwash water, and collect filtrate. Uniform distribution of wash water and collection of filtrate are essential to proper filter operation. The three general types of underdrain assemblages are pipe laterals and gravel, blocks with or without gravel, and false bottom with or without gravel.

Traditionally, the great difficulty in underdrain design has been to provide a barrier to the finest media which will not clog during filtration or backwash. Early attempts to use fine screens or strainers were largely unsuccessful, leading to the use of gravel layers below filter sand. The position of gravel layers may, however, be disrupted during backwashing. Jet action, which is discussed in greater detail elsewhere,[7] causes sand and gravel mixtures to be more easily disrupted than gravel alone. If auxiliary air wash is used, even greater gravel disturbance may occur. Fine gravel, which is usually placed at the sand-gravel interface, is most easily dislocated. A possible solution to this problem is the use of gravel in a coarse-to-fine-to-coarse gradation, which has been shown to be very stable at high water backwash rates.[7] Fine media penetrate the upper coarse gravel layer without apparent ill effect.

Mixed-media beds, which have very fine garnet at the bottom of the bed, are generally constructed with a layer of coarse garnet on top of the silica support gravel. The coarse garnet prevents leakage of the fine garnet and also helps to stabilize the underlying silica gravel.

European-type deep-bed filters utilize relatively coarse and uniformly graded media. As a result, bed stratification is not required and air scour presents less of a hazard to proper bed operation. Also, the use of strainers is more likely to be feasible because of the larger permissible openings. Consequently, false-bottom underdrains with nozzles designed for both air and water distribution and without support gravel are commonly used in deep-bed filters.

Pipe laterals and gravel.   Pipe-lateral underdrains were once popular because of their relatively low cost and their adaptability to use in pressure filters. Problems with relatively high head loss and poor wash-water distribution have resulted in a general decline in their use. They are still encountered, however, when older filters are upgraded.

Pipe underdrain systems generally consist of a centrally located manifold pipe to which smaller, equally spaced laterals are attached. The lateral pipes usually have one or two rows of ¼- to ¾-in-diameter perforations on their bottom sides. They may be fitted with nozzles. Guidelines for lateral design include the following ratios:

Total area of orifices (surface area of bed)	0.0015 to 0.005:1
Cross-sectional area of lateral (total area of orifices served)	2 to 4:1
Cross-sectional area of manifold (total area of laterals served)	1.5 to 3:1

Orifices are normally spaced at 3 to 12 in and laterals at roughly the same spacings as the orifices. Roughly 18 in of gravel is required to cover a lateral network. Usually three to five graded layers are involved, with sizes varying from 1½ to ⅛ in. The bottom layer should extend 4 in above the highest wash-water outlet.

Blocks with gravel.   A commonly used block underdrain consists of vitrified clay blocks which are grouted in place. The size and arrangement of these blocks and typical support gravel layers are shown in Fig. 7.8. In mixed-media applications, the third gravel layer is replaced by garnet of similar size.

The underdrain system described above is intended for use with an auxiliary air-scour backwash. Air scour is usually limited to filters with underdrains which do not require gravel. Recently, a polyethylene underdrain block which is designed for use with overlying gravel and an air/water wash has been introduced (see Fig. 7.9). Dispersion of the air through a relatively large number of closely spaced orifices is intended to reduce the possibility of upsetting the gravel layers.

False bottom with gravel.   One of the most widely used false-bottom underdrains is constructed of precast or cast-in-place reinforced concrete supported on concrete sills. Each system contains uniformly spaced inverted pyramidal depressions. Unglazed porcelain balls are placed in the depressions to distribute flow. Each depression is filled and leveled with 1- to 1½-in gravel before placement of overlying gravel layers. A typical arrangement including the gravel layers is shown in Fig. 7.10. The last silica gravel layer should be replaced by coarse garnet in a mixed-media bed.

False bottom without gravel.   False-bottom underdrains which do not require gravel have impervious bottoms penetrated by strainers and porous bottoms. Fine openings eliminate the need for support gravel. Filter-box depth is thus reduced.

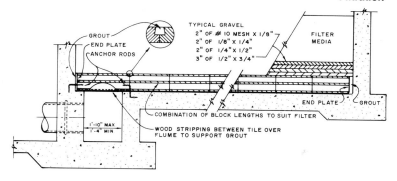

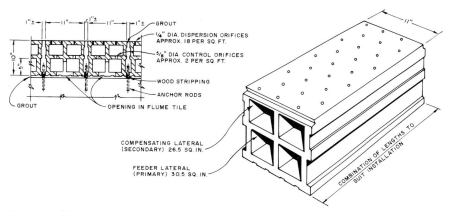

Figure 7.8 Vitrified clay block underdrain with filter media. (*Source: F. B. Leopold Co.*)

A variety of false-bottom and strainer underdrains are available. Three typical units are shown in Fig. 7.11. (All are shown equipped with plunge pipes for air wash.) The false bottoms are usually concrete, polyethylene, or tile blocks; monolithic concrete; or a steel plate. Strainers are usually constructed of stainless steel, plastic, or brass. Plastic strainer orifices are sometimes smaller on the filter side to prevent clogging during filtration, even though such a configuration can contribute to clogging during backwash. Strainer-type underdrains are used primarily in filters employing air/water wash systems; failures resulting from plugging and breakage have been experienced, however. Acceptance of these systems is less widespread than acceptance of the two systems described in the previous sections.

Porous-bottom underdrains. Porous-bottom underdrains with a porous aluminum oxide plate have been used in both block and false-bottom

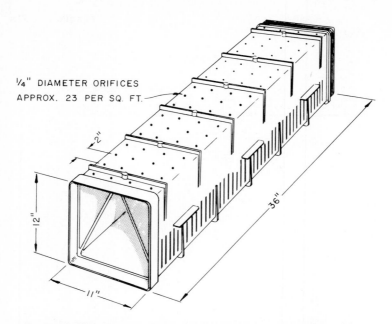

¼" DIAMETER ORIFICES
APPROX. 23 PER SQ. FT.

2"

12"

36"

11"

Figure 7.9 Plastic block underdrain designed for use beneath gravel layers and with air/water wash. (*Source: F. B. Leopold Co.*)

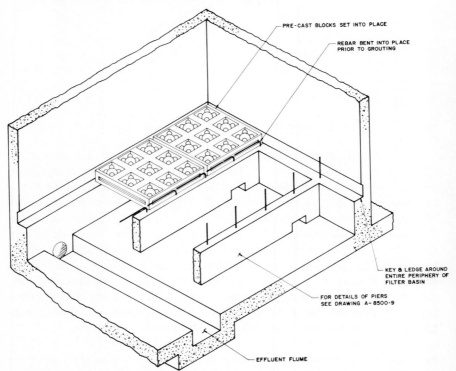

PRE-CAST BLOCKS SET INTO PLACE

REBAR BENT INTO PLACE
PRIOR TO GROUTING

KEY & LEDGE AROUND
ENTIRE PERIPHERY OF
FILTER BASIN

FOR DETAILS OF PIERS
SEE DRAWING A-8500-9

EFFLUENT FLUME

Figure 7.10 Concrete Wheeler-type false-bottom underdrain with support gravel. (*Source: Roberts Filter Manufacturing Co.*)

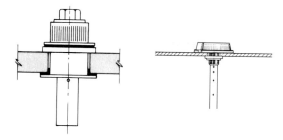

Figure 7.11 Typical strainers used in false-bottom underdrains without gravel. (*Source: (a) Walker Process Corp; (b) Eimco Process Equipment Co.*)

configurations. They are constructed of plates mounted on concrete or steel piers or on clay tile saddles to form blocks. The latter type is shown in Fig. 7.12. Very small pore sizes make porous-bottom underdrains susceptible to plugging and therefore unsuitable for use in softening or iron-and-manganese removal plants or other plants where plugging by chemical deposition may occur. They may also clog with rust or debris during backwashing. Additional problems which may occur include breakage because of the brittle nature of the porous material and failure of caulked joints between plates. Porous bottoms have been used successfully in a few locations, but are less widely accepted than the block or false-bottom and gravel underdrains discussed previously.

Backwashing

As the amount of solids retained in a filter increases, bed porosity decreases. At the same time, head loss through the bed and shear on captured floc increase. Before the head loss builds to an unacceptable level or filter breakthrough begins, backwashing is required to clean the bed.

Failure to clean the filter adequately can lead to a multitude of problems. Initially mudballs will form and accumulate in the bed, causing clogging. Clogged areas contract as head loss increases. Shrinkage opens cracks in the filter surface and sometimes at the filter walls. Cracks can cause short circuiting of the bed during filtration, with subsequent decline in filtrate quality. Clogged areas also contribute to channeling of backwash water, which can lead to bed up-

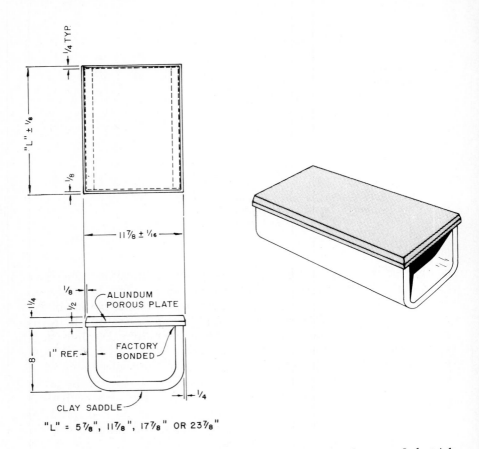

Figure 7.12 Porous filter bottom (ALUNDUM®). (*Source: Norton Company, Industrial Ceramics Division.*)

set. The mechanisms whereby washing problems lead to filter failures are discussed in greater detail elsewhere.[7]

The selection of a washing technique is closely tied to media and underdrain design. In current potable water filtration practice, backwashing invariably includes upflow water flushing. The rate and duration of water flushing are variable, however, and may be supplemented with air scour or surface water wash. The operational sequencing of dual washing systems and the source of the wash water introduce additional variations.

Water source

Common backwash water source options include the following: flow bled from high-service discharge and used directly for washing or to fill an above-ground wash-water tank prior to gravity washing; gravity flow from above-ground finished-water storage; gravity flow from a separate above-ground wash-water tank; or direct pumping from a sump or below-ground clearwell.

Bleeding flow from high-service discharge results in energy loss as a result of the pressure reduction required prior to washing. If direct washing is employed, a pressure-reducing valve or orifice is placed in the wash-water supply line. If bleeding is used to fill a wash-water tank, an altitude valve is used to control the water level in the tank. In either case, the wash-water supply line is often sized to restrict the maximum amount of water which can be delivered. Both options avoid provision of separate wash-water pumps. Direct washing also avoids construction of a wash-water tank, but presents greater difficulty in controlling wash-water flow. Because of the large pressure drop often involved in supplying wash water by high-service bleeding, the potential for cavitation in or following head-dissipating devices in the supply line is significant.

If an above-ground clearwell is not available to provide head for filter washing, wash water may be pumped to a separate tank or directly to the filters. Use of a wash-water tank permits pumping at a lower rate. Tank storage must be sufficient to permit washing of the filters at the maximum backwash rate while they operate at minimum run times.

A number of proprietary filters are available which obtain backwash water by means other than those listed previously. These include several filters which utilize vertical steel tanks divided into upper and lower compartments. Sufficient filtering head is provided so that following downflow filtration in the lower compartment, filtered water flows through a pipe into the upper tank. When terminal head loss in the filter bed is reached, wash water flows from the upper tank back through the filter.

Some filter-control systems permit gravity-flow backwashing of a filter utilizing the effluent from the filters remaining in service. Unusually deep filter boxes are required to provide filtering head in such systems. Backwashing head is obtained by placing an effluent weir several feet above the level of the wash troughs.

Washing method

A thorough review of backwashing methodology has been published by the AWWA Subcommittee on Backwashing of Granular Filters.[45] Three basic methods are available: upflow water wash without auxiliary scour, upflow water wash with surface wash, and upflow water wash with air scour. The application will normally dictate the method to be used. Filter-bed expansion during upflow water washing results in media stratification. Air washing results in bed mixing. If stratification is desired, air scour must be avoided or must precede fluidization and expansion with water.

In current U.S. practice, upflow water wash with surface wash is commonly used wherever mudball formation may occur. Manual cleaning can sometimes be substituted for surface wash in small plants. Upflow water wash alone may be sufficient in some filters which receive low solids loadings. Use of auxiliary air scour is becoming more common in U.S. potable water plants.

Upflow water wash without auxiliary scour.   In the absence of auxiliary scour, washing in an expanded bed occurs as a result of the drag forces on the suspended grains. Grain collisions do not contribute significantly to washing.[45,48,49]

Maximum shear on the grains theoretically occurs (for typical filter sand) at a bed expansion of 80 to 100 percent.[45] The increase in shear with increasing bed porosity, however, is relatively slight beyond the point at which expansion begins. Optimal expansion may be less than 20 percent.[50] Normally when water wash is applied exclusively, an expansion of 20 to 50 percent is used. Water wash at a sufficient rate to substantially expand (10 percent or more) a granular bed is often referred to as high-rate water wash. Wash rates incapable of fully fluidizing a bed (less than 10 percent expansion) may be referred to as low-rate. Experience in the United States with high-rate water wash used alone is extensive. It is generally successful for applications in which iron precipitates have been filtered from groundwater or color has been removed from otherwise high-quality surface water. The relatively weak cleaning action of water wash without auxiliary scour of some type, however, generally renders it unsuitable for filters removing large quantities of suspended solids.

High-rate water wash tends to stratify granular media. In dual- and mixed-media beds, this action is essential and beneficial, but it is not required for uniformly graded single-medium beds. In rapid sand filters, it results in movement of the fine grains to the top of the bed, which has a negative effect on head loss and run length.

Upflow water wash with surface wash.   Surface-wash systems have been widely applied to supplement high-rate upflow washing where mudball formation is likely to be a problem. Either a fixed-nozzle or rotary wash system may be used. Fixed systems distribute auxiliary wash water from equally spaced nozzles in a pipe grid. Most new plants utilize rotary systems in which pipe arms swivel on central bearings. Nozzles are placed on opposite sides of the pipes on either side of the bearing, and the force of the jets provides rotation.

Rotary systems are generally preferred because they provide better cleaning action, usually lower water requirements, and less obstruction for filter access. Possible problems with rotating surface wash units include failure to rotate, failure to clean in corners, abrasion of concrete walls near the point of closest passage of the arm, and locally high velocities caused when passing under wash troughs. Either type of system may fail to provide auxiliary scour where it is most needed. This can be especially true in layered multi-media beds if substantial removals are occurring at media interfaces.

Surface-wash systems are typically suspended about 2 in above the surface of the unexpanded filter bed. Systems have been placed in the unexpanded bed, however, and dual-arm rotary systems which have one arm above and one arm below the unexpanded surface are available. Plugging of nozzles with media has been a problem with the submerged units. Rotary systems may have either straight (Fig. 7.13) or curved pipe arms. Nozzle diameters of ⅛ to ¼ in are common. Single-arm units typically operate at 50 to 100 psi and discharge from 20 to over 200 gpm depending on length. Standard units are available up to approximately 20 ft in diameter. Some models induct air into the wash-water jets.

Advantages of auxiliary water wash include proven effectiveness in alleviating dirty filter problems, improved cleaning (in comparison with water wash alone) without a great change in system complexity, and possibly lessened danger of gravel upset if the quantity of wash water introduced through the underdrain is reduced.

Because surface-wash systems constitute a possible connection between filtered and unfiltered water, backflow prevention devices must be provided in supply lines.

Upflow water wash with air scour. Approaches to the use of auxiliary air scour in backwashing filters are numerous. Air scour has been used alone and with low-rate water backwash in an unexpanded bed or slightly expanded bed. Each procedure is utilized prior to either low- or high-rate water wash.

Air scour provides very effective cleaning action, especially if used simultaneously with water wash. Cleaning is attributable to high interstitial velocities and abrasion between grains. On the other hand, air wash presents substantial potential for media loss and gravel disruption if not properly controlled.

If more than one filtering medium is used and stratification of the bed is desired, high-rate water wash must follow air scour. In a single-

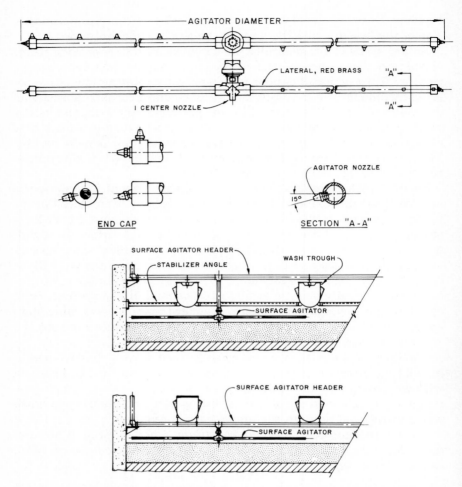

Figure 7.13 Typical surface agitator and arrangements. (*Source: F. B. Leopold Co.*)

medium bed, if a low-rate wash can adequately remove scoured solids, high-rate wash can be avoided.

If air scour occurs simultaneously with water wash, the air flow must usually be stopped prior to wash-water overflow to prevent excessive media loss. Thus, the permissible duration of air washing will be short unless the concurrent water-wash rate is low or the bed is very deep.

Alternatives to the use of a strainer-type underdrain which may still permit the use of air wash include use of a coarse-to-fine-to-coarse gravel gradation or the provision of a separate air distribution system located above the gravel. The latter approach has been implemented at Contra Costa, Calif.,[30] but it is intended primarily to aid in movement of solids to the wash troughs rather than for scour of the media grains.

Experience in Europe indicates that air scour essentially eliminates mudball formation. Difficulties have arisen, however, from failure to remove scoured solids from filter surfaces. Probable contributing factors include low water-washing rates, long horizontal-travel distances to wash-water troughs, and a necessary lag between termination of air scour and initiation of higher-rate water wash.

Backwash rates

In the United States, wash rates are expressed as volumetric flow per unit surface area (gpm/ft^2) or as the equivalent water rise velocity (ft/s, ft/min, or in/min). Required water-washing rates are variable and depend on water temperature, filter type, and washing method. Water viscosity decreases with increasing temperature. Consequently, as wash-water temperature rises, drag forces on media grains are reduced and higher wash rates are required to achieve bed expansion. Each degree Celsius increase in water temperature requires roughly a 2 percent increase in wash rate to prevent a reduction in bed expansion. Backwash systems should be designed for the warmest wash-water temperature which will be encountered.

Media selection also affects washing rate. Rate requirements increase with increasing grain size and media density. Angular grains are more easily expanded than round grains. In beds using more than one type of medium, sizes of different media must be chosen carefully to ensure proper positioning after backwash. Recommended size ratios for dual and mixed beds were discussed in the section, "Granular Media Alternatives." Figure 7.14, taken from Cleasby and Baumann,[51] displays the effect of media size on the wash rate required to achieve 10 percent bed expansion for three common media. Figure 7.15, from the same source, shows the effect of water temperature on the wash rate for silica sand and coal and on the viscosity of water.

Characteristic washing rates and durations vary for each of the washing methods discussed previously. The suitability of a washing method is related to influent water quality, filtering media and bed configuration, and underdrain design. Consequently, not all washing methods are applicable in all cases, and different methods may or may not yield similar results in a particular case.

Upflow water wash without auxiliary scour.   When water wash is used alone, a high-rate wash is employed. Generally a rise rate of 15 to 23

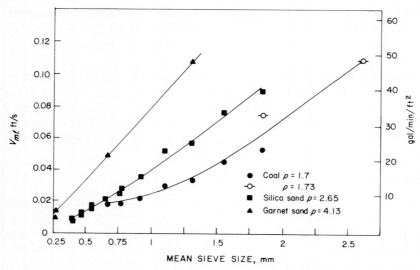

Figure 7.14 Minimum fluidization velocity (V_{mf}) needed to achieve 10 percent bed expansion at 25°C (from Cleasby & Baumann[51]). (*Source: USEPA Technology Transfer.*)

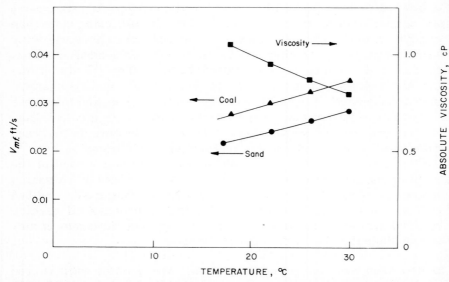

Figure 7.15 Effect of water temperature on V_{mf} of sand and coal, and on absolute viscosity of water (from Cleasby & Baumann[51]). (*Source: USEPA Technology Transfer.*)

gpm/ft^2 is applied. After the water level in the bed has been lowered to near trough level, backwash duration may be 3 to 15 min.

Upflow water wash with surface wash.   Combined surface and water wash usually involves three phases. After the water surface is lowered in the bed, surface wash is activated and operated alone for 1 to 3 min. Low-rate water wash is then applied simultaneously for an additional period of roughly 5 to 10 min. Termination of surface wash precedes a final phase (1 to 5 min) during which a higher wash-water rate is used to expand the bed 20 to 50 percent. This usually requires a backwash use rate of 15 to 23 gpm/ft^2. Wash-water flow during surface agitation is usually limited to that required to expand the bed only slightly. However, if anthracite makes up the top filtering layer, bed expansion above the surface-wash system may be desirable to reduce the likelihood of media loss. Rotary surface-wash systems typically add 0.5 to 2.0 gpm/ft^2 to the wash-water flow. Fixed-nozzle systems deliver 2 to 4 gpm/ft^2.

Upflow water wash with air scour.   Three variations of air and water wash were discussed in the previous section. The first, air scour alone followed by low-rate water wash, is commonly applied in Great Britain to single-medium sand filters with 0.6- to 1.2-mm media. After the water in the filter is lowered to below the wash-water overflow, air is injected at 1 to 2 $scfm/ft^2$ for 3 to 5 min. Water wash of 5 to 7.5 gpm/ft^2 follows. Bed expansion and stratification are not achieved, although relatively cool water temperatures may result in fluidization of the upper sand layers. Problems with gravel disruption have not been experienced if air and water are applied separately and at levels not exceeding 1.5 $scfm/ft^2$ and 7.5 gpm/ft^2, respectively.[45]

Air scour alone followed by high-rate water wash can be applied to rapid sand or dual-media filters, since bed stratification occurs during water wash. This method has been used in the United States with air scour at 3 to 5 $scfm/ft^2$ followed by water wash at 15 to 23 gpm/ft^2.

Simultaneous air scour and water wash is generally limited to the deep, coarse-grained filters common in Europe. For 1- to 2-mm media, air-scour rates of 2 to 4 $scfm/ft^2$ are used with a water flow of 6.3 gpm/ft^2. For 2- to 6-mm media, 6 to 8 $scfm/ft^2$ and 6.3 to 7.5 gpm/ft^2 are used. Simultaneous air and water wash typically lasts 5 to 10 min and is followed by water wash alone for another 5 to 10 min. The rate of final water wash is generally one to two times that used with air scour. In the U.S. installation mentioned previously[30] in which air is distributed above an expanded bed from a fixed piping network, 2 $scfm/ft^2$ of air accompanies 15 gpm/ft^2 of wash water. As noted, however, the air in this case serves to improve transport of solids to wash troughs rather than to increase scour in the bed.

Wash-water disposal/recovery

Following filter washing, disposal or recovery of the backwash water is required. In the past, wash water has been discharged to a surface-water body (which may have been the raw-water source) or to a drainage ditch. Disposal in this manner was both simple and relatively inexpensive. In areas where water conservation was important, wash-water recovery was used to reduce the amount of water withdrawn from the water source. Recent regulations governing discharges of water treatment wastes have made the use of wash-water recovery more widespread.

In conventional plants, wash water can be returned to the head of the treatment facilities. Because wash water is generated in slugs, however, equalization is usually required. Treatment of the wash water prior to return is employed in some conventional plants and is a design consideration. In direct-filtration plants, separate wash-water treatment must be provided. Additional coagulation and flocculation of wash water may not be required, but standby polymer feed facilities may be included. If land area is available, lagoons can be used to provide both equalization and sedimentation.

Wang et al.[52] conducted pilot-scale tests of wash-water recovery at a plant using alum, activated carbon, and chlorine in conjunction with sedimentation and filtration of water from a reservoir. Advantages of recycling included improved settling of basin sludge, lower filter head losses, elimination of discharge to a stream, and recovery of much of the wash water. A small increase in alum use was required. Wash-water recovery may not, however, be feasible at some locations with significant taste and odor problems because of the possibility of intensification of the problem.

Control and monitoring

Control and monitoring of the filtration process are critical to successful operation. Decisions covering control and monitoring methods and facilities must be made during initial design because each affects the physical layout of the filtering facilities.

Filter control may be predicated either on head loss through the filter bed or on the rate of filtration. In either case, smooth transition during changes in filtration rate is highly desirable. The deleterious effects of sudden flow surges on filtrate quality have been amply documented.[29,53] Control methods are generally tested most severely by removal of filters for backwashing and their return to service.

A variety of control methods are in use in the United States. Control methods are often distinguished in the literature as constant-rate, constant-level, influent flow splitting, declining-rate, and so on. In actual practice, however, control systems may incorporate the characteristics implied by more than one of those terms.

Constant-rate filtration can be achieved by placing a rate controller on the filter effluent line. The rate controller consists of a metering device (flow tube), a variable rate-setting control mechanism, and a throttling valve. In the absence of additional controls, the valve responds to the pressure differential in the flow tube, opening to increase flow or closing to restrict flow. Filtration remains at a set rate regardless of the condition of the bed until the number of filters in service is changed. When head loss in the bed reaches the point at which the desired flow cannot be achieved with the valve wide open, backwashing is required. The sum of the rate settings on the filters in service must match the influent flow. If the controls are well designed, the depth of water in each filter box will be fairly stable during most of the run because the rate controller will compensate for the additional head loss as solids accumulate in the bed. The water level in the filter box, however, is not actually regulated (except for limits on extreme levels) and may fluctuate.

Constant-level filtration, in its simplest form, can be achieved by tying operation of the filter effluent valve to a level-sensing device in the filter box. The level in the box varies within a relatively narrow control range. At the top of the range the valve is fully opened, and at the bottom the valve is closed. Such a control scheme serves only to regulate the water level in the filter and prevent dewatering. The rate of filtration is determined by the rate at which water is delivered to the filter.

A method of filter control which has been successfully applied in a large number of plants utilizes both level and rate control. In this scheme, level sensing occurs at the influent header or flume rather than in each filter box. Effluent valves are controlled individually to maintain the same rate through and level in each filter despite possible differences in the conditions of the beds. The controls also limit the maximum rate through each filter. As long as the total influent flow remains constant, a constant filtration rate is achieved.

The total influent flow may also be equally divided using weirs rather than rate controllers. Filters of this type normally discharge over an effluent weir, eliminating the possibility of bed dewatering. The relatively high discharge elevation requires an unusually deep filter box to provide filtering head. From 5 to 6 ft of additional depth is typical.[54] The filtration rate is determined by the plant influent flow. The level in each filter rises as necessary to accept an equal portion of the influent and indicates the head loss. When the level rises to a fixed upper limit, backwashing is initiated.

Filters equipped with effluent weirs rather than rate controllers may also operate without weirs or other devices which equally split the influent. These filters are usually termed declining-rate filters. Flow is distributed on the basis of the relative conditions of the beds. Assuming that influent piping losses are roughly the same for all the filters, a uniform operating water level in all the filters will be achieved. The filtration rate then will be highest in the cleanest bed and lowest in the dirtiest bed. In each bed the filtration rate will decrease as solids accumulate. An orifice or other flow-limiting device is used on each filter to control the maximum flow. To determine which bed is in greatest need of backwashing, some type of effluent rate indication must be provided. Advantages claimed for declining-rate filters include higher water production for a given run length[7] and improved filtrate quality.[55]

Filters may also be operated without rate controllers by pumping directly from the underdrain. If each filter is connected to a single pump, approximately constant-rate filtration is achieved (although as head loss builds, pumping may decrease slightly). If more than one filter is connected to each pump, the cleanest bed will pass the most water.

Valve operating systems may be hydraulic, pneumatic, or electric. Hydraulic systems were developed first, but these are generally no longer installed in new plants because of problems with leakage and with plugging of orifices in the lines by deposition from the fluid. Currently either pneumatic or electrical systems are used. Pneumatic systems are generally less expensive, but they require oil- and moisture-free air. Electrical systems offer greater reliability, but usually at higher cost. In the event that maintenance is required, however, the technical skill required to service electrical controls may be much greater than that required for pneumatic controls.

Monitoring

Filter design should include instrumentation to monitor filtrate turbidity, filtration rate, head loss, and backwash rate. If auxiliary air scour backwash is installed, air-flow monitoring should also be included. Pilot filters may be used as an aid in determining coagulant dosage.

Turbidity.   Continuous monitoring of overall plant effluent turbidity should be practiced, with alarms tied to high levels. A recording-type turbidimeter is valuable because variances from normal operation are displayed graphically. Observations of the effects of fluctuations in raw-water quality, rate changes, equipment malfunctions, chemical feed variations, filter backwashing, and other such occurrences contribute to the operator's understanding of the plant and increase his or her ability to deal with such situations. Continuously reading turbidimeters are available from a number of manufacturers. Piping to such units should be designed to preclude the presence of air bubbles, which can distort readings. Sample taps should be provided at the effluent of individual filters to permit periodic turbidity monitoring, although continuously reading units may not be required. A single turbidimeter is sometimes connected by manifold to all the filters to facilitate periodic monitoring. Turbidimeters are provided for each filter if backwashing is to be automatically activated by high turbidity in the filtrate.

Filtration rate.   Flow tubes are generally used for monitoring flow through individual filters. Design consideration should be given to the need for straight lengths of pipe preceding the meters. Recorders or totalizers are sometimes included. If flow splitting is employed, the filtration rate may be determined from monitoring of the total plant flow.

Head loss.   Head loss in a filter bed is a valuable indicator of filter condition and may be used to automatically activate backwashing. The head loss through the bed is normally monitored by differential pressure-cell devices.

Backwash rate.   Because backwash flow requirements may vary with the seasons and with other conditions, operator knowledge of the rate in use at a particular time is essential. Flow tubes are usually employed as the monitoring device. Recording meters are generally not necessary. A totalizing device is desirable to determine the overall volume of water used in backwashing. An alarm can be provided that is triggered if the wash rate exceeds a predetermined maximum.

Pilot filters.   Pilot filters are bench-scale models of plant filters that are used to determine coagulant dosage. Coagulated water is diverted to pilot filters from the full-scale treatment units. Monitoring of the pilot-filter effluent turbidity provides an indication of the adequacy of the coagulant feed. The effect of the use of pilot filters is to greatly reduce the time lag in coagulant feed system adjustment and thus improve plant operation. Parallel pilot filters are provided to ensure continuous control. Because of the nature of connecting piping to bench filters, higher filter-aid polymer doses than would be used in the full-scale plant are usually required. The effect of increasing the polymer dose is to shorten run times. Consequently, pilot filters are generally not used to predict run lengths or polymer dosage. In most cases, however, these variations do not affect determination of the optimum coagulant dosage.

Operating facilities

Several types of filtration operation and control have been employed in practice. These include local and remote manual, and semi- and fully automatic operation.

Most filter plants currently in operation in the United States have control consoles on the filter floor from which the filters are operated. Because observation of each filter during backwashing provides a check against malfunction and contributes to the operator's understanding of the filters, remote automatic operation of backwash sequences is not usually practiced. The filter control consoles are usually located immediately adjacent to the filters they serve. Nevertheless, remote manual operation, with the remote filter controls located on the plant control console, is used in some plants. This allows a single operator to wash filters and still observe the plant processes indicated on the control console.

In the past, all major valves were controlled by individual manual controls, and all filter operations were operator-directed. However, advances in sensing and control equipment have made the use of remote automatic or semiautomatic control more popular. In semiautomatic operation, backwashing is initiated by the operator but consists of a predetermined sequence which requires no additional attention. Fully automatic filters are backwashed without operator input on the basis of loss of head in the bed, filtrate turbidity, or a fixed maximum run time. Automatic systems permit operation of all filters from a central location, thus reducing personnel requirements. However, remote automatic operation may not permit the operator to observe the backwash cycle directly. Unless they are properly designed, automated systems may be difficult to alter when changing conditions require modification of backwash rate or sequencing. Labor-saving systems should not be installed unless operational flexibility and effective filter performance can be assured.

Energy considerations

Energy consumption in filtration is attributable primarily to the pumping required to provide filtering head and backwashing. If air scour is provided, the compressors will also contribute to the power demand.

Available head for filtering is fixed by design and, for most filters being installed today, falls within a relatively narrow range. The head loss attributable to clean media is unavoidable. Depending on the control method used, however, the head loss resulting from piping and appurtenances can be reduced. Tuepker and Buescher[29] investigated filter control without rate controllers at St. Louis and concluded that energy savings can be realized. Selection of a control strategy should not, however, be based solely upon energy considerations.

Energy savings can also be achieved by increasing run times. Maximization of water production between washes will result in a reduction in the energy required per net unit volume of water produced. A design which permits utilization of the entire filter bed is thus desirable. The type of bed chosen may also affect the amount of energy required for each backwash. Deep, uniform beds do not require full expansion for stratification, as do multimedia beds, but are more difficult to fluidize and are usually equipped with air scour.

If power charges are assessed on the basis of peak usage, energy costs can be reduced through judicious selection of the backwash water source. Backwashing by gravity flow from an elevated tank rather than by pumping from storage substitutes transfer pumping (at a lower rate) for backwash pumping and thus reduces peak demand. If pumped-flow washing is used, peak energy demands can be reduced by providing a larger number of smaller filters. Another alternative is the use of "split" filters which provide for backwashing of one-half the filter media at a time.

Conservation of water within the plant will result in lower raw-water pumping requirements and may result in a significant net energy savings. Wash-water recovery may possibly result in savings of this type. Direct filtration may result in energy savings if the effects of higher loadings and shortened run times are less significant than the energy reductions resulting from elimination of clarification and sludge-handling facilities.

Design trends

Dual- and mixed-media filters are likely to remain the prevalent types of filters being constructed for potable water production in the United States for some years to come. As a result of recent legislation and the capabilities of these filters, the proportion of direct-filtration plants being constructed will probably increase. Wash-water recovery will receive increased attention as energy costs rise and discharge limitations become more stringent. Automation and computer applications in filtration plants will also increase.

An additional concern for the future is that there will be more cases in which filtration requirements will result from or be aggravated by environmental pollution. An example of this is the discovery of asbestos fibers, a suspected carcinogen, in Lake Superior water used for public supply. Pilot studies conducted in Duluth, Minn. in 1974 indicated that removal of amphibole asbestiform fiber by filtration is feasible.[56] For the water studied, direct mixed-media filtration was determined to be the most economical treatment. Alum was found to be more effective than ferric chloride as a coagulant, and nonionic polymer proved most effective as a filter aid. Successful filtration was achieved at loadings of 4 to 6 gpm/ft^2. Based on the findings of the pilot study, a 30-mgd direct-filtration plant has been built at Duluth.[57] One dual-media and three mixed-media filters, designed for 5 gpm/ft^2, are included in the plant. Wash water is recycled following chemical addition, flocculation, and clarification. Sludge containing asbestiform fibers is subjected to freeze-thaw treatment in lagoons. Decant from the lagoons is returned to the plant headworks with reclaimed wash water.

Water quality concerns may also increase interest in particle counting as an index of quality in lieu of or in addition to turbidity measurements. Turbidimeters are widely used in water quality control because they are convenient to use and give instantaneous results. Turbidimeters indicate only light-scattering properties, which are not directly related to the quantity of suspended material present in a water sample. The poor correlation between turbidity and total microscopic count has been amply documented.[58,59]

Automatic particle sizing and counting equipment offers the convenience of turbidimeters and also provides an indication of the quantity (size and number) of particles present. The particle counter thus gives a more accurate measure of water quality than the turbidimeter. Automatic counters cannot, however, be calibrated over an unlimited particle size range and are also unable to distinguish the type of particle being counted and sized.

The use of deep-bed uniformly graded filters is expected to increase because of their ability to operate at hydraulic loading rates 2 to 3 times that of conventional dual- and mixed-media filters. One direct filtration facility recently placed in service in the southwest United States utilizes deep-bed (6-ft depth) anthracite filters operating at rates of up to 13.5 gpm/ft^2. A primary factor in the successful operation of these filters is the addition of ozone prior to flocculation and filtration. Ozonation "preconditions" raw-water particulate matter, thereby enhancing the flocculation process and increasing allowable filter run lengths. Increased attention to variations in raw-water quality and maintenance of appropriate coagulant and filter-aid feed rates is required for successful operation at the higher loading rates.

Other Filtration Techniques

This chapter has been devoted primarily to granular-media filters because they are the prevalent means of filtration in the potable water industry both in the United States and elsewhere in the world. Other types of filtering or straining technology are, however, encountered in water treatment practice. These include microscreens, diatomaceous earth filters, and cartridge filters.

Microscreens

Microscreens are used in water treatment to remove algae or other plankton which may occur in lake and reservoir supplies. In some cases, microscreens are used as pretreatment for granular or diatomaceous earth filtration, but they may also serve as the sole filtration step. Prescreening may be applicable where plankton levels are such that clogging of granular filters is a concern or run lengths are impaired. In some locations, the nature of the plankton present may be such that microscreens are more effective than granular filters in removing them. The use of microscreens without further filtration may be feasible if the raw water is essentially free of color and colloidal turbidity but contains distinct floating or suspended organisms. Such applications are not common.

Microscreens consist of a rotating drum placed in a rectangular tank (see Fig. 7.16). The drum supports a straining fabric, which may be either stainless steel wire cloth or woven polyester cloth. Polyester media are preferable if the water being screened has been chlorinated. Influent enters at one end of the drum and flows outward into the tank. Spray nozzles and a wash-water trough at the top of the drum are provided for washing the media. Commercially available units have drums 4 to 12 ft in diameter and 1 to 16 ft in length. Nominal cloth openings of 17, 21, 23, 35, and 60 μm are used in potable water practice. Coarser mesh sizes are available for industrial and wastewater applications.

Normally, two-thirds to three-fourths of the drum surface area is submerged during operation. Loadings are expressed in terms of flow per submerged unit surface area. In the absence of prior experience,

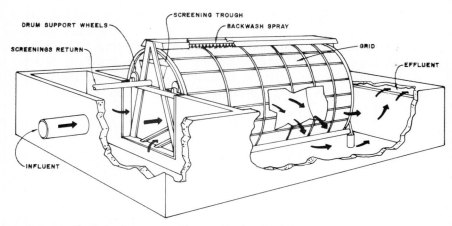

Figure 7.16   Typical microscreen. (*Source: Envirex Inc.*)

the permissible loading at a given location is usually determined by pilot testing. Rates of 5 to 25 gpm/ft^2 of submerged area are typical in water supply applications.

Diatomaceous earth filters

Diatomaceous earth, a natural silicious fossil material, has been used as a filtering medium in potable water plants. Filters utilizing diatomite consist of a pressure vessel containing a number of porous tubular structures on which the diatomite is supported (see Fig. 7.17). An initial layer of roughly ⅛ in of diatomite is applied before water production begins. Because the diatomite layer will develop cracks as pressure drop increases, continuous feed of additional diatomite is required throughout the run. Hydraulic loading rates of 0.5 to 2.0 gpm/ft^2 of media are typical of current operating practice.

Diatomaceous earth filters were initially used during World War II because they could be adapted to portable water plants. Subsequent attempts to utilize this technology in full-scale plants were unsuccessful in a number of cases because of operational deficiencies which have been described elsewhere.[60] Although the operation of diatomite filters is now more adequately understood and guidelines for proper operation are better defined,[61] serious drawbacks remain. These include rigorous operating requirements, high operating costs, increased sludge production, and a lack of proven experience in dealing with raw water which is not of relatively high quality. The primary advantage of diatomaceous earth filtration is a low initial capital cost. Consequently, it is best suited either to very small plants for which the comparable cost of a granular media plant is relatively high, or to

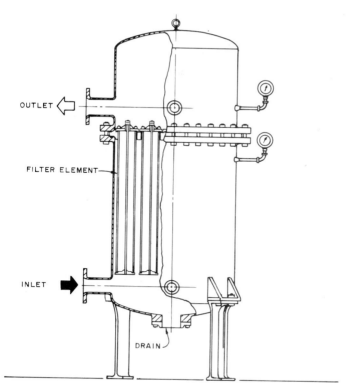

Figure 7.17 Typical cylindrical element. (*Source: Manville Sales Corp.*)

plants which are used only intermittently, such as emergency units and those for swimming pools. In most locations, diatomite filtration is not economically or technically competitive with granular filtration in full-scale potable water supply applications.

Cartridge filters

Cartridge filters are employed prior to membrane desalting processes (reverse osmosis or electrodialysis) to provide protection against fouling. They are available in a range of nominally rated pore sizes and may require either disposal or cleaning when a terminal head loss is reached. The filters most commonly installed before membrane processes are 5 to 25 μm; they are generally provided by equipment suppliers as a part of the total desalting system. Media configurations include wound fiber, bonded fiber, sintered metal, and woven metal mesh. Available wound-fiber cartridges include polypropylene, cotton, acrylic, or modacrylic fibers on polypropylene, stainless steel, or

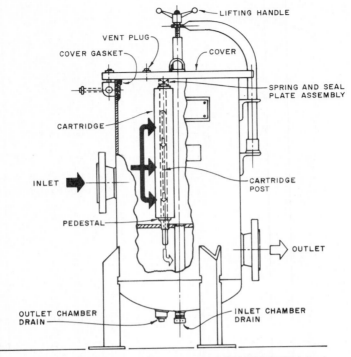

Figure 7.18   Typical cartridge filter. (*Source: AMF CUNO Division.*)

tinned-steel cores. Bonded fibers may be cellulose, fiberglass, wool, acrylic, or viscose rayon with a phenolic or melamine resin binder. Sintered metal and woven metal-mesh cartridges are of stainless steel construction. Wound-fiber cartridges are normally used in potable-water plants.

Multiple cartridges are usually arranged in pressure vessels (see Fig. 7.18). Duplicate pressure vessels allow replacement of cartridges without interrupting water production. Capacities and operating pressures vary widely. Individual cartridges are typically 2 to 3 in wide and 4 to 30 in long.

Use of these filters in potable water supplies in the United States is common only in areas where brackish water supplies are used, primarily Florida and the Southwest.

References

1. M. N. Baker, *The Quest for Pure Water*, AWWA, through Lancaster Press, Lancaster, Pa., 1948.

2. Great Lakes–Upper Mississippi River Board of State Sanitary Engineers, "Recommended Standards for Water Works," Health Education Service, Albany, N.Y., 1976.

3. J. L. Cleasby, "Filtration," in W. J. Weber, Jr. (ed.), *Physicochemical Processes for Water Quality Control,* Wiley-Interscience, New York, 1972, p. 139.

4. C. R. O'Melia and W. Stumm, "Theory of Water Filtration," *Journal AWWA,* vol. 59, no. 11, 1967, p. 1393.

5. C. R. O'Melia and D. K. Crapps, "Some Chemical Aspects of Rapid Sand Filtration," *Journal AWWA,* vol. 56, no. 10, 1964, p. 1326.

6. T. F. Craft, "Review of Rapid Sand Filtration Theory," *Journal AWWA,* vol. 58, no. 4, 1966, p. 428.

7. J. R. Baylis, O. Gullans, and H. E. Hudson, Jr., "Filtration," *Water Quality and Treatment,* 3d ed., Prepared by AWWA, McGraw-Hill, New York, 1971, p. 243.

8. J. Clark, W. Viesman, Jr., and M. Hammer, *Water Supply and Pollution Control,* 3d ed., IEP-DUN-Donnelly, New York, 1977.

9. R. L. Culp, "Direct Filtration," *Journal AWWA,,* vol. 69, no. 7, 1977, p. 375.

10. *AWWA Standard for Filtering Material,* AWWA B100-72, American Water Works Association, New York, 1972.

11. *AWWA Standard for Granular Activated Carbon,* AWWA B604-74, American Water Works Association, New York, 1974.

12. R. W. Oeben, H. P. Haines, and K. J. Ives, "Comparison of Normal and Reverse Graded Filtration," *Journal AWWA,* vol. 60, no. 4, 1968, p. 429.

13. T. F. Craft, "Comparison of Sand and Anthracite for Rapid Filtration," *Journal AWWA,* vol. 63, no. 1, 1971, p. 10.

14. A. H. Rice and W. R. Conley, United States Patent 3,343,680, 1967.

15. W. R. Conley and R. W. Pitman, "Test Program for Filter Evaluation at Hanford," *Journal AWWA,* vol. 52, no. 2, 1960, p. 205.

16. W. R. Conley, "Experiences with Anthracite-Sand Filters," *Journal AWWA,* vol. 53, no. 12, 1961, p. 1473.

17. T. R. Camp, "Discussion: Experience with Anthracite-Sand Filters," *Journal AWWA,* vol. 53, no. 12, 1961, p. 1478.

18. T. R. Camp, "Theory of Water Filtration," *Journal SED-ASCE,* vol. 90, no. 8, 1964, p. 1.

19. D. R. Brosman and J. F. Malina, Jr., *Intermixing of Dual Media Filters and Effects on Performance,* Center for Research in Water Resources, University of Texas, 1972.

20. J. L. Cleasby and G. D. Sejkora, "Effect of Media Intermixing on Dual Media Filtration," *Journal Envir. Engr. Div. (ASCE),* vol. 101, no. 8, 1975, pp. 503.

21. J. L. Cleasby and C. F. Woods, "Intermixing of Dual Media and Multimedia Granular Filters," *Journal AWWA,* vol. 67, no. 4, 1975, p. 197.

22. J. J. McCreary and V. L. Snoeyink, "Granular Activated Carbon in Water Treatment," *Journal AWWA,* vol. 69, no. 8, 1977, p. 437.

23. C. A. Blanck and D. J. Sulik, "Activated Carbon Fights Bad Taste," *Water and Wastes Engineering,* vol. 12, no. 9, 1975, p. 71.

24. R. E. Hensen, "Granular Carbon Filters for Taste and Odor Control," *Journal AWWA,* vol. 64, no. 3, 1972, p. 176.

25. D. G. Hager, "Adsorption and Filtration with Granular Activated Carbon," *Water and Wastes Engineering,* vol. 6, no. 8, 1969, p. 39.

26. C. L. Hamann and R. E. McKinney, "Upflow Filtration Process," *Journal AWWA,* vol. 60, no. 9, 1968, p. 1023.

27. B. J. Haney and S. E. Steimle, "Upflow Filter for Potable Water Production," *Journal EED-ASCE,* vol. 101, no. 8, 1975, p. 489.

28. J. E. Laughlin and T. E. Duvall, "Simultaneous Plant-Scale Tests of Mixed Media and Rapid Sand Filters," *Journal AWWA,* vol. 60, no. 9, 1968, p. 1015.

29. J. L. Tuepker and C. A. Buescher, Jr., "Operation and Maintenance of Rapid Sand and Mixed Media Filters in a Lime Softening Plant," *Journal AWWA,* vol. 60, no. 12, 1968, p. 1377.

30. W. L. Harris, "High Rate Filter Efficiency," *Journal AWWA,* vol. 62, no. 8, 1970, p. 515.
31. W. R. Conley, "High Rate Filtration," *Journal AWWA,* vol. 64, no. 3, 1972, p. 205.
32. G. P. Westerhoff, "Experience with Higher Filtration Rates," *Journal AWWA,* vol. 63, no. 6, 1971, p. 376.
33. W. R. Conley and K. Hsiung, "Design and Application of Multi-Media Filters," *Journal AWWA,* vol. 61, no. 2, 1969, p. 97.
34. C. M. Spink and J. T. Monscvitz, "Design and Operation of a 200 MGD Direct Filtration Facility," *Journal AWWA,* vol. 66, no. 2, 1974, p. 127.
35. W. R. Conley, "Integration of the Clarification Process," *Journal AWWA,* vol. 57, no. 10, 1965, p. 1333.
36. G. G. Robeck, K. A. Dostal, and R. L. Woodward, "Studies of Modifications in Water Filtration," *Journal AWWA,* vol. 56, no. 2, 1964, p. 198.
37. K. A. Dostal and G. G. Robeck, "Studies of Modifications in Treatment of Lake Erie Water," *Journal AWWA,* vol. 58, no. 11, 1966, p. 1489.
38. W. B. Kirchman and W. H. Jones, "High Rate Filtration," *Journal AWWA,* vol. 64, no. 3, 1972, p. 157.
39. A. E. Rimer, "Filtration Through a Trimedia Filter," *Journal SED-ASCE,* vol. 94, no. 6, 1968, p. 521.
40. Committee Report, "State of the Air of Water Filtration." *Journal AWWA,* vol. 64, no. 10, 1972, p. 662.
41. H. Jung and E. S. Savage, "Deep Bed Filtration," *Journal AWWA,* vol. 66, no. 2, 1974, p. 73.
42. A. K. Hsiung, W. R. Conley, and S. P. Hansen, "The Effect of Media Selection on Filtration Performance," Presented at Spring Meeting of Hawaii Section, AWWA, April 1976.
43. G. L. Culp and R. L. Culp, *New Concepts in Water Purification,* Van Nostrand Reinhold, New York, 1974.
44. W. R. Hutchison, "High Rate Direct Filtration," *Journal AWWA,* vol. 68, no. 6, 1976, p. 292.
45. J. L. Cleasby et al., "Backwashing of Granular Filters," *Journal AWWA,* vol. 69, no. 2, 1977, p. 115.
46. G. Fair, J. Geyer, and D. Okun, *Water and Wastewater Engineering,* vol. 2, Wiley, New York, 1968.
47. E. Brater and H. King, *Handbook of Hydraulics,* 6th ed., McGraw-Hill, New York, 1976.
48. T. R. Camp et al., "Backwashing of Granular Water Filters," *Journal SED-ASCE,* vol. 97, no. 12, 1971, p. 903.
49. J. L. Cleasby, et al., "Developments in Backwashing of Granular Filters," *Journal EED-ASCE,* vol. 101, no. 10, 1975, p. 713.
50. R. L. Johnson and J. L. Cleasby, "Effect of Backwash on Filter Effluent Quality," *Journal SED-ASCE,* vol. 92, no. 2, 1966, p. 215.
51. J. Cleasby and E. Baumann, "Wastewater Filtration: Design Considerations," EPA Office of Technology Transfer, EPA/625/4-74/007, NTIS—PB-259 448, July 1974.
52. L. Wang et al., "Continuous Pilot Plant Study of Recycling of Filter Backwash Water," *Journal AWWA,* vol. 65, no. 5, 1973, p. 355.
53. J. L. Cleasby, M. W. Williamson, and E. R. Baumann, "Effect of Filtration Rate Changes on Quality," *Journal AWWA,* vol. 55, no. 7, 1963, p. 869.
54. J. L. Cleasby, "Filter Rate Control without Rate Controllers," *Journal AWWA,* vol. 61, no. 4, 1969, p. 181.
55. J. L. Cleasby, "Filter Control: Try These New Ideas," *Water and Wastes Engineering,* vol. 10, no. 6, 1973, p. 51.
56. J. H. Robinson et al., "Direct Filtration of Lake Superior Water for Asbestiform-Solids Removal," *Journal AWWA,* vol. 68, no. 10, 1976, p. 531.
57. J. L. Patton, "Unusual Water Treatment Plant Licks Asbestos Fiber Problem," *Water and Wastes Engineering,* vol. 14, no. 11, 1977, p. 41.
58. S. Syrotynski, "Microscopic Water Quality and Filtration Efficiency," *Journal AWWA,* vol. 63, no. 4, 1971, p. 237.

59. G. P. Westerhoff, "Filter Loading, Filter Performance, and Water Quality," *Journal AWWA,* vol. 57, no. 2, 1965, p. 157.
60. E. R. Baumann et al., "Diatomite Filters for Municipal Use," *Journal AWWA,* vol. 57, no. 2, 1965, p. 157.
61. E. R. Baumann, "Diatomite Filtration of Potable Water," *Water Quality and Treatment,* 3d ed., Prepared by AWWA, McGraw-Hill, New York, 1971, p. 280.

Finkle, Jerry, ...

... ...

... ...

... ...

Introduction

Once Dr. John Snow established in 1854 that water could be a mode of communication for dreaded diseases like cholera, managers of public water supplies began to develop an active interest in preventing this mode of transmission. At first, slow sand filtration and the use of uncontaminated water supplies were the only means employed. Then, in the 1870s when Louis Pasteur and Robert Koch developed the germ theory of disease, innovations began to occur. In 1881, Koch demonstrated in the laboratory that chlorine could kill bacteria. By 1890, the first electrolytic chlorine generation plant was built in West Germany; in 1905, continuous chlorination was used for the first time in Lincoln, England, to arrest a typhoid epidemic. The first regular use of disinfection in the United States was by G. Johnson at the Bubbley Creek Filtration Plant in Chicago in 1908, about the same time that Dr. Harriette Chick first advanced her famous theory of disinfection. The first use of ozone for disinfection was at Nice, France, in 1910. Since that time, disinfection has become an accepted water supply practice throughout the world. Chlorination has been the dominant method employed, but ozonation has been widely used also, particularly in France, Germany, Canada, and the U.S.S.R. There has been increasing use of chlorine dioxide in European and U.S. disinfection.

Methods currently employed

The consensus on the most appropriate agents for use in disinfecting water supplies is currently undergoing reevaluation. Chlorination is standard U.S. practice, and for good reason. Chlorination is of proven effectiveness, it has low capital and operating costs, and water treatment personnel worldwide have had extensive experience with it. Standard chlorination practice is being challenged, however, because it is now known that chlorine reacts with aquatic organic material present in natural water to form trace levels (between 0.01 and 1.0 mg/L) of the trihalomethanes (THMs), a group of lightweight chlorinated hydrocarbons which are suspected carcinogens. The EPA has promulgated regulations limiting the concentration of THMs in drinking water to 0.1 mg/L. Other chlorinated organics may also be regulated as more reaction products are identified and their toxicity evaluated. Some water utilities may not be able to adequately disinfect their water supply using chlorine without exceeding this limit, or future lower limits (see Chap. 1). A number of options are available for controlling formation of trihalomethanes and other chlorination by-products, and these are widely discussed in the literature. This chapter will be limited to a discussion of chlorination and the use of alternative disinfectants. The principal alternatives are ozonation, chlorine dioxide, and combined chlorine residuals. Others which may be occasionally employed are ultraviolet light, iodine, bromine, bromine chloride, and gamma radiation.

Table 8.1 displays certain physical constants for the three most common disinfecting agents, namely, chlorine, ozone, and chlorine dioxide. It should be noted that all three normally exist as gases, although chlorine dioxide liquefies at a temperature near 10°C. Chlorine is available as a compressed liquid, but ozone and chlorine dioxide must be manufactured on site: ozone because it decomposes, and chlorine dioxide because it is dangerous to store in a concentrated compressed form.

Disinfection Theory

Although a good deal of work on modeling disinfection has recently been done, the principal disinfection theory in use today is still the

TABLE 8.1 Physical Constants for Common Disinfecting Agents

Name	Symbol	Molecular weight	Solubility in water at 1 atm & 25°C, g/L	Boiling point, °C	Melting point, °C	Heat of vaporization, Cal/g
Chlorine	Cl_2	70.91	7.29	−34.5	−101	68.7
Ozone	O_3	48.00	0.006*	−112.0	−192	54.0
Chlorine dioxide	ClO_2	67.45	8.0†	10.9	−59	96.6

*190 O_3 by weight in air.
†Assumes equilibrium with 10% ClO_2 gas phase.

Chick-Watson theory. The Chick-Watson theory was developed by Dr. Harriette Chick[1] and refined by H. E. Watson[2] in 1908. In simplified form, this theory states that the rate of destruction of pathogens by a disinfectant is proportional to the number of pathogens and the concentration of the disinfectant, in the form proposed by Morris.[3]

$$\frac{dN}{dt} = kC^nN$$

In integrated form,

$$\ln \frac{N}{N_0} = kC^nt \tag{8.1}$$

where N = number of pathogens present
N_0 = number of pathogens present at $t = 0$
C = concentration of disinfectant
t = time
k = coefficient of specific lethality
n = dilution coefficient

Table 8.2 shows the specific lethality coefficients for the disinfectants discussed here with respect to four general classes or organisms. The values for ozone, HOCl, OCl⁻, and NH$_2$Cl are taken from Morris.[3] The values for ClO$_2$ were estimated from the literature. These values should be taken as an approximation of the relative lethality of these agents because so many variables affect the results of disinfection experiments that it is hard to compare one set of results with the next. This is particularly true for chlorine dioxide.

Generally, these results show that ozone is the most effective disinfectant for all pathogens, that ClO$_2$ and HOCl are of comparable effectiveness, and that OCl⁻ (the form of free chlorine at alkaline pHs) and NH$_2$Cl (monochloramine) are not very effective.

Free residual chlorination

At the present time, the maintenance of free chlorine residuals is the principal means by which water utilities ensure that the water they

TABLE 8.2   Specific Lethality of Alternative Disinfectants*

Disinfectant	Enteric bacteria	Viruses	Spores	Amoebic cysts
O$_3$	500	5	2	0.5
ClO$_2$	10	1.5	0.6	0.1
HOCl	20	1.0+	0.05	0.05
OCl⁻	0.2	0.02	0.0005	0.0005
NH$_2$Cl	0.1	0.005	0.001	0.02

*1/(mg/L · min), assuming that n is equal to 1.

provide is properly disinfected. Free residual chlorine is a term used to refer to a chlorine residual which is not combined with ammonia or organic nitrogen. Free chlorine residuals comprise $(Cl_2)_{aq}$, HOCl, and OCl$^-$ species, which are strong disinfectants.

When chlorine gas is dissolved in water, it quickly reacts to form hydrochloric acid and hypochlorous acid in the following manner:

$$Cl_2 + H_2O = H^+ + Cl^- + HOCl \tag{8.2}$$

The hydrolysis constant K_H for this reaction can be approximated by the following relationship developed from the data collected by White,[4] in which $pK_H = -\log_{10} K_H$:

$$pK_H = -0.579 + \frac{1190.7}{T_{kelvin}} \tag{8.3}$$

For a temperature of 25°C, this corresponds to a pK_H of 3.42. Calculations will show that almost all the chlorine added to the water is in the form of HOCl. High levels of chloride ion, low pHs, and high temperatures all tend to increase the fraction in the $(Cl_2)_{aq}$ form. But even in hot sea water at pH 6, more than 99.9 percent of the chlorine added is in the HOCl form. Of course, not all the hypochlorous acid is in the HOCl form. Being a weak acid, hypochlorous acid participates in the ionization reactions shown below:

$$HOCl = H^+ + OCl^- \tag{8.4}$$

The ionization constant K_I for this reaction can be approximated by the following relationship developed by Morris,[5] in which $pK_I = -\log_{10} K_I$:

$$pK_I = -10.069 + \frac{3.000}{T_{kelvin}} + 0.025T_{kelvin} \tag{8.5}$$

For a temperature of 25°C, this corresponds to a pK_I of 7.54. Using the pK_I value, the fraction of the chlorine in the HOCl form can be calculated by the following formula:

$$\frac{HOCl}{(Cl_2)_{aq}} = \frac{1}{1} + \frac{K_I}{H^+} \tag{8.6}$$

This fraction is most important because, as the specific lethality data in Table 8.2 show, HOCl is nearly 1000 times more effective than the ionized form OCl$^-$. Figure 8.1 shows the fraction of chlorine present as HOCl at various pHs and at various temperatures. It should be noted that pH is the dominant factor. Changes in temperature merely result in a modest change in the pH at which the chlorine added is half in

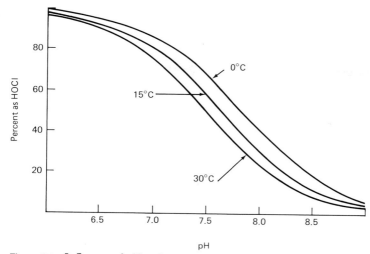

Figure 8.1 Influence of pH and temperature on fraction of aqueous chlorine as HOCl.

the HOCl form and half in the OCl$^-$ form (7.8 at 0°C to 7.5 at 30°C). Generally speaking, the HOCl species dominates at pHs less than 7, and the OCl$^-$ dominates at pHs greater than 8. Between 7 and 8, the speciation of aqueous chlorine is very pH-dependent.

Understanding of the reactions between chlorine and ammonia is important to an adequate understanding of chlorination chemistry. These reactions are complex, and the temperature, pH mixing regime, and Cl_2/NH_3 weight ratio all influence both the rate and the products of the reaction. When a small amount of chlorine is added ($Cl_2/NH_3 < 4$), monochloramine is the dominant species formed. As additional chlorine is added, di- and trichloramine are formed, along with other products such as NO_3^- and N_2 gas. The following are some of the typical reactions which may occur:

Monochloramine: $NH_4^+ + HOCl = NH_2Cl + H_2O + H^+$ (8.7)

Dichloramine: $NH_2Cl + HOCl = NHCl_2 + H_2O$ (8.8)

Trichloramine: $NHCl_2 + HOCl = NCl_3 + H_2O$ (8.9)

Nitrogen: $2NH_4^+ + 3HOCl = N_2 + 5H^+ + 3Cl^- + 3H_2O$ (8.10)

Nitrate: $NH_4^+ + 4HOCl = NO_3^- + H_2O + 6H^+ + 4Cl^-$ (8.11)

These reactions give insight into the chlorine dose required to achieve free residual chlorination. Table 8.3 summarizes the theoretical chlo-

TABLE 8.3   Chlorine Dose Required for NH₃–Cl₂ Reaction

Reaction	mg Cl₂/mg NH₃
Monochloroamine (NH₂Cl)	4.2
Dichloroamine (NHCl₂)	8.4
Trichloroamine (NCl₃)	12.5
Nitrogen (N₂)	6.3
Nitrate (NO₃)	16.7
Recommended design dose for free residual reaction	9

rine dose required for these various chlorination reactions. It should be noted that a great deal of chlorine is required to form nitrate, and only slightly less to form trichloramine. The chlorine-to-ammonia weight ratio required for forming nitrogen, however, is even less than that required for converting all the ammonia to dichloramine. Saunier[6] has shown that nitrogen is the principal species formed during the free residual reaction, but practical experience suggests that doses of 8 mg Cl_2/mg NH_3 are often required, and a dose of 9 to 10 mg Cl_2/mg NH_3 is recommended for design purposes. In practice, however, the NCl_3 concentration increases rapidly as the chlorine doses exceed the optimum, so excessive chlorine doses should be avoided. This is demonstrated by the free residual chlorine curves from Palin[7] shown in Fig. 8.2.

Combined residual chlorination

Combined residual chlorination was first used by Race at Ottawa, Ontario, Canada. At the time, it was argued that chloramines had a germicidal action greater than that of chlorine alone, that their use could ensure that the water produced was free of taste and odors, that a much more long-lasting residual was produced, and that the overall cost of disinfection could be reduced. The sum total of many subsequent studies have shown that (1) the germicidal action of combined chlorine may be substantially less than that of free chlorine, (2) combined chlorine is sometimes better from the taste and odor standpoint when the taste and odor of concern are the result of chlorine by-products, and (3) the combined chlorine residual is indeed longer-lasting than a free chlorine residual.

Specific lethality data in Table 8.2 suggest that for a pH of 7 or below, free chlorine is 200, 200, 50, and 2.5 times more effective in killing bacteria, viruses, spores, and cysts, respectively. This means that to get equivalent removal of bacteria and viruses with chloramine, the chlorine residual must be 200 times higher at the same contact time

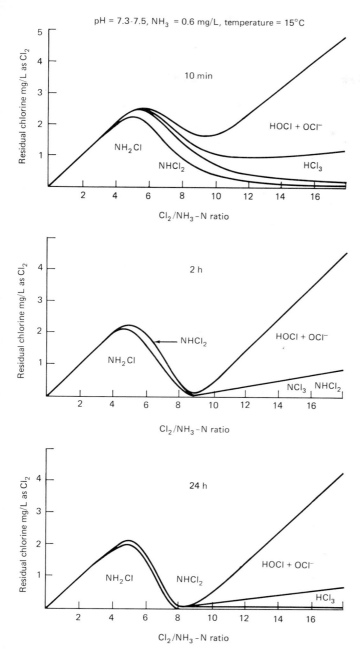

Figure 8.2 Free residual chlorine curves. (*Source: A. Palin, "A Study of the Chloro Derivatives of Ammonia," Water Engineering, vol. 54, December 1950, p. 151.*)

or the contact time must be 200 times longer at the same residual, assuming that n [Eq. (8.1)] is unity. Any combination of concentration times residual that is 200 times greater for chloramines than for free chlorine should give equivalent disinfection. For pHs above 8 to 8.5, this issue is moot because the OCl^- ion is comparable to monochloramine in its disinfecting power. Many of the plants that currently use the chloramine process add chlorine first and maintain a free chlorine residual for some time before ammonia is added.

Chlorine dioxide

In certain circumstances, chlorine dioxide is an excellent choice among disinfectants. Chlorine dioxide is effective in destroying phenols, yet it does not form trihalomethanes in significant amounts. Chlorine dioxide's disinfectant properties are not adversely affected by a higher pH, as those of a free chlorine residual are. Consequently, chlorine dioxide is a much quicker disinfectant at higher pHs. In western Europe, use of chlorine dioxide is increasing, particularly in Holland, Germany, France, and Switzerland in regions where there is an attempt to produce potable water from polluted rivers. In these locations, chlorine dioxide is used for disinfection, often as an adjunct to ozonation.

The chlorine in chlorine dioxide is in the +4 oxidation state, and each mole of chlorine dioxide yields five redox equivalents (electrons) upon being reduced to chlorine ions. In aqueous solution, chlorine dioxide can be reduced by two alternative pathways, as shown below.

$$(8.12)$$

In being reduced to ClO_2^-, chlorine dioxide's redox potential is 1.15 V. In being reduced to Cl^-, its potential is 1.9 V. Chlorine's redox potential in being reduced to Cl^- is 1.4 V. At the pHs normally encountered in water utility practice, chlorine dioxide is most often reduced to the chlorite ion (ClO_2^-); hence, both its redox potential and the redox equivalents are fewer for chlorine dioxide than for chlorine. On the other hand, chlorine dioxide is a good disinfectant, and because it is selective, it does not participate in a number of undesirable side reactions which divert chlorine from its intended purpose. For example, chlorine dioxide does not react with aquatic humus to form trihalomethanes, nor does it react with ammonia to form chloramines. As a result, chlorine dioxide residuals are sometimes purported to last longer than free chlorine residuals under the same circumstances. One of chlorine dioxide's principal advantages as an oxidant is that it effectively removes phenols, a continuing odor problem in certain water supplies. Chlorine dioxide does not dissociate or disproportionate as chlorine does at normal drinking water pHs. Like chlorine, chlorine dioxide exerts a demand when it is first added to a water supply, which must be overcome if a persistent residual is to be maintained. Again like chlorine, chlorine dioxides are photosensitive (light sensitive). However, because chlorine dioxide does not react with water like chlorine, its residuals are easily removed by aeration.

The principal reason for the recent increasing interest in chlorine dioxide in the United States is the fact that it does not form trihalomethanes. On the other hand, the organic by-products of chlorine dioxide are not yet well understood; it may have other undesirable reaction products. Information presently available indicates that the reaction products would include aldehydes, carboxylic acids, and ketones. Few chlorinated by-products are known, although some are likely. The principal inorganic by-products of chlorine dioxide reactions within water treatment are chlorite (ClO_2), chloride (Cl^-), and chlorate (ClO_3^-), in the order listed. Both chlorate and chlorite, particularly the chlorite ion, have been implicated in the formation of methemoglobin. Consequently, most European countries limit the level of chlorine dioxide which can be used, and the EPA has considered doing so in the United States as well. The current EPA recommendation is that the sum of chlorine dioxide, chlorite, and chlorate in the distribution system be less than 1.0 mg/L.

Generation of chlorine dioxide

All chlorine dioxide for drinking-water treatment is generated from sodium chlorite. Most generation techniques use the oxidative process, in which chlorine (either as a gas or in solution) is mixed with a sodium chlorite solution. The stoichiometry of this reaction is (written for molecular chlorine):

$$2NaClO_2 + Cl_2 = 2ClO_2 + 2NaCl \qquad (8.13)$$

In addition to the desired formation of chlorine dioxide, chlorate ion may be formed in the generation system as an undesired by-product in a competing reaction:

$$NaClO_2 + Cl_2 + OH^- = NaClO_3 + HCl + Cl^- \qquad (8.14)$$

The goal in generating chlorine dioxide from chlorine and sodium chlorite is to maximize the chlorine dioxide yield, defined as the molar ratio of chlorine dioxide produced to the theoretical maximum. The term "conversion" is also used when referring to chlorine dioxide generation reactions; this is the molar ratio of the amount of chlorine dioxide formed to the amount of sodium chlorite fed to the system. For Eq. (8.13), yield and conversion will have the same value. For other reactions that produce chlorine dioxide, such as the hydrochloric acid–sodium chlorite reaction, yield and conversion will have different values:

$$5NaClO_2 + 4HCl = 4ClO_2 + 5NaCl + 2H_2O \qquad (8.15)$$

For Eq. (8.15), maximum yield is 100 percent; maximum conversion, 80 percent.

Studies of the mechanism and kinetics of the chlorine–sodium chlorite reaction have shown that conditions favoring the formation of chlorine dioxide are those in which the reactants are present in high concentrations and the chlorine is present as hypochlorous acid or molecular chlorine (Cl_2). Two methods for the generation of chlorine dioxide from chlorine and sodium chlorite are commercially available. They are the aqueous chlorine–sodium chlorite system and the gas chlorine–sodium chlorite system.

Aqueous chlorine–sodium chlorite system

The earliest systems produced chlorine dioxide by simply pumping a sodium chlorite solution into a chlorine solution, followed by a short reaction time. Acceptable yields were achieved by feeding 200 to 300 percent more chlorine than the stoichiometric requirement of Eq. (8.13). The chlorine dioxide solution from a generator of this type contains high levels of chlorine in addition to the chlorine dioxide. A side reaction that occurs in the chlorine dioxide solution under these conditions is

$$2ClO_2 + HOCl + H_2O = 2ClO_3^- + 2H^+ + HCl \qquad (8.16)$$

With the discovery that potentially toxic chlorinated organics are generated by the reaction of chlorine and naturally occurring humic substances in water supplies, plus the growing interest in chlorine dioxide as a replacement for some chlorination practices, generation methods were sought that would produce a chlorine-free chlorine dioxide. One of the most common methods for chlorine dioxide generation currently in use that strives to meet this requirement is the pH-adjusted method.

The pH-adjusted system utilizes hydrochloric acid fed into the chlorine solution before reaction with the sodium chlorite. The acid feed serves to shift the chlorine solution equilibria [the hypochlorous acid dissociation, Eq. (8.17), and the chlorine hydrolysis equilibrium, Eq. (8.18)] favoring hypochlorous acid and molecular chlorine.

$$HOCl = OCl^- + H^+ \qquad (8.17)$$

$$Cl_2 + H_2O = HOCl + HCl \qquad (8.18)$$

The acid feed must be carefully controlled so that the pH of the chlorine dioxide solution can be maintained between 2 and 3. Higher pH values result in decreased yields. At a lower pH, however, Eq. (8.15) becomes significant, again reducing yield because of the maximum conversion of only 80 percent from this reaction. Yields of more than 90 percent have been reported from the pH-adjusted system, with approximately 7 percent excess (unreacted) chlorine remaining in the solution.

Another modification that produces high yields of chlorine dioxide, with minimal amounts of chlorine remaining in the chlorine dioxide solution, requires that the chlorine solution used for generation have a chlorine concentration greater than 4 g/L. The exact relationship of excess chlorine required for 95 percent yield and initial chlorine solution concentration is shown in Fig. 8.3.

Since this concentration of chlorine in solution is near the upper operating limit of commercial chlorine ejectors, and these ejectors operate at constant water flow rates, the yield of this method of generation is dependent on the production rate, with lower production rates resulting in lower yields. This type of generator is normally operated on an intermittent basis to maintain high yield when less-than-maximum production capacity is required. Chlorine dioxide solutions in the 6- to 10-g/L concentration range are prepared and immediately diluted to about 1 g/L for storage and subsequent use as needed.

A schematic of the aqueous chlorine–sodium chlorite system is shown in Fig. 8.4.

Gas chlorine–sodium chlorite system

The most recent development in chlorine dioxide generator technology is a patented system that reacts gas chlorine with a concentrated sodium chlorite solution under vacuum. The chlorine dioxide produced is removed from the reaction chamber by a gas ejector, which is very similar to the common chlorine gas vacuum feed system.

This generation technique produces chlorine dioxide solutions with yields in excess of 95 percent. The chlorine dioxide solution concentration is 200 to 1000 mg/L and contains less than 5 percent excess chlo-

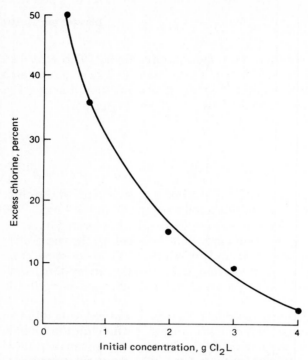

Figure 8.3 Excess chlorine necessary for greater than 95 percent conversion of chlorite to chlorine dioxide. (*Source: M. Aieta and J. Berg, "A Review of Chlorine Dioxide in Drinking Water Treatment," Journal AWWA, vol. 78, no. 6, June 1986, p. 62.*)

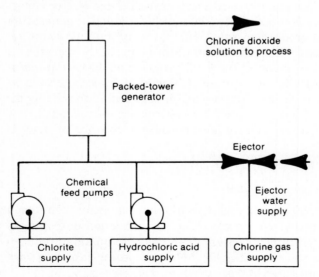

Figure 8.4 Aqueous chlorine–sodium chlorite system schematic with optional acid feed. (*Source: M. Aieta and J. Berg, "A Review of Chlorine Dioxide in Drinking Water Treatment," Journal AWWA, vol. 78, no. 6, June 1986, p. 62.*)

rine, which is defined as the amount of unreacted chlorine remaining in the chlorine dioxide generator effluent. The system is operated on a continuous basis, and achieves a high yield over the entire production range (Fig. 8.5).

Ozonation

Although the first use of ozone in water treatment coincided with the first use of chlorine for that purpose, at the present time ozonation is a common practice in only a small number of countries, notably France, Germany, and Canada. In the United States, interest in ozonation in water treatment has increased recently because of suspected carcinogenic properties of the trihalomethanes that are formed when center organic compounds, naturally present in water, react with chlorine.

Ozone is a highly reactive gas which is formed by electrical discharges in the presence of oxygen. Its most distinguishing characteristic is a very pungent odor. In fact, the word "ozone" is derived from a Greek word which means "to smell." The use of this gas in water treatment requires an understanding of its physical and chemical behavior. The physical chemistry of ozone is important because a number of complex factors affect its solubility, reactivity, autodecomposition, and stability.

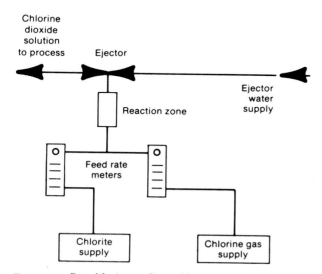

Figure 8.5 Gas chlorine–sodium chlorite system schematic. (*Source: M. Aieta and J. Berg, "A Review of Chlorine Dioxide in Drinking Water Treatment," Journal AWWA, vol. 78, no. 6, June 1986, p. 62.*)

Ozone is an allotrope of oxygen. Substantial amounts of energy are required to split the stable oxygen–oxygen covalent bond to form ozone, and the ozone molecule readily reverts to elemental oxygen during the oxidation-reduction reaction. Ozone is more soluble in water than oxygen. Ozone solubility follows Henry's law, which means that solubility is a direct function of partial pressure. The equation below demonstrates this relationship and shows how the solubility constant K_s, is a function of absolute temperature:

$$O_3 = K_s pO_3 \qquad \text{Henry's law} \qquad (8.19)$$

where O_3 = ozone concentration, mg/L
$\quad K_s$ = solubility constant
$\quad pO_3$ = partial pressure of ozone

$$K_s = \frac{1.29 \times 10^6}{T_{\text{kelvin}} - 3720.5} \qquad (8.20)$$

where T = degrees kelvins

This temperature equation is a simple Van't Hoff relation; its fit to available data is shown in Fig. 8.6. Thus, in an ozone reaction operating at 20° with a 0.05 percent solution of ozone in exit gas, the equilibrium concentration of ozone in the water is about 0.34 mg/L.

The ozone residual present in water decays rapidly, but there are many factors which affect how long it will actually last. Before getting into the rates of decay, a brief discussion of the work of Hoigne[14] is in order. Figure 8.7 shows reaction pathways of ozone as they have been described by three authors. Once ozone enters solution, it follows two basic modes of reaction: direct oxidation, which is rather slow and extremely selective, and autodecomposition to the hydroxyl radical. Autodecomposition to the hydroxyl radical is catalyzed by the presence of hydroxyl radicals, organic radicals, hydrogen peroxide, ultraviolet light, or high concentrations of hydroxide ion. The hydroxyl radical is extremely fast and nonselective in its oxidation of organic compounds, but at the same time, it is scavenged by carbonate and bicarbonate ions to form carbonate and bicarbonate radicals. These radicals are of no consequence in organic reactions. Furthermore, the hydroxyl radicals and organic radicals produced by autodecomposition become chain carriers and reenter the autodecomposition reaction to accelerate it. Thus, low-pH conditions favor the slow, direct oxidation reactions involving O_3, and high-pH conditions or high concentrations of organic matter favor the autodecomposition route. High concentrations of bicarbonate or carbonate buffer, especially carbonate buffer,

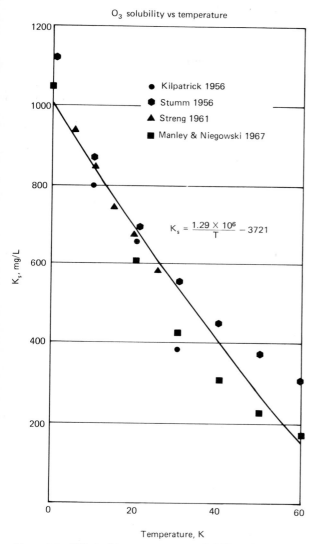

O$_3$ solubility vs temperature

- Kilpatrick 1956
- Stumm 1956
- ▲ Streng 1961
- ■ Manley & Niegowski 1967

$$K_s = \frac{1.29 \times 10^6}{T} - 3721$$

K$_s$, mg/L

Temperature, K

Figure 8.6 Effect of temperature on solubility of ozone.

reduce the rate of autodecomposition by scavenging hydroxyl radicals. This means that ozone residuals last longer at low pH and in highly buffered waters. Figure 8.8 shows the decay of ozone residuals as studied by Stumm in 1956. A crude equation for the autodecomposition of ozone ignoring the effect of carbonate can be developed from Stumm's data as follows:

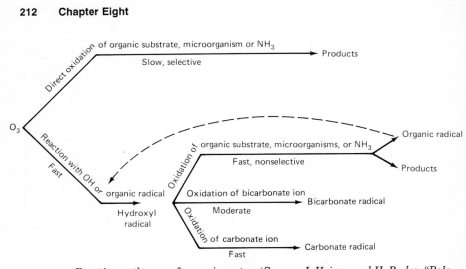

Figure 8.7   Reaction pathways of ozone in water. (*Source: J. Hoigne and H. Bader, "Role of Hydroxyl Radical Reactions in Ozonation Processes in Aqueous Solutions," Water Resources Bulletin, vol. 10, 1976, p. 377.*)

$$\frac{(O_3)_t}{(O_3)_0} = 10^{-At} \tag{8.21}$$

where $(O_3)_t$ = residual at time t
$\quad\ (O_3)_0$ = residual at time 0
$\qquad\quad t$ = time
$\qquad\quad A = 10^{(0.636\,pH\ -\ 6.97)}$

For example, this equation suggests that at pH 8, the half-life of ozone is about 23 min. The half-life of ozone is highly dependent on the water quality (TOC, carbonate, and so on) and the applied ozone dose. For design purposes, ozone half-lives should be determined in the water to be treated and under similar conditions.

Data are available showing ozone's effectiveness in inactivating viruses and killing bacteria. Ozone also seems to be extremely effective in oxidizing chromaphores, resulting in the reduction of color. In many instances, ozonation will reduce the potential for the formation of trihalomethanes.[15] Ozone is also reputed to be effective in removing taste and odor, although less data are available to demonstrate this principle. Ozone has been shown to effectively oxidize phenol, and, although ozone will oxidize Br to HOBr, it has been demonstrated that ozone does not generate trihalomethanes even in the presence of bromide concentrations as high as 0.5 mg/L.

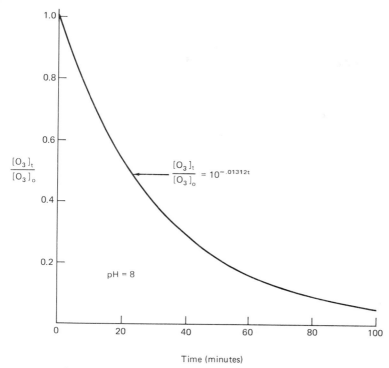

Figure 8.8 Ozone decay with time.

The equation shown in the figure:

$$\frac{[O_3]_t}{[O_3]_o} = 10^{-.01312t}$$

with y-axis labeled $\dfrac{[O_3]_t}{[O_3]_o}$, x-axis labeled Time (minutes), and annotation pH = 8.

Elements of Design

Design of systems to store and feed chlorine gas

Chlorine is most often available commercially in pressurized vessels containing both liquid and gas fractions, as sodium hypochlorite (household bleach), and as calcium hypochlorite. Gaseous chlorine is most often employed because of its significantly lower cost; however, transportation of gaseous chlorine does impose a certain risk of serious accidents, and some utilities have switched to sodium hypochlorite in order to circumvent safety problems in densely populated areas. Calcium hypochlorite has also been used on certain occasions. On-site generation of chlorine gas or sodium hypochlorite is possible, and this approach is receiving increased interest. Design considerations for each approach will be briefly discussed. For greater detail, the reader is referred to White's *Handbook on Chlorination,*[4] an extensive compendium that is widely used in the industry. This discussion uses the *Handbook* extensively as a source.

Storage

Anhydrous chlorine is commercially available in containers of the following sizes:

150-lb cylinders

1-ton cylinders

15- to 17-ton tank trucks

16- to 90-ton railroad tank cars

Cylinders of 100-lb weight are also available, but are rarely used. The dimensions of the 150-lb and 1-ton cylinders are shown in Fig. 8.9. As chlorine tank trucks do not have standard sizes, dimensions should be obtained from the local supplier of chlorine. The dimensions of the various sizes of railroad tank cars available for transporting chlorine are shown in Table 8.4.

In all these vessels, liquid chlorine occupies a maximum of approximately 85 percent of the volume when the product is delivered. This is to provide room for the expansion of liquid chlorine on heating. If the liquid were to get warm enough to expand and fill the entire container, tremendous hydrostatic pressure would result, and the container would rupture. As a result, *no chlorine container should ever be directly heated.* As a safety precaution, the outlet valves on the cylinders are equipped with a small fusible plug that melts at approximately 158°F and releases some liquid chlorine to cool the cylinder before a more serious accident can occur.

Often the chlorine is fed by withdrawing gas from the top of the con-

TABLE 8.4 Railroad Tank Car Dimensions

	Length over strikers*	Overall height†	Height to valve†	Extreme width‡
TMU	42'4"–47'0"	6'8"–7'6"	—	9'6"–10'1"
16-ton	32'2"–33'3"	10'5"–12'0"	9'3¼"–10'0"	9'2"–9'6½"
30-ton	33'10"–35'11½"	12'4½"–13'7"	11'3"–11'9"	9'3"–9'10"
55-ton	29'9"–43'0"	14'3"–15'1"	12'6"–13'4"	9'3"–10'7½"
85-ton	43'7"–50'0"	14'11"–15'1"	13'2"–13'4"	10'5½"–10'6½"
90-ton	45'8"–47'2"	14'11"–15'1"	13'2"–13'4"	10'5½"–10'6½"

*Add 2'6" for length over centerline of coupler knuckles.
†Heights are for empty cars, and are measured from top of rail. Heights for loaded cars may be 4" less.
‡Width over grab irons.
Note: Height to manway platform is 6 to 10" less than height to centerline of valve.

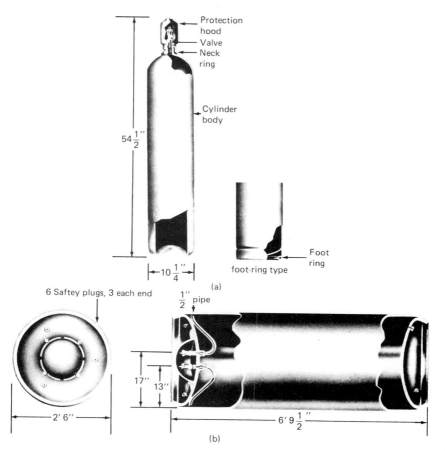

Figure 8.9 Dimensions of standard chlorine cylinders. (a) 150-lb cylinder. (*Courtesy of PPG Industries, Inc., Pittsburgh, Pa.*) (b) One-ton cylinder. (*Courtesy of The Chlorine Institute, Inc.*)

tainer. The reduced pressure above the liquid then causes some of the liquid to evaporate, providing additional gas. The maximum withdrawal rate with this method is about 40 lb/day for a 150-lb cylinder and 400 lb/day for a 1-ton cylinder. Maximum continuous withdrawal rates for containers of other sizes can be approximated by comparing the surface area available to absorb the heat required to replace the heat of evaporation lost. If chlorine is being used in this manner, the containers should be maintained in an environment that can be heated to 65°F. The design-maximum 24-h withdrawal rate of a system designed for withdrawal of gas from the top of the container should not exceed the continuous withdrawal rate of the containers on-line.

Once the logistics of transporting chlorine by tank truck or railroad tank car have been worked out, stationary storage facilities should be considered. The user can purchase chlorine for a better price if the tank car or trailer is on-site only for the period of time it takes to unload it; on the other hand, the use of tank truck trailers and railroad cars for on-site storage is also quite common. Stationary chlorite facilities should be designed in complete accordance with the recommendations of The Chlorine Institute as set forth in their Pamphlet No. 5, *Facilities and Operating Procedures for Chlorine Storage.*[17] The tanks should be designed for 120 percent of the maximum expected working pressure, but not less than 225 psi. To allow for corrosion, the tank wall must be ⅛ in thicker than required by the design formula in the code. Provision must also be made for a weighing device. This can be best accomplished by either a lever scale system or load cells. Load cells are more commonly used.

An air padding system is recommended for unloading the tank car and removing gas from the tank prior to inspection. The compressor for the padding system should have a capacity of not less than 14 scfm at 200 psi. It should be outfitted with a pressure switch and equipped with an 80-gal receiver that meets ASME code, with an air-cooled aftercooler. The air should be dried with a heat-reactivated, desiccant-type air dryer capable of reaching a dew point of −40°F. A humidity alarm should be provided on this part of the system.

Evaporators

If the containers being used are 1 ton or larger, and the withdrawal rates exceed those available with the direct evaporation method described earlier, chlorine evaporators may be used. Evaporators are available in capacities of 4000, 6000, and 8000 lb/day. When an evaporator is used, liquid chlorine is withdrawn from the bottom of the container and transported to the evaporator, where it is converted to a gas. The most common type of evaporator uses an electric resistance heater in a hot-water bath surrounding a vessel in which the liquid chlorine is converted to gas. Sometimes the bath is heated with steam or with a separated, recirculating hot-water system. Figure 8.10 shows a cross section of a typical evaporator. The heat of evaporation of chlorine is very low, approximately 69 cal/g, compared with 540 cal/g for water. However, evaporators should be designed with extra capacity to ensure that the existing gas is superheated and will not recondense on the downstream side. When an evaporator is being used beyond its capacity, misting occurs. A chlorine gas filter should be installed on the exit gas line from the evaporators to remove impurities in the chlorine that would be detrimental to the chlorinator. Evapora-

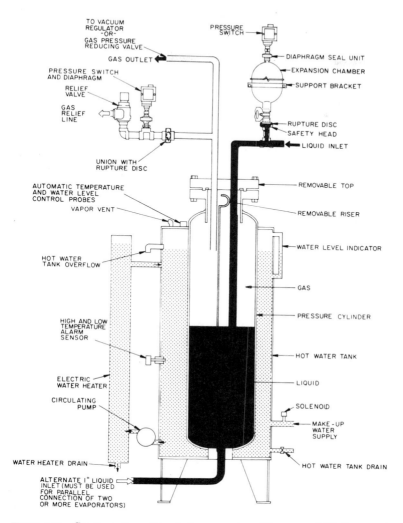

Figure 8.10 Cross section of typical evaporator. (*Courtesy of Wallace and Tiernan Division of Pennwalt Corp.*)

tors should be equipped with an automatic shutoff valve to prevent liquid chlorine from passing to the chlorinators.

When possible, all portions of the chlorine feed system which contain liquid chlorine should be designed and operated with all the liquid in the system as a continuous medium. To shut down the evaporator, it is only necessary to close the effluent valve on the evaporator. No other valves between the evaporator effluent valve and the liquid chlorine container should be shut. If very long liquid chlorine lines make this impossible, chlorine expansion chambers should be provided. It should be emphasized that liquid chlorine has a high temperature-expansion coefficient. Unless expansion is permitted, the temperature increase in trapped liquid will result in pressure high enough to rupture the pipes.

Chlorinators

A conventional chlorinator consists of the following units: an inlet-pressure-reducing valve, a rotameter, a metering control orifice, and a vacuum-differential regulating valve. A simple schematic is shown in Fig. 8.11. The driving force for the system comes from the vacuum which is created by the chlorine injector. The chlorine gas comes to the

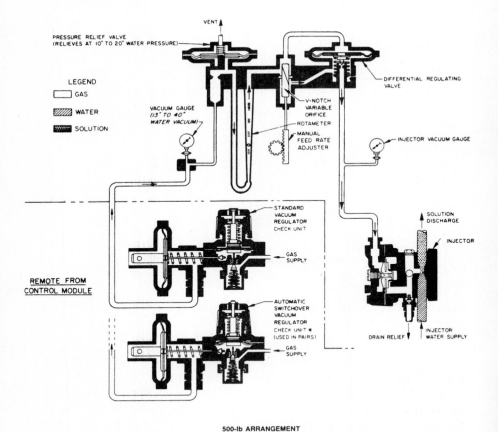

500-lb ARRANGEMENT

Figure 8.11 Flow diagram for conventional chlorinator. (*Courtesy of Wallace and Tiernan Division of Pennwalt Corp.*)

chlorinator and is converted to a constant pressure (usually a mild vacuum) by the influent-pressure-reducing valve. The chlorine then passes through the rotameter, where the flow rate is measured under conditions of constant pressure (and consequently constant density), then through a metering or control orifice. A vacuum differential regulator is mounted across the control orifice so that a constant pressure differential (vacuum differential) is maintained to stabilize the flow for a particular setting on the control orifice. The flow through the control orifice can be adjusted by changing the opening on the orifice. The control orifice has a typical range of 20 to 1, while the vacuum-differential regulator has a range of about 10 to 1. Thus, the overall range of these devices combined is about 200 to 1. On the other hand, a typical rotameter has a range of about 20 to 1. Thus, the chlorinator should be selected based on design capacities, and the rotameter installed at any particular time should be appropriate for current demands.

Chlorine gas pipelines

Between the chlorinator and the injector, the chlorine gas flows in a vacuum. Although the head loss of the gas flow is rather small, it is critical that the vacuum created by the injector be transmitted to the chlorinator without significant dissipation. As a consequence, the diameter of the chlorine vacuum lines should always be designed rather than arbitrarily selected. The following analysis is heavily dependent on the work of White.[4]

According to White,[4] lines should be sized to limit the total pressure drop over the pipe length to between 1.5 and 1.75 in of mercury under maximum injector vacuum levels (22 to 23 in of mercury). Following White,[4] the formula below can be used to estimate pressure drop:

$$P = \frac{11.89 L f W^2}{10^9 p d^5}$$ (8.22)

where P = total pressure drop, in of mercury
L = length of line, ft
f = friction factor
W = chlorine flow, lb/day
p = chlorine density, lb/ft^3
d = inside pipe diameter, in

The chlorine density can be estimated from Fig. 8.12 if the pressure and temperature are known. For PVC gas lines, the friction factor can be estimated from the following formula once the Reynold's number is determined:

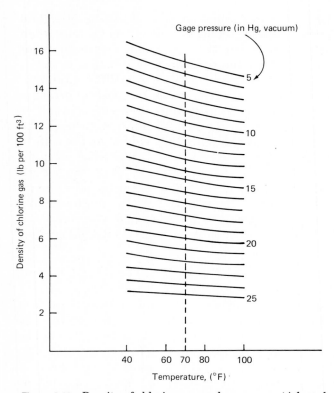

Figure 8.12 Density of chlorine gas under vacuum. (*Adapted from A. S. Ross and O. Mass, "The Density of Gaseous Chlorine," Canadian Journal of Research, vol. 18B, 1940, pp. 55–65.*)

$$\log f = 1.75 - 0.722 \log N_{\text{re}} \tag{8.23}$$

The Reynold's number can be estimated by the following formula:

$$N_{\text{re}} = \frac{0.263W}{ud} \tag{8.24}$$

where u = viscosity of gas, cP
      d = inside pipe diameter, in

In a 40 to 60° temperature range, the viscosity can be estimated by the following formula:

$$u = 0.0115 + 0.00003T \ (\text{°F})$$

The design procedure is to select pipe sizes and calculate the pressure drop. If the drop is too large, then a larger pipe diameter should be used.

Initial mixing of chlorine

When disinfection is being accomplished entirely by free chlorine, it is important to distribute the chlorine dose uniformly across the flow cross section. Traditionally, good designs have accomplished this with open-channel or pipeline diffusers. It can be shown, however, that truly complete mixing across the flow cross section only takes place some distance downstream from diffusers of this type. When free chlorine residuals are being used, this may not be a critical problem. But when water contains significant amounts of ammonia (10 percent of the chlorine dose or more), initial mixing takes on new importance. Under these conditions there is evidence that chlorine is more effective during the first few seconds following its addition. With ammonia present, failure to mix the chlorine solution rapidly with *all* the water can result in a "break-point" reaction with part of the water and little or no reaction with the remainder. The break-point reaction is not reversible. Thus, part of the water receives excess chlorine, and the remainder little or none. Consequently, good initial mixing becomes a much more important process step, and initial mixing devices should be designed to spread the chlorine throughout the flow cross section in the shortest possible time with the least possible backmixing. This can be accomplished by in-line mixers, by sophisticated gas aspirator devices, by installing the chlorine diffuser in a hydraulic jump, or by installing a pump-diffuser system. Flash-mixing chambers such as those used for coagulants in a conventional water treatment plant are not very satisfactory because they result in backwashing.

Materials

Dry chlorine gas will not attack carbon steel at normal temperatures; as a consequence, liquid chlorine is packaged in steel containers. On the other hand, like liquid oxygen, liquid chlorine will sustain combustion of steel once any portion of the steel/chlorine contact surface has been heated to the kindling point (438°F). The reaction proceeds as follows:

$$2Fe_{metal} + 3Cl_2 \underset{gas}{\rightarrow} 2FeCl_3 \tag{8.25}$$

Because of this potential danger, heat should never be applied to a chlorine container, and all chlorine piping should be clearly labeled. If a steel pipe containing liquid chlorine or even chlorine gas at reduced pressure is accidentally cut with a welder's torch, the pipe will ignite and continue to burn as long as there is a chlorine supply available. Small amounts of moisture will also cause chlorine to attack steel. As a trace amount of moisture is unavoidable, some of the corrosion product ($FeCl_3$) is always found in chlorine containers and in chlorine lines.

Table 8.5 gives a summary of the preferred materials for handling chlorine in the three basic parts of the system: the supply system, the vacuum gas lines, and the chlorine water lines. The supply system includes the storage tank and all piping and fittings up to the pressure-reducing valve (PRV) on the chlorinator inlet, including the evaporator, if it is present. The vacuum system refers to all the piping, fittings, and other elements in which the chlorine gas is in a vacuum, including the area between the chlorinator inlet PRV and the injector. The chlorine water system includes all piping above and below water downstream of the injector.

In the supply system, all parts should be carbon steel. Piping should be schedule-80 seamless-weld carbon steel. Reducing fittings should be used rather than bushings, and ammonia-type unions with lead gaskets should be used rather than ground-joint unions. All parts should meet Chlorine Institute standards. Mainline valves should be ball type or rising-stem type, made of cast iron. The ball type is preferred because it is easier to operate and because the lever indicates the position of the valve at a glance.

Piping systems can be assembled by welding or by threading, although welding is preferred. If threaded piping is used, Teflon tape should be specified as the thread lubricant. Only diaphragm-type pressure gauges should be installed in chlorine systems, and these should employ silver diaphragms and Hastalloy-C housing.

TABLE 8.5   Materials Selection for Chlorine Handling

	Location	Form of chlorine	Acceptable materials
Supply system	Storage and piping from storage through to chlorinator inlet	Liquid chlorine Gaseous chlorine under pressure	Sched 80 stainless Carbon steel Cast iron
Vacuum gas system	Chlorinator outlet to injector inlet	Gaseous chlorine under vacuum	Sched 80 PVC Reinforced fiberglass
Chlorine water lines	Injector to diffuser	Chlorine solution	Sched 80 PVC

Design of system to store and feed sodium hypochlorite

In recent years, large metropolitan areas have been more frequently considering the use of hypochlorite rather than chlorine gas because of an increased emphasis on safety where large amounts of gas are stored. If cost were the only criterion, liquid chlorine would always be chosen rather than sodium hypochlorite. Despite the considerable additional cost of hypochlorite over chlorine gas (2 to 4 times), and cumbersome handling problems, in 1967 the City of New York changed from gas to hypochlorite at some wastewater plants, and since 1969, the Metropolitan Sanitary District of Greater Chicago has made increasing use of hypochlorite. Several other cities have followed suit.

Sodium hypochlorite (liquid bleach) is formed by combining chlorine and sodium hydroxide. In some instances, it is made at the site, with both of these products generated electrolytically. In other instances, it is manufactured from chlorine and sodium hydroxide that have been separately shipped to the manufacturing site. The reaction which proceeds in this instance is as follows:

$$2NaOH + Cl_2 \rightarrow NaOCl + NaCl + H_2O \qquad (8.26)$$

Often a slight excess of sodium hydroxide is added to increase the stability of the chlorine in the product. When the hypochlorite is added to water, it hydrolyzes to form hypochlorous acid (HOCl), the same active ingredient which occurs when chlorine gas is used. The hypochlorite reaction slightly increases the hydroxyl ions (pH increase) by the formation of sodium hydroxide, whereas the reaction of chlorine gas with water increases the hydrogen-ion concentration (pH decrease), forming hydrochloric acid. In most waters, these differences are not significant, but when high chlorine doses are used in poorly buffered waters, these effects should be considered. They can be evaluated by calculation or by simple laboratory tests.

In the commercial trade, the concentration of sodium hypochlorite solutions is usually expressed as a percentage. The "trade percent" is actually a measure of weight per unit volume, with 1 percent corresponding to a weight of 10 g of available chlorine per liter. Common household bleach, at a trade concentration of 5.25 percent, has approximately 5.25 g/100 mL or 52.5 g of available chlorine per liter. Swimming pool bleach usually has a trade concentration of 12.5 percent. These are approximate concentrations, and should always be confirmed for a particular shipment by laboratory procedures.

Since increasing the concentration of any salt will lower the freezing point of a solution, the freezing points of various solutions of sodium hypochlorite are a function of their concentrations, with the more dilute concentrations approaching the freezing point of pure water. Figure 8.13 shows the freezing temperature of hypochlorite solutions as a function of concentration in the concentration ranges normally experienced.

The chlorine concentration in hypochlorite solutions is adversely affected by high temperature, by light, by low pH, and by the presence of certain heavy metal cations. Iron, copper, nickel, and cobalt are the most common problem-causing cations. The concentration of the hypochlorite itself also has a major impact on hypochlorite degradation. Table 8.6 shows the half-life of a hypochlorite solution as a function of chlorine concentration and temperature.

When purchasing bulk sodium hypochlorite, purchasing specifications should be used, delineating the acceptable ranges for available chlorine (15 to 17 percent) and pH (11 to 11.2) as well as maximum contaminant limits for iron (2 mg/L) and copper (1 mg/L). Specifications should also require that shipments be free of sediment and other deleterious particulate material. Upon arrival, shipments should be analyzed for the concentration of chlorine, the pH, and the concentration of metal contaminants. The NAS Codex[16] also suggests that the content of trihalomethanes and carbon tetrachloride be limited.

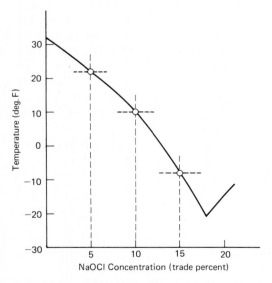

Figure 8.13   Freezing temperatures of hypochlorite solutions.

TABLE 8.6   Influence of Temperature and Strength on Decay of Hypochlorite
Solutions

% Cl$_2$	Half-life			
	100°C	60°C	25°C	15°C
10.0	0.079	3.5	220	800
5.0	0.25	13	790	5000
2.5	0.63	28	1800	—
0.5	2.5	100	6000	—

Materials.   The best material for large-scale sodium hypochlorite storage has not yet been established. Chicago has had satisfactory experience with hand-fabricated fiberglass tanks, and fiberglass-lined concrete tanks have not been entirely successful. PVC-lined carbon steel tanks have been used on occasion. Hypochlorite tanks should be vented, and provision should be made for sampling the contents. The connection to the delivery vehicle should be Hastalloy-C or titanium nipples securely braced to the tank. The fill pipe itself can be PVC–Saran-lined steel or Resistoflex (a Kynar trademark).

Schedule-80 PVC, Kynar, rubber-lined steel, and Saran-lined steel are acceptable materials for hypochlorite piping. The plastics are generally more convenient. Valves should be plug valves made of steel, lined with PVC or polypropylene. Diffusers can also be designed using PVC or Kynar. Because of the high salinity of hypochlorite solutions, these diffusers should be designed for high velocities to ensure mixing throughout the channel cross section. The rate of flow is most commonly controlled by a diaphragm valve. Steel valves lined with PVC, Kynar, hard rubber, or Saran are acceptable.

Feeding

Hypochlorite is fed by gravity systems, pump systems, and educator systems. Gravity systems are preferred because of the simplicity of their design and their reliability. In these installations, the difference in static head between the hypochlorite storage tanks and the point of application is used to provide gravity flow. The flow is then modulated using a flowmeter and the diaphragm valve described earlier. If a sufficient hydraulic gradient does not exist between a storage tank and the point of application, an intermediate constant-head tank can be used. In any instance, a constant-head tank will provide improved flow control.

As long as hypochlorite feed rates are less than 200 gal/h, they can be effectively provided through the use of a positive-displacement diaphragm pump. For larger systems, centrifugal pumps are used, with downstream modulating valves to control the flow rate. These systems have not been found as satisfactory as gravity feed or the use of diaphragm pumps.

Eductor systems use the same principle as chlorine gas injector systems. An eductor is used to draw a vacuum, which pulls the hypochlorite from the storage tank to the point of application. Again, the flow is controlled by a modulating valve.

On-site generation of hypochlorite

Commercial chlorine is generated through the use of an electrolytic cell such as that shown in Fig. 8.14. Two types of cells are commonly used: the mercury cell, originally developed in Austria in 1982, and the dia-

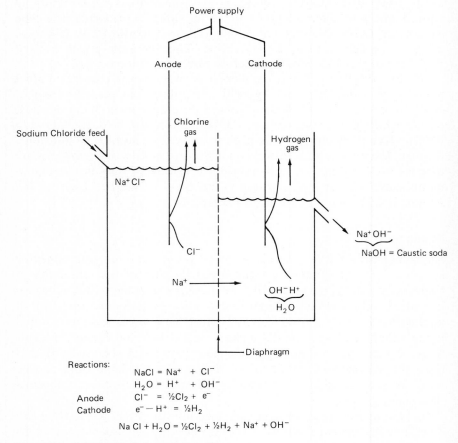

Reactions:

$$NaCl = Na^+ + Cl^-$$
$$H_2O = H^+ + OH^-$$

Anode $\quad Cl^- = \frac{1}{2}Cl_2 + e^-$

Cathode $\quad e^- - H^+ = \frac{1}{2}H_2$

$$Na\,Cl + H_2O = \frac{1}{2}Cl_2 + \frac{1}{2}H_2 + Na^+ + OH^-$$

Figure 8.14 Schematic of electrolytic cell.

phragm cell, first used on a large commercial scale in 1929. Approximately 75 percent of the chlorine in the United States is produced by the diaphragm-type cell. Most of these cells are similar to the Hooker Type S cell shown in Fig. 8.15. This cell uses a graphite anode and a steel-mesh cathode coated with an asbestos diaphragm. Purified salt brine (NaCl) is fed to the cell through an opening in the top. The electrolytic reactions described in Fig. 8.14 take place, with chlorine gas being produced at the anode and hydrogen gas and sodium hydroxide being produced at the cathode. The liquor coming out of the cathode cell typically contains about 11.5 percent sodium hydroxide and 50 percent salt. The original Type S cell produced about 660 lb/day of chlorine. The new Type S-3 cells in current use produce between 600 and 1600 lb/day. Conventional commercial chlorine-generating cells require a great deal of maintenance. The porous asbestos diaphragm which separates the anodes from the cathodes becomes clogged with use and must be replaced every 100 to 200 days. The clogging is usually indicated by higher voltages and higher hydrostatic pressures required on the brine feed. For larger installations, the Hooker-type cell may prove satisfactory. Similar commercial-scale diaphragms are a design manufactured by the Diamond Alkali Company, which produces a very low hydrogen content in the chlorine gas; a bipolar cell produced by the Dow Chemical Company, in which as many as 50 cells can be abutted to form a single operating

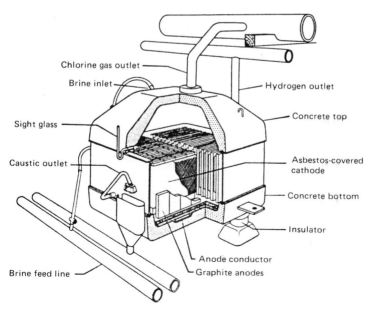

Figure 8.15 Hooker Type S-3A cell. (*Courtesy of OxyTech Systems, Inc.*)

unit; and the Chloromat cell, a design of special interest to the water industry, which utilizes expanded electrodes and is designed to reduce the amount of routine maintenance normally required for larger conventional diaphragm cells. Another cell configuration of interest is the Chloropac cell, which is particularly well suited for sea water. At the present time, not many on-site hypochlorite generation systems are being used at municipal facilities. As a result, any utility seriously considering on-site generation should carefully investigate alternatives and err on the side of conservatism. Most hypochlorite generation systems now in use have been constructed for manufacturers of household bleach swimming pool disinfection. Since these installations are primarily of the manufacturing sort, the level of risk, the level of maintenance, and the level of operator training associated with them may differ from those to which the water treatment industry is accustomed.

In evaluating alternative on-site hypochlorite generation systems, the operating cost of the process, the concentration of the brine produced, the availability of salt of sufficient quality, and necessary conjunctive treatment processes should all be considered. The principal operating costs are the cost of salt, the cost of any on-site salt purification necessary, the cost of power (commercial units typically use between 1.2 and 1.5 kWh/lb), the replacement of diaphragms of membranes and electrodes, and, most importantly, skilled labor.

The concentration of brine is important because more dilute brine concentrations mean that more on-site storage is required. There is considerable variation in the maximum brine concentration which can be produced by the different processes. A commercial hypochlorite generation facility may include facilities for refining salt quality, evaporating and concentrating the product using a tripe evaporator, and filtration. Hence, the simpler municipal installations will ordinarily produce much more dilute brine with a higher NaCl content.

Control of chlorination

Proper design of the control system for chlorination facilities is as important as any other aspect of their design. Methods currently used are manual setting based on flow and periodic or continuous residual measurements; continuous feedforward control based on continuous flow measurements and feedback control based on continuous residual measurements; and compound, closed-loop control based on continuous measurements of both flow and chlorine residual. Each of these methods is illustrated in Fig. 8.16. Details of control-signal manipulation are not shown.

The manual control method is limited by the diligence of the operator. If either the flow or the chlorine residual change, the operator

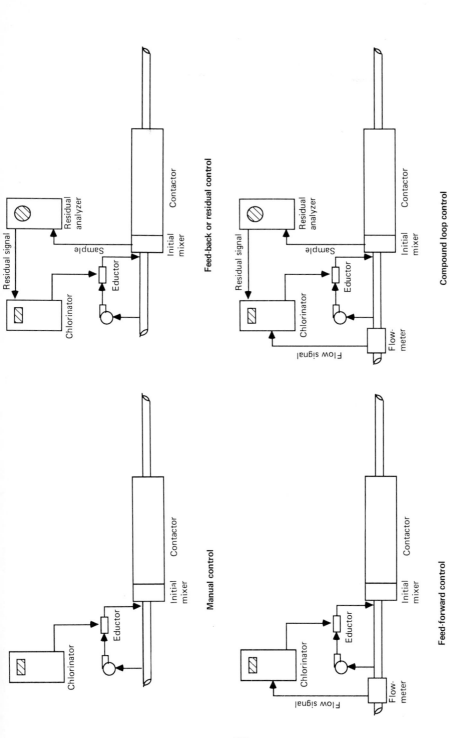

Manual control

Feed-back or residual control

Feed-forward control

Compound loop control

Figure 8.16 Alternative chlorination control methods.

229

must make adjustments; consequently, this method gives a wide range of performance. The feedforward method is a significant improvement because the flow has been eliminated as a variable provided the operator is diligent in maintaining the control system. For water supplies where chlorine demand is very stable, feedforward control is preferred. Feedback control is theoretically superior to feedforward control because the chlorine residual is being directly used to control chlorine addition. Unfortunately, this is not always the case, because chlorine residual analyses drift off course unless they are regularly maintained. Feedforward control is better than feedback control alone. Whenever chlorine demand is variable, compound-loop control is preferred.

Compound-loop control is sometimes accomplished by controlling the differential vacuum regulator on the chlorinator with the flow signal and setting the chlorine gas-metering orifice with the signal from the residual analyzer. Alternatively, it can be provided by electronically adding both control signals and using the results to control the differential vacuum. The first approach allows the chlorinator to operate over a dynamic range of 200:1, whereas the differential vacuum will only allow a dynamic range (maximum feed/minimum feed) of 20:1. However, in most installations, a dynamic range of 20:1 is satisfactory.

With either feedback or compound-loop control, lag time is one of the principal design parameters. Lag time refers to the time between the moment when the chlorine is added to the effluent and the time when the residual-analyzer signal comes to the chlorinator. Lag time includes the transit time from the point where the chlorine is initially mixed to the sampling point, the transmission time between the sample point and the chlorine residual analyzer (in the sample line), and the analysis time. The analysis time is usually a minor factor. If the lag time is too much longer than the response time of the analyzer, then the level of the chlorine dose will sawtooth. White[4] suggests that the lag time be maintained at an average level of 2 min, with a maximum of 5 min. Low-flow conditions should be considered. The following are some of the most common design errors: poor chlorine sample conditions, analyzer located too far from sampling point, and effluent chlorine dose paced to influent flow.

It should be understood from the beginning that the purpose of the chlorine residual analyzer discussed here is to control the chlorine dose. If continuous monitoring of the chlorine residual following the chlorine contact period is desired, another chlorine residual analyzer is required.

The principal consideration in locating the sampling point for the control analyzer is goodness of mixing. If the sample is taken before adequate mixing has occurred, the result will be erratic readings unsuitable for control. For the majority of initial mixing designs, sampling should be provided immediately downstream of the initial mixing device. Ordinarily, chlorine residuals are stable enough for control measurements after just a few seconds of contact. If no initial mixing device is present, then the sampling point should be far enough downstream to ensure that good mixing has occurred. For turbulent flow, 10 pipe diameters is probably sufficient; however, low-flow conditions should be considered, and if adequate mixing cannot occur in a reasonable period of time, an initial mixing device will be necessary for control purposes. Chlorine residual analyzers should always be located as near as possible to the sampling point, even if special housings are required. Sample lines should be designed for velocities of about 10 ft/s, and the transit time between the sampling point and the residual analyzers should be minimized. Finally, the chlorine dose should always be paced to the flow most representative of the point of addition. A common error in design is an arrangement in which the effluent chlorine dose is paced using influent flow measurements. There are too many events which occur between a plant's influent and its effluent, and such a design often results in an erratic chlorine dose and an unmanageable operating system.

Chlorine residual analysis

Two methods for continuous chlorine residual analysis are currently available: the automatic amperometric titrator, and the ion selective probe. In an automatic amperometric titrator, the cell has an indicating electrode made of copper concentrically mounted around a platinum reference electrode. Water flows into the space between the two, and a potential is imposed between the electrodes, resulting in a current flow which is proportional to the amount of chlorine in the sample. Ordinarily, a pH 4 buffer is used, and the free chlorine is measured. The use of a buffer with excess potassium iodide will cause the unit to titrate the total chlorine residual, while an excess of combined chlorine will interfere with attempts to measure the residual. For details on the operation of these devices, see White. One type of amperometric titrator is shown in Fig. 8.17.

Special considerations for chloramine systems

In designing facilities for combined residual chlorination, the residual ratio of ammonia to chlorine should be considered. White recommends a ratio of 3 parts of chlorine to 1 part of ammonia. A survey of 24 utilities currently using combined residual chlorination revealed Cl_2/NH_3 ratios currently employed ranging from 1 to 4, the median being 3. As the Cl_2/NH_3 ratio gets higher, the cost of the ammonia required to

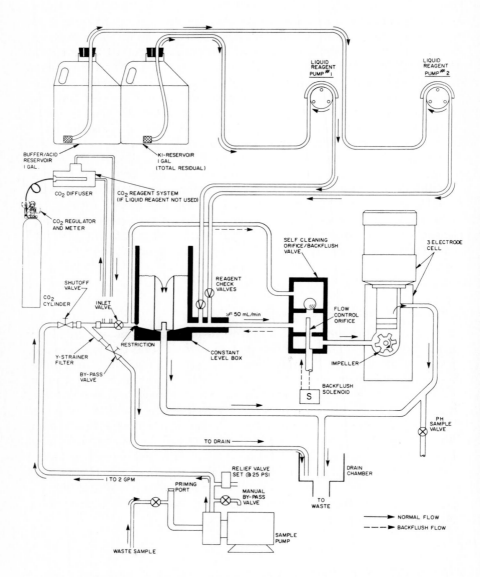

Figure 8.17 Flow diagram of amperometric chlorine residual analyzer. (*Courtesy of Wallace and Tiernan Division of Pennwalt Corp.*)

maintain a given level of chlorine residual increases. For alkaline pHs, the maximum long-term combined residual will be at a ratio of less than 5; for more acid pHs, a higher ratio applies (see Fig. 8.2). Above this dose, substantial amounts of combined chlorine will be lost to nitrogen and nitrate ions. Chlorinous odors are also observed at ratios above approximately 4. Very low water ammonia ratios risk excessive corrosion of copper and brass elements of the distribution system.

Between 1930 and 1940, a large number of plants installed facilities for using combined chlorine residuals. An AWWA survey of 36 states in 1940 showed that 2541 supplies treated their water supply with chlorine and 407 used combined chlorine residuals. Thus, at its peak, combined residual chlorine was used in about one out of every seven water supplies. Following this, the discovery of break-point chlorination, the difficulty of obtaining ammonia during World War II, and pressure from public health officials to use a more effective free chlorine residual caused combined residual chlorination to decrease in popularity. Recently, however, interest in combined residual chlorination has again increased because combined residuals do not react with the natural aquatic humus present in water to form trihalomethanes (THM). In most instances the use of a combined chlorine residual is the most inexpensive way to limit THM formation.

The general design of chlorination facilities is discussed in the section, "Free Residual Chlorination." The design of systems for combined residual chlorination requires knowledge of the design of ammonia systems as well as chlorination systems. Ammonia is available on the commercial market in three useful forms: anhydrous ammonia, aqueous ammonia, and ammonia sulfate. Aqueous and anhydrous ammonia are the forms most commonly used. Anhydrous ammonia is available as a compressed liquid in containers nearly identical to those used for chlorine. In fact, most of the equipment used in connection with chlorine can also be used with ammonia with minor modification. Chlorinators can be used as ammoniators through the use of a simple modification kit. Ammonia has a heat of vaporization of 328 cal/g and may be fed from the top of the cylinder like chlorine, although not at the same rate. The capacity of a 1-ton ammonia cylinder by the evaporation method is about 84 lb/day. Like chlorine, ammonia liquids should be transported in black iron pipe with cast iron fittings. Although ammonia, like chlorine, can be fed by injector systems it is highly soluble in water, and simple direct-feed ammoniator designs are common. Although an ammonia injector-type system eliminates the need for transporting toxic ammonia under pressure to distant locations in the plant, ammonia is a base, unlike chlorine, and it will soften the water at the point of injection, producing a precipitate of calcium carbonate. This can cause severe scale problems in the injection system. Users of anhydrous ammonia report that carbonate precipitates also build up at diffuser ports when anhydrous ammonia is fed directly. These problems are particularly troublesome in hard water, so ammonia injector systems may require that soft water be used. In any case, the anhydrous ammonia delivered should be filtered to remove the contaminants that are often found in this product.

Often ammonia is fed through stainless steel diffusers designed with a significant back pressure. The holes in ammonia diffusers of this type should be ⅛ in or larger. Diffusers should be carefully laid on a horizontal grade, because at low doses and low plant flows, poor distribution will result if variations of hydrostatic pressure occur. Successful designs feed ammonia by gravity, drawing liquid ammonia from the bottom of the storage vessel through a flowmeter and regulating valve to the point of injection. The vapor pressure from the liquid ammonia is the prime mover in this instance. Metering pumps are sometimes used to improve dosage control. Generally, the ammonia dosage is not critical, and a manual or flow-pace control system is satisfactory. The ideal control system would permit a feed rate proportional to the product of the flow and the chlorine residual.

Aqueous ammonia is delivered in solutions that are 33 percent ammonia by weight. Aqueous ammonia is usually fed via a diaphragm metering pump (Hypalon or Teflon surfaces) and through PVC lines. Iron pipe is also acceptable. In concentrated form, ammonia reacts chemically with copper. Consequently, under no circumstances should any brass, bronze, or other copper alloy be used in any ammonia feed system. The vapors above the solution in an aqueous ammonia tank are extremely potent. Therefore, provision should be made for disposing of the displaced vapors in the tank in a safe manner, such as transfer back to the delivery vehicle, when the storage tank is being refilled.

Pressure release valves on these tanks should pass through a water-type scrubber before going to the atmosphere. When ordering aqueous ammonia, debris-free chemical should be specified, since aqueous ammonia is sometimes delivered with considerable debris present; alternatively, facilities may be installed to strain undesirable debris from the product before it is used. Clogging with precipitated calcium carbonate is often reported to be a problem with diffusers using aqueous ammonia. Softening of the carrier water may be necessary to avoid excessive maintenance.

Solid ammonium sulfate is usually fed into a simple mixing tank using a gravity or volumetric feeder. Once mixed, the solution can be transported using the same methods described earlier for aqueous ammonia. If the local water is hard, scaling problems may occur, and softening of this carrier water should be considered.

Design of systems to store and feed chlorine dioxide

Chlorine dioxide cannot be stored once it is generated because it is not safe. Numerous stimulants may cause the pure gas to explode, including an increase in temperature, exposure to light, changes in pressure, and exposure to organic contaminants. As a result, chlorine dioxide is generally generated on-site.

With the chlorine-chlorite process, the reaction to produce chlorine dioxide is generally carried out in a reaction chamber containing some packing material. The reactants are introduced into the reaction chamber, where chlorine dioxide is formed. The chlorine dioxide is educted from the reactor and mixed with water, and the chlorine dioxide solution exits from the top. The progress of the reaction can be subjectively judged by the development of a green color in the liquid exiting from the generator. The exiting mixture is piped to a diffuser. Most chlorine dioxide installations in U.S. water treatment plants were installed to deal with taste and odor problems and employ the chlorine-chlorite method. The presence of chlorine in the chlorine dioxide was not an issue. As a result of recent advances in chlorine dioxide generator technology, several manufacturers now supply equipment that provides a high yield of chlorine dioxide without excess chlorine in the final product. Figure 8.18 is a sketch of the overall process design for each of the systems discussed above. When selecting alternative equipment for adding chlorine dioxide, careful consideration should be given to the dynamic range of the chemical dose available. Some chlorine dioxide systems are not well suited to water treatment plants where the required dose can vary a great deal.

Sodium chlorite (the main chlorine dioxide precursor used in the water industry) is available as a solid, orange-colored powder which is about 80 percent $NaClO_2$ by weight and in the form of liquid solutions which are 25 to 32 percent $NaClO_2$ by weight. If granular sodium chlorite is used, it should be stored in a separate building equipped with sloped floors, drains, and facilities for hosing down spills. The building should be constructed of materials with maximum fire resistance, and it should be designed with the material's explosive potential in mind. If liquid solutions are chosen, the 25 percent solutions are available immediately upon request from a variety of suppliers.

Design of Systems to Generate, Store, and Feed Ozone

Ozone generation

Figure 8.19 shows the basic configuration of an ozone generator. An electromotive force (voltage) is impressed across two electrodes with a

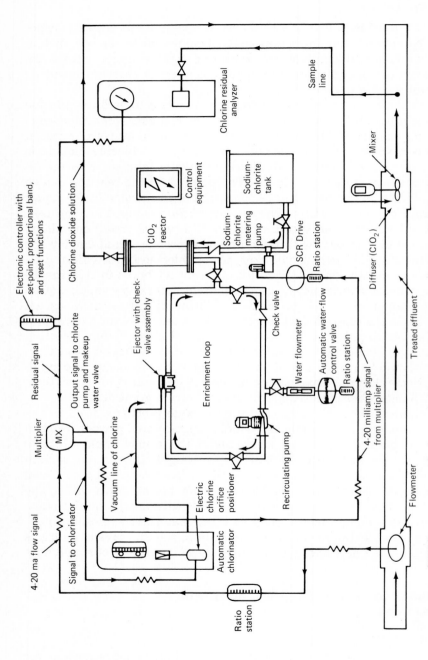

Figure 8.18 CIFEC automatic residual control chlorine dioxide system. (*Courtesy CIFEC, Paris, France.*)

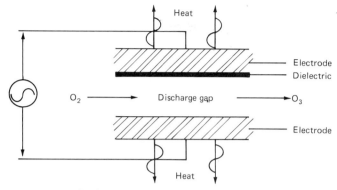

Figure 8.19 Basic ozonator configuration. (*Source: H. Rosen, "Ozone Generation and Its Relationship to the Economical Application of Ozone in Wastewater Treatment," in F. L. Evans III (ed.), Ozone in Water and Wastewater Treatment, Ann Arbor Science Publishers, Ann Arbor, Mich., 1972.*)

dielectric and discharge gap in between. Air is passed through corona discharge between the two electrodes, and some of the oxygen in the air is converted to the ozone allotrope. Design principles suggest that the voltage necessary to produce ozone is a function of the product of the gap pressure and the gap width.

$$V = K_1 pg \tag{8.27}$$

where V = necessary voltage
 p = gap pressure
 g = gap width

In a similar sense, the yield of the ozonator is directly proportional to the frequency, the dielectric constant, and the square of the voltage applied and inversely proportional to the thickness of the dielectric.

$$\text{Yield} = K_2 (feV^2)/d \tag{8.28}$$

where f = frequency
 V = voltage
 e = dielectric constant
 d = thickness of dielectric

This equation suggests some problems that are inherent in the design of ozonators. It suggests that the dielectric be made as thin as possible. Very thin dielectrics are, however, more susceptible to failure. In the same sense, the yield is related to the square of the voltage, indicating that high voltages are very desirable. On the other hand, dielectric failure also occurs when high voltages are used. At the present time, it would appear that the most promising method for increasing ozonator capacity is to increase the frequency of the current used. For a long time problems of electrical design prevented this, but a number of ozone system manufacturers now offer high-frequency equipment. Other design improvements involve better-quality dielectrics and better methods of removing heat from the ozone cell. Three basic types of ozone-generating systems are now in use: the Otto plate, the conventional horizontal tube, and the Lowther plate. Each of these designs is briefly sketched in Fig. 8.20. The Otto plate was designed in 1905. Although rather inefficient, this design is still being used in parts of western Europe. Its principal disadvantages are that it is inefficient and that only low pressures can be used within the unit. High pressures are desirable so that the ozone can be bubbled through deep ozone contact chambers.

The tube-type generator is composed of a number of tubes of the configuration shown in Fig. 8.21. The outer electrodes are typically stainless steel tubes fitted into a large vessel and surrounded by cooling water. A concentric glass tube with a conducting coating on the inside is placed inside each stainless steel tube. A potential is applied between the inside coating of the glass tube and the outside steel tube, and air or oxygen is then passed through the gap in between. Variations of this tube-type design are by far the most common ozone generators in use today.

Discounting improvements in the tube-type generator, the Lowther plate unit is the most recent development. Whereas the other two units are usually water-cooled, this unit is air-cooled. It is made up of a gas-tight arrangement of an aluminum heat dissipator, a steel electrode coated with a ceramic dielectric, a silicone-rubber spacer, and a second ceramic-coated steel electrode with inlet and outlet. The silicone-rubber spacer sets the width of the discharge gap. Several of these units can be pressed together and manifolded to increase generator production.

Materials

In designing systems for ozonation, the highly aggressive character of ozone should be kept in mind. All rubber, most plastics, neoprene, EPDM, and aluminum are unacceptable materials for use with ozone. The only acceptable materials are $3/16$-in stainless steel, 305 stainless steel, glass, Hypalon, Teflon, and concrete. There is some dispute about the usefulness of Type 1 PVC. Manufacturers have often recommended Type 1 PVC, but its quality does not seem to be uniform from place to place, and incidents of PVC failure occur regularly.

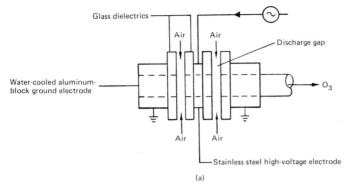

Air   Air

Discharge gap

Glass dielectrics

Water-cooled aluminum-
block ground electrode

O₃

Air   Air

Stainless steel high-voltage electrode

(a)

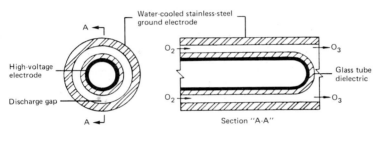

Water-cooled stainless-steel
ground electrode

High-voltage
electrode

Discharge gap

Glass tube
dielectric

O₂   O₃

O₂   O₃

Section "A-A"

(b)

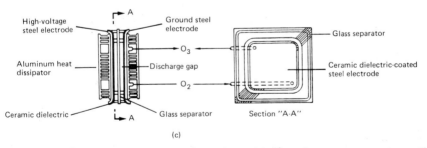

High-voltage
steel electrode

Ground steel
electrode

Glass separator

Aluminum heat
dissipator

Discharge gap

Ceramic dielectric-coated
steel electrode

Ceramic dielectric

Glass separator

Section "A-A"

O₃

O₂

(c)

Figure 8.20 Alternative ozonator configurations. (*a*) Otto plate-type generator unit; (*b*) tube-type generator unit; (*c*) Lowther plate generator unit. (*Source: H. Rosen, "Ozone Generation and Its Relationship to the Economical Application of Ozone in Wastewater Treatment," in F. L. Evans III (ed.), Ozone in Water and Wastewater Treatment, Ann Arbor Science Publishers, Ann Arbor, Mich., 1972.*)

Contactor configurations

Four types of ozone contactor configurations are commonly used. They are shown in Figs. 8.22 through 8.25. A common feature of all these configurations is the use of a deep contact basin to allow maximum opportunity for ozone dissolution. The oldest configuration is the Otto

Figure 8.21 Typical tube-type generators at Choisy Le Roy, France. (*Courtesy of Trailigaz Ozone of America, Inc.*)

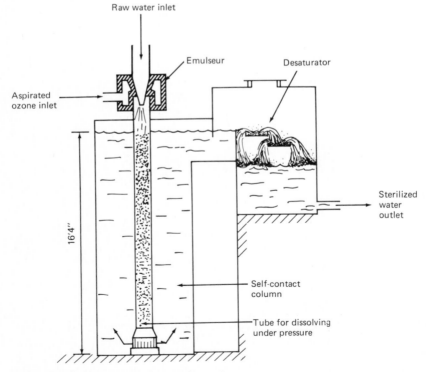

Figure 8.22 The Otto contactor configuration.

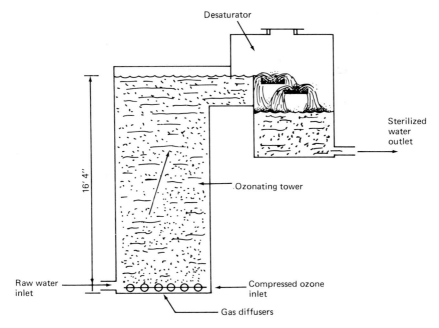

Figure 8.23   The concurrent contactor configuration.

configuration, shown in Fig. 8.22, which involves aspirating the ozone in the raw-water inlet and carrying the mixture to the bottom of a deep tank where the bubbles and water flow concurrently. The principal shortcoming of this design is that most effective aspirator designs cannot create sufficiently small bubbles over a wide enough range of ozone doses and influent flow rates.

The concurrent configuration shown in Fig. 8.23 is also very common in Europe. Because the ozone is introduced into the contact chamber through gas diffusers, this design does not suffer from flow and dose limitations. However, its concurrent design does not result in maximum ozone utilization and contact efficiency.

The countercurrent configuration shown in Fig. 8.24 is probably the most common basic configuration now in use. Quite often more than one chamber is used in a series. In this instance, the most highly treated water sees the highest concentration of ozone and is presumably polished to the greatest degree possible. At the same time, the ozone exiting the chamber sees raw water of the poorest quality, and under these conditions the maximum amount of ozone is utilized.

The stirred-tank configuration shown in Fig. 8.25 is a good design from the standpoint of chemical engineering principles, as it should ensure maximum gas transfer and maximum bubble hold time. In wa-

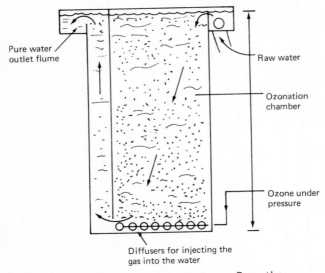

Pure water
outlet flume

Raw water

Ozonation
chamber

Ozone under
pressure

Diffusers for injecting the
gas into the water

Figure 8.24 The countercurrent contactor configuration.

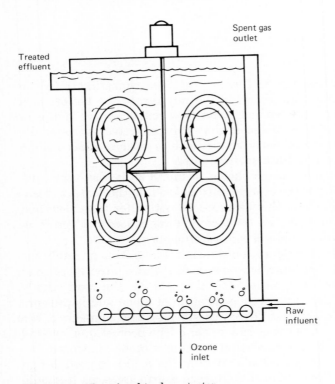

Spent gas
outlet

Treated
effluent

Raw
influent

Ozone
inlet

Figure 8.25 The stirred-tank contactor.

ter treatment, however, the efficiency of these units is not well established, since few field installations exist at the present time. All underwater metal parts in ozone contact chambers should be made from stainless steel.

Off-gas disposal

One of the principal design problems in ozone contact systems is the disposal of off-gases from ozone contactors. This has not yet been satisfactorily solved. Assuming that ozone contactors utilize from 90 to 100 percent of the ozone which is applied, the air exiting from the contactor may have ozone concentrations as high as 0.1 percent by volume. This compares with a threshold odor level of 0.05 ppm for ozone and an 8-h OSHA standard of 0.1 ppm. To date, regulations have not been established on the levels of ozone which may be discharged to the atmosphere, but there is no question that large volumes of air containing 0.1 percent ozone cannot be casually discharged. Five principal methods of off-gas disposal may be considered: (1) reinjection, (2) heating to cause autodecomposition, (3) chemical reduction with a reducing agent, (4) catalytic reduction with a metal oxide, and (5) dilution.

Reinjection generally involves the construction of two ozone contact basins. The fresh ozone is introduced into the downstream contact basin, then the off-gases are repumped and reinjected into the upstream contact basin. Given the efficiencies of ozone consumption in each contact stage and the loss of ozone during the repumping process, the ozone residual in the air exiting from the reinjection stage can be as low as 0.001 percent, or 10 ppm. Thus, reinjection alone does not completely solve the problem. Rather, reinjection must be used in tandem with some of the other techniques described.

Chemical reduction is another method for removing ozone residuals from off-gases. The chemical reduction could be accomplished by passing the off-gases from the ozone contact chamber in countercurrent flow with an ozone-specific reducing agent in a scrubber much like those used for removing fumes from industrial off-gases. The key to this method is the selection of an inexpensive reducing agent which is not also oxidized by the oxygen present in the air. No uniformly satisfactory reducing agent has been developed to date.

Ozone rapidly dissipates when it is heated. Consequently, in some designs the ozone contactor off-gases are heated to a temperature at which decomposition of the ozone is nearly instantaneous. Temperatures as high as 250°C have sometimes been indicated. The obvious disadvantage of this method is the amount of heat required. In some European designs, the hot air exiting from the ozone decomposer is recycled to a preheater to warm the air which is about to enter the decomposer. This reduces energy requirements, but increases capital costs.

Catalytic reduction involves presenting the ozone off-gases with a surface which catalyzes the decomposition of ozone to elemental oxygen. A number of oxide surfaces, including iron oxide, have been demonstrated to accomplish this purpose. At the present time, however, most successful ozone decomposers are of a proprietary nature, and until more information is available, it is not possible to accurately assess how resistant these devices are to fouling of the catalyst and to long-term destruction by the wet ozone-containing off-gases. On the other hand, these devices are now receiving wide acceptance in European installations.

Dilution is a very simple approach to dealing with the off-gases from ozone contact chambers. A stack is built, and a low-pressure, high-volume fan is used to blend clean air with the air containing residual ozone. If sufficient velocities occur going up the stack, dilution can be accomplished not only by the amount of air that is pumped into the stack to mix with the ozone off-gases but by the amount of air that is entrained in the off-gas plume as it exits from the stack. If the dilution stack is tall enough, additional plume dilution will also be available.

References

1. H. Chick, "An Investigation of the Laws of Disinfection," *Journal of Hygiene,* vol. 8, 1908, p. 92.
2. H. Watson, "A Note of the Variation of the Rate of Disinfection with Change in the Concentration of the Disinfectant," *Journal of Hygiene,* vol. 8, 1908, p. 536.
3. C. Morris, "Aspects of the Quantitative Assessment of Germicidal Efficiency," in J. Johnson (ed.), *Disinfection in Water and Wastewater,* Ann Arbor Science, Ann Arbor, Mich., 1975.
4. G. White, *Handbook of Chlorination,* 2d ed., Van Nostrand, Princeton, N.J., 1986.
5. C. Morris, "The Acid Ionization Constant of HOCl from 5 to 35°C," *Journal of Physical Chemistry,* vol. 70, 1966, p. 3798.
6. B. Saunier, *Kinetics of Breakpoint Chlorination and of Disinfection,* Ph.D. Thesis in Civil Engineering at U.C. Berkeley, 1976.
7. A. Palin, "A Study of the Chloro Derivatives of Ammonia," *Water and Water Engineering,* vol. 54, 1950, pp. 151–200, 248–258.
8. J. Race, *Chlorination of Water,* Wiley, New York, 1918.
9. E. M. Aieta and J. D. Berg, "A Review of Chlorine Dioxide in Drinking Water," *Journal AWWA,* vol. 77, no. 6, 1986, p. 64.
10. M. Kilpatrick et al., "The Decomposition of Ozone in Aqueous Solutions," *Water Research,* vol. 10, 1976, p. 377.
11. W. Stumm, "Chemical Aspects of Water Ozonation," *Schw. Z. Hydrol.,* vol. 18, 1956, p. 201.
12. A. Streng, "Solubility of Ozone in Aqueous Solution," *Journal of Chemical and Engineering Data,* vol. 6, 1961, p. 431.
13. T. Manley and S. Niegowski, "Ozone," in *Encyclopedia of Chemical Technology,* 2d ed., vol. 14, Wiley, New York, 1967, p. 410.
14. J. Hoigne, "Mechanisms, Rates, and Selectivity of Oxidation of Organic Compounds

Initiated by Ozonation of Water," in R. G. Rice and A. Netzer (eds.), *Handbook of Ozone Technology and Applications,* vol. 1, International Ozone Association, 1982, pp. 341–379.
15. R. R. Trussell and M. D. Umphres, "The Formation of Trihalomethanes," *Journal AWWA,* vol. 70, no. 11, 1978, p. 604.
16. *NAS Chemicals Codex,* 2d ed., National Academy of Science, 1985.
17. *Facilities and Operating Procedures for Chlorine Storage,* Pamphlet no. 5, The Chlorine Institute.

Taste and Odor Control

Introduction

Ever since the first person put water to lips, people have been evaluating the purity of the substance by its taste or odor. Still today, even people who are informed about subtle contaminants in drinking water rely upon their own organoleptic sensors to judge its acceptance. It is well known by professionals in the water industry that a water can be unhealthy yet still taste and smell good, but sophisticated analyses are necessary to detect those unhealthy contaminants. Nevertheless, unpleasant taste or odor is a relied-upon indicator to the water supplier that the product has been tainted and, in fact, may present an acute toxicity problem, depending upon the cause.

For these reasons, the industry has developed ways in which to rank taste and odor type and intensity so that it can measure the effectiveness of control measures and ultimately the acceptability by the customers. Methods described in the twelfth edition of *Standard Methods*[10] presented scientific procedures for determining the intensity of tastes and odors as well as a method of describing, defining, and characterizing the type of odor. After that edition, *Standard Methods* found it impossible to include a section on qualitative descriptions and focused only on the quantitative aspects (e.g., *Standard Methods,* 16th ed.).[29] A threshold odor number (TON) is found by serial dilutions using odor-free water based on the most dilute sample in which an odor can be detected. The detection is very subjective, and some people have been found to be both insensitive to certain odors and extremely sensitive to others. Recently, a method called flavor profile analysis (FPA) was developed to avoid some of the TON deficiencies. The FPA involves a panel of trained people who evaluate the flavor of the water. Flavor here is described as a combination of taste, odor, and feeling. Each of a list of known chemicals is added to water at a known concentration, and the panel evaluates the intensity. These are then considered standards against which the panel can evaluate unknown flavors.

Tastes and odors are caused by a variety of agents, mostly organic in nature. Decayed vegetation, algae, and industrial chemicals are the most common. Other causes can be sulfur, metals, and salts. Basically, the organic problems are likely to affect surface water, whereas the others are more of a groundwater problem.

Palmer (1962)[35] cited relationships between different types of algae and the odors they produce. He grouped the odors into four general categories: "aromatic," "fishy," "musty" or "earthy," and "septic." Seppovaara (1971)[36] indicated concentration thresholds for these algae above which the Helsinki Water Department detected the specific odors mentioned above. Muller et al. (1982)[37] reported examples of various tastes and odors provoked by mass developments of algae (diatoms and green and blue-green algae) for cell concentrations ranging from 500 to 50,000/mL. A 1984 American Water Works Association Research Foundation study (Barnett, 1984)[32] presented the results of a North American Water Utilities survey designed to document and describe algal-induced taste and odor problems and the treatments used to solve them. Blue-green algae, especially *Anabaena,* were identified most often in taste and odor episodes. It is noteworthy that only 24 percent of the respondents identified attached growths of algae during taste and odor episodes, which is understandable because few waterworks personnel have been trained to monitor periphyton in the reservoir. Yet attached algal growths can be significant sources of tastes and odors, especially in lakes, at times when planktonic algal population densities are low (Izaguirre et al., 1983).[38] Tabachek and Yurkowski (1976)[39] reported the production of strong earthy odors by attached algae in Canadian lakes even during the winter. Slater and Blok (1983)[40] reviewed the odorous compounds produced by blue-green algae. Juttner (1983)[41] reviewed the literature and presented data of his own concerning the volatile, odorous excretion products of several families of algae. The earthy/musty tastes and odors create more problems in public water supplies than any of the other types, and the producers of the earthy/musty compounds geosmin and 2-methylisoborneol (MIB) seem to be restricted to certain blue-green algae, notably *Anabaena* and *Oscillatoria,* and certain actinomycetes and possibly some fungi (Wood et al., 1983).[42] Some odorous compounds are rarely found in the immediate environment of living algae, but are released after their death by autolysis or bacterial decomposition of the algae or their metabolites. Certain bacteria, such as *Pseudomonas* species, can convert certain amino acids to hydrogen sulfide, methyl mercaptan, and dimethylpolysulfides (Whitfield and

Freeman, 1983).[43] Muller et al. (1982)[37] pointed out that various amines, which can have fishy odors, originate from the decomposition of amino acids.

For the most part, tastes and odors are not related to a public health threat. Consequently, the U.S. EPA has decided to establish a secondary standard for odor of 3 TON. However, since little is known about the chemical nature of these taste and odor procedures, the health question is still unanswered.

Control of taste and odor (T&O) can be classified into prevention measures and treatment measures, which will be discussed separately.

Prevention Measures

Source of supply

In order to prevent a problem, one must first determine the possible cause. For example, to prevent industrial chemicals, an aggressive stream-monitoring program and routine sanitary survey of the watershed is necessary. Results of these surveys need to be used to take action against those industries creating the problem. Efforts of this type are tedious, but results can be very rewarding.

Impounded surface supplies are more subject to biological problems than are flowing streams. However, when a flowing river becomes relatively quiescent like a lake or reservoir during a drought, it is possible that more biological sources of off flavor may come to bear (Burlingame et al., 1986).[44] The most common are algal blooms and thermal stratification. Algae in themselves can cause taste and odors, and the chemical products of algae control can likewise create problems. Thermal stratification is generally only a problem in deep reservoirs where cold water stays at the bottom, causing stagnant conditions. The lack of oxygen enhances biological decay of bottom sediment containing vegetation and metals. When this thermocline is disturbed by changing water temperatures, those decayed products are brought upward into the water intake.

Preventive measures are directly related to the causes. For algae control, limiting the sources of nutrients (nitrogen, phosphorus, and carbon) can limit algal growths. Once algae develop, application of an algicide, like copper sulfate, can be effective (although the killing of algae sometimes results in taste and odor also, as other organics are produced). Where attached algal growths exist, small crystals of copper sulfate will tend to dissolve before sinking to the bottom. Larger chunks or granules heavy enough to sink rapidly to the bottom in water 30 ft (9 m) deep have been effectively used for control of attached growths (McGuire et al., 1984).[30] Wholesale broadcasting of copper sulfate may not be effective and may be harmful to other biological forms. Divers or other sampling techniques may prove valuable in identifying target application areas. At the Metropolitan Water District of Southern California, copper sulfate treatment is initiated when 5 ng/L or more of 2-methylisoborneol (MIB) is detected 1 ft (0.3 m) above algal growths on reservoir bottoms (Means and McGuire, 1986).[31] This action helps to prevent the level of MIB from reaching 10 ng/L in the water column, a level which has resulted in considerable consumer complaints. In alkaline waters, it may be necessary to add citric acid to prevent complexing of the copper (Barnett, 1984).[32]

Keeping the proper biological balance using fishlike alewife can prevent algal blooms. Narayan and Nunez[11] reported a successful biological control method using one of the *Bacillus* strains of bacteria to biodegrade geosmin, an organic taste- and odor-producing chemical. Adequate control measures for biological processes have not been developed, and consequently those processes have not been used. Especially important is the fact that a local health department would probably not allow the introduction of bacteria to a reservoir without knowing the full ecological implications.

Installing a perforated pipe around a reservoir bottom at the deepest section and pumping in just enough air to cause uplift at the thermal interface has been shown to be a quite effective and very low cost method of preventing a thermocline in deep reservoirs. When done continuously, this small air introduction will prevent a thermocline from developing and will increase the dissolved oxygen content of the water, which further prevents septic conditions. Large volumes of water can be moved in a relatively short time, but without creating turbulence. For example, in a 15-ft-deep reservoir, 20 cfm of air distributed over 1000 ft of tubing can lift 86 mgd. In deeper lakes, continuous air feed has moved water miles away from the aeration area. See Chap. 4, "Aeration," for more design details.

Many utilities, however, have found odor-producing algae and their by-products restricted to the water above the thermocline. If enough dissolved oxygen is present to prevent the formation of hydrogen sulfide and other malodorants, water from below the thermocline can be used, avoiding taste and odor problems found above the thermocline (Barnett et al., 1983; McGuire et al., 1981).[33,34] In fact, the use of microaeration to maintain a reasonable level of dissolved oxygen below the thermocline without disrupting the thermocline can be successfully applied (Barnett et al., 1983).[33]

Distribution system

Yes, taste and odor problems can originate in the distribution system. Iron and copper dissolving into the water, stagnation from a storage vessel, and leaching of a coating constituent are among those that have been experienced.

Prevention, then, entails proper corrosion control to the tap. A nonaggressive water will not dissolve metallic pipe components, some of which can produce distasteful water, others of which are unhealthy. Maintaining the proper pH–mineral balance or using inhibitors can affect this control.

From a taste and odor control viewpoint, storage vessels should be designed with separate inlet and outlet pipes so that flow patterns prevent stagnation and any chemical treatment needed is more successful. This will prevent stale water tastes as well as possible microbiological growths.

Most paints and lining formulations contain aromatic solvents such as toluene and xylene. If these coatings are not properly cured prior to water contact, the solvents can be released into the water, thereby causing severe taste and odor problems (Krasner and Means, 1986).[45] Other paint constituents, such as barium, also can dissolve, creating a potential health hazard.

Treatment Measures

Because little is known about the exact chemical cause of a taste or odor problem, the treatment has historically been more of an art than a science. However, that experience has taught us some general guidelines for successful taste and odor control. There are two categories of effective treatment for taste and odor. One is chemical transformation, and the other is removal.

Chemical transformation is herein defined as the use of a chemical to (1) oxidize the taste- and odor-producing molecule, or (2) cause a chemical substitution. Oxidation is generally accepted as the mechanism which affects taste- and odor-producing compounds, but the chemistry to support this belief is just now being developed. Treatment by addition of chlorine, ozone, potassium permanganate, chlorine dioxide, and hydrogen peroxide is clearly intended to oxidize, and all have been shown to be effective.

Oxidant design criteria

For the most part, design details under this heading involve chemical feeding systems, which are covered in another chapter. However, some recommendations are needed regarding design dosage and application points.

Undoubtedly the most complex oxidant system to design is ozone generation. However, because it is so complex, all ozone suppliers sell systems as a package. The water plant designer need only be concerned with applying the proper ozone dosage in a proper adsorber chamber. Review of recent experiences with ozone treatment has shown that a dosage of 0.5 to 1.5 mg/L applied to a low-turbidity water is necessary to satisfy all ozone demand, including taste and odor, and provide about a 0.1-mg/L residual at the contactor outlet. Ozone doses of 2.5 to 2.7 mg/L, with a 10-min contact time, were required to effectively remove numerous tastes and odors at Lyonnaise des Eaux (Suffet et al., 1986).[46] Fishy tastes and odors were completely removed; however, fruity odors (such as decanal) were produced during ozonation.

Ozone should be applied through a porous diffuser at a pressure of about 15 psig into the bottom of a contact chamber which provides 5 to 10 min contact time. The excess ozone emanating from the water surface should be recovered and reabsorbed rather than discharged to the atmosphere. Ozone can be generated by electrical excitation of oxygen using atmospheric dried air or pure oxygen. Generally, dry air is used for drinking-water applications because the higher yield of oxygen is not required. Other oxidants, such as chlorine, chlorine dioxide, potassium permanganate, and hydrogen peroxide, can be fed with relative ease. Approximate design doses for these should be a maximum of 5 ppm. When planning a chlorine, chlorine dioxide, or hydrogen peroxide system, allow flexibility to feed the chemical at either the pre- or postfiltration point. Potassium permanganate must be fed only as a prefiltration chemical because of its inherent purple color.

Very little experience has been gathered on hydrogen peroxide, perhaps because no commercial product is yet approved as a drinking-water additive. Chlorine, potassium permanganate, and chlorine dioxide have been extensively used for taste and odor control, even more so than ozone in this country. Schull[15] reported great success with use of potassium permanganate in 1962, reducing TON from 30 to 3 using 0.75 ppm in conjunction with 3 ppm powdered carbon.

Des Moines, Iowa, related success a few years later, as TON was reduced from 35 to 5 with 1.5 ppm potassium permanganate and 5 ppm powdered carbon.[16]

Some years later, it was shown by Popalsky,[17] using a gas chromatograph, that potassium permanganate was actually creating an odor-producing chemical by oxidation of some naturally occurring organic compound. Substituting powdered carbon at 10 ppm for the 4 ppm potassium permanganate avoided the undesirable production and still maintained control of other taste- and odor-producing chemicals.

Chlorine dioxide, like ozone, is a very unstable oxidant and must be generated on site from sodium chlorite. There are a few methods available for this purpose: (1) chlorine solution–sodium chlorite solution, (2) acid solution–sodium chlorite solution, and (3) chlorine gas–sodium chlorite solution. The first process is about 80 percent efficient and requires excess chlorine, which can result in trihalomethane (THM) formation. The second process is likewise 80 percent efficient, but avoids THM development. The third is 95 percent efficient and does not require excess chlorine, so THM development is avoided. Some by-products are known to be unhealthy, namely chlorite ion and chlorate ion. Therefore, the EPA has limited the total of those two ions plus chlorine dioxide residual to 1 ppm.

Chlorine dioxide has been used for this purpose for decades. Bean[12] reported greater success in 1957; however, he also experienced an aftertaste when fed in excess. This aftertaste, described as kerosene-like, was also experienced by McCarthy in 1944.[13] The use of chlorine dioxide has also been shown to eliminate chlorinous taste and odors where high free chlorine residual was practiced.

Chlorination systems are discussed in Chap. 8. Wajon et al. (1985)[47] found swampy odors in western Australian distribution systems as a result of the presence of dimethylpolysulfides. The use of 2 mg/L free chlorine with 1-h contact time effectively reduced these odors. Some California utilities who switched their primary disinfectant to chloramines for trihalomethane (THM) control encountered fishy/swampy taste and odor problems (Beard et al., 1984; Krasner et al., 1986).[48,49] Certain odorous compounds released by certain microorganisms appear to be ineffectively oxidized by chloramines. Treatment was accomplished by prechlorination/postammoniation, with sufficient free chlorine dose and contact time to properly oxidize odors prior to ammonia addition. Certain fishy/swampy odors required 2 mg/L free chlorine with 1-h contact time to control the odors, as in Australia. Where background ammonia is present, break-point chlorination may be required to handle off-odors. Unfortunately, THMs will be produced during the free chlorine contact time. In designing a treatment plant for chloramine disinfection, the ability to add free chlorine or some other preoxidant for taste and odor control should be included.

Unfortunately, none of these oxidants are effective in reducing earthy/musty odors resulting from geosmin or MIB (Lalezary et al., 1986).[50]

All these oxidants will react with a variety of other water constituents, such as iron, manganese, and other organics, which will compete for the oxidants. Therefore, it is best to test each water for the oxidant demand and base the design of the feeding system on that demand test. It is also best to consider oxidation only partially successful for taste and odor control. Other chemicals are best adsorbed, so both processes should be employed at a plant.

Adsorption design criteria

Two adsorption methods are worthy of discussion here: powdered activated carbon (PAC) and granular activated carbon (GAC). Both obviously remove taste- and odor-producing substances by the same chemistry; however, there are vast differences in efficiency and costs, as well as application method. Since adsorption is the process of physical removal of dissolved organic molecules by trapping these molecules in the pores within the activated carbon particle, it stands to reason that carbon has a definite life which expires when saturated. It can be rightfully concluded that dose and contact time are directly related to removal efficiency. There are other factors which can influence efficiency, such as competition, molecular size, and carbon pore size distribution, to name a few. However, for designing a water treatment facility to remove taste and odor (rather than a specific organic contaminant), these factors need not be determined. Operational experience can dictate the need to further specify the exact type of carbon for the specific organic compounds present.

Powdered activated carbon. This material is made from a variety of raw materials, the most common being tree bark, coal, and lignite. The material is powdered because it is fed to the water as a slurry and is intended to slowly settle, thereby allowing sufficient contact time to adsorb. It is supplied as a dry powder, and can be stored either dry or in a slurry. Slurry storage is the recommended method for larger installations to eliminate handling of bags. If slurry storage is selected, then the carbon can be received in bulk trucks or railcars, mixed in a concentration of 0.5 to 1.0 lb/gal to reduce settling (over 1.0 it becomes nonfluid and impossible to handle), and constantly mixed. An air sparge system in the bottom of the concrete slurry storage vessel will significantly aid in wetting the powder. Once wetted, the slurry can be pumped at a proportional rate with periodic water flushing to prevent caking in the feed lines (see Chap. 13).

The limiting factor on the use of PAC is the carryover of particles to the filters at high feed rates. Certainly the settling of these particles can be enhanced by improved coagulation, but a general guideline to use for design purposes is to limit feed rates to 200 lb per million gallons. Lalezary et al. (1985)[51] found that the use of 20 mg/L PAC required the use of 15 mg/L alum and 2 mg/L cationic polyelectrolyte to prevent filter breakthrough. The feed system should also provide multiple application points, which can improve efficiency. Recommended points are (1) inlet to mixing chamber, (2) inlet to flocculator, (3) inlet to sedimentation basin, and (4) outlet from sedimentation basin. Only on rare occasions has it been necessary to feed PAC to the filter inlet because that practice can readily result in filter breakthrough. However, under a taste and odor emergency, one might resort to that method.

Ancient civilizations used charcoal to freshen their water, so carbon has been used for water treatment for thousands of years. More recently, there have been hundreds of articles written on the benefits of activated carbon. Activation produces a carbon particle containing many macro- and micropores into which a chemical can be adsorbed.

Ettinger and Middleton[20] found powdered activated carbon to be most effective, requiring normally only a few ppm, but sometimes as much as 100 ppm. While adsorption takes place almost instantly, contact time of 30 min can facilitate better adsorption efficiency.

Sigworth[21] reported better success when PAC was applied ahead of chlorine, because the chlorine could react with some organic material prior to adsorption. The classical chlorine-phenol reaction to form the distasteful chlorophenol is an example. If PAC is added first, it will remove phenol from the water and prevent the chlorine from reacting with it. Another critical parameter is that chlorine and PAC are not added simultaneously. Chlorine can oxidize the carbon surface and reduce PAC adsorption capacity (Lalezary et al., 1985).[51]

An extensive study was conducted in 1967 on various methods of removing the musty odor associated with *Actinomycetes*. Dougherty and Morris[22] reported that only PAC was capable of reducing the TON from 300 down to 2. It required 25 ppm and 30 min to accomplish the task.

Now that it is known that geosmin and MIB are the earthy/musty odorants produced by certain *Actinomycetes* and blue-green algae, more rigorous studies of PAC treatment have been made. Burlingame et al. (1986)[44] used PAC doses from 6 to 42 mg/L to control geosmin. The removal varied from 43 to 73 percent as the PAC dose increased. Yagi et al. (1983)[52] reported that MIB and geosmin were significantly reduced with PAC doses of from 10 to 25 mg/L, but that more than 100 mg/L PAC was required to remove 100 mg/L of geosmin.

PAC can be effective for treating general taste and odor producers up to a threshold odor number of about 35. Montiel (1983)[53] reported that PAC was effective for reducing organic odorous compounds, but that up to 200 mg/L may be required to reduce the taste threshold number from 15 to 2. Bartels and Suffet (1986)[54] used 50 mg/L PAC in studies and achieved high removal rates for many compounds. For TON values higher than 35 and for persistent values around 35, it is necessary, and probably more cost effective, to use granular carbon filters, as Flentje and Hager found in the early 1960s.[23]

Granular activated carbon.   The most common raw materials used for the manufacture of GAC are bituminous coal and lignite. Other more specialty carbons (nonwater grade) are made from coconut shells, walnut shells, peach pits, and the like. GAC is placed into a contactor, and water is filtered through the bed, thereby providing intimate contact for efficient removal of organic matter.

Even though GAC has been used in this country for almost 50 years, the chemistry of taste and odor removal is somewhat unknown. Many scientists still consider it a phenomenon because GAC has such a long life for removal of general taste and odor producers. Much more specific research is being done today to better understand this phenomenon, and therefore to better design GAC systems. Nevertheless, the past experience with it has provided some guidelines.

To begin with, it is helpful to understand how the various carbons are evaluated. Carbon manufacturers have standardized some indices to measure adsorption capacity. Iodine number and molasses are the most widely used, and they refer to the weight of iodine (or molasses) which can be adsorbed by a given weight of carbon under controlled laboratory conditions. The higher the number, the greater the capacity. Even though many GACs have different densities, the indices still provide a good comparison of these materials. For the waterworks professional, however, there is a dilemma. Neither iodine nor molasses is likely to be the problem plaguing the water, so the indices do not relate directly to the taste and odor problem. Lalezary et al. (1985)[51] found that PACs with similar iodine numbers had different adsorption capacities for the odorants geosmin and MIB. Ideally, the carbons should be evaluated on a concentrate of the raw water or water spiked with known odorants, but this is not practical because most problems are sporadic and the compounds causing the odor problem may be unknown. Consequently, many systems have found it necessary to run long-term (1- to 2-year) pilot columns to demonstrate the effectiveness of GAC and to select from a few available products. A pilot study should be designed to allow for several empty-bed contact times (EBCT) from a minimum of 2½ min to 10 min. This can be accomplished by either one bed with four sample taps, or four discrete beds with 2½ min EBCT each.

Occasionally, it is necessary to install GAC without the benefit of any pilot data. On these occasions, the designer can call upon all the past experiences to judge the EBCT and carbon type. As a general rule, 5 min EBCT will provide excellent taste and odor control for a surface stream for a period of 3 to 5 years using either a bituminous or lignite carbon. Several algae conditions and total organic carbon levels above 10 ppm are examples where this general rule does not apply.

Some data show that GAC particle size is important in prolonging adsorption life, as reported by Dostal et al. in 1965.[24] In that study, 20 × 50 mesh GAC lasted twice as long as 8 × 30 mesh. Higher-activity carbon did not have the same effect. Empty-bed contact time of 5 min reduced TON to 5, but to get to the goal of 3, 7½ min EBCT was necessary. Other specific organic chemical data generated by this report also documented the organic chemical removal efficiency of GAC.

Using GAC as a filter and an adsorber with a depth of 24 in GAC at a filtration rate of 2 gpm/ft^2 reduced TON from 140 to 4, Hager and Flentje reported in 1965.[25] As a comparison, GAC as an adsorber only performed just as well at a higher surface loading (5 gpm/ft^2), but required a depth of 10 ft, which increased EBCT.

Hanson[26] found that GAC was the only way to treat lake water and render it palatable to the customer. Replacing 2 ft of sand with GAC provided this control for 3 years at a treatment cost equal to PAC.

GAC can be used solely as an adsorber after filtration (or when no filtration is necessary, such as with groundwater), or as a combined filter-adsorber. Because most of the experience in this country has been with retrofitting GAC into existing treatment plants, it was convenient and less costly to replace some or all of the rapid filter media with the GAC. In those instances the carbon size is selected to match either the anthracite layer of a dual-media filter or the sand in a rapid sand filter. Most carbons exhibit backwashing characteristics similar to those of anthracite, so that conversion is generally easy to make. However, converting sand to GAC necessitates a lower and more controlled backwash rate or the GAC will be washed away. It is also more important for the operator to adjust backwash rate as water temperature changes because of the lower density of GAC. Some carbons have been known to require a backwash rate around 20 gpm/ft^2 to get 25 percent expansion. Consequently, it is imperative that the carbon supplier provide the backwash characteristics to the designer before any decision is made.

Some additional considerations related to GAC as a filter adsorber need to be discussed. Where water quality conditions would result in deposition of manganese or calcium carbonate, GAC should not be used because these inorganic deposits will seal the adsorption sites and render the carbon useless in a matter of months. If the carbon is to be regenerated, it is important to prevent sand from intermixing with the carbon. Ideally, no sand should be used with carbon; however, this is not possible in dual-media filters. Therefore, the effective size of the sand should be approximately one-half that of the carbon.

Carbon will dechlorinate all water passed through it and will usually breed bacteria. Consequently, it is imperative to provide sufficient postchlorination contact time to attain adequate disinfection and disinfectant residual.

If the carbon is to be regenerated repeatedly, then it is probably more practical to use it after filtration as an adsorber only. With this method, the carbon can be more readily removed, without any possibility of sand or inorganic contaminants. Postfiltration adsorbers have the added benefits of (1) providing greater EBCT because the bed can be designed to suit specific needs, and (2) not disturbing the stratification of spent GAC (on top) and virgin GAC (on the bottom) by frequent backwashing, which will improve bed life. In addition, based on work done in European countries, beds more than 3 ft deep preclude sloughing of bacteria. Bacteria actually are encouraged to inhabit the GAC bed, thereby biodegrading organic compounds and removing micronutrients. Consequently, beds should be designed for that 3-ft minimum depth. Provision for backwashing the bed should still be designed, but is likely to be required only on rare occasions.

To facilitate easy removal of the spent carbon, the contactor should be equipped with a bottom-side drain, which can be connected to a water ejector, or with a trough, which can drain by gravity to a storage vessel. More details on such a system can be found in Chap. 13.

Future trends

Taste and odor control is expected to evolve into more of a science than an art. Recent projects have begun to determine the chemical characterization of tastes and odors. As more specific inorganic and organic chemicals in drinking water become regulated because of some potential adverse health effects, most drinking water shall be treated to a greater extent than at present. When this occurs, taste and odor control will probably be a secondary benefit, and will no longer be a separate design consideration. For example, GAC contactors at Regina/Moose Jaw, Saskatchewan, eliminated algae-produced tastes and odors, as well as providing a significant reduction in THMs (Gammie and Giesbrecht, 1986).[55] In Japan, a GAC filter which had been in use for more than a year and had no remaining THM adsorptive capacity was found to still be effective in removing geosmin and MIB (Yagi et al., 1983).[52]

References

1. J. R. McCullough, "Aeration Revitalizes Reservoir," *Water Sewage Works,* June 1974.
2. J. N. Hinde, "Reservoir Mixing and Aeration Systems," *Water and Wastes Engineering,* March 1970.
3. J. A. Merritt, "Ozone for Water and Wastewater Treatment," *Virginia Water Pollution Control Federation Conf.,* April 1980.
4. "Ozone Treatment of Potable Water," *Pollution Science and Technology* Reprint, June 1973.
5. C. A. Blanck, "In-Plant Control of Taste and Odor in the Plains Region of the American Water Works System," *Taste and Odor Seminars* held by Illinois Section of AWWA. 1979.
6. R. H. Moser, "U.S.A. Experience with Granular Activated Carbon Adsorption," *NATO/CCMS Symposium on Adsorption Techniques in Drinking Water Treatment,* May 1979.
7. J. E. Amoore, "The Chemistry and Physiology of Odor Sensitivity," *AWWA WQTC,* Denver, Colo., December 1984.

8. J. C. Mallevialle, C. Anselme, and S. W. Maloney, "Identification of Taste and Odor Compounds in the Drinking Waters of France," *AWWA WQTC*, Denver, Colo., December 1984.

9. I. H. Suffet, G. L. Brock, T. L. Yoye, and S. W. Maloney, "Identification and Treatment of Taste and Odor Producing Compounds," *AWWA WQTC*, Denver, Colo., December 1984.

10. *Standard Methods for the Examination of Water and Wastewater*, 12th ed., American Public Health Association, American Water Works Association, Water Pollution Control Federation, 1965.

11. L. V. Narayan and W. J. Nunez III, "Biological Control: Isolation and Bacterial Oxidation of the Taste and Odor Compound Geosmin," *Journal AWWA*, vol. 66, no. 9, 1974, p. 532.

12. E. L. Bean, "Taste and Odor Control at Philadelphia," *Journal AWWA*, vol. 49, no. 2, 1957, p. 205.

13. J. A. McCarthy, "Chlorine Dioxide for the Treatment of Water Supplies," *Journal of the New England Water Works Association*, vol. 58, 1944.

14. H. W. Augenstein, "Use of Chlorine Dioxide to Disinfect Water Supplies," *Journal AWWA*, vol. 66, no. 12, 1974, p. 716.

15. K. E. Schull, "Operating Experiences at Philadelphia Suburban Treatment Plants," *Journal AWWA*, vol. 54, no. 10, 1962, p. 1232.

16. J. R. Maloney, "Odor Control with Carbon and Permanganate at Des Moines," *Journal AWWA*, vol. 60, no. 10, 1968, p. 1195.

17. J. R. Popalsky and F. W. Pogge, "Detecting and Treating Organic Taste and Odors Compounds in the Missouri River," *Journal AWWA*, vol. 64, no. 8, 1972, p. 505.

18. J. J. Boland and W. E. DeArment, "Potassium Permanganate Removal of Tastes and Odors from Paper Mill Wastes," *Journal AWWA*, vol. 57, no. 11, 1965, p. 1451.

19. AWWA, *The Quest for Pure Water*, 2d ed., American Water Works Association, Denver, Colo., 1981, vol. 1.

20. M. B. Ettinger and F. M. Middleton, "Plant Facilities and Human Factors in Taste and Odor Control," *Journal AWWA*, vol. 48, no. 10, 1956, p. 1265.

21. E. A. Sigworth, "Control of Odor and Taste in Water Supplies," *Journal AWWA*, vol. 49, no. 12, 1957, p. 1507.

22. J. D. Dougherty and R. L. Morris, "Studies on the Removal of Actinomycetes Musty Tastes and Odors in Water Supplies," *Journal AWWA*, vol. 59, no. 10, 1967, p.1230.

23. M. E. Flentje and D. G. Hager, "Reevaluation of Granular Carbon Filters for Taste and Odor Control," *Journal AWWA*, vol. 56, no. 2, 1964, p. 191.

24. K. A. Dostal, R. C. Pierson, D. G. Hager, and G. G. Robeck, "Carbon Bed Design Criteria Study at Nitro, West Virginia," *Journal AWWA*, vol. 57, no. 5, 1965, p. 663.

25. D. G. Hager and M. E. Flentje, "Removal of Organic Contaminants by Granular Carbon Filtration," *Journal AWWA*, vol. 57, no. 11, 1965, p. 1440.

26. R. E. Hanson, "Granular Carbon Filters for Taste and Odor Removal," *Journal AWWA*, vol. 64, no. 3, 1972, p. 176.

27. *Activated Carbon in Drinking Water Technology*, AWWA Research Foundation, Denver, Colo., 1983.

28. S. W. Krasner, M. J. McGuire, and V. B. Ferguson, "Tastes and Odors: The Flavor Profile Method," *Journal AWWA*, vol. 77, no. 3, 1985, p. 34.

29. *Standard Methods for the Examination of Water and Wastewater*, 16th ed., American Public Health Association, American Water Works Association, Water Pollution Control Federation, 1985.

30. M. J. McGuire, R. M. Jones, E. G. Means, G. Izaguirre, and A. E. Preston, "Controlling Attached Blue-Green Algae with Copper Sulfate," *Journal AWWA*, vol. 76, no. 5, 1984, p. 60.

31. E. G. Means and M. J. McGuire, "An Early Warning System for Taste and Odor Control," *Journal AWWA*, vol. 78, no. 3, 1986, p. 77.

32. R. H. Barnett, "Research on Control of Taste and Odor Producing Algae in Surface Reservoirs," *Proc. AWWA WQTC*, Denver, Colo., December 1984.

33. R. H. Barnett, E. L. Reynosa, A. R. Trussel, R. R. Clark, and L. Y. C. Leong, "The Lake Casitas Taste and Odor Investigation," *Proc. AWWA WQTC*, Norfolk, Va., December 1983.

34. M. J. McGuire, S. W. Krasner, C. J. Hwang, and G. Izaguirre, "Closed-Loop Stripping Analysis at the Parts-per-Trillion Level as a Tool for Solving Taste and Odor Problems," *Journal AWWA*, vol. 73, no. 10, 1981, p. 530.

35. C. M. Palmer, "Algae in Water Supplies," U.S. Public Health Service Publication 657, 1962.

36. A. Seppovaara, "The Effect on Fish of the Mass Development of Brackish Water Plankton," *Aqua Fennica*, 1971.

37. H. Muller, F. Juttner, and U. De Haar, *Schadstoffe im Wasser*, Band III: *Algenburtige Schadstoffe*, Bonn, Germany, 1982.

38. G. Izaguirre, C. J. Hwang, S. W. Krasner, and M. J. McGuire, "Production of 2-Methylisoborneol by Two Benthic Cyanophyta," *Water Science and Technology*, vol. 15, no. 6/7, 1983.

39. J. L. Tabachek and M. Yurkowski, "Isolation and Identification of Blue-Green Algae Producing Muddy Odor Metabolites, Geosmin and 2-Methylisoborneol, in Saline Lakes in Manitoba," *Jour. Fish Res. Bd. Can.*, vol. 33, 1976.

40. G. P. Slater and V. C. Blok, "Volatile Compounds of the Cyanophyceae—A Review," *Water Science and Technology*, vol. 15, no. 6/7, 1983.

41. F. Juttner, "Volatile Odorous Excretion Products of Algae and Their Occurrence in the National Aquatic Environment," *Water Science and Technology*, vol. 15, no. 6/7, 1983.

42. S. Wood, S. T. Williams, and W. R. White, "Microbes as a Source of Earthy Flavours in Potable Water—A Review," *International Biodeterioration Bull.*, vol. 19, no. 3/4, 1983.

43. F. B. Whitfield and D. Freeman, "Off-Flavours in Crustaceans Caught in Australian Coastal Waters," *Water Science and Technology*, vol. 15, no. 6/7, 1983.

44. G. A. Burlingame, R. M. Dann, and G. L. Brock, "A Case Study of Geosmin in Philadelphia's Water," *Journal AWWA*, vol. 78, no. 3, 1986, p. 56.

45. S. W. Krasner and E. G. Means, "Returning Recently Covered Reservoirs to Service: Health and Aesthetic Considerations," *Journal AWWA*, vol. 78, no. 3, 1986, p. 94.

46. I. H. Suffet, C. Anselme, and J. Mallevialle, "Removal of Tastes and Odors by Ozonation," *AWWA Annual Conf.*, Denver, Colo., June 1986.

47. J. E. Wajon, R. I. Kagi, and R. Alexander, "The Occurrence and Control of Swampy Odour in the Water Supply of Perth, Western Australia," A report to the Water Authority of Western Australia, 1985.

48. J. D. Beard, J. Borgerding, and M. Lanier, "THM Reduction Experiences," *California–Nevada Section, AWWA Annual Fall Conf.*, Reno, Nev., 1984.

49. S. W. Krasner, S. E. Barrett, M. S. Dale, and C. J. Hwang, "Free Chlorine Versus Monochloramine in Controlling Off-Tastes and Odors in Drinking Water," *Proc. AWWA Annual Conf.*, Denver, Colo., June 1986.

50. S. Lalezary, et al., "Oxidation of Five Earthy-Musty Taste and Odor Compounds," *Journal AWWA*, vol. 78, no. 3, 1986, p. 62.

51. S. Lalezary, S. M. Pirbazari, M. Dale, T. S. Tanaka, and M. J. McGuire, "Pilot-Plant Studies for the Removal of Geosmin and 2-Methylisoborneol by Powdered Activated Carbon," *Proc. AWWA Annual Conf.*, Washington, D.C., June 1985.

52. M. Yagi, M. M. Kajino, U. Matsuo, K. Ashitani, T. Kita, and T. Nakamura, "Odor Problems in Lake Biwa," *Water Science and Technology*, vol. 15, no. 6/7, 1983.

53. A. J. Montiel, "Municipal Drinking Water Treatment Requirements for Taste and Odour Abatement: A Review," *Water Science and Technology*, vol. 15., no. 6/7, 1983.

54. J. H. M. Bartels and I. H. Suffet (eds.), *Taste and Odor in Drinking Water Supplies*, American Water Works Association Research Foundation, 1986.

55. L. Gammie and G. Giesbrecht, "Full-Scale Operation of Granular Activated Carbon Contactors at Regina/Moose Jaw, Saskatchewan," *Proc. AWWA Annual Conf.*, Denver, Colo., June 1986.

Softening

Introduction

The primary purpose of water softening is to reduce the content of dissolved minerals, particularly calcium and magnesium, in order to minimize scale-forming tendencies. Other ions which may produce hardness include iron, manganese, strontium, barium, zinc, and aluminum; however, these ions are generally not present in significant quantities. Softening of hard water can provide additional benefits, such as

- Biological growth control
- Enhancement of use for boiler feed and cooling purposes
- Removal of many trace inorganics
- Some slight degree of trace organics removal

In light of current environmental and energy concerns, evaluation of the advantages of water softening must go beyond consideration of scale-forming tendencies.

Hardness is expressed in terms of the sum of the concentrations of polyvalent ions, the principal ones being calcium and magnesium. This sum can be expressed in several ways, including milliequivalents/liter (for the chemically oriented) or, more commonly, in terms of the equivalent milligrams/liter of calcium carbonate. Another expression, now out of vogue except in some specialized fields, is grains/gallon, where 17.1 mg/L (as $CaCO_3$) is equal to 1 grain/gal.

Total hardness is defined as the sum of the magnesium and calcium hardness. The total hardness can also be differentiated into carbonate and noncarbonate hardness. Carbonate hardness is the portion of the total hardness which is present in the form of bicarbonate salts [$Ca(HCO_3)_2$ and $Mg(HCO_3)_2$] and carbonate compounds ($CaCO_3$ and

$MgCO_3$). Noncarbonate hardness is the portion of that calcium and magnesium that is present as noncarbonate salts, such as calcium sulfate ($CaSO_4$), calcium chloride ($CaCl_2$), magnesium sulfate ($MgSO_4$), and magnesium chloride (MgCl).[1] The sum of the carbonate and the noncarbonate hardness is equal to the total hardness.

Sawyer[2] classified the degree of water hardness as follows:

Hardness	mg/L as $CaCO_3$
Soft	0 to 75
Moderate	75 to 150
Hard	150 to 300
Very hard	Above 300

The degree of hardness accepted for a finished water varies with the consumer or industry served. In 1968, AWWA established a water quality goal for total hardness of 80 to 100 mg/L expressed as calcium carbonate.[3]

It has often been proposed that an ideal water would have a total hardness of 75 to 85 mg/L (as $CaCO_3$) and a magnesium hardness of not more than 40 mg/L to minimize magnesium hydroxide scaling at elevated temperatures, although the actual magnesium concentration that can be present before precipitation of magnesium salt is a function of the pH of the finished water. In recent years, many cities have allowed the hardness in finished water to approach 110 to 150 mg/L to reduce chemical costs and sludge production. The general use of synthetic detergents has reduced the importance of hardness for soap consumption; however, industrial requirements for a higher-quality feed water for high-pressure boilers and cooling towers have generally increased. As industrial waste treatment costs increase, the demand for higher-quality water has increased dramatically in order to maximize the number of cycles before concentration limits are reached and thus reduce blowdown to the sewer. Industries purchasing water from municipal supplies have generally been faced with additional water treatment costs, dependent upon the quality of the municipal supply and the intended plant or process use. The degree of treatment provided to the processed water, therefore, is determined, to some degree, by the user requirements.

The Safe Drinking Water Act, passed in 1974, established several interim primary drinking water regulations (NIPDWRs) for a number of microbiological, organic, and inorganic water supply contaminants. This same law required the EPA to identify treatment technologies to achieve these limits. As an outgrowth of this requirement, considerable research has been published describing contaminant-removal efficiencies for various water treatment technologies.[4] Several amendments to this act have been promulgated, including monitoring requirements for corrosion and sodium.

Water softening, and in particular high-pH lime treatment (pH near 11), has been shown to be effective in removing a number of heavy metals. The removal is due to precipitation of the hydroxides and/or carbonates of those metals or to a combination of solubility-product reactions and concurrent complex formation. Lead, cadmium, silver, barium, trivalent chrome, arsenic ($+5$), and inorganic mercury are removed to a significant degree by softening. Removal of these metals tends to increase with increasing pH.

Barium, for example, is least soluble at pH ~ 10.5 and becomes more soluble at higher pH. This may be due to formation of relatively insoluble $BaCO_3$ up to pH 10.5, and formation of more soluble $Ba(OH)_2$ at higher pH.

Radium 226 and radium 228 are removed by lime softening. Typical removal is around 70 percent. Radium removal increases with hardness removal and pH during softening.[4] The current MCL for radium 226 plus radium 228 is 5 pCi/L, which is much less than the reported solubilities of radium. Although direct precipitation may not be a major mechanism for radium removal, radium may be removed by coprecipitation or adsorption with $CaCO_3$ or $Mg(OH)_2$.

High-pH softening has been shown to disinfect the treated water and to prevent algal growth in the treatment plant.[6,7,8] Because high pH increases the production of trihalomethanes, many plants no longer prechlorinate raw water, relying instead on chlorination just prior to, and/or after, filtration. This change has resulted in problems with algal and slime growths in the settling basins, and to a lesser extent in the filters. These problems are significantly reduced where high-pH softening is used.

Traditionally, the bacteriocidal effect has been attributed to the effect of the pH attained in the softening process, with the higher pH values in excess lime treatment causing greatly enhanced bacterial reductions; however, virus removal has correlated better with $Mg(OH)_2$ and $CaCO_3$ precipitation than with pH. The suggested mechanism for virus removal appears to be enmeshment in a forming precipitate, with removal and perhaps inactivation occurring as a result of precipitate formation. The surface characteristics of the virus at pH values above 10.5 are very suitable for adsorption to and enmeshment in the colloidal precipitate.[9]

The removals are not high enough to preclude the need for other disinfection; rather, they provide a margin of safety, especially for surface-water sources that are subject to contamination.

Certain organic compounds can be removed by lime softening. Generally, higher-molecular-weight, hydrophilic compounds are more easily removed.[10] Up to approximately 30 to 50 percent of THM precursors such as humic and fulvic acids can be removed. The presence of magnesium enhances removal. Volatile organic carbons such as chloroform are poorly removed by lime-soda softening.[11]

Silica and fluoride are also removed with high-pH softening. Silica removal is particularly important when the treated water is used by industry for boiler or cooling-tower makeup. Often hot process lime–soda ash softening is utilized in industrial applications to speed up the softening reactions. Most hardness-forming substances are less soluble in hot water than in cold, and often industrial applications utilize hot water or waste heat recovery.

In recent years, the advantages offered by water softening have been partially offset by the high energy requirement of the process. Lime, the primary chemical used in water softening, requires considerable energy in its production. In some areas of the United States, where lime is abundant, the initial cost of lime is less significant than the high cost of handling and processing the lime sludge. Often communities utilize large storage lagoons to contain this sludge; however, environmental concerns have required many water plants to dispose of the lime sludge in a much more expensive and energy-intensive manner.

Number and Location of Softening Plants

There are currently more than 1000 domestic-use water-softening plants. Ohio has been reported to have one-third of all the municipal water-softening plants in the country.[12] While softening plants are found in most sections of the country, the majority of the large plants are located in the Midwest and in Florida.

Types of Softening Processes

There are presently two major types of softening plants: lime–soda ash and ion-exchange. The primary emphasis of this chapter will be on lime–soda ash softening. Discussion of process variations of the lime–soda ash process will be presented later in this chapter and will include excess-lime treatment, selective calcium removal, and split-flow treatment. Softening can take place in conjunction with iron removal, coagulation for turbidity removal, or both.

Water softening by means of ion exchange will not be discussed in detail in this chapter. There are few large, municipal ion-exchange softening plants, partly for economic reasons, but also because of problems associated with disposing of the brine wastes produced. Addition-

TABLE 10.1   Summary of Domestic-Use Softening Plants

Softening process	Number of plants	Average daily production, mgd	Total daily production, mgd
Softening	353	0.85	299
Coagulation–softening	265	8.50	2246
Softening–iron removal	366	0.95	348
Coagulation–softening–iron removal	45	3.60	162

ally, sodium-cycle ion exchange for potable-water production increases the sodium level in the treated water.

As noted in Table 10.1, many of the larger softening plants are performing both coagulation and softening in the treatment of surface waters. This chapter will address the design of the processes used and special problems associated with the sludges produced in these plants.

Theoretical Review: Chemistry of Water Softening

Lime–soda ash softening

Water softening involves a number of complex and dynamic chemical interactions. The discussion that follows simplifies the chemistry involved, highlighting the predominant reactions that occur.

Lime, the primary chemical used in water softening, is used to neutralize carbon dioxide, to convert bicarbonate to carbonate alkalinity, and to precipitate calcium carbonate and magnesium hydroxide. Quicklime, CaO, is first slaked to produce calcium hydroxide, according to

$$CaO + H_2O = Ca(OH)_2 \tag{10.1}$$

The reactions between calcium hydroxide and carbon dioxide and bicarbonate alkalinity are shown in Eqs. (10.2) and (10.3). The reactions first convert the alkalinity present to carbonate alkalinity, which then precipitates as insoluble calcium carbonate:

$$CO_2 + Ca(OH)_2 = CaCO_3 + H_2O \tag{10.2}$$

$$Ca(HCO_3)_2 + Ca(OH)_2 = 2CaCO_3 + 2H_2O \tag{10.3}$$

The optimum pH to produce minimum soluble calcium is about 10.3, depending upon water temperature, total dissolved solids, and other factors that affect the solubility of inorganic compounds. In precipitating the calcium ion, two moles of calcium carbonate are formed for every mole of calcium ion removed from the water, as shown in Eq. (10.3).

Magnesium hardness, present as magnesium bicarbonate, is removed in a stepwise fashion, as shown in Eqs. (10.4) and (10.5).

$$Mg(HCO_3)_2 + Ca(OH)_2 = CaCO_3 + MgCO_3 + 2H_2O \qquad (10.4)$$

$$MgCO_3 + Ca(OH)_2 = CaCO_3 + Mg(OH)_2 \qquad (10.5)$$

Magnesium hydroxide does not precipitate quantitatively, as suggested by Eq. (10.5), since the solubility of magnesium hydroxide is dependent upon pH. Generally a pH of 11.0 to 11.3 is necessary to reduce the magnesium ion concentration to low values. Unless the initial carbonate alkalinity exceeds the calcium concentration, considerable soluble calcium exists at this elevated pH; thus, the excess hydroxide alkalinity must be converted to carbonate alkalinity in order to produce a water of minimum calcium hardness. This process, generally termed "stabilization" or "recarbonation," requires carbon dioxide addition, as shown in Eq. (10.6).

$$Ca^{++} + 2OH^- + CO_2 = CaCO_3 + H_2O \qquad (10.6)$$

Once calcium carbonate is formed, its properties are such that resolubilization takes place only at a very low rate. To remove noncarbonate hardness—calcium or magnesium hardness present in excess of the alkalinity—soda ash is required. Equations (10.7) and (10.8) illustrate noncarbonate hardness removal.

$$MgSO_4 + Ca(OH)_2 = Mg(OH)_2 + CaSO_4 \qquad (10.7)$$

$$CaSO_4 + Na_2CO_3 = CaCO_3 + Na_2SO_4 \qquad (10.8)$$

No softening occurs in Eq. (10.7), as magnesium hardness is only exchanged for calcium hardness. Soda ash is used in Eq. (10.8) to remove the calcium noncarbonate hardness either originally present or formed as a result of Eq. (10.7).

These equations allow reasonably good approximations of the amounts of lime and soda ash required to soften a water. The lime required to remove carbonate hardness and magnesium can be calculated as shown in Eq. (10.9):

$$
\begin{aligned}
CaO \text{ (lb/mil gal)} = {}& 10.6\, CO_2 \text{ (mg/L)} \\
& + 4.7\, [\text{alkalinity (mg/L)} \\
& + \text{magnesium hardness (mg/L)} + x] \qquad (10.9)
\end{aligned}
$$

where CaO is 100 percent pure, CO_2 is expressed as CO_2, alkalinity is expressed as $CaCO_3$, and x is the required excess hydroxide alkalinity as $CaCO_3$.

The magnesium hardness that is shown is the amount to be removed in softening, and not the amount that is present. The desired excess alkalinity can be determined from the magnesium hydroxide solubility relationship; it is typically in the range of 30 to 70 mg/L, expressed as $CaCO_3$.

The calculation for the soda ash required to remove noncarbonate hardness is shown in Eq. (10.10).

$$Na_2CO_3 \text{ (lb/mil gal)} = 8.8 \text{ [noncarbonate hardness (mg/L)} - x] \quad (10.10)$$

where Na_2CO_3 is 100 percent pure, noncarbonate hardness is expressed as $CaCO_3$, and x is the noncarbonate hardness that is left in the water.

CaO is usually 88 to 95 percent pure; thus, the results must be divided by the actual chemical purity. Since soda ash is essentially pure, no adjustment to the calculation is required. If $Ca(OH)_2$ were used in place of CaO, the required amount of CaO should be adjusted by dividing by $^{56}/_{74}$, the ratio of the molecular weights.

Other softening processes

Caustic soda, NaOH, can be used in place of lime and/or soda ash. Less sludge is produced, and the caustic soda is easier to handle, store, and feed. Caustic soda is generally purchased as a 50 percent aqueous solution. The reactions for softening are shown below:

$$CO_2 + 2NaOH = Na_2CO_3 + H_2O \quad (10.11)$$

$$Ca(HCO_3)_2 + 2NaOH = CaCO_3 + Na_2CO_3 + 2H_2O \quad (10.12)$$

$$Mg(HCO_3)_2 + 2NaOH = Mg(OH)_2 + 2Na_2CO_3 + 2H_2O \quad (10.13)$$

$$MgSO_4 + 2NaOH = Mg(OH)_2 + Na_2SO_4 \quad (10.14)$$

$$CaSO_4 + Na_2CO_3 = CaCO_3 + Na_2SO_4 \quad (10.15)$$

The sodium carbonate formed in Eqs. (10.11), (10.12), and (10.13) is available to precipitate the calcium noncarbonate hardness, as shown in Eq. (10.15). A combination of lime and caustic soda can be used, with the ratio dependent upon the calcium noncarbonate removal required. This will allow some savings in chemical cost compared with the use of caustic soda alone, since caustic soda is more expensive than lime. Use of caustic soda may be desirable for low-alkalinity water, since alkalinity reduction with caustic soda is half that with lime softening. A disadvantage of using caustic soda is the increase in finished-water sodium concentration.

Split-treatment softening is used at several plants where the raw water is of low turbidity and high in magnesium. The lime dose required to treat the entire flow is added to the first basin, elevating the pH to 11.0 to 11.3 and removing calcium and almost all the magnesium hardness. The settled water is then blended with a by-passed portion of the raw water, producing a pH of about 10.3, which precipitates only calcium carbonate hardness in the bypassed flow. The principal advantage of split treatment is the elimination of carbon dioxide stabilization of the high-pH water, which can be a significant cost savings in plant operation. An additional advantage, depending on sludge handling, is segregation of the relatively pure calcium carbonate in the second-stage sludge from the first-stage sludge, which consists of magnesium hydroxide and raw-water contaminants, such as color, turbidity, and silica, that are removed at the high pH because of the coagulating effect of the precipitated magnesium hydroxide.

As a result of the significant sludge production in the basin which combines the treated and the bypassed flow, designs for split-flow softening may need to provide additional sludge removal equipment in this basin. Consideration must also be given to possible encrustation of the recarbonation equipment if it is housed in this basin. When designing split-flow systems for high-iron-content waters, the engineer should also verify that the selected design and bypass flow will yield permissible iron concentrations in the finished water.

Hot-process softening is predominantly used in industrial applications and therefore will not be discussed in this chapter.

A process developed by A.P. Black in the 1970s uses magnesium as a recycled coagulant.[13,14,15] The process is centered around recovery of magnesium as magnesium bicarbonate from the sludge using CO_2, as shown in Eq. (10.16).

$$Mg(OH)_2 + 2CO_2 = Mg(HCO_3)_2 \qquad (10.16)$$

Experience has shown that 85 to 90 percent of the magnesium precipitated as magnesium hydroxide can be recovered from the sludge. The recovered magnesium is recycled to be reprecipitated, with the magnesium hydroxide acting as a coagulant for both turbidity and calcium carbonate removal. The process has been applied to both hard and soft waters with resulting economic benefits, particularly where lime recovery has been feasible.[16,17]

In the treatment of water with high turbidity using the Black process, froth flotation can be used to purify the calcium carbonate sludge to allow recalcination. The principal advantage of the process is reduction of sludge through recovery of lime and the coagulant, magnesium.

In the design of water-softening plants, the actual water chemistry that occurs must be carefully considered. In the next section, design concepts are discussed with reference to both softening and water chemistry.

Elements of Design

The design of a conventional lime–soda ash softening plant is largely determined by the amount of water to be softened, the raw-water characteristics, and the quality requirements of the treated water. Sludge treatment and disposal must be considered, along with special requirements such as space limitations, aesthetics, chemical recovery and reuse, and operational characteristics.

Pretreatment

Pretreatment, when necessary, generally consists of carbon dioxide removal or presedimentation. As discussed in the previous section, carbon dioxide requires lime to remove. Additionally, calcium carbonate sludge is formed, and this must be disposed of. Forced-draft aeration is often used for well water containing a high concentration of carbon dioxide, reducing the carbon dioxide level to less than 10 mg/L. Aeration also oxidizes iron or manganese that may be present, but has the disadvantage of adding oxygen to the water. Dissolved oxygen generally leads to an increased rate of corrosion in the distribution system.

The economic advantages of aeration must be weighed against the disadvantages; thus, aeration is used only where the carbon dioxide levels are quite high. Chemical oxidation of iron and manganese can easily be accomplished where aeration is not utilized.

Presedimentation is used primarily by those plants treating surface water of extremely high turbidity, such as those supplies on the Missouri and Mississippi rivers. Some of these plants use organic polymers to enhance the suspended-solids removal. Presedimentation provides a more uniform water quality at the treatment plant, removes a major portion of the suspended solids with little chemical cost, and offers the potential for cost savings in sludge treatment and disposal. Because of the cost of dewatering and land disposal of these solids and the minor impact on highly turbid rivers, state and federal agencies have occasionally allowed return of presedimentation sludge directly to the river. This greatly reduces the quantity of sludge to be disposed of in a more costly manner.

Rapid mix and flocculation

Rapid mixing serves a number of important purposes, including dissolving of the relatively insoluble calcium hydroxide, mixing of recycled sludge with both the raw water and chemical feed, and mixing of chemical prior to splitting the flow to more than one flocculation basin.

Recycling of previously formed calcium carbonate crystals to the rapid mix is extremely important. The precipitation reactions are accelerated and will more closely approach true solubility when the mix is seeded with these previously formed crystals.[18,19,20,21] Recycling of sludge will allow precipitation to occur on the recycled crystals, which serve as nuclei. This reduces precipitation on the mechanical equipment. More important, however, this reaction furthers growth of larger calcium carbonate particles. Larger calcium carbonate crystals will settle more readily, thicken to a greater extent, and dewater much more easily and with a lower final moisture content. Recent work shows that 50 to 100 percent sludge recycle, based on solids produced, will effectively control particle size.[23] This same study found that particle growth approached an equilibrium value after about four cycles. Figure 10.1 illustrates the effect of sludge recycling on particle growth. Curve A is a sample of sludge taken before recycling was practiced. Curve B represents a sample of sludge taken after several cycles at 25 percent recycling based on solids produced, i.e., if 100 lb/h

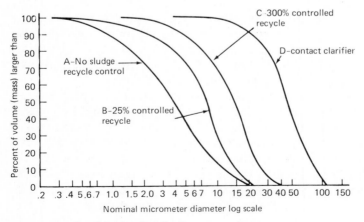

Figure 10.1 Particle-size distribution comparison.

of solids is formed as a result of water treatment, 25 lb of solids are recycled to the rapid mix. Curve C represents 300 percent sludge recycling. Curve D was a sample of sludge taken from a contact clarifier with an extremely high recycle rate and high numbers of sludge recycles.

The importance of sludge recycling depends to some degree upon the sludge dewatering and disposal processes used. Adequate recycling can dramatically affect sludge thickening and dewatering costs.

The flocculation basin allows the softening reactions to proceed to completion and the smaller particles to agglomerate into sufficiently large-sized particles to settle effectively at a faster rate.

Both synthetic organic polymers and inorganic coagulants are commonly used to enhance particle agglomeration and, in the case of surface waters, turbidity removal. While the rapid mix is typically designed to provide the required amount of energy input, the flocculation basin generally is designed with several stages in series to allow sufficient time for completion of the reaction with enough energy input to keep the solids suspended and in contact. Variable-speed flocculation is desirable to respond to seasonal mixing requirements and to achieve optimum velocity gradients for development of particles which will settle rapidly.

The softening reactions are best accommodated in a solids-contact basin. As previously discussed, this type of unit provides a high degree of continuous sludge recirculation and contact, producing a more stable water and larger calcium carbonate crystals. The depth and density of the sludge blanket can be controlled by sludge wasting and flocculation agitation. Sludge is continually recirculated from the sludge blanket to the flocculator, with recirculation rates from several hundred to several thousand percent, based on solids production.

Sedimentation

Where solids-contact clarifiers are used, the sedimentation basin is of the upflow type, with the design based on an overflow rate commonly in the range of 1440 to 2000 gpd/ft^2 and higher. Where coagulation for turbidity removal is required, less than 1440 gpd/ft^2 loading is normal. Generally, a hydraulic retention time of less than 3 h results. If the basins are of conventional horizontal design, retention time of up to 4 h is common. Continuous sludge removal is employed in either case to handle the large quantity of solids produced. Heavy-duty, high-torque-capacity rake mechanisms are required because of the high density and viscosity of the sludge.

Softening waters that are high in magnesium usually produces a sludge that settles and thickens poorly, although the gelatinous nature of the magnesium hydroxide provides a high-clarity effluent. For this reason, lower clarifier overflow rates are used, similar to those of plants designed for turbidity removal.

The suspended solids present in the sedimentation basin overflow are very small calcium carbonate crystals. These particles are non-compressible and do not shorten filter runs as much as particles of alum or iron floc. For this reason, higher levels of suspended solids in the sedimentation basin overflow can be tolerated without affecting the filter operations. When excess lime treatment is practiced, the overflow weirs and troughs will tend to encrust with precipitated calcium carbonate. The carbon dioxide in the atmosphere stabilizes the water at the water surface, particularly where the weir overflow aerates the water. A submerged weir takeoff from the settling basins minimizes this problem; however, care should be taken to avoid small orifices which become encrusted. V-notch overflow weirs tend to encrust rapidly, negating the added value offered by this design.

Recarbonation.   There are two basic purposes for recarbonation in lime-softening plants:

1. pH adjustment and elimination of $CaCO_3$ supersaturation

2. Neutralization of hydroxide alkalinity and precipitation of calcium carbonate from excess lime softening

In conventional lime softening with selective calcium carbonate removal, the water remains supersaturated with $CaCO_3$ after the reaction basin and may have a pH greater than 10.0. Carbon dioxide reacts with the supersaturated $CaCO_3$, converts it to calcium bicarbonate, and reduces pH by the following reaction:

$$CaCO_3 + CO_2 + H_2O \leftrightharpoons Ca(HCO_3)_2 \qquad (10.17)$$

If some excess lime is present, and converting it to calcium bicarbonate would not significantly increase hardness, the following reaction is possible:

$$Ca(OH)_2 + 2CO_2 \leftrightharpoons Ca(HCO_3)_2 \qquad (10.18)$$

Carbon dioxide should be added after the reaction basin and before filtration with conventional softening. A polyphosphate (~0.5 mg/L) may be added to avoid the possibility of calcium carbonate encrustation of the filter sand.

With excess lime softening, the hydroxide alkalinity must be converted to carbonate alkalinity for precipitation of calcium carbonate by the following reaction:

$$Ca(OH)_2 + CO_2 \leftrightharpoons CaCO_3 \downarrow + H_2O \qquad (10.19)$$

Converting to bicarbonate alkalinity would excessively increase the hardness concentration and would be more expensive. The excess lime is typically precipitated and settled out in a secondary basin. Supersaturated $CaCO_3$ from this basin should be neutralized according to Eq. (10.17) prior to filtration to prevent encrustation of the filter medium.

Split-flow lime softening greatly reduces recarbonation requirements, since free CO_2 and bicarbonate alkalinity in the bypass water neutralize excess calcium hydroxide. Depending upon the chemistry of the raw water, some recarbonation may still be required for pH adjustment. Where coagulation or larger quantities of chlorine are required, the acidity of these chemicals may sufficiently decrease pH.

Plants designed to remove significant levels of magnesium require two stages of stabilization. In the first stage, the pH is reduced to 10.3, precipitating calcium carbonate. Recycling of previously formed calcium carbonate will assist in the reaction for the reasons discussed earlier. Most plants are designed to provide secondary flocculation and settling of the calcium carbonate formed. A more economical design alternative provides 30 to 45 min reaction to complete the calcium carbonate formation. Secondary carbonation then reduces the pH of the water to the desired level prior to filtration. The calcium carbonate formed does not resolubilize on secondary stabilization, but does place a significant suspended solids loading onto the filters. The solids produced on first-stage carbonation are proportional to the hydroxide alkalinity present; therefore, this alternative would be less desirable for those plants that must operate at high pH levels to remove nearly all the magnesium present.

Secondary carbonation is used to convert the carbonate to bicarbonate alkalinity. This reaction occurs almost instantaneously and often is accomplished in the flume conveying the settled water to the filters. The design of improvements to increase the efficiency of the carbon dioxide transfer will depend upon the relative carbon dioxide costs.

There are several methods for recarbonating lime-softened water. In the past, carbon dioxide was obtained by burning fossil fuels with excess air, scrubbing the stack gases, and blowing the gas under pressure to the point of application. Because of the equipment required (burners, scrubbers, piping, control valves, blower/compressor), considerable maintenance was required to handle the moist, corrosive gas. In addition, the presence of sulfur and phenolic materials in the case caused taste and odor problems in the finished water.

A more common method of recarbonation is the use of underwater burners. With this method, natural gas and air are mixed and blown to an underwater burning apparatus, where the gas mixture is ignited at the bottom of a recarbonation basin. Alternatively, the natural gas/air mix can be burned above ground and blown into an underwater diffuser. Natural gas has few impurities to contaminate the water. However, carbon monoxide is produced by the equipment, and therefore low areas should be properly ventilated to exhaust any carbon monoxide gas accumulation.

The amount of carbon dioxide generated is controlled by regulating the amount of natural gas burned. Typically, 0.115 lb CO_2 is produced for every cubic foot of natural gas burned. The transfer efficiency of CO_2 into water is approximately 75 percent. Natural gas costs vary with location and usually range from \$2.50 to \$5.00 per 1000 standard cubic feet (\$43.50 to \$87.00 per ton CO_2 produced).

Proper sizing of underwater burners is critical, since the turndown ratio is only about 2:1. Additional variation in CO_2 feed requirements must be obtained by using multiple burners. This should be carefully considered with water plants having a wide range of flow-rate and CO_2 requirements.

Liquid carbon dioxide systems are being used more frequently for recarbonation. They consist of a storage tank, refrigeration unit, vaporizer, vapor heater, and gas controls and meters. The pure CO_2 gas is diffused into the water by fine bubble diffusers or a dispersion mixer and gas sparger plate in the recarbonation basin. Typical transfer efficiencies of CO_2 into water are 80 to 85 percent. A wide range of CO_2 dosages are possible with the liquid CO_2 system. This is useful when water demand is variable, or when process operations such as switching from excess lime to split-flow softening change CO_2 requirements.

Liquid CO_2 costs range from \$50 to \$100 per ton, depending on location. This is similar to CO_2 costs with underwater burners. However, the electrical requirements for blowers in the underwater burner system are usually greater than those for refrigeration and vapor heating in the liquid CO_2 system. Capital costs for underwater burner and liquid CO_2 systems are similar. Maintenance and operation of the recarbonation equipment should also be considered in the selection of process equipment.

Filtration

There are no significant differences between the design of the filter system for a softening plant and that for a conventional plant. Mixed or multimedia filters ensure longer filter runs and lower wash-water requirements. Careful pH control is necessary to prevent calcium carbonate encrustation on the filter media. Good operating practice includes, at a minimum, daily checks on the alkalinity of the water above the filter, with adjustment of the stabilization pH as necessary. If the pH of the stabilized water is too low, the filtered water will be corrosive. The filter will provide modest short-term corrections to an unstable water, increasing the alkalinity if the pH is too low and reducing the alkalinity if it is too high. Polyphosphates are sometimes fed to control filter media encrustation.

The use of a mechanical surface sweep to assist filter backwashing is essential. The agitator breaks up cementation of filter media and helps remove suspended solids in the backwash water.

In softening plants treating low-turbidity water, there is less concern about filtered-water turbidity than in conventional plants. In both cases, however, recording turbidimeters on each filter are of considerable help in filter operation. Many filters are backwashed on a time-duration basis rather than on the basis of head loss or deterioration of filter effluent quality. It is not unusual for fine calcium carbonate to pass through a filter, producing a high turbidity in the effluent. A recording turbidimeter will assist the plant operator in determining when to backwash a filter, as well as help control other plant operating parameters, such as polymer feed and control of the water stabilization process.

Filter backwash water may be returned to the plant influent. This water has been softened and contains primarily calcium carbonate and magnesium hydroxide as suspended solids. Generally a surge basin is provided, returning the backwash water at less than 10 percent of plant raw-water flow. The recycled suspended solids will assist the softening reactions in a manner similar to recycling of sludge.

Chemical feed, handling, and storage

Lime is by far the chemical used in greatest quantity. In many cases, as much as a ton of lime per million gallons of water treated is required. Larger plants generally take delivery by 70-ton railcars, although most plants receive lime by truck. The amount of storage required depends upon the daily plant requirement, variations in that requirement, distance and dependability of supply, and method of transportation. Normally, storage is provided for at least a 30-day supply, with longer storage desirable.

Lime is typically transferred by both pneumatic and mechanical conveying systems. The lime truck generally has a self-contained unload system; however, railcar unloading generally requires the use of a vacuum/pressure pneumatic system. Baghouses minimize lime dust problems when pneumatic conveying is used. A typical installation provides transfer systems from lime storage to feed bins or day bins.

Volumetric or gravimetric feeders, dependent upon the feed accuracy required, are used to feed quicklime to either a paste or slurry slaker. Grit removal is generally provided to protect pumps, valves, and other equipment. Sludge recycling to the lime-slurry feed helps prevent encrusting of lime feed lines and valves. Lime feed lines should be constructed to allow easy access for cleaning. Lime-slurry feed should be by gravity, although pH control systems may require positive slurry feed and control.

Soda ash is purchased both in bulk and in 100-lb bags, depending on usage requirements and the source of supply. Like lime, soda ash is fed both volumetrically and gravimetrically. The dry chemical is fed to a dissolving tank.

Liquid caustic soda is generally received as a 50 percent solution and stored in a steel or fiberglass tank. In cold climates, provision should be made to prevent freezing. Solution metering pumps are used to accurately feed the chemicals.

The purchase of pure carbon dioxide is becoming common practice. Carbon dioxide is captured as a by-product from industries such as ammonia plants, breweries, or refineries. The sale price will depend upon the degree of cleanup required prior to pressurization, distance from the source, and other factors. Carbon dioxide is trucked under pressure as a liquid, and stored in insulated, pressurized tanks. The carbon dioxide is vaporized and fed as a gas through a rotameter, or in some instances a chlorinator-type feeder is used. Use of pure carbon dioxide may offer advantages compared with on-site generation, such as:

- Ease in handling and feeding
- Ease in automated feed control
- Low maintenance and capital costs
- Lower purchase price in some cases

Where lime recalcination is practiced, carbon dioxide is available in the exhaust gas for only the cost of conveyance to the use point within the plant.

Regardless of the plant design or chemicals used, water softening has very high chemical costs and produces large quantities of sludge to be disposed of. The next section of this chapter deals with in-plant processes that help minimize the cost and environmental impacts of water softening.

Design Principles and Practices: In-Plant Sludge Consideration

The section on water chemistry discussed the fact that more sludge is produced than chemicals are fed. A 1969 study of softening plants found an average of 3.5 lb of solids produced for every pound of calcium carbonate hardness removed, considerably higher than the theoretical ratio.[12] While the sludge production will depend on raw-water and plant operational characteristics, the total quantity of sludge produced may well average greater than a ton of dry solids per million gallons of water treated. Coagulation-softening plants may produce many times this amount during periods of high water turbidity.

Lime recovery

The most successful water plant sludge disposal operations to date are in plants that recalcine softening sludge and reuse the lime produced. However, for recalcination to be economical, the calcium carbonate fed to the lime kiln must be relatively pure (90 percent or higher), with a minimum moisture content (30 percent or less), and with a lime production rate to 50 tons CaO per day or higher being desirable.

In lime recalcination, a number of unit operations are required, as shown in Fig. 10.2. The processes include:

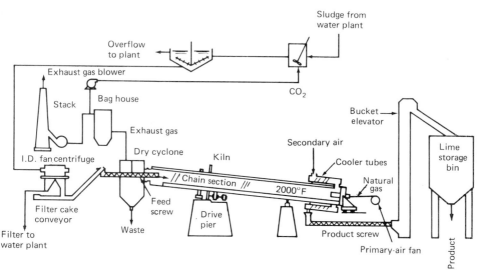

Figure 10.2 Recovery of lime for reuse—rotary kiln process.

- The magnesium hydroxide fraction of the sludge, when present, is dissolved using carbon dioxide produced in recalcination.

- The carbonated sludge is thickened and dewatered to 30 percent solids or greater. The overflow is recycled to the plant influent.

- The underflow from the thickener is dewatered using either a solid bowl centrifuge, a vacuum filter, or a gravity belt filter press.

- The sludge is dried and then fed to the lime kiln, which is fired with fuel oil or natural gas. Many commercial lime companies use anthracite coal, pulverized on-site, as a more economical fuel.

- The calcium carbonate is converted to calcium oxide as the carbon dioxide is driven off by the heat.

Lime recovery is currently practiced at nine water plants in the United States, with varying degrees of success. The recalcining processes employed at the more recent installations include rotary kilns, fluidized-bed reactors, and multiple-hearth furnaces. The energy requirement per ton of lime produced depends primarily on the moisture content of the feed sludge, but is significantly affected by the use of energy recovery devices and the calcining process chosen. The softening reactions produce about 30 percent more lime than is fed, depending upon raw-water characteristics. Often, this excess lime is sold.

Full-scale lime recovery for plants treating water with high turbidity has not been attempted. However, studies conducted at Columbus, Ohio, investigated the use of two-stage centrifugation to purify the calcium carbonate, taking advantage of differences between particle size and specific gravity.[23] Modest results were obtained, although high purity generally required considerable wastage of calcium carbonate.

Froth flotation was studied at Johnson County, Kan. Greater than 90 percent purity and recovery were obtained. Froth flotation studies at another plant found less promising calcium carbonate recovery, believed to be a result of small particle size calcium carbonate. The treatment plant was conventional in design with external sludge recycling. The initial study at Johnson County was in a plant using contact clarifiers.

Lime recalcination offers new advantages as a result of escalating costs for energy and pollution abatement requirements. Present state-of-the-art design allows on-site lime recalcination at essentially the same energy requirements as when calcining limestone. Energy savings result, however, as

- Commercial operations must quarry, transport, and crush the limestone.

- Round-trip haul of the lime to the water plant adds to the energy requirement.

- Round-trip haul of the dewatered water plant sludge adds additional energy costs.

In many cases, water plants are being required to dewater the sludge, haul it to a landfill, and pay a substantial disposal cost. Lime recalcination can offer an attractive alternative in many cases.

Lagoon storage

Because of the large volume of sludge produced by lime softening and the relatively low cost of land for lagooning, many plants construct large-volume or multiple-cell lagoons for storage and/or air drying of the lime sludge. Howson[24] developed the following conclusions regarding lagoon storage:

1. The cheapest means of transporting sludge from the treatment plant to the sludge disposal site is by pipeline.

2. Although sludges vary in their character, composition, and volume, it may be assumed that on a dry basis there will be approximately 2.5 lb of sludge produced per pound of commercial lime used in the softening process.

3. Most softening-plant sludges air-dry in well-designed lagoons with supernatant removed to facilitate drying to about 50 percent moisture. New sludge should not be added to a lagoon until previous applications have dried.

4. When lime-softening sludge is reduced to 50 percent moisture content, it will occupy only about 16 percent as much volume as when applied at 90 percent moisture, or 8 percent as much volume as when applied at 95 percent moisture.

5. It is believed that sludge deposited in a lagoon where it is always submerged will not compact to less than about 70 percent water. In this condition it occupies twice as much storage space as when dried to 50 percent. The wet sludge is very difficult to handle.

6. When sludge is dried to 50 percent moisture, the total volume per year produced by a 1-mgd ($0.044\text{-m}^3/\text{s}$) plant removing 100 mg/L hardness is about ⅔ acre-ft (820 m^3).

7. There should be at least three lagoons for lime-softening sludge, each capable of holding approximately 1 year's supply of wet

sludge. Applications of sludge to the lagoons should be rotated as consolidation to 50 percent is reached.

8. As a general figure, where sludge can be lagooned to 10-ft (3 m) depth, it is desirable to have 3 to 5 acres (1.2 to 2 ha) available for sludge beds for each 1 mgd (0.044 m^3/s) plant capacity in order to provide for the future.

9. Lagoons should be operated on a "fill and let dry" basis. Sludge should be applied to a depth of 3 to 5 ft (1 to 1.7 m), which usually shrinks to 6 to 10 in (15 to 20 cm) depth when dried to 50 percent moisture.

10. Because of the desirability of applying as much as 3 ft (1 m) at a time, berms should be built 3 to 5 ft (1 to 1.7 m) above maximum sludge level when filled. Berms should be broad enough (about 12 ft or 4 m) to permit operation of a drag line and to permit raising their top elevation.

11. In operating lagoons for sludge disposal, it is desirable to fill at one end and decant or otherwise withdraw supernatant at the other end. Relatively long and narrow lagoons are preferable.

12. It is desirable to keep the water level in lagoons as low as possible to facilitate compaction.

13. Lime sludge does not dewater properly under water. Compaction under water does not result in solids concentration of more than 30 to 40 percent solids. Lagoons should never be operated as ponds.

Lagooned lime sludge generally is removed using construction equipment and ultimately disposed as landfill or applied on agricultural land.

In northern states with low evaporation rates, such as Ohio, several water plants have used shallow drying-freezing beds with underdrains to dewater lime sludge. The depth of these beds permits an application of 1 ft 6 in to 3 ft of sludge. This sludge dewaters and, if allowed to drain over a winter freeze, tends to become grainlike in texture. The lime sludge is then loaded with conventional front-end tractors and hauled to landfill.

Other Product Recovery

Precipitated calcium carbonate has considerable value, depending on the particle size, brightness, and other factors. Using a private contract operation, one plant has been producing dried precipitated calcium carbonate for sale as an industrial chemical. Low-turbidity raw water is a prerequisite for this alternative.

Pilot projects for the recovery of various magnesium compounds have been performed at two water plants. Based on results from these studies, the cost of production of high-purity magnesium compounds was found to be significantly below the current market price.[21] Only those plants treating raw water for magnesium removal would have this alternative available.

While these two alternatives represent unusual situations, additional opportunities for by-product recovery may be found as the cost of disposal increases. The primary function of a water plant is production of high-quality water; however, economics may dictate that consideration be given to new alternative treatment and recovery processes.

References

1. "Introduction to Water Treatment," vol. 2, *Principles and Practices of Water Supply Operations,* American Water Works Association, Denver, Colo., 1984.
2. C. N. Sawyer, *Chemistry for Sanitary Engineers,* McGraw-Hill, New York, 1960.
3. "Quality Goals for Potable Water: A Statement of Policy Adopted by the AWWA Board of Directors on January 28, 1968, Based on the Final Report of Task Group 2650P—Water Quality Goals, Elwood L. Bean, Chairman," *Journal AWWA,* vol. 60, 1968, p. 1317.
4. *Manual of Treatment Techniques for Meeting the Interim Primary Drinking Water Regulation,* U.S. Environmental Protection Agency, 600/8-77-005, April 1978.
5. G. S. Logsdon, T. J. Sorg, and J. M. Symons, "Removal of Heavy Metals by Conventional Treatment," *Proc. 16th Water Qual. Conf.,* Univ. Bull. 71, University of Illinois Urbana-Champaign, 1974.
6. G. Berg, R. B. Dean, and D. R. Dahling, "Removal of Poliovirus 1 from Secondary Effluents by Lime Flocculation and Rapid Sand Filtration," *Journal AWWA,* vol. 60, no. 2, 1968, p. 193.
7. M. L. Riehl, H. H. Weiser, and R. T. Rheins, "Effect of Lime Treated Water Upon Survival of Bacteria," *Journal AWWA,* vol. 44, 1952, p. 466.
8. Malay Chaudhuri and R. S. Engelbrecht, "Removal of Viruses from Water by Chemical Coagulation and Flocculation," *Journal AWWA,* vol. 62, 1970, p. 563.
9. O. J. Sproul, "Virus and Bacterial Removal in Water Softening," *13th Water Qual. Tech. Conf.,* Univ. Bull. 69, University of Illinois Urbana-Champaign, 1971.
10. S. J. Randtke, et al., "Removing Soluble Organic Contaminants by Lime-Soda Softening," *Journal AWWA,* vol. 74, no. 4, 1982, p. 192.
11. M. Y. Liao and S. J. Randtke, "Predicting the Removal of Soluble Organic Contaminants by Lime Softening," *Water Research,* vol. 20, no. 1, 1986, p. 27.
12. *Waste Sludge and Filter Washwater Disposal from Water Softening Plants,* Ohio Department of Health, September 1978.
13. A. P. Black, B. B. Shuey, and P. J. Fleming, "Recovery of Calcium and Magnesium Values from Lime-Soda Softening Sludges," *Journal AWWA,* vol. 63, 1971, p. 616.
14. C. G. Thompson, J. E. Singley, and A. P. Black, "Magnesium Carbonate—A Recycled Coagulant," *Journal AWWA,* vol. 64, no. 11, 1972.
15. C. G. Thompson, J. E. Singley, and A. P. Black, "Magnesium Carbonate—A Recycled Coagulant, Part II," *Journal AWWA,* vol. 64, 1972, p. 94.
16. A. P. Black and C. G. Thompson, "Plant Scale Studies of the Magnesium Carbonate

Water Treatment Process," EPA National Environmental Research Center, Office of Research and Development, EPA-660/2-75-006, May 1975.
17. C. G. Thompson and G. A. Mooney, *Recovery of Lime and Magnesium in Potable Water Treatment*, U. S. Environmental Protection Agency, EPA-600/2-76-285, December 1976.
18. W. A. Sperry, "The Lime Softening of Water and the Use of the Sludge as an Aid Thereto," *Journal AWWA*, vol. 6, 1919, p. 215.
19. H. O. Hartung, "Experience with Up-Flow Type Basins," *Water and Sewer Works*, vol. 1, 1944, p. 91.
20. R. F. McCauley and R. Eliassen, "Accelerating Calcium Carbonate Precipitation in Softening Plants," *Journal AWWA*, vol. 51, 1955, p. 106.
21. J. L. Tuepker and H. O. Hartung, "Effect of Accumulated Lime-Softening Slurry on Magnesium Reduction," *Journal AWWA*, vol. 52, 1960, p. 106.
22. "Pilot Plant Studies at the Elm Fork Treatment Plant," Dallas Water Utilities, in press.
23. M. A. Burris, K. W. Cousens, and D. M. Mair, "Softening and Coagulation Sludge—Disposal Studies for a Surface Water Supply," *Journal AWWA*, vol. 68, 1976, p. 247.
24. L. R. Howson, "Lagoon Disposal of Lime Sludge," *Journal AWWA*, vol. 53, 1961, p. 1169.

Chapter
11

Iron and Manganese Removal

Iron and Manganese in Nature

Iron and manganese are the fourth and seventeenth most abundant elements, constituting, respectively, about 4.5 and 0.1 percent of the approximately one hundred elements in the earth's crust, which is known as the lithosphere.[1] Only oxygen, silicon, and aluminum are more abundant than iron. They comprise about 48, 28, and 8 percent of the lithosphere, respectively. Other constituents of natural water, calcium, sodium, potassium, and magnesium, make up about 3.5, 2.5, 2.5, and 2.25 percent of the lithosphere, respectively. The compounds of two of these, calcium and magnesium, along with those of aluminum, iron, and manganese, are recognized as the causes of hardness in natural waters.[2,3]

Iron and manganese occur in rocks and minerals of the earth's crust. Iron occurs in silicate minerals of igneous rocks, whereas manganese compounds are found most often in metamorphic and sedimentary rocks. Both are found in minerals mostly as carbonates, oxides, silicates, and sulfides.[4] They also are found in clays, soils, and sediments.

Iron and manganese are found throughout the plant and animal kingdoms. Both are required for the growth of microorganisms. Iron is one of the macronutrients, along with calcium, magnesium, and potassium, and is required by virtually all organisms. Manganese is one of the micronutrients which, along with cobalt, copper, and molybdenum, is commonly required by most microorganisms.[5] Iron and manganese are two of the most common contaminants found in unacceptable levels in drinking-water supplies.[65]

Iron and manganese in groundwater supplies

Iron is present in many groundwater supplies, whereas manganese is present only occasionally, and then usually along with iron.[3] Usually the manganese is the minor constituent; it is considerably less abundant in the lithosphere.

Groundwater, which is frequently high in carbon dioxide and low in dissolved oxygen, will readily dissolve or convert insoluble iron- and manganese-bearing minerals to soluble ferrous and manganous bicarbonates[2] having, respectively, the divalent ferrous iron, Fe^{2+}, and the divalent manganous manganese ion, Mn^{2+}. It has been established that inorganic carbonate and bicarbonate iron complexes are not a constituent of most groundwater, meaning that the ferrous ion, Fe^{2+}, is the only inorganic form of iron of any significance in carbonate-bearing groundwater.[7]

The carbon dioxide found in groundwater probably originated in the decomposition of organic matter in the soil. Ferric iron, a constituent of many iron-bearing minerals, is reduced to ferrous iron through the action of microorganisms in the anaerobic environment of a deep well. Similarly, there is evidence that manganese of higher valences than two, a constituent of many manganese-bearing minerals, such as the tetravalent manganese in manganese dioxide, MnO_2, is reduced to manganous manganese through the action of microorganisms in the anaerobic environment of a deep well.[5]

Although iron and manganese are normally present in groundwater as soluble bicarbonates, soluble ferrous and manganous sulfate, with their respective ferrous iron ion, Fe^{2+}, and manganous manganese ion, Mn^{2+}, are to be found in groundwater containing sulfur, particularly hydrogen sulfide. In a recent survey, 52 percent of the untreated groundwater supplies had iron concentrations greater than 0.05 mg/L and 26 percent exceeded 0.26 mg/L.[63] Also, organically bound iron and manganese can be found in some groundwater. For example, humic acids, sometimes called "the yellow acids," derived from humus, the organic portion of the soil resulting from the partial decay of leaves and other vegetation, react with the ferrous iron ion to form colored organic complexes.[8]

Records on the concentration of iron in groundwater indicate that it normally ranges from a few hundredths to about 25 mg/L; however, there are exceptions. In one state, for instance, the dissolved iron in wells ranges from a few hundredths to over 70 mg/L,[3] and in another state it reaches a maximum of over 90 mg/L. Manganese is usually present in groundwater in a concentration of less than 1.0 mg/L;[9] however, there are exceptions.

A more general observation is that water of high alkalinity often has a lower iron and manganese concentration than water of low alkalinity. Also, the iron concentration of water from gravel wells is often less than that of the water from rock wells because the gravel wells often draw water from a single aquifer rather than multiple aquifers. Any colloidal or precipitated iron, if formed, is removed by underground filtration.[10]

Iron and manganese in surface-water supplies

Iron exists in oxygenated surface-water supplies in various forms of ferric iron. It may be present in suspensions of silt, clay, and fine particulates of hydrated ferric oxides; in a colloidal form; in a chelated or other complex organic form with humic acids, always colored;[8,11] in other organic complexes, often colored;[2,4] in inorganic complexes;[2,4] and in "solution." The last relates to the fact that ferric iron is in solution only to the extent that the formation of chelates and organic complexes increases its solubility. In filtered samples of oxygenated surface water, the concentration of iron seldom reaches 1 mg/L,[2] but it can be in excess of this in a colored water in which the iron is a constituent of the soluble color. In a recent survey, 76 percent of the untreated surface-water supplies had iron concentrations greater than 0.05 mg/L, and 38 percent exceeded 0.26 mg/L.[63]

As for manganese, there is evidence that in surface-water supplies it is present in suspensions of a tetravalent (quadrivalent) state;[2] in organic complexes;[4] in the trivalent state as a relatively stable soluble complex;[2] in inorganic complexes;[4] and in solution as a manganous manganese ion, Mn^{2+}, to the extent that the word "solution" applies to those organic complexes that further increase the solubility of manganese. In surface water, the concentration of manganese is rarely in excess of 1 mg/L.[2] However, under certain conditions, often spring turnover, for example, dissolved manganese may be formed in sudden, high concentrations in both reservoirs and rivers, causing problems. The causes and effects of high manganese concentrations are discussed below.

Manganese and iron are present in practically all reservoirs; there appear to be very few deep-water reservoirs that do not show an increase in soluble manganese (Mn^{2+}) near the bottom. The buildup of the manganous manganese ion, Mn^{2+}, in the hypolimnion of a reservoir makes it possible for the Mn^{2+} concentration to increase markedly in the epilimnion after the sometimes abrupt spring turnover.

Several studies[12-17] of the mechanism of the buildup of the manganous manganese ion in the hypolimnion have been conducted. In one study,[15] it was concluded that "biologic activity" is involved in the solution and increase of the manganese in the hypolimnion. This conforms with the biological evidence reported for deep wells and applicable to the hypolimnions of lakes and reservoirs, that is, the evidence[5] that manganese compounds that have a valence greater than 2 are reduced to manganous manganese through the action of microorganisms in the anaerobic hypolimnion environment.

Although the manganese concentration can get higher than 20 mg/L in some of the lakes of the Tennessee Valley Authority[18] and in certain reservoirs,[12] it is more common to encounter a manganese concentration of 0.1 to 1.0 mg/L.[19] The manganese concentration more often approximates one-half to one-third of the concentration of iron, or conversely, the iron concentration is often approximately two to three times as great as the manganese concentration.[10]

When reservoir turnover does occur, the plant operator makes the best of a bad situation by obtaining raw water from the reservoir level with the lowest manganese concentration. Manganese in rivers is associated with the release of water from the hypolimnions of lakes and reservoirs; the flows from other anaerobic environments, such as bogs, marshes, and swamps; and the metal-bearing drawings from iron ore and certain other ore mines. The soluble manganese may be carried many miles downstream.

The iron and manganese problem

The literature is replete with the effects of the presence of iron and manganese in public water supplies. Iron and manganese produce ugly and insoluble rusty brown, yellow, gray, or black stains, blotches, and streaks[20] on clothing during laundering, on plumbing fixtures, and on everything they touch. Manganese is particularly tenacious. In extreme cases, iron and manganese interfere with culinary use, turning tea black and darkening boiled vegetables, for example.[21] Sometimes the presence of iron and manganese becomes a disaster in industrial wet-processing operations. Iron also imparts a taste described as a bitter, sweet, astringent, or "iron" taste,[22] detectable by some persons at levels of 1 to 2 mg/L.[2,22]

Water containing iron and manganese promotes the growth of iron- and manganese-tolerant bacteria in mains, with accompanying increases in friction loss and power consumption.[21] When large masses of bacteria break loose, they clog nozzles, lines, and valves.[20] Also, precipitation of iron in distribution systems causes the familiar redwater problems in the home and in industry.[21] If consumers have water softeners, they become fouled and must be repeatedly cleaned to prevent an excessive loss in efficiency. In addition, as the bacteria decay, they impart a particularly bad taste and odor to the water, making it objectionable to drink or use for sanitary purposes.[20]

Experience has shown that the domestic consumer finds the water objectionable when iron is present in amounts greater than 0.2 mg/L, and the tenacity of manganese is so great that its concentration should not be more than 0.1 mg/L and preferably less than 0.05 mg/L.

For some industrial applications, iron must be reduced to 0.1 mg/L and manganese to less than 0.05 mg/L. Some water utility directors believe that water delivered to consumers should be completely devoid of manganese; for some industries, this is imperative. On the other hand, the average domestic consumer can tolerate 0.01 to 0.02 mg/L of manganese.[18] An AWWA task group[23] suggested that an "ideal quality water" have limits of 0.05 mg/L for iron and 0.01 mg/L for manganese.

The U.S. Drinking Water Standards, revised in 1962,[25] gave separate recognition to iron and manganese. A limit of 0.3 mg/L was set for iron. There was some difficulty in setting a limit for manganese, since a water free of manganese is imperative for some industries.

The National Secondary Drinking Water Regulations,[26] those related to the aesthetic qualities of drinking water, were effective January 19, 1981. They stipulate that the secondary maximum contaminant level (SMCL) for iron and manganese be 0.3 mg/L and 0.05 mg/L, respectively.

The secondary regulations are not enforceable at the federal level, but may be adopted by a state, or a state may establish higher or lower levels, depending upon local conditions. It is essential that iron and manganese, if present in a water supply, be removed to the SMCL levels estimated by a state for these constituents, so that the water may be aesthetically acceptable as well as potable.

Removal of various forms of iron and manganese

Although iron and manganese, both soluble and insoluble, are found in many forms in oxygenated surface-water supplies, their presence in filtered samples of the water is quite limited, seldom or rarely exceeding 1 mg/L, as previously noted. As a result, their removal after any pretreatment is usually incidental to the conventional processing of the water by coagulation and flocculation (Chap. 5), sedimentation (Chap. 6), and filtration (Chap. 7).

Coagulation and filtration alone cannot be depended on to remove soluble manganese. Pretreatment (excluding aeration) with one or more oxidants, as described under their application, oxidizes the soluble manganese to the very insoluble manganese dioxide. The presence of a coating of the dioxide on the sand grains in a filter not only aids in reducing the manganese to the SMCL of 0.05 mg/L, but helps to produce finished water whose manganese content approaches the suggested limit of 0.01 mg/L, an "ideal-quality water."

The organic color in surface water is usually associated with soft water containing little or no alkalinity.[27] Apparently, only a small fraction of the organic color is complexed with iron. If the color in the effluent resulting from any pretreatment and the conventional processing of the water by coagulation, flocculation, sedimentation, and filtration exceeds the objective of 10 units[4] or less, and certainly if it exceeds the SMCL of 15 units,[26] it is probably because the definite narrow pH range for coagulation is not being maintained.

When alum is used as a coagulant, different degrees of color removal from different water have been observed.[11] It is suggested that color removal improves with increased presence of iron. As chelates and organic complexes, iron forms colloidal dispersions or suspended colloids that apparently are more receptive to removal than the uncomplexed organic color colloids.[11] Many investigators have found ferric sulfate to be an excellent coagulant when used in a pH range of 6 to 8.5.

If the oxygenated surface-water supply requires softening by the lime-soda process (see Chap. 10), any iron, soluble or insoluble, and any manganese, soluble or insoluble, are removed along with the other hardness. The process is very effective in removing the difficult to remove manganese, because of the high pH in the reactor.

Groundwater supplies have only three forms of iron and manganese that must be removed to their SMCL or less. They are the ferrous iron ion, Fe^{2+}, and its usually colored organic complexes, in significant concentrations up to a normal maximum of 25 mg/L; the manganous manganese ion, Mn^{2+}, and its organic complexes, in concentrations that rarely exceed 1 mg/L; and the color, only a small fraction of which is complexed with iron and possibly manganese.

Colored water is not necessarily surface water.[8] Organic color in groundwater is usually associated with soft water in shallow wells. When a colored groundwater contains 5 to 10 mg/L of iron, thereby requiring sedimentation, three kinds of treatment are possible. Treatment can conform to pretreatment by aeration followed by conventional processing of the water through coagulation and flocculation, sedimentation, and filtration, using the coagulation procedure outlined for colored surface water.[8,27] Alternatively, treatment can consist of pretreatment by aeration and chlorine, chlorine dioxide, or ozone; or coagulation, flocculation, and settling and addition of iron in the form of ferric sulfate as a floc former, if required, in a solids-contact-type (sludge blanket) reactor that permits the higher oxides of iron and manganese to play a role in the oxidation of any iron and manganese that may be in solution. Or treatment may consist simply of filtration.

When the colored groundwater contains 5 to 10 mg/L of iron, treatment can take place in an iron and manganese removal plant, where it consists of aeration, detention, and filtration with chlorine, chlorine dioxide, or ozone as a part of the pretreatment. (Note: Chlorine alone may not be adequate.) However, with lower concentrations of iron, treatment preferably takes place in the solids-contact type of plant described above, except that 1 to 3 grains of ferric sulfate per gallon is added as a floc former. As an oxidant for color removal, chlorine dioxide is more effective than chlorine, and ozone is more effective than chlorine dioxide.[28]

The ferrous iron ion, Fe^{2+}, and the manganous manganese ion, Mn^{2+}, can be simultaneously removed with the other hardness in groundwater using zeolite water softeners (Chap. 10). Care must be taken to prevent air from entering the water softener. If this occurs, iron precipitates form, resulting in clogging or fouling of the ion-exchange resin bed. The iron and manganese leakage will not average more than 1 percent of the influent, or either 0.1 mg/L of iron or 0.05 mg/L of manganese, whichever is greater. The ion-exchange capacity of the resin must not exceed 50 percent of the raw water's total hardness, up to 50 mg/L maximum iron. Records indicate that water containing several milligrams per liter of iron and manganese has been treated in zeolite water softeners to obtain an essentially iron-free and manganese-free soft water. However, removing iron and manganese by other methods, such as aeration, detention, and filtration, prior to utilizing ion exchange for softening, is now a more common municipal water treatment practice.

Water softeners remove hardness to a desired minimum level; in municipal supplies the standard is 3 to 5 grains per gallon. Part of the unsoftened water must bypass the softeners and be reblended with the treated water.

If the blended finished water contains iron and manganese in excess of their SMCLs, manganese zeolite units, discussed later in the text, are placed in the bypass line to remove the iron and manganese but not the other hardness. This is a very simple and effective way to treat groundwater containing 1.0 mg/L or less iron and manganese.

The removal of ionized iron and manganese by the hydrogen cation exchanger of a demineralizer system is incidental to the demineralization of the water. Usually, the water used for demineralizing is a good-quality finished water.

The ferrous iron and manganous manganese ions in anaerobic carbonate-bearing water can be almost completely precipitated as carbonates at a pH of 8.0 and 8.5, respectively, by the addition of lime or soda ash.[4] When this anaerobic water is softened by the lime-soda process, where the pH is about 11.0, the ferrous ion and the manganous manganese are precipitated as their hydroxides, $Fe(OH)_2$ and $Mn(OH)_2$.

Much less soluble iron and manganese compounds result when the ferrous iron ion, Fe^{2+}, is oxidized to the ferric ion, Fe^{3+}, and precipitated as ferric hydroxide, $Fe(OH)_3$, and the manganous manganese ion, Mn^{2+}, is oxidized to the tetravalent (quadrivalent) manganese ion, Mn^{4+}, and precipitated as manganese dioxide, MnO_2; through their agglomeration, they are readily removed from the water by filtration.

Using two of the most frequently quoted solubility equilibrium constants, the solubility of ferric hydroxide at a pH of 6.0 is about 3.3×10^{-9} mg/L, and the constant indicates that the insolubility increases 1000-fold for each unit increase in pH. Manganese dioxide is just as insoluble. Thus, the solubility of the precipitates is so negligible as to be of academic interest only.

The actual precipitation and agglomeration of the iron and manganese are not instantaneous. Important to the design and operation of a treatment plant including iron and manganese removal are the conditions under which these hydrous derivatives can be completely precipitated in a reasonable period of time. The time required to accomplish this is dependent on the oxidant and on the chemical environment in the water in which oxidation and precipitation occur. Information related to this, along with information on the application of the oxidants, is presented below.

Design Principles and Practices

Chemistry of the oxidation of iron and manganese

Chemical oxidation processes were used early in the eighteenth century for conversion and modification of undesirable substances in water.[29] In these few early instances, simple aeration of public water supplies was used to enhance the oxidation of decomposed vegetation and animal matter to less offensive forms.[30] During the latter half of the nineteenth century, aeration of public water supplies became a more general practice. This included the use of atmospheric oxygen for the removal of iron. After the turn of the twentieth century, stronger and more effective oxidants than oxygen began to be used in water treatment plants for iron and manganese removal. These additional oxidants were chlorine, chlorine dioxide, potassium permanganate, and ozone.

These oxidants do not actually react with the divalent ferrous iron, Fe^{2+}, or the divalent manganous manganese ion, Mn^{2+}, as indicated by these symbols. Instead, they react with their respective divalent ions,[31] the hexaaquoiron(II) ion, $Fe(H_2O)_6^{2+}$, and the hexaaquomanganese(II) ion, $Mn(H_2O)_6^{2+}$. Although it is understood that these divalent aquo ions do exist and do play an important role in oxidation by oxidants and in sorption by certain hydrous metallic oxides and hydroxides, they are generally written as Fe(II) and Mn(II) to indicate their valence. Similarly, trivalent ferric iron is written Fe(III), and tetravalent (or quadrivalent) manganese as Mn(IV).

In the oxidation of the divalent ferrous iron, Fe(II), to the trivalent ferric iron, Fe(III), the oxidation state of the iron is increased by one valence. In the oxidation of the divalent manganous manganese, Mn(II), to the tetravalent manganese, Mn(IV), the oxidation state of the manganese is increased by two valences. Therefore, discounting any difference in the molecular weights of iron and manganese, the divalent manganese requires twice as much oxidant as does the divalent iron. However, since the molecular weight of manganese is 1.63 percent less than that of iron, the divalent manganese, Mn(II), actually requires 2.033 times as much oxidant as does the divalent iron, Fe(II).

The chemistry of iron and manganese oxidation is not clearly understood, as there are no simple relationships among the species present, the pH, and the redox potential. The designer's intent is to cause insoluble forms of iron and manganese to form during oxidation, with the precipitates being removed by subsequent processes. The precipitates formed appear to be affected by the rate of oxidation, with more rapid oxidation resulting in hydroxyl precipitates and slower reactions resulting in the formation of carbonates.[69]

The existence of considerable concentrations of ferrous iron in anaerobic groundwater and the excessive presence of manganese in the hypolimnion of reservoirs is well documented. Not so well publicized is the fact that water treatment plant operators who treat raw water from a reservoir are also well aware that occurrence of a high iron concentration in the hypolimnetic zone during periods of stagnation and stratification of the reservoir is common.[32]

The most commonly used oxidants are oxygen, chlorine, chlorine dioxide, and potassium permanganate. The amount of oxidant required, the alkalinity consumed, and an estimate of the sludge produced are given in Tables 11.1 and 11.2. The use of ozone will be discussed separately.

Reaction Kinetics

Reaction with oxygen

The rate of oxygenation of ferrous iron for any given pH in the presence of ample oxygen is a function of the ferrous iron concentration,

TABLE 11.1 Oxidation of Iron

Reaction	Oxidant, mg/mg Fe^{2+}	Alkalinity used, mg/mg Fe^{2+}	Sludge,* lb/lb Fe^{2+}
A. Oxygen $4Fe(HCO_3)_2 + O_2 + 2H_2O = 4Fe(OH)_3 + 8CO_2$	0.14	1.80	1.9
B. Chlorine $2Fe(HCO_3)_2 + Ca(HCO_3)_2 + Cl_2 = 2Fe(OH)_3 + CaCl_2 + 6CO_2$	0.64	2.70	1.9
C. Chlorine dioxide $Fe(HCO_3)_2 + NaHCO_3 + ClO_2 = Fe(OH)_3 + NaClO_2 + 3CO_2$	1.21	2.70	1.9
D. Potassium permanganate $3Fe(HCO_3)_2 + KMnO_4 + 2H_2O = 3Fe(OH)_3 + MnO_2 + KHCO_3 + 5CO_2$	0.94	1.50	2.43

*Sludge weight based on $Fe(OH)_3$ as the precipitate. It is highly probable that portions of the sludge will consist of $FeCO_3$.

TABLE 11.2 Oxidation of Manganese

Reaction	Oxidant, mg/mg Mn^{2+}	Alkalinity used, mg/mg Mn^{2+}	Sludge,* lb/lb Mn^{2+}
A. Oxygen $2MnSO_4 + 2Ca(HCO_3)_2 + O_2 = 2MnO_2 + 2CaSO_4 + 2H_2O + 4CO_2$	0.29	1.80	1.58
B. Chlorine $Mn(HCO_3)_2 + Ca(HCO_3)_2 + Cl_2 = MnO_2 + CaCl_2 + 2H_2O + 4CO_2$	1.29	3.64	1.58
C. Chlorine dioxide $Mn(HCO_3)_2 + 2NaHCO_3 + 2ClO_2 = MnO_2 + 2NaClO_2 + 2H_2O + 4CO_2$	2.46	3.60	1.58
D. Potassium permanganate $3Mn(HCO_3)_2 + 2KMnO_4 = 5MnO_2 + 2KHCO_3 + 2H_2O + 4CO_2$	1.92	1.21	2.64

*Sludge weight based on MnO_2 as the precipitate. It is highly probable that portions of the sludge will consist of $MnOOH$ and $MnCO_3$.

with the rate decreasing as the iron concentration decreases. Chemically speaking, this is a first-order reaction, which mathematically results in a straight line for any given pH when the logarithm of the ferrous iron concentration is plotted as a function of time.[32]

The oxygenation of ferrous iron is very strongly pH-dependent, increasing 100-fold for each unit increase in pH at a given temperature in the presence of a constant excess of dissolved oxygen in the water.[32] The oxygenation is less dependent on temperature, but nevertheless increases about tenfold for a 27°F rise in temperature. In bicarbonate water with a temperature of 60°F, the oxygenation reaction proceeds very slowly at a pH of 6.5, but at a pH of 6.9 and 7.2, the times required for a 90 percent completion of the reaction are approximately 43 and 8 min, respectively.[30,32] At the same temperature and a pH of 7.9, the oxygenation is 90 percent complete in less than 1 min.

High alkalinity also favors the oxygenation of ferrous iron.[33] In order to obtain immediate oxidation of the ferrous iron in low-alkalinity groundwater, it is necessary to raise the bicarbonate alkalinity to 100 to 130 mg/L,[9] expressed as $CaCO_3$. The solubility of iron and manganese is frequently controlled by the carbonate form in the pH range of 6.5 to 9.5.[68]

Most organic impurities in the water are known to hasten oxygenation reactions.[32] However, ferrous iron is quite capable of forming organic complexes, mostly colored, with humic acids, as noted previously; it also forms mostly colored complexes with tannic acids and other products of vegetative decay. These complexes can completely retard the oxidation of the ferrous iron for several days, even in the presence of dissolved oxygen.[34] Thus, aeration may be ineffective in water with complex organics.

The cupric copper ion, Cu^{2+}, is an efficient catalyst in the oxygenation of ferrous iron. Even trace quantities of this ion have a pronounced effect on the reaction rate. Its effectiveness is not reduced when it becomes complexed with organic matter. The catalyst has no effect on the temperature dependence of the reaction, however.

The divalent manganous manganese ion, Mn(II), as well as anions which form complexes with Fe(III), such as the monovalent dihydrogen phosphate ion, $H_2PO_4^-$, and the monovalent metaphosphate ion, $(PO_3^-)_n^1$, are also capable of acting as catalysts to hasten the oxygenation of ferrous iron.[32] Silica likewise catalyzes the oxidation reaction.[35]

It is often assumed that the precipitates of hydrous ferric oxides or hydroxides have a catalytic effect on oxidation of the ferric iron in aerated bicarbonate water. This is not evident in the oxygenation of the ferrous iron in the pH range most conducive to oxidation; the rate of oxygenation is independent of the Fe(III) concentration.[32] Also, the addition of ferric hydroxide at a lower pH failed to have any catalytic effect on the oxidation of ferrous iron in aerated water.[36]

The oxygenation of water containing manganous manganese normally leads to its precipitation as manganese dioxide or to its removal from the water in the manner described below. The rate of oxygenation of Mn(II), like that of Fe(II), is strongly pH-dependent. The rate of oxygenation is relatively slow below a pH of 9.5, but when that pH is reached, the rate of oxygenation increases substantially.[37]

The oxygenation of manganous manganese not only depends on the pH and other variables, but is further complicated by autocatalysis by manganese dioxide.[30] Since the rate of oxygenation is relatively slow at a pH of less than 9.5, the effect of the presence of manganese dioxide on the removal of Mn(II) is of the utmost importance. It has been shown that the major effect of manganese dioxide is to absorb Mn(II).[37]

The sorption of Mn(II) on manganese dioxide increases about 2.5-fold, from about 0.3 mg Mn(II) per mg MnO_2 expressed as Mn(IV), or per 1.58 mg MnO_2, at a pH of 7.0, to about 0.75 mg Mn(II) per mg MnO_2 expressed as Mn(IV), or per 1.58 mg MnO_2, at a pH of 8.0. It means that Mn(II) can be effectively removed from the water by sorption on manganese dioxide in the pH range shown in Fig. 11.1 without raising the pH to a level that, in most cases, is too high to be practical. All that is required is to have the Mn(II) in the water come in contact with previously precipitated manganese dioxide. The

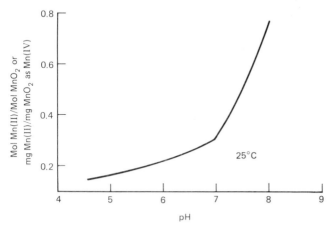

Figure 11.1 Mn(II) sorption by MnO_2 as a function of pH. (*Reprinted with permission from J. J. Morgan and Werner Stumm, "The Role of Multivalent Metal Oxides in Limnological Transformation as Exemplified by Iron and Manganese," Proc. 2d Intl. Conf. Water Pollution Research, Pergamon Press PLC, Oxford, England, 1964.*)

autocatalytic action is "self-serving," producing additional manganese dioxide, and thereby making more of it available for further sorption of any Mn(II) that may be present in the water.

The Mn(II) is also adsorbed on ferric hydroxide or the hydrated oxides. The sorption of Mn(II) on these precipitates, expressed as ferric hydroxide, is also pH-dependent, increasing as the pH increases, and markedly so after the pH reaches 8.2, as shown in Fig. 11.2.[30,40] The sorption of Mn(II) on ferric hydroxide increases about threefold, at about 0.2 mg Mn(II) per mg $Fe(OH)_3$ expressed as Fe(III) or per 1.9 mg $Fe(OH)_3$ at pH 8.7. It means that Mn(II) can be effectively removed from the water by sorption on ferric hydroxide or hydrated oxides in the pH range shown in Fig. 11.2 without raising the pH to a level that, in most cases, is too high to be practical. All that is required is to have the Mn(II) in the water come in contact with previously precipitated ferric hydroxide or hydrated oxides. Thus, the pH range most propitious for the precipitation of ferric hydroxide or ferric oxides by oxygenation is also the pH range most favorable for the sorption of Mn(II) on both ferric hydroxide or ferric oxides and manganese dioxide.

A study of the rate of oxygenation into the high pH range shows that with 10 mg/L of Mn(II) and without mixing, which helps to keep sorption of the Mn(II) at a minimum, the reaction is 90 percent complete in a little less than 15 min at a pH of 9.95; by interpolation of the data, the Mn(II) is reduced to 0.05 mg/L or less in a few minutes at a pH of about 10.1.[36]

Manganous manganese, like ferrous iron, is quite capable of form-

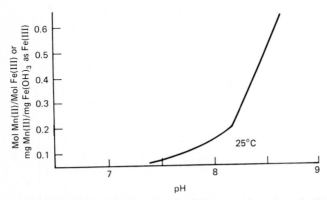

Figure 11.2 Mn(II) sorption by $Fe(OH)_3$ as a function of pH. (*Reprinted with permission from J. J. Morgan and Werner Stumm, "The Role of Multivalent Metal Oxides in Limnological Transformation as Exemplified by Iron and Manganese," Proc. 2d Intl. Conf. Water Pollution Research, Pergamon Press PLC, Oxford, England, 1964.*)

ing organic complexes, mostly colored, with humic acids and other products of vegetative decay. These complexes, like those of ferrous iron, retard the oxygenation of the manganous manganese.

Reaction with chlorine

When chlorine gas or hypochlorites are added to water, they hydrolyze to establish an equilibrium between the undissociated hypochlorous acid, HOCl, and the hypochlorite ion, OCl^-. At a pH of 5.0 or less, the chlorine is present almost entirely as the undissociated hypochlorous acid; at a pH of 7.5, it is 50 percent undissociated hypochlorous acid and 50 percent hypochlorite ion; but at a pH of 10.0 or greater, it is present as the hypochlorite ion. The total chlorine applied to a water at any pH is referred to as free available chlorine. The amount remaining after the chlorine demand of the water is satisfied is referred to as a free available chlorine residual or simply free chlorine residual, except under certain conditions when ammonia-nitrogen is present.

When ammonia-nitrogen is present in the water in a concentration that is sufficient or more than sufficient to unite with the free available chlorine, chloramines are formed. The amount of chloramine remaining after any chlorine demand has been satisfied is referred to as a combined chlorine residual, or simply a chloramine residual. In a process developed in 1940, often called break-point chlorination, chlorine is present in excess of the ammonia-nitrogen in an amount sufficient to oxidize the ammonia-nitrogen as a part of the chlorine demand of the water. The excess or unreacted portion of the applied chlorine is, of course, a free chlorine residual. Chlorination to the point where such a residual is created is frequently called free residual chlorination.

The actual oxidant for the oxidation of Fe(II) and Mn(II) in the water is free available chlorine, proportioned, depending on the pH of the water, between the undissociated hypochlorous acid and the hypochlorite ion, as described above. Chlorination followed by filtration is often used for iron and manganese removal for water with an iron concentration of less than 2 mg/L.[64]

Chlorination of the water to a chlorine residual, be it a free chlorine residual or, in the presence of ammonia-nitrogen, a chloramine residual, immediately oxidizes the ferrous iron to ferric iron. As a result, the iron is immediately precipitated by the alkalinity of the water as ferric oxide or ferric hydroxide. In other words, the oxidation of the ferrous iron, like that of hydrogen sulfide, is part of the immediate chlorine demand of the water.

The chlorination of water containing manganous manganese to a free chlorine residual, even by the break-point chlorination process if necessary, leads to precipitation of hydrous manganese dioxide over a wide pH range. The rate of oxidation of the manganous manganese is pH-dependent. It takes about 12 h at a pH of 6.0. At a pH of 8.0 and alkalinities of 50 mg/L or more expressed as $CaCO_3$, the required time may be approximately 2 to 3 h.[18] As the pH increases further, the time required keeps diminishing until the pH reaches that required for the softening of the water by the lime-soda process, where the oxidation appears to be completed within a few minutes.[18] The presence of cupric copper ions in water containing free available chlorine tends to speed the oxidation of Mn(II).

Reaction with chlorine dioxide

The first commercial installation of chlorine dioxide (Chap. 13) was at Niagara Falls in 1944. Originally, the process was developed and installed for the control of taste and odor resulting from phenolic contaminants. It soon gained reasonably wide acceptance as an oxidant for the removal of other taste and odor compounds. During the years of its use, it has also been found useful in the removal of organic color, as noted previously, and for iron and manganese removal, particularly the latter.[51] When chlorine dioxide is applied to water, it is presumed to oxidize the ferrous iron at least as fast as does free available chlorine. The efficiency and speed of chlorine dioxide oxidation of Mn(II) appear to depend to a large degree on the pH of the water, just as with chlorination. The best results are obtained when the pH is more than 7.0.[18] This is known to be a rather rapid reaction, as indicated by the response when chlorine dioxide is added to a manganese-bearing water.

Reaction with potassium permanganate

Potassium permanganate was first employed for water treatment in England about 1913,[30] although it was found to be effective in an aeration and filtration plant treating water for the removal of iron and manganese in 1907. At that time, however, the addition of such a chemical, even lime, was considered expensive and troublesome, and required close supervision of daily variations in the water to avoid overdosing or underdosing, which would always be an important consideration.[43] Overdosing can result in a residual pink color which will give rise to consumer complaints. In recent years, potassium permanganate has gained widespread use in water treatment both for taste and odor control (Chap. 9) and for removal of iron and manganese. Removal of 12.8 mg/L of iron along with 1.2 mg/L of manganese has been reported.[66] The oxidation of ferrous iron by potassium permanganate is known to be a rather rapid reaction, and presumably follows the other oxidants in being somewhat faster than the oxidation of the Mn(II). The rate of oxidation of the manganous manganese by potassium permanganate is pH-dependent. At pH 4.0, 5.0, 6.0, and 7.0, it takes about 30 min, 10 min, 4 min, and 1½ min, respectively, to complete the reactions. At a pH of 7.5 or greater, the oxidation is completed immediately after the addition of the potassium permanganate.

Application of primary oxidants

Application of oxygen.   Aeration is a necessary first step in removing the iron and manganese from anaerobic water. Aeration results in the rapid absorption of oxygen from the atmosphere and releases hydrogen sulfide and carbon dioxide (Chap. 4). The release of carbon dioxide raises the pH of the water and promotes the precipitation of the ferrous iron as a ferric hydroxide, carbonate, or oxide. Open aeration will not remove all the free carbon dioxide, and the reduction is less with highly alkaline or highly buffered water.[21]

The first iron-removal plant in the United States was placed in operation in 1893 at Atlantic Highlands, N. J., and it used aeration and filtration. During the first two decades of this century, aeration and filtration plants continued to be constructed to treat groundwater with iron concentrations up to 5 mg/L. The plants were effectively accomplishing aeration, detention, and filtration.[41] Settling following aeration had been considered, but over the years it was found that it did not add greatly to the effectiveness of iron removal unless the quantities of iron were so high as to require coagulation to hasten sedimentation. In addition to the precipitate, a rather stable sol is formed which does not settle well and gives a rather opalescent appearance to the water. To remove the iron in this condition, of course, filtration is necessary.[21] During these early years, gravity filters were used almost exclusively, but pressure filters began to be widely employed in water treatment plants in the 1920s.

Many of the early aerators, which later became known as contact aerators, were composed of trays containing crushed coke, and iron-bearing water from wells was sprayed on beds of coke which were 6 to 10 ft in depth. At first called "tricklers," these were the predecessors of what became known as "contact filters." In order to provide a large solids contact surface, the filter medium usually consisted of anthracite, coke, gravel, marble, or limestone.[21]

Many advantages were claimed for contact filters, and by 1950 numerous installations of this type were said to be economically justified. One advantage, certainly, was that the contact filters provided the beneficial effects of a much greater contact surface than did the contact aerators.[21] The "tricklers" apparently originated in New England,[41] and for much of the water in that area, the iron and manganese were removed in plants consisting of aerators, contact filters (usually coke) of considerable volume, sedimentation tanks, and final filters.[42]

When a fine medium is used in a contact filter, a large amount of surface area is provided, and there is sufficient space to accumulate the precipitated iron. Such a filter is produced by the use of anthracite. Since the contact filter strains out other suspended matter as well as the iron precipitates, it was concluded that a sedimentation tank or sand filter could be eliminated.[21] Since then, even as they became more frequently used, the word "contact" in relation to such filters has become less frequently used in the technical literature on iron and manganese removal.

Contact aerators, particularly the early multiple-tray aerator using coke trays (see Chap. 4) and the staggered-slat trays that came into use later, have continued to be employed for the removal of iron and manganese in aeration, detention, and filtration plants. They are described later in this chapter.

As pressure and forced-draft aerators were introduced, they soon became widely employed in aeration and filtration plants and in aeration, detention, and filtration plants for the removal of iron. It should be pointed out, however, that because of the presence of the ferric precipitates, plants using pressure or forced-draft aerators should be able to scavenge from the water, through sorption, very small concentrations of any manganese that may be present.

Aeration and filtration plants and aeration, detention, and filtration plants are used when the groundwater contains 5 to 10 mg/L of iron. It is claimed that the most common method of removing iron and manganese from municipal water supplies in the United States involves the second type of plant, employing one of the previously mentioned types of multiple-tray contact aerators.[4] On the other hand, it is also claimed that the method of aeration and filtration employed in the earliest plants for iron removal still predominates today.[4]

Not until 1901 was it shown that carbon dioxide is liberated when iron is precipitated.[43] When aeration, detention, and filtration plants were placed in operation in this country, lime or soda ash was frequently added to the detention basin following aeration to raise the alkalinity to 100 to 130 mg/L and hasten the precipitation of iron.

If the cupric copper ion, Cu^{2+}, applied as copper sulfate, $CuSO_4 \cdot 5H_2O$ (weighing 3.93 times as much as the Cu) (Chap. 13), is used as an oxygenation catalyst, it is generally applied ahead of the aerator. At one plant, the oxidation of ferrous iron to ferric iron required 180 min. With 0.01 mg Cu/L, little effect was noticed. However, with 0.1 mg Cu/L, the time was reduced to 30 min, and with 1.0 mg Cu/L, the time was further reduced to 10 min. At another location, the oxidation required 90 min, but when 0.1 mg Cu/L was added, the time was reduced to 18 min.[44]

If the iron concentration in the groundwater is 5 to 10 mg/L, pretreatment by aeration can be followed by the conventional processes of coagulation, flocculation, sedimentation, and filtration. Without coagulation and flocculation, the oxidized iron may take 12 to 24 h or more for effective settling, whereas in a properly coagulated water settling will normally take place in approximately 2 h.[21] If Mn(II) is present, pretreatment with one or more oxidants is required, as noted previously for surface water containing Mn(II), and as mentioned under the application of these other oxidants.

Besides the sorption of Mn(II) in a typical iron and manganese removal plant, it was realized at least as early as 1916 that manganese is effectively removed by filtration through sand on which a coating of manganese dioxide has developed.[45] Over the years many conventional water treatment plants have continued to remove manganese in this manner.

In an iron- and manganese-removal plant, the solids contact reactor also affords the coagulation, flocculation (Chap. 5), and sedimentation (Chap. 6) required for groundwater containing 5 to 10 mg/L of iron. In such a plant, the reactor is preceded by an aerator and followed by a filter, as discussed later in this chapter. Lime may be employed for pH adjustment (Chap. 13). Additional iron in the form of ferric sulfate (15 to 50 mg/L) as a floc former may be required.

After coagulation and flocculation, the water passes upward through the sludge blanket, supported by the rise rate or overflow rate in gallons per square foot of effective surface area per minute. The sludge blanket, for this particular application, normally has a suspended solids concentration of about 0.8 to 1.0 percent, or 8000 to 10,000 mg/L, consisting mostly of ferric oxides or ferric hydroxide along with calcium carbonate and some hydrous manganese dioxide. This makes available the very best contact filter, one that cannot clog and that has an infinite sorption capacity. As the water passes upward through the sludge blanket, it absorbs the residual Mn(II), that is, the manganous manganese ions that were not oxidized during coagulation. Some of these absorbed ions are subsequently oxidized by the dissolved oxygen in the water and precipitated as manganese dioxide.

Operating at the proper oxidation state and pH is extremely important if satisfactory removal rates are to occur. Low-alkalinity water is likely to have residual iron and manganese concentrations controlled by hydroxyl species, while higher-alkalinity water will frequently be controlled by the carbonate species present in the pH range of 6.5 to 9.5.

The minimum solubility of ferric hydroxide occurs over a pH range of 7 to 10, while the minimum solubility of ferrous hydroxide occurs near pH 12.[68,69] Because of the complex factors affecting these reactions, designers frequently choose to use bench-scale tests, pilot plants, or full-scale testing to determine the optimum process and operating conditions.

Chlorine application.   In many instances, the addition of chlorine following aeration in either aeration, detention, and filtration plants or aeration, sedimentation, and filtration plants aids in the oxidation. As an example, when iron consistently passes through the filters, prechlorination may be practiced as a remedial measure. Some of the procedures that may be used to control bacterial growths in the filters include not only more frequent backwashing and installing a surface and air wash, but also disinfecting the filter with chlorine at doses of up to 1000 mg/L.[4,48]

Some surface-water supplies in the south have a shallow storage reservoir or lake ahead of the water treatment plant. Much of this water has a low pH and low alkalinity and is manganese-bearing. Heavy doses of chlorine, providing a high free available chlorine residual to the water at the inlet end of bodies of water providing 24 h or more of detention, have very successfully oxidized the manganous manganese, causing it to precipitate as manganese dioxide.[49] When prechlorination of the raw water is used to remove manganese in surface water in a conventional water treatment plant, free residual chlorination must be practiced; a minimum of 0.5 mg/L of free available chlorine must be maintained throughout the treatment area. The designer needs to be aware that this procedure may cause the formation of chlorination by-products such as trihalomethanes if precursor material is present.

Manganous manganese is oxidized as it passes through the settling basin in the filters. Although oxidized Mn(II) is insoluble in water, the particles are very small, do not settle well, and at first have a tendency to pass through the filters. Within a short time after the chlorination process is started, however, the sand grains of the filter will become jet black if manganese alone is present, and a deep mahogany color if iron is also present. This is due to the coating of manganese dioxide alone or manganese dioxide and the ferric oxides or ferric hydroxides. When the sand grains are coated as described, the filters no longer pass manganese because of the sorption and autocatalytic processes mentioned previously. The deposit on the sand grains is necessary to prevent the passage of manganese, and should never be cleaned off.

Experience with the use of cupric copper ions as a catalyst in the presence of free available chlorine for the oxidation of Mn(II) was noted as early as 1948 in Louisiana.[18] In the aeration, chlorination, settling, and filtration plant at Lake Charles, the addition of copper sulfate (0.2 mg/L as copper, Cu) ahead of the aerators completely removed the manganese in less than 30 min when the chlorine demand was slightly oversatisfied.[50] Wong showed that chlorination followed by filtration on dual media (anthracite and sand) gave better results than filtering on anthracite alone.[64] Iron and manganese concentrations in the range of 1 to 5 mg/L were almost completely removed at a filtration rate of 5 gpm/ft^2. As previously mentioned, a disadvantage of this process is the potential formation of chlorinated organic compounds such as trihalomethanes.[64]

Application of chlorine dioxide.   In Georgia, the addition of chlorine dioxide to the detention basin in iron- and manganese-removal plants consisting of aeration, detention, and filtration very successfully removes the iron and manganese in groundwater containing up to 2 mg/L of iron and manganese combined.[49]

Although chlorine dioxide is very effective in removing manganese from high-manganese surface water, the point of application in the plant is important to its effectiveness. When chlorine was applied to the raw water at the entrance to the mixing chamber and chlorine dioxide was applied to the water as it left the settling basin for the filters, the filter runs dropped from 15 to 25 h to about 2 to 3 h. However, when the chlorine dioxide application was moved back to the middle of the baffled mixing chamber, excellent manganese removal was obtained without decreasing the normal filter runs. Other benefits were a noticeable improvement in floc formation and better settling characteristics.[49]

The use of chlorine dioxide as pretreatment in colored water containing organically complexed iron and manganese has been discussed previously. Chlorine dioxide has an advantage over chlorine in that it does not form trihalomethanes, although very little is known about any health hazards associated with its by-products. In addition to the reactions previously indicated for iron and manganese, the chlorite (ClO_2) which is formed as a by-product will also cause reduced manganese to precipitate as manganese dioxide. Organically bound iron and manganese are also reportedly oxidized.[70]

Application of potassium permanganate. Potassium permanganate has two important applications. One is its use as an oxidant, like chlorine and chlorine dioxide, to be added to a water supply to remove iron and manganese, particularly the latter. The other is its use as an oxidant with manganese zeolite filters.

In the conventional processing of surface water by coagulation, flocculation, sedimentation, and filtration, it has been recommended that potassium permanganate be added to the raw-water intake or lowlift pump station to allow a longer contact time for the permanganate to do its work.[52] However, experience has shown that the simultaneous addition of potassium permanganate and coagulant at the rapid mix tank, at a normal pH, usually gives good results.[49,52] This conforms with the rapidity of the reactions of the permanganate with the manganous manganese at a pH of 6.0 or greater, as previously described.

Chlorine may be added first to oxidize the iron and to satisfy at least a portion of the chlorine demand.[18] The oxidation can then be completed by the permanganate.[18] The order of chemical addition is very important when Mn(II) is to be removed. The order in plant practice should adhere to that used in the laboratory to determine chemical dosages.[18,53] For example, at one plant,[53] the order at first was chlorine (5- to 10-min contact), alum, lime, and potassium permanganate. When polyelectrolytes were used, the order became chlorine, lime, potassium permanganate, alum, and polyelectrolytes.

The manganese in a surface-water supply with a pH of 6.5 to 7.0 can readily be removed in a solids-contact type of reactor, using alum as a coagulant, by applying sufficient potassium permanganate at least 4 min ahead of the alum. This allows complete oxidation of the Mn(II) and reduction of the manganese in the permanganate to manganese dioxide, which is coagulated along with the alum.[54] The removal of manganese from water by means of insoluble higher oxides of manganese and instantaneous action of natural or artificial zeolites whose bases are replaced by manganese dates back at least to 1908, when a German patent was issued for the process.[55] Today, this is known as the manganese zeolite process.

The manganese zeolite process differs from the sodium ion-exchange process in that it is strictly an iron- and manganese-removal process and not a water softening process, and it is regenerated with a solution of potassium permanganate instead of a solution of common salt.[18] The manganese zeolite is made from processed green sand by alternate treatments with a manganous compound and potassium permanganate, producing higher oxides of manganese in and on the granules of green sand.[56]

The original manganese zeolite units were regenerated in batches with potassium permanganate to restore their oxidizing capacity.

However, this becomes uneconomical at high flows and high iron/ manganese concentrations, as the regeneration requires an excess of regenerant, which is wasted. In addition, the beds clog rapidly when the water has high iron content. By 1968, therefore, the process was rapidly being replaced by a continuous potassium permanganate feed system.[56]

This system, like the batch-regeneration system, employs sorption and oxidation,[30] but it carries the processing one step further by also using oxidation as a first step ahead of the manganese zeolite bed. Thus, potassium permanganate is added ahead of the manganese zeolite filter, which, in this system, uses a layer of anthracite on top of the bed. The Fe(II) and Mn(II) in the groundwater are oxidized by the potassium permanganate, and the resulting precipitates accumulate on and in the anthracite layer. The bed and anthracite, therefore, operate basically as filter media. When the iron and manganese deposits have built up, the unit is backwashed like an ordinary sand filter.[56]

In addition to its basic function as a filter bed, the manganese zeolite actually acts as a buffer. It oxidizes any residual Fe(II) and Mn(II) if the potassium permanganate dosage is slightly low, and removes any excess unreacted permanganate, partially regenerating the manganese zeolite bed, when the dosage is high. The bed acts like a water tower floating on the line, providing capacity in times of high demand and storing up excess in times of low demand.[56]

With a manganese zeolite filter, it is generally desirable to raise the pH of the groundwater with an alkali to between 7.5 and 8.0. In this pH range, not only the Fe(II) but also the Mn(II) is oxidized by the potassium permanganate almost instantaneously, as noted previously.[56]

The widest application of the manganese zeolite process is in the range of 0.5 to 5.0 mg/L of Fe(II) and Mn(II). There are, however, certain applications where the concentration of Fe(II) and Mn(II) can be much higher. In fact, the process has easily handled 18 mg/L of Fe(II) in combination with several mg/L of Mn(II).[57]

The use of potassium permanganate for the oxidation of manganese in organic complexes has been monitored,[30,58] although detailed information appears to be lacking. Since potassium permanganate is such a powerful oxidizing agent, it seems very logical that it would have that capability.

Ozone

Two hundred years have elapsed since Van Marum noted the pungent odor of ozone in 1781. It was not until 1867 that it was found to be composed of triatomic oxygen, O_3. The first use of ozone for water treatment was in 1893, for water sterilization in Holland. The first major treatment plant installation was in Nice, France, in 1906. Before 1970, there were only two drinking-water plants using ozone in the United States. Today there are more than two dozen plants using ozone, mostly for oxidation of impurities, not for final disinfection.[67]

Ozone has not been widely employed in this country for several reasons. It cannot compete in cost with chlorine, and while it is possible to maintain a chlorine residual throughout a water distribution system, ozone has a half-life of only 20 min in water, and its decomposition is catalyzed by many metals, such as iron. Many regulatory bodies require a chlorine residual throughout the distribution system, precluding the use of ozone. However, ozone treatment remains an alternative to other oxidants for the oxidation of iron and manganese.[61]

Although ozonation is an effective treatment technique for iron and manganese removal, it is seldom used for this purpose in the United States. It may be ineffective when humic or fulvic materials are present. Overdosing with ozone can also cause pink water, as permanganate may be a product of the reaction.

Design and Process Criteria for Iron- and Manganese-Removal Plants

Although there are a very large number of iron- and manganese-removal plants in operation, employing various combinations of principles and equipment already discussed, for the purposes of this portion of Chap. 11, seven different plants will be described:

- Aeration and filtration using pressure aeration
- Aeration, detention, and filtration using forced-draft aeration
- Aeration, detention, and filtration using multiple-tray aerators
- Manganese zeolite filter system
- Zeolite softener with manganese zeolite on bypass portion
- Aeration, settling, and filtration
- Chlorination and filtration

Effective filtration is a major component of successful iron and manganese removal. The medium should be carefully selected and usually has a large effective size (>1.5 mm). Green sand is normally not used, except for small systems, as it has a small effective size. For smaller systems, green sand can be intermittently treated with permanganate, which allows for unattended operation.[69] A manganese dioxide coating can be formed on the medium by initially feeding with caustic soda. The coating will become established in a few months, and the hydroxide feed can then be discontinued.

Aeration and filtration using pressure aeration

In operation, as water is pumped from the well, it passes through an orifice on the main line, with a fixed portion passing through an air saturator tank. A level control in the air saturator tank will activate air flow from the compressor. Flows are then recombined downstream from the orifice and delivered to a pressure filter. This system will saturate only a portion of the flow with oxygen (air) to prevent supersaturation of the flow to the filter. Figure 11.3 gives a schematic representation of this type of system.

Alternatively, the air saturator tank may be mounted so that the total flow passes through it, and a controlled amount of air may be introduced through a diffuser or sparger.

Oxidized iron precipitated from solution is removed by the pressure filter. Either sufficient iron-free backwash water must be provided from the system, or nonaerated water must be fed to the filter for backwash and rewash.

Effluent of the pressure filter is delivered to service. Generally, some storage facility—elevated or hydropneumatic—is incorporated.

Aeration, detention, and filtration using forced-draft aeration

Well water is directed through an aerator (more fully described below) where air (oxygen) is introduced for the oxidation of iron and manganese to their higher valences. The system may be fed by a well pump activated on demand or from a detention basin. When air passes over the water in the aerator, it will also remove a portion of the carbon dioxide (depending on the design), thereby raising the pH of the water and hastening the oxidation and precipitation of the hydroxides of iron and manganese. Although forced-draft aerators with detention basins prior to filtration have been used for iron and manganese removal, their principal application has been in treating water with 5 to 10 mg/L of iron. A schematic representation of such a system is shown in Fig. 11.4.

A detention basin is needed to provide time for the reaction because the reactions are not instantaneous. It must be remembered that pH has a direct bearing on these reaction times. A review of the literature indicates that the detention time can vary from 15 min to 1 h; present design standards call for a detention time of 20 to 30 min in the de-

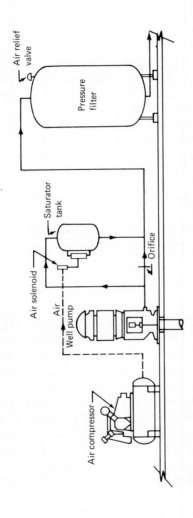

Figure 11.3 Aeration and filtration (using pressure aeration for iron removal).

308

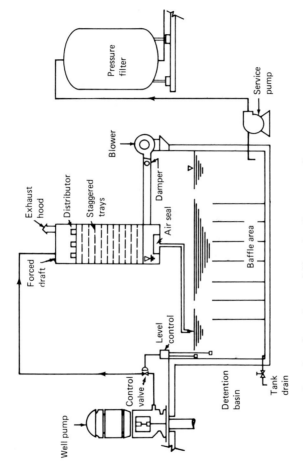

Figure 11.4 Aeration, detention, and filtration (iron removal).

309

tention basin. The oxidized insoluble iron is removed on the filters; hence, there is a limit on the quantity of iron to be removed in this system. Baffles may be used to assure required detention times.

Should the design anticipate 5 to 10 mg/L of iron, the detention basin is replaced by either a sedimentation basin (Chap. 6) preceded by coagulation and flocculation (Chap. 5), or a solids-contact clarifier which includes coagulation and flocculation in a reaction compartment (see Aeration, Settling, and Filtration, below). It follows that the more time provided in the settling basin, the more complete the reaction and the more insolubles precipitated, reducing the load going to the pressure filter following the basin.

In the forced-draft aerator, illustrated in Fig. 11.4, air is introduced into the bottom of the unit by a blower. The air flows upward, contacting the thin films of water flowing downward over a series of staggered trays. The unit is completely enclosed and normally operates at 1 to 3 in static air pressure. The inlet flow is introduced at the top through a baffled distribution system that allows the air to exhaust while maintaining the static pressure.

An alternative to this unit is an induced-draft aerator. In this unit, the blower is mounted on the top and pulls the air upward through screened bottom inlets. Forced-draft or induced-draft aerators are generally square or rectangular, with one removable side for tray cleaning. Originally, the trays were redwood or fir, but they are now aluminum or plastic. The exterior of these units can be marine plywood, coated steel, aluminum, or reinforced fiberglass. Forced-draft or induced-draft aerators are more efficient than staggered-tray or coke-tray units. Forced-draft or induced-draft units operate at a flow 50 percent greater than the staggered-tray or coke-tray units; hence, smaller units can be installed.

Aeration, detention, and filtration using multiple-tray aerators

This system is essentially the same as the preceding one, except for the aeration units. It is commonly used for iron and manganese removal when the combined level of iron and manganese is 5 to 10 mg/L.

The coke-tray aerator unit shown in Fig. 11.5 is in common use today. The flow of water rains down through a distribution system of trays, normally filled to a depth of 4 to 6 in with 2- to 4-in pieces of coke or slag. Perforations in the bottom of the coke trays allow the water to flow through to the collection pan. Units are either square or round, with three to five trays. Air flows over the pans, contacting the thin films of water on the coke and oxidizing the ferrous iron and manganous manganese. After a period of operation, the coke will de-

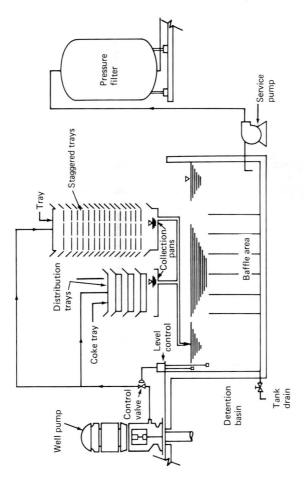

Figure 11.5 Aeration, detention, and filtration (iron and manganese removal).

Pressure filter

Service pump

Staggered trays

Tray

Distribution trays

Coke tray

Collection pans

Level control

Baffle area

Well pump

Control valve

Detention basin

Tank drain

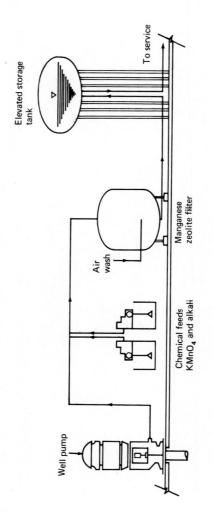

Figure 11.6 Manganese zeolite filter (iron and manganese removal).

velop a coating which actually assists the oxidation process. However, the oxidation products coating the coke will eventually clog distribution and must be cleaned off or the coke replaced.

In a staggered-tray aerator unit, flow is through a distribution tray over a series of staggered trays. Air enters the unit through louvered sides. Generally, for this unit to achieve the equivalent thin film area presented by the coke-tray aerator, it must be taller. The staggered-tray unit and its companion, the cascade aerator, have generally been replaced by coke-tray units or by induced-draft and forced-draft aerators.

Manganese zeolite filter system.   Potassium permanganate and alkali (if required to raise the pH) are fed on the basis of an average permanganate demand. The chemical feed units are activated by the control that activates the well. Oxidation of iron and manganese is accomplished in the line to the filters. The point of chemical application should be as close to the well as possible to allow a greater reaction time (see Fig. 11.6). The oxidation products, precipitates, are removed in the filter in the upper layer of large-sized anthracite particles providing filtration in depth. Since chemicals are fed on the basis of "average" demand, when they are overfed the permanganate is adsorbed on the manganese zeolite. Manganese zeolite is a black, granular material with a screen size of 16 to 50 mesh and a weight of 98 lb/ft^3. Each cubic foot has a capacity of 0.09 lb of iron and manganese. Operating conditions provide filter flows of 3 to 5 gpm/ft^2 with backwash rates of 8 to 10 gpm/ft^2. An "air wash" is generally required when iron entering the system exceeds 3 to 5 mg/L. The higher filter rates are for multiple units, when one unit of a battery is off line for backwash or regeneration. In operation, the effluent of a properly adjusted filter will not have the color indicating the presence of unreacted permanganate.

The system provides the advantages of the pressure air saturator system with single pumping. In addition, depending on the concentration of iron present, units can operate at rates of up to 5 $gal/(min)(ft)^2$. Since the backwash rate requirement is 80 percent of that for a sand filter, less backwash water is used.

Currently manganese zeolite is produced by one manufacturer in the United States. The natural green sand (zeolite) is mined, cleaned, classified, and then activated with manganous chloride to convert it to manganese zeolite.

Zeolite softener with manganese zeolite on bypass portion

This system will provide water with the level of hardness desired, but without iron or manganese. Flow from the well is delivered proportionally to a zeolite softener on the basis of the percentage of hardness removal desired. The zeolite softener will remove the hardness cations, as well as the free cations (not molecules) of iron and manganese. No oxidant or treatment chemicals can enter the well water prior to the zeolite softener, or the unit will soon plug with the oxidation products.

The bypass flow around the zeolite softener is fed chemicals as required (see the discussion of the operation of the manganese zeolite unit above). Flow through the manganese zeolite removes the precipitates of iron and manganese with little or no effect on the hardness cations. When the water is blended with the zeolite softener effluent, the resulting water is at the hardness level desired and essentially free of iron and manganese. This system is schematically represented in Fig. 11.7.

Aeration, settling, and filtration

Where quantities of iron, manganese, or both are high (10 mg/L or greater), this system provides a more efficient removal of the oxidized products prior to filtration. Flow from the well is passed through an aerator. Although a coke aerator is shown in Fig. 11.8, the use of the coke tray and tray aerators is limited to raw water containing less than 30 to 40 mg/L carbon dioxide. As indicated above, in the discussion on aeration, detention, and filtration using forced-draft aeration, the forced- (or induced-) draft aerator unit is smaller than the coke-tray or staggered-tray units, as well as more efficient for both oxidation and carbon dioxide removal. The higher the pH of the water treated, the more rapidly the hydroxides of iron and manganese are formed and precipitated. Process limitations in respect to pH, hardness, and other parameters were discussed in detail earlier in this chapter.

Flow from the aerator is led to a solids-contact clarifier. The detention time in the center reaction compartment (coagulation and flocculation) is not less than 20 min. A higher pH value is achieved not only by use of the aerator, but also with supplemental feeding of an alkali, preferably lime. An acceptable rise rate is 0.6 to 0.8 gpm/ft^2 of effective surface area, which represents a detention time of more than 2 h. Some designers establish the rise rate at the sludge separation zone, in which case the rate should not exceed 1.0 gpm/ft^2. The sidewater depth (SWD) is generally 10 to 12 ft, with a maximum of 17 ft.

Most designs provide an increasing upward cross-sectional area within the clarifier, establishing a blanket of precipitated materials. Since all water passes through this blanket, more complete utilization of chemicals plus the catalytic effect of the previously precipitated materials are obtained. The water is then collected in top launders. As

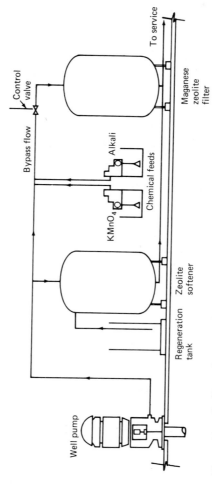

Figure 11.7 Zeolite softener with manganese zeolite on bypass portion (iron and manganese removal).

315

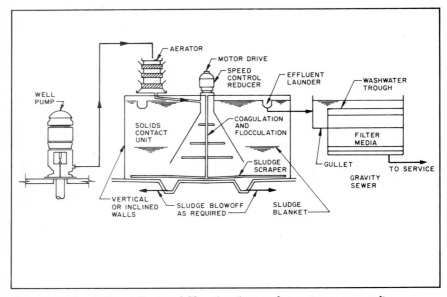

Figure 11.8 Aeration, settling, and filtration (iron and manganese removal).

the sludges form, they become increasingly more dense and settle to sludge-collection hoppers within the unit. The same precautions noted above for sludge disposal apply.

Flow from the clarifier passes to a pump suction tank for repressurization by a transfer or service pump. The water is then pumped either through pressure filters, as shown in Fig. 11.8, or to gravity filters at a higher elevation, or, depending on elevation, it may flow from the clarifier by gravity to gravity filters. Water collected under the gravity filters is then pumped to service.

Sludge withdrawal through a sludge pit is controlled by an adjustable, time-controlled, desludging valve. Where more dense sludges are handled, the sludge withdrawal system should be given a pressure backflush with filtered water after each use, without creating a cross-connection.

Chlorination and Filtration

Other oxidants may be substituted in the previously discussed processes. For example, a commonly used method is chlorination followed by filtration on a monomedia filter. Some pH adjustment may be necessary for optimum removal, and detention times of 10 to 30 min after chlorine addition have been used. A popular filter medium is anthracite. A schematic of this system is shown in Fig. 11.9.[69]

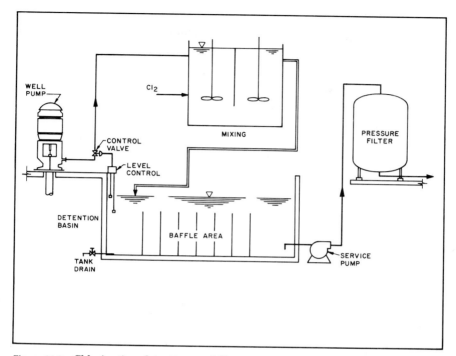

Figure 11.9   Chlorination, detention, and filtration (iron and manganese removal).

References

1. K. T. Stetson, "The Earth, Earth's Constitution," *Encyclopedia Americana,* vol. 9, Americana Corporation, New York, Chicago, Washington, D.C., 1954, p. 487.
2. *Standard Methods for the Examination of Water and Wastewater,* 16th ed., APHA, AWWA, WPCF, Washington, D.C., 1985.
3. H. E. Riehl (ed.), *Hoover's Water Supply and Treatment,* 8th ed., Bull. 21, National Lime Association, Washington, D.C., 1957.
4. J. T. O'Connor, *Iron and Manganese in Water Quality and Treatment,* 3d ed., AWWA through McGraw-Hill, New York, 1970, chap. 11.
5. T. D. Brock, *Biology of Microorganisms,* Prentice-Hall, Englewood Cliffs, N. J., 1970.
6. V. J. Calise and R. F. Dietz, *Iron and Manganese Removal from Municipal and Industrial Water Supplies,* Presented at Joint Meeting of Florida Section of AWWA and the Florida Sewage and Industrial Waste Association, Orlando, Fla., November 7, 1955.
7. P. C. Singer and W. Stumm, "The Solubility of Ferrous Iron in Carbonate-Bearing Water," *Journal AWWA,* vol. 62, no. 3, 1970, p. 198.
8. W. K. Oldham and E. F. Gloyna, "Effect of Colored Organics on Iron Removal," *Journal AWWA,* vol. 61, 1969, p. 610.
9. L. R. Robinson, Jr., and R. I Dixon, "Iron and Manganese Precipitation in Low Alkalinity Ground Waters," *Water and Sewage Works,* vol. 115, 1968, p. 514.
10. T. M. Riddick, N. L. Lindsay, and A. Tomassi, "Iron and Manganese in Water Supplies," *Journal AWWA,* vol. 50, 1958, p. 688.
11. J. Shapiro, "Effect of Yellow Organic Acids on Iron and Other Metals in Water," *Journal AWWA,* vol. 56, 1964, p. 1062.

12. E. S. Hopkins and G. B. McCall, "Manganese in Deep Reservoirs," *Ind. Eng. Chem.*, vol. 33, 1941, p. 1491.
13. H. C. Myers, "Manganese Deposits in Western Reservoirs and Distribution Systems," *Journal AWWA*, vol. 53, 1961, p. 579.
14. R. S. Ingols and R. D. Wilroy, "Observations on Manganese in Georgia Water," *Journal AWWA*, vol. 54, 1962, p. 203.
15. R. S. Ingols and R. D. Wilroy, "Mechanism of Manganese Solution in Lake Waters," *Journal AWWA*, vol. 55, 1963, p. 282.
16. C. P. C. Poon and F. J. DeLuise, "Manganese Cycle in Impoundment Water," *Water Resour. Bull.*, vol. 3, no. 4, 1967, p. 26.
17. R. Schweisfurth, "Causes of Manganese Concentration Increase in Reservoirs," *Staedtehygiene*, vol. 20, no. 7, 1969, p. 167; *Chem. Abstracts* 71, 1969, p. 94621u.
18. A. E. Griffin, "Significance and Removal of Manganese in Water Supplies," *Journal AWWA*, vol. 52, 1960, p. 1326.
19. J. J. Morgan and W. Stumm, "Analytical Chemistry of Aqueous Manganese," *Journal AWWA*, vol. 57, 1965, p. 107.
20. E. J. Connelley, Jr., "Removal of Iron and Manganese," *Journal AWWA*, vol. 50, 1958, p. 697.
21. G. E. Hauer, "Iron and Carbon Dioxide Removal," *Journal AWWA*, vol. 42, 1950, p. 555.
22. J. M. Cohen et al., "Taste Threshold Concentrations of Metals in Drinking Water," *Journal AWWA*, vol. 52, 1960, p. 660.
23. E. L. Bean, "Progress Report on Water Quality Criteria," *Journal AWWA*, vol. 54, 1962, p. 1313.
24. S. B. Applebaum, "Iron and Manganese Removal," *Water and Sewage Works*, vol. 94, 1947, p. 439.
25. *Drinking Water Standards*, U.S. Public Health Service Pub. no. 956, U.S. Government Printing Office, Washington, D.C., 1962.
26. Editor's Note, "EPA Secondary Regulations Promulgated: Effective 1981," *Opflow*, vol. 5, 1979, p. 1.
27. A. P. Black et al., "Stoichiometry of the Coagulation of Color-Causing Organic Compounds with Ferric Sulfate," *Journal AWWA*, vol. 55, 1963, p. 1347.
28. A. P. Black and R. F. Christman, "Chemical Characteristics of Fulvic Acids," *Journal AWWA*, vol. 55, 1963, p. 897.
29. M. N. Baker, "The Quest for Pure Water," AWWA through Lancaster Press, Lancaster, Pa., 1948.
30. W. J. Weber, Jr., *Physicochemical Processes for Water Quality Control*, Wiley-Interscience, New York, 1972.
31. F. A. Cotton and G. Wilkinson, *Advanced Inorganic Chemistry*, 3d ed., Wiley-Interscience, New York, 1972.
32. W. Stumm and G. F. Lee, "Oxygenation of Ferrous Iron," *Ind. Eng. Chem.*, vol. 53, 1961, p. 143.
33. R. Jobin and M. M. Ghosh, "Effect of Buffer Intensity and Organic Matter on the Oxygenation of Ferrous Iron," *Journal AWWA*, vol. 64, 1972, p. 590.
34. T. L. Theis and P. C. Singer, "Complexation of Iron(II) by Organic Matter and Its Effect on Iron(II) Oxygenation," *Environmental Science and Technology*, vol. 8, 1974, p. 569.
35. J. E. Schenk and W. J. Weber, Jr., "Chemical Interactions of Dissolved Silica with Iron(II) and (III)," *Journal AWWA*, vol. 60, 1968, p. 199.
36. E. Nordell, *Water Treatment for Industrial and Other Uses*, 2d ed., Reinhold, New York, 1961.
37. J. J. Morgan, "Chemical Equilibria and Kinetic Properties of Manganese in Natural Waters," *Proc. 4th Rudolfs Conference, Principles and Applications of Water Chemistry*, Wiley, New York, 1967.
38. G. M. Fair, J. C. Geyer, and D. A. Okun, *Water and Waste Water Engineering*, Wiley, New York, 1968.

39. J. J. Morgan and W. Stumm, "Colloid Chemical Properties of Manganese Dioxide," *Jour. Coll. Sci.*, vol. 19, no. 4, 1964, p. 437.

40. J. J. Morgan, "The Chemistry of Aqueous Manganese II and IV," Thesis, Harvard University, Cambridge, Mass., 1964.

41. J. W. Ellms, *Water Purification*, 2d ed., McGraw-Hill, New York, 1928.

42. G. M. Fair and J. C. Geyer, *Water Supply and Waste Disposal*, Wiley, New York, 1961.

43. C. Zapffe, "The History of Manganese in Water Supplies and Methods for Its Removal," *Journal AWWA*, vol. 25, 1933, p. 655.

44. W. Kauffmann, "Influence of Small Quantities of Copper and an Active Form of SiO_2 on Iron Removal," *Journal AWWA*, vol. 39, 1947, p. 808.

45. H. P. Corson, *Manganese in Water Supplies*, Univ. Ill. Bull., Water Survey Series No. 13:144 (1916); *Chem. Abstracts* 11, 1917, p. 1704.

46. Private communication from K. Simmons, General Filter Company, Ames, Iowa, 1981.

47. J. T. O'Connor and B. E. Benson, "Iron Removal Using MgO," *Jour. Sanit. Eng. Div., Am. Soc. Civil Eng.*, vol. 96, no. Sa6, 1970, p. 1335.

48. E. W. Steel and T. J. McGhee, *Water Supply and Sewerage*, 5th ed., McGraw-Hill, New York, 1979.

49. Private communication from S. B. Weill, Wallace & Tiernan, Division Pennwalt Corp., Atlanta, Ga.

50. W. B. Gurney and G. H. West, "Iron and Manganese Removal at Lake Charles," *Proc. 12th Annual Short Course*, La. State Univ., Engr. Exp. Sta. Bull. 18, 1950, p. 31.

51. R. N. Aston, "Developments in the Chlorine Dioxide Process," *Journal AWWA*, vol. 42, 1950, p. 151.

52. H. G. Swope, "Potassium Permanganate for Iron and Manganese Removal," *Water and Sewage Works*, vol. R-208, 1976.

53. R. D. Adams, "Manganese Removal by Oxidation with Potassium Permanganate," *Journal AWWA*, vol. 52, 1960, p. 219.

54. Private communication from K. Ficek, Carus Chemical Company, Div. of Carus Corporation, LaSalle, Ill.

55. R. Gans, Ger. Patent 211,118, Jan. 23, 1908; *Chem. Abstracts* vol. 3, 1909, p. 2725.

56. W. A. Wilmarth, "Removal of Iron, Manganese, and Sulfides," *Water and Wastes Engineering*, vol. 5, 1968, p. 52.

57. K. M. Sayell and R. R. Davis, "Removal of Iron and Manganese from Raw Water Supplies Using Manganese Greensand Zeolite," *Ind. Water Eng.*, vol. 12, 1975, p. 20.

58. A. H. Reidies and E. Mack, "Die Verwendung von Kaliumpermanganat in der Wasseraufbereitung in den USA," *Vom Wasser*, vol. 30, Verlag Chemie, GmbH, Weinheim/Bergstr., 1963.

59. F. L. Evans, III, *Ozone in Water and Wastewater Treatment*, Ann Arbor Science Publishers, Ann Arbor, Mich., 1972.

60. W. O. LePage, "The Anatomy of an Ozone Plant," *Journal AWWA*, vol. 73, 1981, p. 105.

61. R. R. Ferguson and R. O. Day, "Iron and Manganese Removal with Ozone, Part II," *Water and Sewage Works*, vol. 122, 1975, p. 61.

62. C. M. Robson, "Ozone's Many Applications Expands Its Image," *Water and Sewage Works*, vol. R-130, 1979.

63. R. G. Miller et al., "The Occurrence of Aluminum in Drinking Water," *Journal AWWA*, vol. 76, 1984, p. 84.

64. J. M. Wong, "Chlorination-Filtration for Iron and Manganese Removal," *Journal AWWA*, vol. 76, 1984, p. 76.

65. "An AWWA Survey of Inorganic Contaminants in Water Supplies, Committee Report," *Journal AWWA*, vol. 77, 1985, p. 67.

66. M. D. Curry and M. Reynolds, "Using By-Products of an Iron Removal Process to Improve Water Treatment," *Journal AWWA,* vol. 75, 1983, p. 246.
67. R. G. Rice, "Trends in Ozonation," *Journal AWWA,* vol. 77, 1985, p. 26.
68. L. D. Benefield and J. F. Judkins, *Process Chemistry for Water and Wastewater Treatment,* Prentice-Hall, Englewood Cliffs, N.J., 1982.
69. J. M. Montgomery, Consulting Engineers, Inc., *Water Treatment Principles and Design,* Wiley, New York, 1985.
70. E. M. Aieta and J. D. Berg, "A Review of Chlorine Dioxide in Drinking Water Treatment," *Journal AWWA,* vol. 78, 1986, p. 6.

12

Solids Handling, Disposal, and Recovery

Introduction

Increasing restrictions on sludge disposal over the past decade have led to heightened concern for adequate sludge disposal practices. In the 1950s, discharge of sludges to surface water was the most prevalent means of disposal, with 80 to 90 percent of all utilities disposing of sludge in this manner.[29] The 1972 Water Pollution Control Act reversed this trend. Under this act, water utilities are considered to be industries, and discharges to water must meet the requirements of federal laws. The National Pollution Discharge Elimination System (NPDES) established a permit system for water treatment plant discharges. Discharge limitations are currently established on a case-by-case basis. A number of NPDES permits have been issued to water treatment plants, generally using state standards applicable at the time of issuance. Wide variations in permit limitations are found among states; however, sludge discharge into most small or medium-sized streams is prohibited by law in most states.[30]

With restrictions on discharge to surface water, an increasing number of utilities have turned to landfilling as the ultimate sludge disposal method. Many states classify water treatment sludge as an industrial waste, restricting disposal to closely regulated landfills. However, other states allow disposal of sludge in landfills designed for municipal waste.[31] The disposal of liquid or semiliquid sludges at sanitary landfills is becoming increasingly more difficult,[19] and the costs of landfill disposal are also continuing to rise. As a result, more attention must be paid to dewatering sludge prior to disposal. Dewatering creates sludge with a more solid consistency, making it more readily accepted by landfill operators. More significantly, dewatering greatly reduces the volume of sludge to be transported and disposed of, and thus offers the potential for significant cost savings to the water utility.

Sludge Types, Quantities, and Characteristics

The sludge generated from water treatment processes includes suspended solids removed from the raw water and chemical precipitates either added to or removed from the raw water. The various types of sludge resulting from water treatment processes include:

- Waste filter backwash water
- Aluminum or iron coagulant sludges
- Iron and manganese precipitates
- Softening plant sludges

Because sludge disposal is becoming increasingly more difficult, increased consideration must be given to:

- Type of solids
- Quantities of sludge
- Sludge characteristics that may influence sludge dewaterability

Filter Backwash Water

Waste filter backwash water can be troublesome to handle; it has low solids content even after thickening, and usually dewaters poorly. The solids concentration of filter backwash water may vary from 50 to 400 mg/L. A great portion of the solids are difficult to gravity-separate without coagulant aids. Filter backwash water deserves careful consideration not only with regard to solids disposal, but because of the potential recovery of a significant volume of water.

Filter backwash water typically represents 2 to 5 percent of the total water processed, or 20,000 to 50,000 gal per million gallons treated. The solids quantity depends on the filter efficiency and the amount of solids applied to the filter. The amount of solids applied to the filter depends significantly on the pretreatment provided. Where flocculated water is applied directly to the filter, the solids loading is a function of the coagulant dosage and the raw-water turbidity. Where sedimentation precedes the filter, typical suspended solids concentrations escaping the sedimentation basin often range from 4 to 10 mg/L. In water treatment plants, more data are available regarding turbidity applied to filters. Attainable sedimentation-basin effluent turbidities can be less than 1 TU (turbidity unit); however, typical sedimentation effluent turbidities are 2 to 6 TU.

If a suspended solids concentration of 4 to 10 mg/L is applied to the filter, filter backwash water will contain 35 to 85 lb of solids per million gallons processed. If direct filtration of flocculated water is practiced, the solids applied are often higher.

Filter backwash solids are typically difficult to separate from the liquid. Wash-water recovery ponds sized to hold backwash water for 24 h or more may recover up to 80 percent of the solids with the use of polymers or other coagulant aids. The reclaimed water is reprocessed through the treatment plant or discharged to a surface water.

Coagulant Sludges

Aluminum or iron coagulants result in inorganic sludges containing such compounds as aluminum hydroxide and ferric hydroxide along with the clay, silts, organics, and inorganics precipitated by the coagulant. The nature of the sludge produced is highly variable, depending upon the raw-water quality. Seasonal variations in a single raw-water source also affect such characteristics of the sludge as its thickening density and dewaterability.

The characteristics of coagulant sludges vary with the proportion of material removed from the water. High-turbidity waters usually result in sludges that are more concentrated and less difficult to dewater, whereas low-turbidity waters present a more difficult sludge-processing problem. In general, settled iron sludges have a higher solids concentration than alum sludges, while the addition of polymer or lime increases the solids concentration of both. Coagulant sludges are essentially biologically inert, having low biodegradable organic content, and retain a near-neutral pH.

Coagulant sludges such as iron and alum may be characterized as follows:

Solids content	Sludge character
0–5%	Liquid
8–12%	Spongy, semisolid
18–25%	Soft clay
40–50%	Stiff clay

Alum

Alum sludge is a voluminous gelatinous sludge, with poor compactability. It will generally concentrate to 0.5 to 2.0 percent

(5000 to 20,000 mg/L) in sedimentation basins. When filter alum $[Al_2(SO_4) \cdot 14H_2O]$ is added to water, it forms aluminum hydroxide $[Al(OH)_3]$. For every pound of alum added, 0.26 lb of aluminum hydroxide is formed. The quantity of aluminum escaping the filters and appearing in the finished water is dependent on the pH.

Determination of coagulant dosage and sludge quantities, if not derived from field experience at existing facilities, should be developed from a series of jar or pilot tests. Tests and sludge quantity analyses should be made seasonally to account for variations in water quality.

The suspended matter in the raw-water supply is usually reported in turbidity units (TU). There is no absolute correlation between turbidity units and total (dry weight) suspended solids (TSS); however, based on observed values where both parameters have been measured, the ratio of TSS to TU normally varies from 1.0 to 2.0 and often can be as high as 10.0. To estimate the solids residue from alum coagulation, two examples are shown below:

Example 1.   Low-Turbidity Water Supply

Raw-water turbidity	10 TU	
Alum dose	30 mg/L	
Aluminum hydroxide sludge	30 mg/L × 8.34 × 0.26 =	65 lb/mil gal
Raw-water solids	10 TU × 1.5* × 8.34 =	125 lb/mil gal
	Total	190 lb/mil gal

*1.5 is the assumed ratio of TSS/TU.

Example 2.   High-Turbidity Water Supply

Raw-water turbidity	150 TU	
Alum dose	60 mg/L	
Aluminum hydroxide sludge	60 mg/L × 8.34 × 0.26 =	130 lb/mil gal
Raw-water solids	150 TU × 1.5* × 8.34 =	1876 lb/mil gal
	Total	2006 lb/mil gal

*1.5 is the assumed ratio of TSS/TU.

Generally, sludges from treating high-turbidity raw water will thicken to higher concentrations than will sludges from treating low-turbidity water. For the two examples shown above, the sludge volume at 1.0 percent concentration will represent 2300 gal/mil gal and 24,000 gal/mil gal, respectively, or 0.2 and 2.4 percent of the treated water flow.

When considering recovery of alum, the aluminum content and dissolved inorganic and organic solids are of importance.[4,5,6] Various reported alum sludge characteristics are shown in Table 12.1.

TABLE 12.1 Alum Sludge Characteristics

		Rochester‡	Shoremont‡	Kodak‡	Sturgeon Point‡	Indianapolis§	Concord§	Tampa§	Moline§	Washington§
Raw-water turbidity	Jtu	—	—	—	—	45	42	0.6	71	18
Alum dosage	mg/L	25	18	24	15	24	41	100	43	20
Other dosage	mg/L	17*	7†	10*	—	—	—	—	—	—
Sludge solids	lb/10^6 gal	210	116	143	100	—	—	—	—	—
Organic solids	%	—	—	—	—	21	46	33	15	42
Total aluminum	mg/L	—	—	—	—	2400	2400	3500	2950	3750

*Clay.
†Clay, carbon, starch.
‡From R. M. Gruinger, "Disposal of Waste Alum Sludge from Water Treatment Plants," *Journal WPCF*, vol. 47, 1975, p. 535.
§From D. A. Cornwell and J. A. Susan, "Characteristics of Acid Treated Alum Sludges," *Journal AWWA*, vol. 71, no. 10, 1979, p. 604.

Iron salts

Iron coagulants include ferric sulfate [$Fe_2(SO_4)_3$], ferrous sulfate ($FeSO_4 \cdot 7H_2O$), and ferric chloride ($FeCl_3$). The precipitate formed is ferric hydroxide [$Fe(OH)_3$]. Like alum sludges, ferric hydroxide is hydrophilic and thickens poorly. The amount of sludge formed should be determined from experience or from jar tests conducted on the proposed water supply. To estimate the solids residue from ferrous sulfate coagulation, an example is shown below:

Low-turbidity water supply		
Raw-water turbidity	10 TU	
Ferric sulfate dose	15 mg/L	
Ferric hydroxide sludge	$15 \times (^{107}/_{278}) \times 8.34 =$	48 lb/mil gal
Raw-water solids	$10 \text{ TU} \times 1.5^* \times 8.34 =$	125 lb/mil gal
	Total	173 lb/mil gal

*1.5 is the assumed ratio of TSS/TU.

A 1.0 percent concentration of sludge for the above example represents 2100 gal/mil gal or 0.2 percent of the treated water flow.

Iron and Manganese Precipitates

Soluble iron and manganese are oxidized by aeration or the addition of permanganate, chlorine, or ozone, to form precipitates such as ferric hydroxide, ferric carbonate,[32] or manganese dioxide. Following oxidation, these precipitates can be removed in sedimentation or filtration processes. The sludge produced is inert and is typically red or black in color.

For each milligram per liter of iron or manganese in solution, 1.5 to 2 mg/L of sludge production may be anticipated. However, since the concentrations of iron and manganese found in most natural water are typically low, overall iron and manganese sludge volume is generally much lower than the volume of coagulation or softening sludge.[2]

Based on field experience,[32] iron and manganese sludge removed from filters by backwashing settles sufficiently in 2 h to allow decanting and recycling of backwash water to the head of the water plant. The sludge volume remaining varies considerably. Typical values are 10 to 30 percent of the total backwash water volume.

Softening-Plant Sludges

Softening of water with lime and/or soda ash produces sludge containing precipitants such as calcium carbonate, calcium sulfate, magnesium hydroxide, silica, iron oxides, aluminum oxides, and unreacted lime. Coagulated organics and inorganics typically constitute a small fraction of the sludge mass. When highly turbid waters are treated, the turbidity is normally removed by coagulation prior to softening. Softening sludge is relatively inert and stable. Lime sludges are also biologically inert as a result of their high pH, which is due to unspent lime and high alkalinity. The sludge normally is easier to concentrate than coagulant sludges. The solids content of lime sludges typically ranges between 2 and 15 percent.[2]

The quantity of lime-softening sludge produced at water treatment plants varies greatly, depending on the hardness of the raw water, the raw-water chemistry, and the desired finished-water quality. The volume of softening sludge produced is typically much greater than that produced by coagulation processes. Reported quantities are shown in Table 12.2. The lime-softening sludge solids will normally concentrate in the sedimentation basin to 10 percent. At 10 percent concentration, 2200 lb/mil gal will produce a sludge volume of 2600 gal/mil gal of treated or input water.

Lime-softening sludge dewaterability varies with the amount of magnesium hydroxide that has been captured with the sludge. Magnesium hydroxide will range from a few percent to as much as 30 percent. Sludges that are low in magnesium hydroxide may be dewatered to cakes having 60 percent solids, whereas cake solids may be as low as 20 to 25 percent with higher magnesium hydroxide concentrations. The magnesium hydroxide solids are gelatinous and similar in nature to aluminum and iron coagulant solids. The calcium carbonate solid is more discrete and crystalline, and thus is more readily dewatered.

Lime-softening sludges are primarily calcium carbonate with varying amounts of other constituents, as shown in Table 12.3. The character of lime sludges at varying moisture contents is generalized as follows:

Solids content	Sludge character
0–10%	Liquid
25–35%	Viscous liquid
40–50%	Semisolid, toothpaste consistency
60–70%	Crumbly cake

Many utilities report that lime sludge cakes in the 50 to 65 percent moisture content range are sticky and difficult to discharge cleanly from dump trucks.

Design Considerations and Criteria

Methods for processing and disposing of the waste solids should be investigated in the planning phase. Sludge disposal may represent a

TABLE 12.2 Softening-Plant Sludge Quantities†‡

	Flow, mgd	Chemical dosages, lb/mil gal		Ratio, lb solids/lb lime dose	Reported sludge, lb/day
		Lime	Soda ash		
Austin, Tex.	45	750	—	3.8	91,200
Corpus Christi, Tex.	56.3	428	—	2.6	46,600
Dallas, Tex.	36.5	342	—	2.2	80,000
Des Moines, Iowa	30.2	1830	197	2.8	560,000
El Paso, Tex.	19.0	825	145	3.4	—
Fort Wayne, Ind.	27.0	1746	268	2.0	135,000
Grand Rapids, Mich.	6.0	1350	—	2.0	18,000
Kansas City, Mo.	97.9	1410	—	1.8	—
Louisville, Ky.	109.8	348	—	4.5	116,000
Minneapolis, Minn.	73.5	1014	284	2.0	138,000
New Orleans, La.	120.3	637	143	1.6	304,000
Oklahoma City, Okla.	11.9	1045	—	2.5	183,000
Oklahoma City, Okla.	21.0	336	—	.1.4	174,000
Oklahoma City, Okla.	14.7	906	—	2.1	272,000
Omaha, Neb.	46.8	705	63	2.0	70,600
Toledo, Ohio	80.4	602	24	2.0	168,000
Topeka, Kan.	15.7	1500	.250	1.8	—
Wichita, Kan.	34.2	900	—	1.5	12,300
Pontiac, Mich.	10.0*	2200	—	2.5	—
Miami, Fla.	180.0*	1800	—	2.2	—
Lansing, Mich.	20.0*	2200	—	2.3	—
Dayton, Ohio	96.0*	2140	—	2.5	—
St. Paul, Minn.	120.0	990	—	2.4	—

*Plant capacity.
†From AWWA *Water Treatment Plant Waste Committee Report*, unpublished data, December 1971.
‡From AWWA, *Water Quality and Treatment*, 3d ed., McGraw-Hill, New York, 1971.

TABLE 12.3 Lime-Softening Sludge Characteristics

	Boulder City, Nev.*	Miami, Fla.*	Wright Aero, Cincinnati, Ohio*	St. Paul, Minn.*	Lansing, Mich.*	Wichita, Kan.†	Vandenberg, Calif.‡	Columbus, Ohio§
Silica, iron, aluminum oxides	2.6	1.5	4.4	2.0	—	0.6–2.0	7	2–5
Calcium carbonate	87.2	93.0	88.1	85.0	80–90	89–98	85	87–91
Calcium hydroxide	—	—	—	—	—	—	1	—
Magnesium hydroxide	7.0	1.8	2.2	6.2	4–6	0.4–3.5	7	2.4

*From P. C. Singer, "Softener Sludge Disposal—What's Best," *Water and Waste Engineering*, vol. 11, no. 12, 1974, p. 25.
†From Black and Veatch, Engineers–Architects, "Report on Water Treatment Plant Waste Disposal," Wichita, Kan., December 1969.
‡From Charles Lawrence, "Lime Soda Sludge Recirculation Experiments at Vandenberg Air Force Base," *Journal AWWA*, vol. 55, no. 2, 1963, p. 177.
§From M. A. Burris et al., "Coagulation Sludge Disposal Studies for a Surface Water Supply," *Journal AWWA*, vol. 68, no. 5, 1976, p. 247.

substantial portion of the investment and operating costs of providing treated water and may influence the raw-water source selection and the method of treatment. When evaluating design alternatives for processing and disposing of waste solids, the following items should be considered:

- Minimizing sludge quantities by sludge quantity reduction and recovery of coagulants
- Sludge handling and transport
- Sludge dewatering techniques
- Sludge disposal
- Recovery and reuse of coagulants or lime

Minimizing Sludge Quantities

Sludge handling and disposal costs can be reduced by:

- Reducing sludge production through process modifications
- Recovering spent coagulants and lime for reuse

Process modifications for sludge quantity reduction

Polymers can be used to replace or enhance the performance of coagulants such as alum or ferric chloride. For some water, the ratio of alum dose to polymer dose required for effective coagulation is approximately 50:1; this results in a sludge production ratio of aluminum hydroxide to polymer of 7:1.[19] Thus, a significant reduction of sludge volume is realized.

In lime-softening plants where a significant fraction of the hardness is attributed to magnesium, split-flow lime softening can reduce total sludge production compared with excess lime softening. A high pH is necessary for the removal of magnesium hardness. In addition, most of the calcium hardness must be removed before magnesium hardness will precipitate. In split flow, the lime dose required to treat the entire flow is added in the first softening basin. Magnesium and calcium hardness precipitate in the primary softening basin as a result of the elevated pH. Unreacted lime enters the recarbonation basin or second softening basin, where it removes additional calcium hardness from the bypassed raw water. Because less lime is used than in excess lime softening, total sludge production may be lower.

Alternative water supplies (i.e., softer water) that may result in smaller sludge quantities can be considered. Where softening of a water supply is required, alternative processes can be selected. The softening plant can be operated to selectively remove only the calcium fraction of the total hardness. Higher magnesium concentrations may reduce the life of hot water heaters and boilers, however. Ion exchange may be also selected depending on the geographical location. Although increased sodium in the finished water is undesirable, regeneration of lime from chemical process sludges is rarely economical.

Recovery of coagulants

Recycling and recovery of coagulants has been examined as a means of helping to resolve the waste disposal problem of water treatment plant solids. Recalcination of spent lime is a proven technology in many locations, as discussed in Chap. 10. The recovery and reuse of coagulants has been more elusive. Recent technology in alum recovery shows promise, and research efforts are being made to recover and reuse spent iron coagulants.

Alum.   The traditional scheme for alum recovery consists of thickening, reducing the pH, and separating residual precipitates from the dissolved aluminum decant. The recovered alum solution is decanted from the separation stage and reused. Aluminum recoveries of 60 to 80 percent have been reported at pH levels of 3.0; however, some locations require pH values as low as 1.0. To form 1.9 lb of alum, 1.9 lb of sulfuric acid is required to react with 1 lb of aluminum hydroxide. This acidic alum recovery process was eagerly pursued in several Japanese water treatment plants, but concern about the potential buildup of heavy metals in the recovered alum stopped further use of the process in 1972. Metals such as chromium and iron can be converted to a soluble form during acidification. Other metals and impurities may be present in the sulfuric acid, and these impurities may become concentrated in the recovered alum.[19] Further detractions for the process included the expense and the critical operating control required.

More recently a promising liquid ion-exchange process is being applied to alum sludge recovery.[26] Thickened alum sludge is acidified to a low pH (about 2.0), separated from remaining precipitates in a sedimentation tank, and subjected to liquid ion exchange. The aluminum is extracted into a liquid carrier that is immiscible in water and separated. The aluminum in the separated liquid carrier is stripped with sulfuric acid, and the carrier liquid is recycled. The extractant is selective for aluminum, which results in no buildup of impurities or heavy metals. A 95 percent recovery of alum is achievable under laboratory conditions.

If sodium aluminate proves to be a good coagulant for a specific water, then the alkaline method of alum recovery may be applicable. The aluminum can be redissolved from the alum sludge by raising the pH to 12 to 12.5 with sodium hydroxide. This converts the aluminum hydroxide to sodium aluminate. Aluminum recoveries of 90 to 95 percent are reported.

Iron coagulants. The recovery of iron coagulants involves acidification of the ferric hydroxide and a recovery technique very similar to that described for the acidic alum recovery process. The pH must be reduced to 1.5 to 2.0 to attain 60 to 70 percent recovery of iron. Because of the expense and the poor dewatering characteristics of the sludge, there has been little interest in this process. On a laboratory scale,[11] a sulfide-reducing agent used to convert the ferric to ferrous ion in conjunction with acid resulted in 60 percent recovery of iron and a pH of 3.0.

Lime. A coagulant recovery technique for lime-softening plants has also been developed.[27] It is based on a combination of water softening and conventional coagulation procedures which can be applied to all types of water. Magnesium carbonate is used as the coagulant, with lime added to precipitate magnesium hydroxide as the active coagulant. The resulting sludge is composed of $CaCO_3$, $Mg(OH)_2$, and the turbidity removed from the raw water. The sludge is carbonated by injecting CO_2 gas, which selectively dissolves the $Mg(OH_2)$. The carbonated sludge is filtered, with the magnesium being recovered as soluble magnesium bicarbonate in the filtrate. The magnesium bicarbonate coagulant is then recycled to the point of chemical addition to the raw water, where it is precipitated as $Mg(OH)_2$, and a new cycle is initiated. The filter cake produced in the separation step contains $CaCO_3$ and the turbidity removed from the raw water.

The process may be expanded to recover the lime. The filter cake ($CaCO_3$ plus turbidity particles) is slurried and processed in a flotation unit to separate the turbidity particles from the $CaCO_3$. The purified $CaCO_3$ can then be dewatered and recalcined to quicklime. Recalcination of lime is discussed more extensively in Chap. 10.

Handling and Transport

Methods for transporting water treatment plant solids are similar to other material-handling methods. Sludge in liquid form may be pumped through pipelines or trucked. Alternatively, sludge in cake form may be trucked or barged.

Dilute concentrations of coagulant sludges flow by gravity, or may be pumped using centrifugal pumps with nonclog impellers. Gravity sewers should be designed to maintain nonsettling velocities at minimum flows. Lime sludge or thickened alum sludge (8 to 15 percent) should be pumped with a positive displacement pump. Precautions are required to protect pumps and pipeline materials from corrosion and abrasion. Scaling of pipelines has not been reported to be a severe problem, since the chemicals are stable. Abrasion of pump impellers is common with all water treatment plant sludges. In some instances pneumatic ejectors have been used to transport sludges[16] to avoid abrasion problems with pump elements. Conveyor belts or screw conveyors are commonly used for thickened lime sludge (30 percent or greater) and thickened coagulant sludges (15 percent or greater).

Trucking of sludges to remote sites has often resulted in solids compression as a result of vibration and release of free water. The truck should be watertight. Lime sludge frequently is very sticky and adheres to the truck container. Special surfaces on the container shell should be considered to reduce adherence.

Sludge Dewatering Techniques

The general goal of dewatering techniques is to reduce the bulk of the sludge and produce a material that is suitable for convenient disposal or recovery processes.

Gravity thickening

Gravity thickening of solids is practiced to reduce the bulk of material to be disposed of, to provide a more consistent feed material, and to reduce the size of subsequent dewatering units. Recovery of filter wash water by thickening is often provided in open lagoons. Polymer addition is used to increase particle size and reduce solids carryover in the reclaimed wash water.

Basin coagulant sludge drawn off at less than 1 percent solids can often be thickened to 2 percent solids. Aluminum and iron hydroxides may be conditioned with the aid of polymers. However, while polymers will affect particle size and enhance settling velocity, and may also improve capture efficiency and reduce the detention time required for a given degree of thickening, they will have minimal effect on the ultimate degree of compression (Fig. 12.1).[17] Typical design parameters reported for alum sludge thickening are 100 to 200 gal/(day)(ft^2) when conditioned with polymers. Alum sludges mixed with clay or lime have exhibited thickened concentrations of 3 to 6 percent and 9 percent, respectively,[3,16] at higher overflow rates than sludges without clay or lime.

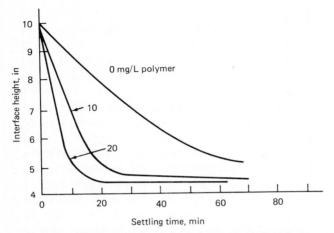

Figure 12.1 Effects of polymer dosage on the rate of thickening of metal hydroxide suspensions. (*Source: W. R. Knocke, "Thickening and Conditioning of Chemical Sludges," Proc. ASCE Environmental Engineering Conference, San Francisco, Calif., July 1978.*)

Lime sludge thickening provides more concentrated solids and a more consistent feed material for dewatering units. Solids loading from 60 to 200 lb of solids per square foot of thickener surface area per day are common. Reported thickening performance for the lime-softening sludge solids is presented in Table 12.4. High magnesium hydroxide concentrations reduce sludge dewaterability and thus will reduce the density of the thickened sludge.

Vacuum filtration

Vacuum filtration of metal hydroxide coagulant sludges is often ineffective. The dilute solids (even if thickened), a high compressibility, and resistance to flow of water through the sludge result in low yields and poor recoveries of hydroxide sludges. When chemically conditioned with polymers and when large concentrations of inert

TABLE 12.4 Gravity Thickening Performance on Lime-Softening Sludges*

Location	Solids input, %	Solids output, %
Boca Raton, Fla.	1–4	28–32
Dayton, Ohio	2–4	15–25
Lansing, Mich.	12–16	20–25
Ann Arbor, Mich.	9	20
Miami, Fla.	30	40
Cincinnati, Ohio	5	15

*From P. C. Singer, "Softener Sludge Disposal—What's Best," *Water and Waste Engineering,* vol. 11, no. 12, 1974, p. 25.

solids are present, vacuum filters can dewater alum sludges to 20 percent solids.[34] The use of a diatomaceous earth precoat on the vacuum filter has also been suggested as a means of attaining a 20 percent cake (including the precoat solids).

The vacuum filter is effective for dewatering lime-softening sludges. Yields of 10 to 20 $lb/(ft^2)(h)$ are typical for sludges with high magnesium hydroxide content, and yields of 40 to 90 $lb/(ft^2)(h)$ have been reported for sludges with low magnesium hydroxide content. Although cake solids content is typically 40 to 50 percent, some applications attain as high as 70 percent solids content.[9] Supplemental chemical conditioners are not used, and solids recovery ranging from 96 to 99 percent can be expected.[18]

Filter press

The filter press is applicable for dewatering metal hydroxide coagulant and lime-softening sludges; however, it has primarily been used for metal hydroxide coagulant sludges. Filter presses are often used for difficult sludges because the batch operation can keep the solids under pressure for extended periods of time until the desired consistency is attained. Filter presses are less frequently used for lime-softening sludges.

With alum or iron salt sludges, either polymer conditioning, lime conditioning, or diatomaceous earth precoat is often required. Fly ash may also be appropriate. Cake solids content of 20 to 50 percent results with pressing cycle times of from 2½ to 22 h.[19] Typical cycle times are 8 h. Filter cloth life is reported to be 12 to 18 months.[20]

Pilot filter presses used to dewater alum sludge[1] resulted in filter cake solids content of 40 to 50 percent using 25 percent lime and 2 percent precoat. Cycle times ranged from 1.5 to 2 h.

Belt press

Belt presses applied to coagulant sludges result in cake solids of 15 to 20 percent when aided by 10 to 20 lb of polymer per ton of solids. The capture efficiency ranges from 90 to 99 percent. A belt press evaluated on alum sludge at the Erie County, N. Y., plant[21] produced 8 to 12 percent solids using 10 to 14 lb of polymer per ton of solids. Filtrate solids concentrations were 25 to 60 mg/L.

Centrifuges

The basket centrifuge operates semicontinuously. Batches of sludge are fed to the unit for concentration of solids. Recoveries are about 90 percent without polymer and 99 percent with 1 to 2 lb of polymer per ton of waste solids. Mixtures of lime and alum sludges experience thickened cake concentration of 15 to 40 percent.[21] Thickening of alum sludge alone using basket centrifuges produced an 11 percent cake after a 40-min cycle.[1] Waste filter backwash has also been concentrated using basket centrifuges, producing a 6 percent cake in 20 min without polymer and a 10 percent cake in 80 min with polymer.

The bowl centrifuge is a continuous process in which the slurry is fed into the bowl and the cake is drawn up a bench and discharged while the concentrate overflows a dam. The unit operates in a manner similar to a clarifier under higher gravitational forces. The bowl centrifuge may be used to selectively separate magnesium hydroxide from calcium carbonate or to produce a cake. The separation of magnesium hydroxide precipitate from calcium carbonate precipitate is desirable when the waste lime sludge is to be recalcined; however, separation is difficult to achieve with many waters. Magnesium hydroxide may also be recovered by carbonation of the calcium carbonate/magnesium hydroxide sludge; this will solubilize the magnesium and result in a high magnesium content in the centrate. Separation of the magnesium and calcium precipitates with a centrifuge results in 60 to 75 percent of the magnesium in the centrate. With the recarbonation/magnesium carbonate recovery process, magnesium recovery of 80 percent in soft water and nearly 100 percent in hard water is achievable.

Applying the bowl centrifuge to alum sludges produces widely varying results. It is reported at Lancaster, Pa., that using 1 to 2 lb of polymer per ton of solids yields 98 percent recovery with a 30 percent cake. In other locations with low-turbidity water, as much as 4 lb of polymer per ton of solids may be required to produce a 15 percent cake. The Sturgeon Point Plant in Erie County, N. Y., reported 24 to 28 percent cake with about 98 percent recovery using 3 lb per ton of polymer.[3] Alum sludges containing high levels of raw-water turbidity, clay additives, or lime may be expected to produce higher cake solids concentrations with lower polymer requirements than pure alum sludges.

When the bowl centrifuge is used for dewatering lime-softening sludge, it yields a cake solids concentration ranging from 33 to 70 percent, as shown in Table 12.5. Minneapolis experiences a seasonal variation in solids concentration. During summer conditions, the raw water is softer and the lime dosage is lower; however, greater water production results in about the same quantity of waste solids. Sludge produced during the summer is more difficult to dewater and requires polymer to achieve 90 percent recovery.

Drying beds

Drying beds consist of sand underdrained with gravel and perforated pipe. In dry climates, shaped, shallow, earthen basins without

TABLE 12.5   Solid Bowl Centrifuge Results for Lime Sludge (Percent Solids)

Location	Feed	Cake	Centrate	Comment
Dayton, Ohio*	15–25	60	—	
Lansing, Mich.*	20–25	62–67	—	
Ann Arbor, Mich.*	20	60–65	—	
Miami, Fla.*	40	65	—	
Cincinnati, Ohio*	15	65–70	—	
Minneapolis, Minn.†	8.6	33.5	1.02	2.1 lb polymer/ton
Minneapolis, Minn.†	8.6	55	3.8	
Minneapolis, Minn.†	13.8	62.7	1.65	

*From M. A. Burris et al., "Coagulation Sludge Disposal Studies for a Surface Water Supply," *Journal AWWA,* vol. 68, no. 5, 1976, p. 247.

†From L. G. Hagstrom and N. A. Mignone, "Centrifugal Sludge Dewatering Systems Can Handle Alum Sludge," *Water and Sewer Works,* vol. 125, no. 5, 1978, p. 54.

underdrains are used which rely solely upon evaporation to separate solids from the water. With either type of drying bed, sludge storage facilities must also be provided for periods when climatic conditions prevent effective dewatering. Several designs incorporate additional drying beds that are used to hold sludge until the right season. The size of drying beds should be based on the effective number of uses that may be made of each bed and the depth of sludge that can be applied to the bed:

$$A = \frac{V}{N \times D \times 7.5}$$

where A = drying bed area, ft^2
N = number of uses for beds each year
D = depth of sludge to be applied, ft
V = annual volume of sludge for disposal, gal

The number of times that the beds may be used is dependent upon the drying time and the time required to remove the solids and prepare the bed for the next application. The bed is usually considered dewatered when the sludge can be removed by earth-moving equipment (such as a front-end loader) and does not retain large quantities of sand. Alum sludges generally attain solids concentrations of 15 to 30 percent, and lime-softening sludges attain 50 to 70 percent solids content. Alum sludges require from 3 to 4 days to drain;[18] but the use of polymers may accelerate this to 1.5 to 3 days.[22] These are optimal times and do not reflect realistic field conditions. Both field tests and a detailed study of climatic variations are required in order to apply this option. It is estimated that the number of bed uses will range from 1 to 20 per year, depending upon the climate; the usage rate may be increased if polymers are used. In northern locations, drying beds are sometimes designed for one use per year, partially to take full advantage of the natural freezing.

The depth at which sludge may be applied will range from 8 to 30 in for coagulant sludge and from 12 to 48 in for lime sludge. Greater sludge depths will require proportionally longer drying times. Alum sludge at Kirksville, Mo., required 20 h per percent solids concentration for an 8-in application, and 60 h per percent solids concentration for a 16-in application. In order to obtain a dewatered cake on the bed with a finished thickness suitable for removal with a front-end loader, at least 16 to 24 in of sludge should be applied. For example, for a 1 mgd average treated water quantity, 2000 lb of sludge per million gallons treated, and 20 bed uses per year, a 2 percent concentration sludge applied at a 16-in depth will require:

$$A = \frac{4,357,000}{20 \times 1.33 \times 7.5} = 22,000 \text{ ft}^2$$

If the drying beds are designed for use once per year to take advantage of natural freezing, a maximum sludge depth of 10 to 12 in is recommended.

Freezing

Freezing of waste alum solids causes the water in the gelatinous material to crystallize; upon thawing, the water does not return to the solid, but leaves a granular (coffee-ground consistency) solid. Solids concentrations of up to 20 percent may be attained. The sludge must be totally frozen for this technique to be effective, requiring shallow depths. Freezing is economically practical only in colder climates. Artificial freezing has been applied; however, the power costs are prohibitive ($85/ton @ $0.05/kWh).[23] The Onondaga County, N. Y., Water District's treatment facility applies lagoon-thickened alum sludge to freeze-thaw beds at a depth of 3 to 9 in. Applied sludge concentration was 8.0 percent. During one season, sludge was applied at 2.5 lb/ft^2. After freezing, thawing, and decanting, the sludge had concentrated to 25 percent. Final disposal of the sludge is to landfill.[25]

Disposal

Lagoons

The storage of dilute sludge in lagoons concentrates the solids. Coagulant solids will concentrate to 6 to 10 percent[10] over a period of months. If a water treatment plant produces 2000 lb/mil gal of solids, 25 to 50 acre-feet of storage capacity will be required for every decade of operation for an average 1-mgd treatment plant. Softening sludge, on the other hand, can be expected to concentrate to 20 to 30 percent,[12] and may attain a 50 percent concentration over a period of years. For a 2000-lb/mil gal solids production rate, about 10 acre-feet of storage capacity is required every decade for a plant with an average 1-mgd treatment rate. While this option may be attractive for small treatment plants, it often is impractical for larger treatment plants.

In many instances, lagoon storage of water treatment plant solids is considered the ultimate disposal. However, eventually the lagoon fills and the land is unusable for other purposes or must be reclaimed. Ultimate disposal of solids is effectively limited to application to land or incorporating into landfills. Disposal to natural water and the ocean is discouraged.

Landfills

Disposal of water treatment plant solids in sanitary landfills requires concentration of the solids to a semisolid or cake form. Following dewatering, water treatment plant sludge may be disposed of using sludge-only trenches or area fill techniques. Alternatively, the sludge may be co-disposed with refuse; dry refuse and sludge are mixed to attain a compactables45cell with no free moisture.

Land application

Sludge disposal directly to the surface of the land has been attempted. Alum sludge solids tend to clog soil pores and prevent seed germination; however, breaking up the crust mitigates this problem. Lime sludge has often been promoted as a soil additive for certain soil types, such as clays. It has been claimed that it stabilizes clay soils (from shrinking or swelling) and increases the pH of acidic soils.

Discharge to sanitary sewers

The practice of disposing water treatment plant solids to sanitary sewers has become more common. The economies of scale provided by treating water treatment and wastewater treatment solids together is attractive. Dilution of the inorganic sludges with organic sludges makes the sludge more acceptable for land disposal.

The discharge of sludge to sanitary sewers must be coordinated with the municipal wastewater treatment plant. The impact of the chemical nature and volume of the sludge on the wastewater facility needs to be considered.

The additional solids loading will need to be assessed as it affects plant solids handling capacity; a greater operation and maintenance effort may be required to process the additional solids. Discharges to the sewer should be monitored and controlled to minimize the possibility that sludges of relatively inert material will fill the digesters and upset the wastewater sludge treatment process.

Many wastewater utilities are concerned that the water treatment plant solids will adversely affect their process. However, coagulants are used extensively in waste treatment to remove phosphorus. There even may be benefits in the wastewater treatment plant operation as a result of enhanced sedimentation. The application of 200 to 300 mg/L waste lime sludge at the Daytona Beach, Fla., wastewater treatment plant in 1949 provided 45 percent BOD removal and 75 percent suspended solids removal in the primary clarifier.[23] This is more efficient than the typical experience. Dallas, Tex., in an attempt to both dispose of waste lime sludge and effectively use it for waste treatment, employed a similar process at the city's waste treatment facility.[14]

Culp and Wilson[15] studied the effect of adding alum sludge to an activated sludge wastewater treatment facility. They reported no identifiable benefit or detriment to the treatment process or to the anaerobic digester. The increase in wastewater sludge quantities was reported to be in proportion to the added water treatment solids.

Discharge of lime sludge to sanitary sewers should be carefully examined. Softening sludge may produce encrustations on weirs, channels, and piping.[35] The volume of softening sludge disposed of is also typically large, and this may prohibit disposal.

Economics

The costs of facilities and of the operation and maintenance associated with solids disposal may be estimated from information presented by Gumerman et al.[28] Short of detailed studies on a specific facility, this reference provides estimating techniques that are appropriate for gross planning estimates. Using the information provided, costs for disposal of example sludges have been estimated based on October 1978 costs. These are presented in Tables 12.6, 12.7, and 12.8. Typical examples have been selected to give a general idea of the magnitude of the costs involved for solids disposal; however, as presented in other sections of this chapter, several other alternatives are available and may be more appropriate.

Trends

Many new treatment facilities and improvements to older facilities are including filter wash-water recovery basins. Where water is not valuable, the decant liquid is often returned to the surface-water sup-

TABLE 12.6   Wash-Water Recovery Example

Average production	10 mgd	
Quantity of backwash water	300,000 gal/day	
Recovery Ponds Construction Cost		

	Capacity or size	Cost
Recovery ponds	2.0 acre · ft	$ 20,000
Land	1.0 acre	25,000
Polymer feed	10 lb/day	20,000
Return pumps	500 gpm	80,000
Site work		20,000
General contractor overhead and profit		25,000
Engineering		20,000
Legal, fiscal, and administrative		2,000
Interest during construction		17,000
	Total estimated cost	$229,000

Annual Operating and Maintenance Cost

	Labor, h	Power, kWh	Misc. supplies	Chemicals
Ponds	50	—	$ 100	—
Polymer	200	6,000	300	2000 lb
Return pumps	500	19,000	400	
Total	750	25,000	$ 800	

Summary

	Annual cost
Capital cost @ 8% (20 years)	$23,000
Labor, 750 h @ $10	7,500
Power, 25,000 kWh @ 5¢	1,250
Misc. supplies	800
Polymer, 2000 lb @ $4	8,000
Total	$40,550
Unit cost/1000 gal production	$0.01

ply. In spite of reluctance by wastewater treatment utilities, in more and more instances discharging coagulant sludges to sanitary sewers is being found to be a satisfactory practice. In locations where the wastewater treatment plant is not receiving the waste, lagoons remain the most prevalent means of coagulant sludge disposal.

Disposal in landfills will probably continue to be the predominant disposal method for sludge. Less frequently used, but desirable in some locations, will be the application of lime to clay or acid soils for conditioning. However, as landfill area decreases and the cost of landfilling increases, the resurgent interest in coagulant recovery should continue. The feasibility of recovery techniques, such as recalcination and alum recovery, will need to be determined on a case-by-case basis.

TABLE 12.7   Alum Sludge Disposal Example

Average production	10 mgd	
Quantity of coagulant sludge	200 lb/mil gal @ 5000 mg/L	

Centrifuge/Landfill Construction Cost

	Capacity or size	Cost
Centrifuge	60 gpm	$230,000
Polymer	10 lb/day	20,000
Haul truck	1 8-yd^3 truck	29,000
Site work		39,000
General contractor overhead and profit		48,000
Engineering		37,000
Legal, fiscal, and administrative		4,000
Interest during construction		30,000
	Total estimated cost	$437,000

Annual Operating and Maintenance Cost

	Labor, h	Power, kWh	Misc. supplies	Chemicals
Centrifuge	1100	170,000	$ 3000	
Polymer conditioning	200	13,000	300	800
Sludge hauling	240	—	1670	—
Total	1540	183,000	$ 4970	800

Summary

	Annual cost
Capital cost @ 8% (20 years)	$44,000
Labor, 1540 h @ $10	15,400
Power, 183,000 kWh @ 5¢	9,150
Misc. supplies	4,970
Polymer, 800 lb @ $4	3,200
Total	$76,720
Unit cost/ton solids	$ 210
Unit cost/1000 gal production	$0.02

TABLE 12.8 Lime Sludge Disposal Example

Average production	10 mgd
Quantity of lime sludge	2000 lb/mil gal @ 10% solids

Vacuum Filter/Landfill Construction Cost

	Capacity or size	Cost
Vacuum filter	750 ft^2	$ 650,000
Haul truck	28-yd^3 truck	58,000
Site work		99,000
Contractor overhead and profit		113,000
Engineering		92,000
Legal, fiscal, and administrative		10,000
Interest during construction		82,000
	Total estimated cost	$1,104,000

Annual Operating and Maintenance Cost

	Labor, h	Power, kWh	Misc. supplies
Vacuum filter	5200	940,000	$50,000
Hauling	1000	—	10,000
Total	6200	940,000	$60,000

Summary

		Annual cost
Capital cost @ 8% (20 years)		$112,000
Labor, 6200 h @ $10		62,000
Power, 940,000 kWh @ 5¢		47,000
Misc. supplies		60,000
	Total	$281,000
Unit cost/ton solids		$77
Unit cost/1000 gal treated		$0.08

References

1. *AWWA Water Treatment Plant Waste Committee Report,* unpublished data, December 1971.
2. AWWA, *Water Quality and Treatment,* 3d ed., McGraw-Hill, New York, 1971.
3. R. M. Gruinger, "Disposal of Waste Alum Sludge from Water Treatment Plants," *Journal WPCF,* vol. 47, 1975, p. 535.
4. D. A. Cornwell and J. A. Susan, "Characteristics of Acid Treated Alum Sludges," *Journal AWWA,* vol. 71, no. 10, 1979, p. 604.
5. D. A. Cornwell, "An Overview of Liquid Ion Exchange with Emphasis on Alum Recovery," *Journal AWWA,* vol. 71, no. 12, 1979, p. 741.
6. D. A. Cornwell and R. M. Lemunyon, "Feasibility Studies on Liquid Ion Exchange for Alum Recovery from Water Treatment Plant Sludges," *Journal AWWA,* vol. 72, no. 64, 1980, p. 64.
7. M. A. Burris et al., "Coagulation Sludge Disposal Studies for a Surface Water Supply," *Journal AWWA,* vol. 68, no. 5, 1976, p. 247.
8. Black and Veatch, Engineers-Architects, "Report on Water Treatment Plant Waste Disposal," Wichita, Kan., December 1969.
9. P. C. Singer, "Softener Sludge Disposal—What's Best," *Water and Waste Engineering,* vol. 11, no. 12, 1974, p. 25.
10. Charles Lawrence, "Lime Soda Sludge Recirculation Experiments at Vandenberg Air Force Base," *Journal AWWA,* vol. 55, no. 2, 1963, p. 177.
11. Paul E. Pigeon et al., "Recovery and Reuse of Iron Coagulants in Water Treatment," *Journal AWWA,* vol. 10, no. 7, 1978, p. 397.
12. American Water Works Association Research Foundation, *Disposal of Wastes from Water Treatment Plants,* FWPCA publication PB 186157, August 1969.
13. J. Williamson, Jr., "Something New in Sewage Treatment," *Water and Sewage Works,* vol. 96, 1949, p. 159.
14. H. H. Benjes, Jr., "Treatment of Overflows from Sanitary Sewers," Presented at the 9th Texas WPCA conference, Houston, Tex., July 1970.
15. R. L. Culp and W. I. Wilson, "Is Alum Sludge Advantageous in Wastewater Treatment," *Water and Waste Engineering,* vol. 16, no. 7, 1979, p. 16.
16. W. S. Foster, "Get the Water Out of Alum Sludge," *American City and County,* vol. 90, no. 9, 1975.
17. R. W. Knoche, "Thickening and Conditioning of Chemical Sludges," *Proc. ASCE Environmental Engineering Conference,* San Francisco, Calif., July 1978.
18. P. E. Dlouhy and A. P. Hager, "Vacuum Filtration Solves Problems of Water Softening Sludge," *Water and Waste Engineering,* vol. 5, no. 7, 1968.
19. AWWA Committee, "Water Treatment Plant Sludges—An Update of the State of the Art," *Journal AWWA,* vol. 70, no. 9, 1978, p. 498.
20. J. W. Krasaukas, "Review of Sludge Disposal Practices," *Journal AWWA,* vol. 61, no. 5, 1969, p. 225.
21. L. G. Hagstrom and N. A. Mignone, "Centrifugal Sludge Dewatering Systems Can Handle Alum Sludge," *Water and Sewer Works,* vol. 125, no. 5, 1978, p. 54.
22. C. O. Taflin et al., "Minneapolis Keeps on Trucking," *Water and Waste Engineering,* vol. 12, no. 5, 1975, p. 24.
23. J. T. Novak and Mark Langfort, "Use of Polymers for Improving Chemical Sludge Dewatering on Sand Beds," *Journal AWWA,* vol. 69, no. 2, 1977, p. 106.
24. J. H. Wilhelm and C. E. Silverblatt, "Freeze Treatment of Alum Sludge," *Journal AWWA,* vol. 68, no. 6, 1976, p. 312.
25. "Water Plant Waste Treatment," *American City and County,* vol. 94, no. 3, 1979.
26. G. P. Westerhoft and D. A. Cornwell, "A New Approach to Alum Recovery," *Journal AWWA,* vol. 70, no. 12, 1978, p. 709.
27. A. P. Black and C. G. Thompson, "Plant Scale Studies of the Magnesium Carbonate Water Treatment Process," U.S. Environmental Protection Agency, Publication EPA-660/2-75-006, May 1975.
28. R. C. Gumerman, R. L. Culp, and S. P. Hansen, "Estimating Water Treatment

Plant Costs," 4 vols, U.S. Environmental Protection Agency, EPA Publication EPA-600/2-79-162, August 1979.

29. J. B. Dean, "Disposal of Wastes from Filter Plants and Coagulation Basins," *Journal AWWA,* vol. 45, no. 11, 1953, p. 1229.

30. AWWA, ASCE, CSSE, *Water Treatment Plant Design,* American Water Works Association, New York, 1969.

31. AWWA Committee Report, "Water Treatment Plant Sludges—An Update of the State of the Art: Part 2," *Journal AWWA,* vol. 70, no. 10, 1978, p. 548.

32. J. Cleasby, "Iron and Manganese Removal—A Case Study." *Journal AWWA,* vol. 67, no. 3, 1975, p. 147.

33. J. M. Montgomery, Consulting Engineers, Inc., *Water Treatment: Principles and Design,* Wiley, New York, 1985.

34. S. L. Bishop, "Alternate Processes for Treatment of Water Plant Wastes," *Journal AWWA,* vol. 70, no. 9, 1978, p. 503.

35. T. D. Reynolds, *Unit Operations and Processes in Environmental Engineering,* Wadsworth Publishing Company, Belmont, Calif., 1982.

13

Chemicals and
Chemical Handling

Introduction

This chapter discusses the properties and characteristics of 50 chemicals commonly used in present-day treatment of potable water. Recommendations are included for the storage, handling, feeding, and safe use of these chemicals as required by designers and supervisors of water treatment operations.

These data emphasize the physical aspects of chemicals and their handling. Discussion of process reactions and the chemistry involved has been held to a minimum; additional facts relating to the theory of treatment are referred to in AWWA's handbook, *Water Quality and Treatment.*

Two related tables present chemical data. Table 13.1 lists commonly used water treatment chemicals in alphabetical order regardless of process usage or function. Table 13.2 groups chemicals according to use and refers to applicable detailed data in Table 13.1. Common generic chemical names have been used in all cases; it is hoped that this will permit effective use of the data by those unfamiliar with the scientific nomenclature of chemical compounds.

Review of the Properties and Characteristics
of Water Treatment Chemicals

Process chemicals

Some of the compounds discussed in this chapter are new to potable water treatment. Major advances have been made in the use of polyelectrolyte organic coagulant aids, fluoride-bearing agents, and chlorine dioxide. Other compounds such as granular activated carbon,

TABLE 13.1 Alphabetical Listing of Commonly Used Water Treatment Chemicals

Chemical name and formula	Common or trade name	Shipping containers	Suitable handling materials	Available forms	Weight, lb/ft^3	Solubility, lb/gal	Commercial strength, percent	Characteristics
Activated alumina (see aluminum oxide)								
Activated carbon, C	"Aqua Nuchor," "Hydrodarco," "Herite"	Bags, bulk	Dry iron, steel; wet rubber, silicon, iron, stainless steel	Black granules, powder	15	Insoluble (suspension used)		
Aluminum oxide, Al_2O_3	Activated alumina	Bags, drums	Iron, lead, steel	Powder granules (up to 1½ in diameter)		Insoluble	100	
Aluminum sulfate, $Al_2(SO_4)_3$ $14H_2O$ (dry)	Alum, filter alum, sulfate of alumina	100–200-lb bags, 300–400-lb bbls, bulk (carloads), tank truck, tank car	Dry iron, steel, solution lead-lined rubber, silicon asphalt, 316 stainless steel	Ivory-colored powder, granule, lump, liquid	38–45 60–63 62–67 10 (lb/gal)	4.2 (60°F)	15–22 dry	pH of 1 percent solution 3.4
Aluminum sulfate (liquid)	50% alum	Tank cars and tank trucks	See dry form	Liquid	11.2 (lb/gal)	—	8.5	
Ammonium aluminum sulfate, $Al_2(SO_4)_3$, $(NH_4)_2$-$SO_4 \cdot 24H_2O$	Ammonia alum, crystal alum	Bags, bbls., bulk	Duriron, lead, rubber silicon, iron stoneware	Lump, nut, pea, powdered	64–68 62 65 60	0.3 (32°F) 8.3 (212°F)	11 (Al_2O_3)	pH of 1 percent solution 3.5

Ammonium silicofluoride, $(NH_4)_2SiF_6$	Ammonium fluorsilicate	100-lb and 400-lb drums	Steel, iron, lead	White crystals		1.7 (63°F)	100	White, free-flowing solid
Ammonium sulfate, $(NH_4)_2SO_4$	Sulfate of ammonia	100-lb bags	Ceramics, plastics, rubber; iron (dry)	White or brown crystal	42.5	6.3 (68°F)	25 (NH_3)	Cakes in dry feed: add $CaSO_4$ for free flow
Anhydrous ammonia, NH_3	Ammonia	50-, 100-, 150-lb cylinders, in bulk tank cars and trucks	Glass, iron, monel metal, nickel, steel	Colorless gas		3.9 (32°F) 3.1 (60°F) 1.8 (125°F)	99–100 (NH_3)	
Aqua ammonia, NH_4OH	Ammonia water, ammonium hydrate, ammonium hydroxide	Carboys, 750-lb drums, 8000-gal tank cars or trucks	Glass, iron, monel	Colorless liquid		Complete	29.4 (NH_2) 26°Be	
Bentonite	Colloidal clay, volclay, wilkinite	100-lb bags, bulk	Iron, steel	Powder, pellet, mixed sizes	60	Insoluble (colloidal sol used)		
Bone charcoal	"Fluor-carb"	Bags, drums, bulk	Wood, iron, steel	Granules	Variable			Black: best used in beds for persolution
Calcium fluoride, CaF_2	Fluorspar	Bags, drums, bbls., hopper cars, trucks	Steel, iron, lead	Powder		Very slight	85 (CaF_2), less than 5 (SiO_2)	

TABLE 13.1 Alphabetical Listing of Commonly Used Water Treatment Chemicals *(Continued)*

Chemical name and formula	Common or trade name	Shipping containers	Suitable handling materials	Available forms	Weight, lb/ft³	Solubility, lb/gal	Commercial strength, percent	Characteristics
Calcium hydroxide, $Ca(OH)_2$	Hydrated lime, slaked lime	50-lb bags, 100-lb bbls, bulk (carloads), bulk trucks	Asphalt, cement, iron, rubber, steel	White powder, light, dense		0.14 (68°F) 0.12 (90°F)	85–99 $(Ca(OH)_2)$ 63–73 (CaO)	Hopper agitation required for dry feed of light form
Calcium hypochlorite, $Ca(OCl)_2 \cdot 4H_2O$	"HTH," "perchloron," "pittchlor"	5-lb cans; 100-, 300-, 800-lb drums	Glass, rubber, stoneware, wood	White granule, powder, tablet	52.5		70 (available Cl_2)	1–3 (available Cl_2 solution used)
Calcium oxide, CaO	Burnt lime, chemical lime, quicklime, unslaked lime	50-lb bags, 100-lb bbls, bulk (carloads)	Asphalt, cement, iron, rubber, steel	Lump, pebble, granule		Slaked to form hydrated lime	75–99 (CaO)	pH of saturated solution, on detention time temp. amount of water critical for efficient slaking
Chlorinated lime, CaO, $2CaOCl_2 \cdot 3H_2O$	Bleaching powder, chloride of lime	100-, 300-, 800-lb drums	Glass, rubber, stoneware, wood	White powder	48		25–37 (available Cl_2)	Deteriorates
Chlorine, Cl_2	Chlorine gas, liquid chlorine	100-, 150-lb cylinders; 1-ton tanks; 16-, 30-, 55-ton tank cars	Dry-black iron, copper, steel, wet gas-glass, hard rubber, silver	Liquefied gas under pressure	91.7	0.07 (60°F) 0.04 (100°F)	99.8 (Cl_2)	

Chemical	Common name	Shipping containers	Suitable handling materials	Appearance	Weight, lb per cu ft	Solubility	Percent composition	Remarks
Chlorine dioxide, ClO_2	Chlorine dioxide	Generated as used	Plastics, soft rubber (avoid hard rubber), aluminum	Yellow-red gas		0.02 (30mu)	26.3 (available Cl_2)	
Copper sulfate, $CuSO_4 \cdot 5H_2O$	Blue vitriol, blue stone	100-lb bags, 450-lb bbls, drums	Asphalt, silicon, iron, stainless steel	Crystal, lump, powder	75–90 73–80 60–64	1.6 (32°F) 2.2 (68°F) 2.6 (86°F)	99 ($CuSO_4$)	
Disodium phosphate, $Na_2HPO_4 \cdot 12H_2O$	Basic sodium phosphate, DSP, secondary sodium phosphate	125-lb kegs, 200-lb bags, 325-lb bbls.	Cast iron, steel	Crystal	60–64	0.4 (32°F) 6.4 (86°F)	19.19 5 (P_2O_5)	Precipitates Ca, Mg; pH of 1 percent solution, 9.1
Ferric chloride, $FeCl_3$ (35–45 percent solution)	"Ferrichlor," chloride of iron	5–13-gal carboys, trucks, tank cars	Glass, rubber, stoneware, synthetic resins	Dark brown syrupy liquid		Complete	37–47 ($FeCl_3$) 20–21 (Fe)	Hygroscopic (store lumps and powder in tight container), no dry feed; optimum pH, 4.0–11.0
$FeCl_3 \cdot 6H_2O$	Crystal ferric chloride	300-lb bbls.		Yellow-brown lump			59–61 ($FeCl_3$) 20–21 (Fe)	
$FeCl_3$	Anhydrous ferric chloride	500-lb casks; 100-, 300-, 400-lb kegs		Green-black powder			98 ($FeCl_3$) 34 (Fe)	
Ferric sulfate, $Fe_2(SO_4)_3 \cdot 9H_2O$	"Ferrifloc," ferrisul	100–175-lb bags, 400–425-lb drums	Ceramics, lead, plastic, rubber, 18-8 stainless steel	Red-brown powder 70 or granule 72	60–70	Soluble in 2–4 parts cold water	90–94 (Fe) (SO_3) 25–26 (Fe)	Mildly hygroscopic coagulant at pH 3.5–11.0

TABLE 13.1 Alphabetical Listing of Commonly Used Water Treatment Chemicals (*Continued*)

Chemical name and formula	Common or trade name	Shipping containers	Suitable handling materials	Available forms	Weight, lb/ft³	Solubility, lb/gal	Commercial strength, percent	Characteristics
Ferrous sulfate, $FeSO_4 \cdot 7H_2O$	Copperas, green vitriol	Bags, bbls., bulk	Asphalt, concrete, lead, tin, wood	Green crystal, granule, lump	63–66		55 ($FeSO_4$) 20 (Fe)	Hygroscopic; cakes in storage; optimum pH 8.5–11.0
High-magnesium lime	Dolomitic lime	Bags, bbls., bulk	Wood, iron, steel	Lump, pebble, ground	50–63	Slakes slowly	58 (CaO) 40 (Mg)	
Hydrofluosilicic acid, H_2SiF_6	Fluosilicic acid	Rubber-lined drums, trucks, or railroad tank cars	Rubber-lined steel, PVC	Liquid		Approx. 1.2 (68°F)	35 (approx.)	
Hydrogen fluoride, HF	Hydrofluoric acid	Steel drums, tank cars	Steel	Liquid			70 (HF)	Below 60 percent steel cannot be used
Ozone, O_3	Ozone	Generated at site of application	Aluminum, ceramics, glass	Colorless gas				
Potassium aluminum sulfate, $K_2SO_4 \cdot Al_2(SO_4)_3 \cdot 24H_2O$	Potash alum, potassium alum	Bags, lead-lined bulk (carloads)	Lead, lead-lined rubber, stoneware	Lump, granule, powder	62–67 60–65 60	0.5 (32°F) 1.0 (68°F) 1.4 (86°F)	10–11 (Al_2O_3)	Low, even solubility; pH of 1 percent solution, 3.5

352

	Common name	Shipping containers	Materials of construction	Appearance		Solubility	Assay (%)	Remarks
Potassium permanganate, $KMnO_4$	Purple salt	Bulk, bbls., drums	Iron, steel, wood	Purple crystals		Infinite	100	Danger of explosion in contact organic matters
Pyrosodium sulfite	Sodium metabisulfite	Bags, drums, bbls.	Iron, steel, wood	White crystalline powder		Complete in water	Dry 67 (SO_2), sol 33.3 (SO_2)	Sulfurous odor
Sodium aluminate, $Na_2OAl_2O_3$	Soda alum	100–150-lb bags, 250–440-lb drums, solution	Iron, plastics, rubber, steel	Brown powder or liquid (27°Bé)	50–60	3.0 (68°F) 3.3 (86°F)	70–80 $(Na_2 Al_2O_4$ min. 32 $Na_2 Al_2O_4)$	Hopper agitation required for dry feed
Sodium carbonate, Na_2CO_3	Soda ash	Bags, bbls., bulk (carloads), trucks	Iron, rubber, steel	White powder, extra light, light, dense	23 35 65	1.5 (68°F) 2.3 (86°F)	99.4 (Na_2CO_3) 58 (Na_2O)	Hopper agitation required for dry feed of light and extra light forms; pH of 1 percent solution, 11.3
Sodium chloride, $NaCl$	Common salt, salt	Bags, bbls., bulk (carloads)	Bronze, cement, rubber	Rock, fine		2.9 (32°F) 3.0 (68°F)	98 $(NaCl)$	
Sodium chlorite, $NaClO_2$	Technical sodium chlorite	100-lb drums	Metals (avoid cellulose materials)	Light orange powder, flake			82 $(NaClO_2)$ 30 (available Cl_2)	Generates ClO_2 at pH 3.0

TABLE 13.1 Alphabetical Listing of Commonly Used Water Treatment Chemicals (*Continued*)

Chemical name and formula	Common or trade name	Shipping containers	Suitable handling materials	Available forms	Weight, lb/ft^3	Solubility, lb/gal	Commercial strength, percent	Characteristics
Sodium fluoride, NaF	Fluoride	Bags, bbls., fiber drums, kegs	Iron, lead, steel	Nile blue or white powder, light, dense	50 75	0.35 (most temps.)	90–95 (NaF)	pH of 4 percent solution, 6.6
Sodium hexametaphosphate, Na(PO$_3$)$_6$	"Calgon," glassy phosphate, vitreous phosphate	100-lb bags	Hard rubber, plastics, stainless steel	Crystal, flake, powder	47	1–4.2	66 (P$_2$O$_5$ unadjusted)	pH of 0.25 percent solution, 6.0–8.3
Sodium hydroxide, NaOH	Caustic soda, soda lye	100–700-lb drums; bulk (trucks, tankcars)	Cast iron, rubber, steel	Flake, lump, liquid		2.4 (32°F) 4.4 (68°F) 4.8 (104°F)	98.9 (NaOH) 74–76 (NaO$_2$)	Solid, hygroscopic; pH of 1 percent solution, 12.9
Sodium hypochlorite, NaOCl	Sodium hypochlorite	5-, 13-, 50-gal carboys; 1300–2000-gal tank trucks	Ceramics, glass, plastics, rubber	Light yellow liquid			12–15 (available Cl$_2$)	
Sodium silicate, Na$_2$OSiO$_2$	Water glass	Drums, bulk (tank trucks, tank cars)	Cast iron, rubber, steel	Opaque, viscous liquid		Complete	38–42°Bé	Variable ratio of Na$_2$O to SiO$_2$; pH of 1 percent solution, 12.3

Name/Formula	Synonym	Shipping containers	Suitable materials	Form		Solubility	Strength	Remarks
Sodium silicofluoride, Na_2SiF_6	Sodium silicofluoride	Bags, bbls., fiber drums	Iron, lead, steel	Nile blue or yellowish white powder	72	0.03 (32°F) 0.06 (72°F) 0.12 (140°F)	99 (Na_2)	pH of 1 percent solution, 5.3
Sodium sulfite, Na_2SO_3	Sulfite	Bags, drums, bbls.	Iron, steel, wood	White crystalline powder		Complete in water	23 (SO_2)	Sulfurous taste and odor
Sulfur dioxide, SO_2	Sulfurous acid anhydride	100–150-lb steel cylinders, ton containers, tank cars, tank trucks	Aluminum, brass, Durco D-10, stainless steel 316	Colorless gas		20 percent at 32°F, complete in water	99 (SO_2)	Irritating gas
Sulfuric acid, H_2SO_4	Oil of vitriol, vitriol	Bottles, carboys, drums, trucks, tank cars	Concentrated iron, steel; dilute glass, lead, porcelain, rubber	Solution	(60–66°) Bé	Complete	60°Bé 77.7 (H_2SO_4) 66°Bé 93.2 (H_2SO_4)	Approx. pH of 0.5 percent solution, 1.2
Tetrasodium pyrophosphate, $Na_4P_2O_7 \cdot 10H_2O$	Alkaline sodium, pyrophosphate, TSPP	125-lb kegs, 200-lb bags, 300-lb bbls.	Cast iron, steel	White powder	68	0.6 (80°F) 3.3 (212°F)	53 (P_2O_5)	pH of 1 percent solution, 10.8
Tricalcium phosphate	"Fluorex"	Bags, drums, bulk, bbls.	Iron, steel	Granular	Variable	Insoluble		Also available as white powder
Trisodium phosphate, $Na_3PO_4 \cdot 12H_2O$	Normal sodium phosphate, tertiary sodium phosphate, TSP	125-lb kegs, 200-lb bags, 325-lb bbls.	Cast iron, steel	Crystal—course, medium, standard	56 58 61	0.1 (32°F) 13.0 (158°F)	19 (P_2O_5)	pH of 1 percent solution, 11.9

TABLE 13.2   **Process Use of Chemicals**

Process	Chemicals
Coagulant	Aluminum sulfate Bauxite Ferrous sulfate Ferric sulfate Ferric chloride Sodium aluminate Calcium hydroxide Calcium oxide
Coagulant aids	Bentonite Calcium carbonate Carbon dioxide Sodium silicate
Disinfection and chlorination	Anhydrous ammonia Ammonium hydroxide Ammonium sulfate Chlorine Chlorine dioxide Sodium chlorite Chlorinated lime Calcium hypochlorite Sodium hypochlorite
Dechlorination	Activated carbon Ion-exchange resins Sodium bisulfate Sodium sulfite Sulfur dioxide
pH adjustment	Calcium carbonate Carbon dioxide Hydrochloric acid Calcium oxide Calcium hydroxide Sodium hydroxide Sulfuric acid
Fluoridation and fluoride adjustment	Ammonium silicofluoride Calcium fluoride Hydrofluosilicic acid Sodium fluoride Sodium silicofluoride Activated alumina (aluminum oxide)
Taste and odor control	Activated carbon Bentonite Chlorine Chlorine dioxide Copper sulfate Potassium permanganate
Mineral oxidation	Chlorine Chlorine dioxide Ozone Potassium permanganate

TABLE 13.2   Process Use of Chemicals (Continued)

Process	Chemicals
Stabilization and corrosion control	Calcium oxide Calcium hydroxide Sodium carbonate Sodium hexametaphosphate
Softening	Carbon dioxide Calcium oxide Calcium hydroxide Sodium carbonate Sodium chloride

potassium permanganate, and caustic soda have shown a use renaissance. A change in the use of compounds such as sodium silicate and chlorine has occurred, while the use of certain mainstay compounds remains the same. The latter group includes alum, chlorine, soda ash, lime, powdered activated carbon, and copper sulfate. Noteworthy improvements affecting the delivery, feeding, and storage of these chemical agents include the introduction of aluminum sulfate in liquid form, carbon slurry storage, lime slurries from bulk deliveries of hydrated lime, and storage of saturated soda ash slurry in softening plants. Lime reclamation is practiced increasingly.

New knowledge about existing materials together with the availability of new corrosion-resistant materials have made the job of both the treatment plant designer and operator easier. When possible, recommendations for up-to-date use of these materials are included in the data presented here.

Activated alumina

See Aluminum oxide.

Activated carbon

Activated carbon is a form of charcoal that has acquired the property of absorbing various substances from water through treatment by a carefully controlled combustion process. It is available in two forms, powdered and granulated, and it has high affinity for absorbing chlorine and taste- and odor-causing substances.

Activated carbon particles have a large surface area. The grade of activated carbon used for water treatment has a specific surface area ranging from 500 to 600 m^2/g. The particles appear to be solid, but are actually honeycombed with an infinite number of minute tunnels or pores on the molecular order of size. Pore dimensions are expressed in angstroms. The materials responsible for taste and odor in water, such as the products of industrial waste, sewage, and plant and animal organisms, are thought to be absorbed in pores not greater than 20 Å in diameter. In the highly activated carbons, about 75 percent of the surface exists as pores of less than 20 Å in diameter.

Activated carbon is prepared from wood charcoal, paper char, petroleum coke, lignite, coal, charred peach pits, coconut husks, and other carbonaceous materials. The carbons used in the water industry are prepared principally from paper char, hardwood charcoal, or lignite. Powdered activated carbon is a very finely ground material; more than 90 percent passes a 300-mesh screen (AWWA Standard B600).

Granular activated carbon can be ground and screened to any desired size. In the size used in some water treatment plants, 100 percent will pass an 8-mesh screen, and at least 90 percent will be retained on a 12-mesh screen. Other such carbons have effective sizes of 0.8 to 0.9 and 0.55 to 0.65 mm.

Granular carbon is usually placed in filters through which the entire flow of water passes, so that chlorine or tastes and odors may be removed. Carbon treatment is usually applied after standard filtering, so that the granular carbon bed will not become clogged or coated with colloidal material from the unfiltered water. Because the contact time is usually short with this type of treatment, the general effect of granular carbon filters in taste and odor removal is a polishing action. Where taste and odor problems are fairly constant at a low intensity, granular-carbon filters are quite satisfactory. A typical chemical feed schematic for powdered activated carbon appears in Fig. 13.1.

Aluminum oxide

Aluminum oxide (Al_2O_3), also known as activated alumina, is a highly porous, granular material with a preferential adsorptive capacity for moisture from gases, vapors, and some liquids. It is also used as a carrier to remove fluorides from drinking water. When the aluminum becomes saturated with fluorides, it must be regenerated. This is accomplished by first backwashing with water in order to remove the accumulated solids, then backwashing with a weak caustic solution to remove fluorides. The residual caustic is then neutralized with a weak acid, followed by water rinses. Activated alumina is available in granules ranging in size from a powder to approximately a 1.5-in diameter. The 8- to 14-in and the ¼- to 8-in mesh are the sizes most generally used. In the fluoride removal process, the water is percolated through beds of alumina. The beds can be arranged as either pressure or gravity filters, and piped for backwashing and regeneration.

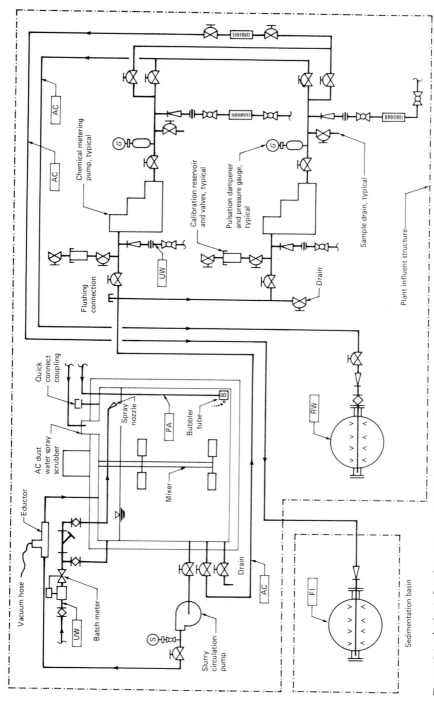

Figure 13.1 Activated carbon system. (*J. M. Montgomery Consulting Engineers.*)

Aluminum sulfate (AWWA Standard B403)

By far the most important coagulating agent is aluminum sulfate. Most commercial grades have the formula $Al_2(SO_4)_3 \cdot 14H_2O$. Aluminum sulfate is available in lump, ground, or liquid form. The lump form particles range in size from 0.5 to 3.0 in.

Ground aluminum sulfate for use in dry feed machines should be of such size that not less than 90 percent will pass a National Bureau of Standards No. 10 sieve, and 100 percent will pass a National Bureau of Standards No. 4 sieve. It is a grayish white crystalline solid completely soluble in water with a tendency to absorb moisture from the air. Under such conditions, it tends to deliquesce to a fine white powder. This does not affect its efficiency but requires a slight change in the weight fed.

Liquid aluminum sulfate is a clear, amber-colored liquid sometimes called "50 percent" alum. This is because a gallon of liquid alum weighs 11.2 lb and contains 5.6 lb of dry aluminum sulfate. Actually, it usually contains 8.5 percent or more available water-soluble alumina (Al_2O_3), as compared with the 17 percent Al_2O_3 available in dry alum. A typical chemical feed schematic for liquid aluminum sulfate appears in Fig. 13.2.

Ammonia

See Anhydrous ammonia

Ammonium hydroxide

Aqua ammonia is the ammonium hydroxide of commerce. At 60°F, it consists of a stable solution of 20.4 percent NH_3, with a specific gravity of 0.8974, a density of 16.48 lb/ft^3, and boiling and freezing points of 81°F and 107°F, respectively. Its vapor pressure varies from about 4.5 lb/in^2 absolute (psia) at 32°F to 50 psia at 104°F. A typical chemical feed schematic for aqua ammonia appears in Fig. 13.3.

Ammonium silicofluoride

Ammonium silicofluoride is produced by neutralizing hydrofluosilicic acid with either aqua or anhydrous ammonia. It is sold as a white, odorless, free-flowing crystalline material. One hundred percent will pass a 20-mesh screen, and 90 percent will be retained on a 100-mesh screen. Its solubility is high, comparing favorably with that of sodium fluoride.

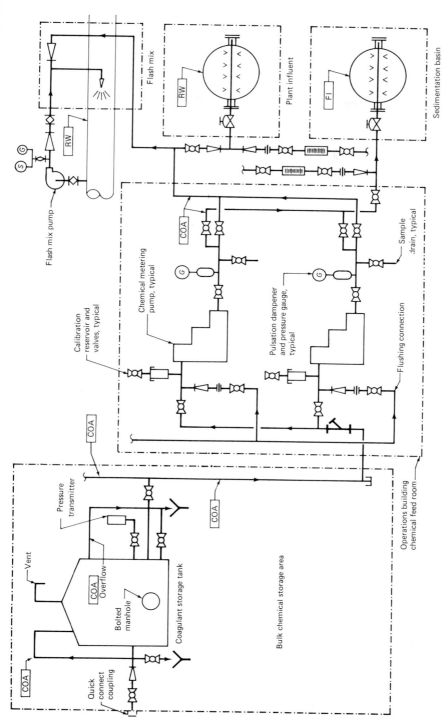

Figure 13.2 Coagulant alum/ferric chloride system. (*J. M. Montgomery Consulting Engineers.*)

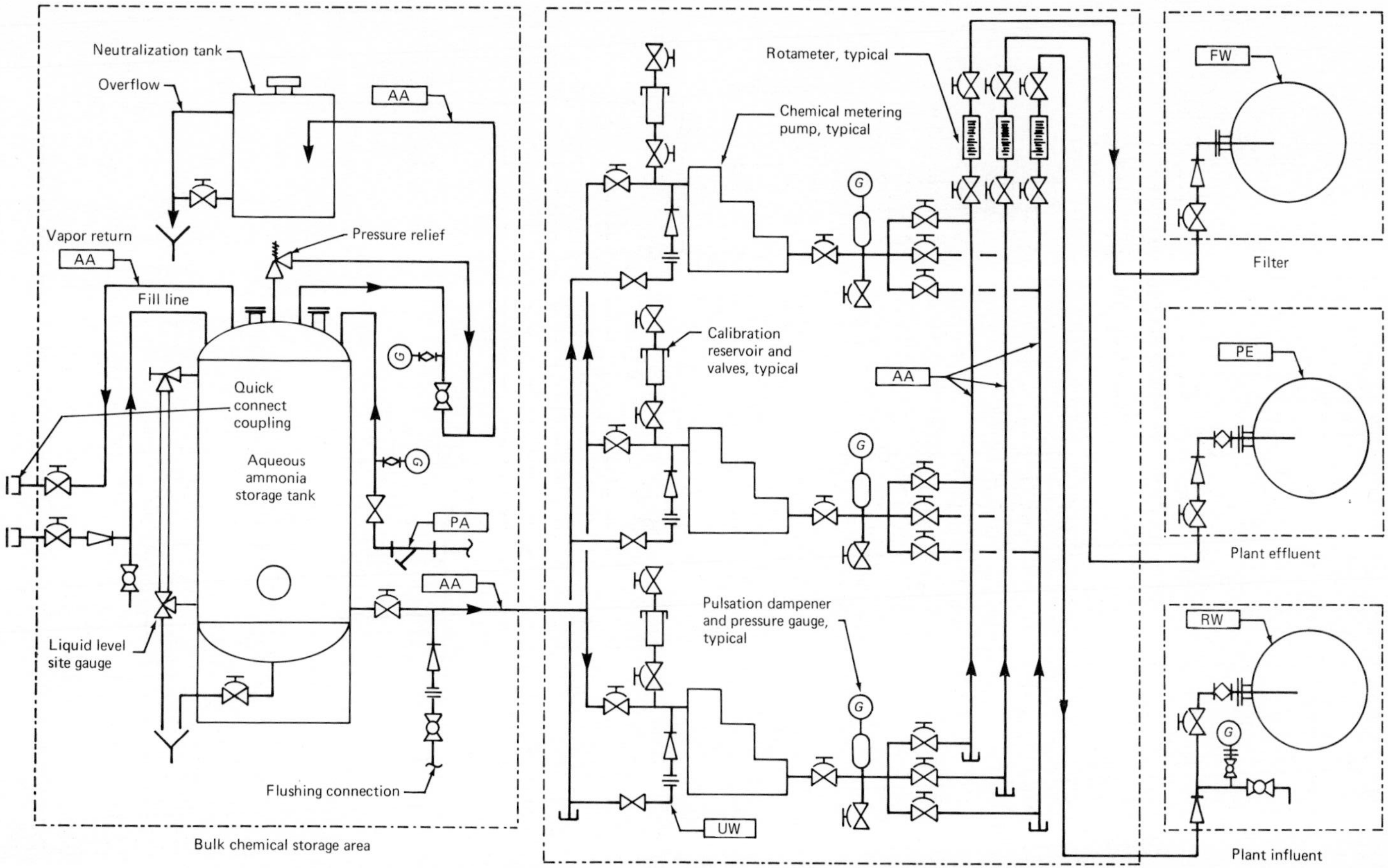

Figure 13.2 Aqua ammonia system. (*J. M. Montgomery, Consulting Engineers.*)

Labels within figure:

Filter — FW

Plant effluent — PE

Plant influent — RW — G

Rotameter, typical

Chemical metering pump, typical

Calibration reservoir and valves, typical

Pulsation dampener and pressure gauge, typical

AA

UW

Neutralization tank

Overflow

Pressure relief

Vapor return — AA

Fill line

Quick connect coupling

Aqueous ammonia storage tank

Liquid level site gauge

Flushing connection

Bulk chemical storage area

PA

AA

Ammonium sulfate (AWWA Standard B302)

Ammonium sulfate is used as a source of ammonia in the formation of chloramines. It may vary widely in purity; specifications should be very carefully written and should conform to the AWWA standard. Because it is a by-product, it should be carefully examined for the presence of heavy metals. It is a white, crystalline solid that is readily soluble in water.

Anhydrous ammonia

Various physical and chemical characteristics of anhydrous ammonia were summarized in Table 13.1. In the gaseous state, ammonia is colorless and about 0.6 times as heavy as air. The liquid, also colorless, is about 0.68 times as heavy as water. Unconfined liquid ammonia rapidly vaporizes to gas. The temperature, pressure, and density characteristics of anhydrous ammonia are shown in Fig. 13.4.

Bauxite (AWWA Standard B401)

Bauxite is a mineral containing a preponderance of hydrated aluminum oxide. Bauxite is used in a few water treatment plants for manufacture of alum on the plant site.

Bentonite

Bentonite, a form of clay that swells on absorbing moisture, is sometimes used as a coagulant aid in waters of very low turbidity. (See Chap. 5.)

Calcium carbonate

This is available in a number of forms, both prepared and naturally occurring. Known as whiting or precipitated chalk, it is an inert material, only slightly soluble in water.

Calcium fluoride

See Fluorspar.

Calcium hydroxide

See Lime.

Calcium hypochlorite

Present-day commercial high-test calcium hypochlorite products, such as HTH, introduced in 1928, contain at least 70 percent available

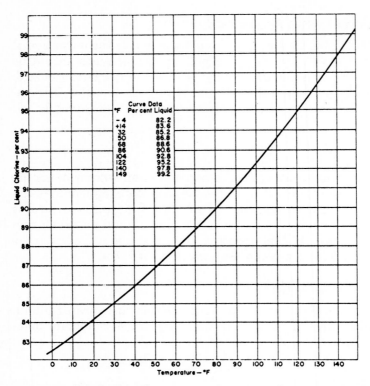

Figure 13.4 Relationship of pressure–temperature to density–temperature in anhydrous ammonia.

chlorine and have from less than 3 percent to about 5 percent lime (which reduces the amount of sludge formed in an aqueous solution). All commercial calcium hypochlorites also contain, among minor amounts of other impurities, some calcium carbonate and other insolubles. In hard water, an additional amount of calcium carbonate is formed. Thus, some sediment occurs that might remove material from solution, but this is considerably less than the amount of sediment formed if bleaching powder is dissolved to obtain a solution containing an equivalent content of available chlorine.

An off-white, granular (free-flowing or compressed-tablet) material, calcium hypochlorite, although a highly active oxidizer, is relatively stable. Under normal storage conditions, commercial preparations lose about 3 to 5 percent of their available chlorine content in a year. Contact with water or the atmosphere induces a pronounced increase in the decomposition rate; additionally, it greatly increases the reaction rate with organic materials.

Decomposition is exothermic and proceeds rapidly if any part of the material is heated to 350°F, yielding oxygen and chlorine as well as a powdery dust that has an irritating action; heat also is evolved, which further supports and increases the decomposition rate. The granular form is essentially nonhydroscopic and resists moist caking tendencies when properly stored. Though calcium hypochlorite is a stable, nonflammable material that cannot be ignited, contact with heat, acids, combustible, organic, or oxidizable materials may cause fire. It is readily soluble in water, varying from about 21.5 g/100 mL at 0°C to 23.4 g/100 mL at 40°C. Tablet forms dissolve more slowly than the granular materials, and provide a fairly steady source of available chlorine over an 18- to 24-h period.

Calcium oxide

See Lime.

Carbon

See Activated carbon.

Carbon dioxide

This gas may be produced under atmosphere-type conditions by the burning of carbonaceous materials such as wood, coal, coke, fuel oil, or gas at atmospheric pressure. Another kind of carbon dioxide generator, the pressure-type CO_2 generator, uses a ratio of fuel to air so carefully regulated that complete combustion takes place.

The pressure in the combustion chamber forces the gas to the CO_2 diffusers, eliminating the blower needed by the atmospheric-type generator. Better diffusion of the CO_2 is obtained by forcing a water spray against the gas as it is released from the diffuser openings, breaking up the bubbles and ensuring better control. In a method now being offered to the water industry, gas and air are burned together in subsurface burners, producing carbon dioxide at the point of application.

Carbon dioxide is a high-specific-gravity, clear, colorless, and odorless gas that becomes liquefied under pressure and solidifies when the pressure is released. When confined, carbon dioxide tends to seek the lowest level possible. In water, its solution produces carbonic acid. Carbon dioxide functions as a coagulant aid primarily by adjusting the pH or solubilities so that proper coagulation is obtained.

Chlorinated lime

This material, although primarily used as a disinfectant, is sometimes used in treating water supplies, particularly swimming pools. It is a white powder prepared by chlorinating slaked lime. It decomposes in water, releasing 39 percent available chlorine for disinfecting action.

Chlorine (AWWA Standard B301)

Various physical and chemical characteristics of the element chlorine are summarized in Table 13.1. In the gaseous state, chlorine is greenish yellow in color and about 2.48 times as heavy as air; the liquid is amber-colored and about 1.44 times as heavy as water. Unconfined liquid chlorine rapidly vaporizes to gas; 1 volume of liquid yields about 450 volumes of gas.

Chlorine is only slightly soluble in water, its maximum solubility being approximately 1 percent at 49.2°F. At temperatures below 49.2°F, chlorine combines with water forming chlorine "ice," a crystalline hydrate ($Cl_2 \cdot 8H_2O$).

The temperature–pressure characteristics of chlorine are shown in Fig. 13.5. Chlorine confined in a container may exist as a gas, a liquid, or a mixture of both. Thus, any consideration of liquid chlorine includes consideration of gaseous chlorine. As will be noted, the vapor pressure of chlorine in a container is a function of temperature, and is independent of the contained volume of chlorine; therefore, gauge pressure is not an indication of container content.

The volume–temperature characteristics of chlorine in a container loaded to the limit authorized by Department of Transportation (DOT) regulations (as later discussed) are shown in Fig. 13.6. It is apparent that if a container is filled to this limit, it becomes completely full of liquid at approximately 154°F; temperatures beyond that point may give rise to pressure that could result in hydrostatic rupture of the container. Safety devices are provided to relieve the excessive pressures that accompany dangerous temperature elevations.

Under specific conditions, chlorine reacts with most elements, sometimes with extreme rapidity. Because of its great affinity for hydrogen, chlorine removes hydrogen from some compounds. One example is its reaction with H_2S to form hydrochloric acid and sulfur. It also reacts with ammonia or nitrogen-containing compounds to form various mixtures of chloramines. It reacts in much the same way with organic materials to form chlorinated derivatives. Some of these reactions can be explosive, for example, those with hydrocarbons, alcohols, and ethers. Although neither explosive nor flammable, chlorine (like oxygen) is capable of supporting combustion of certain substances. It should, accordingly, be handled and stored away from other com-

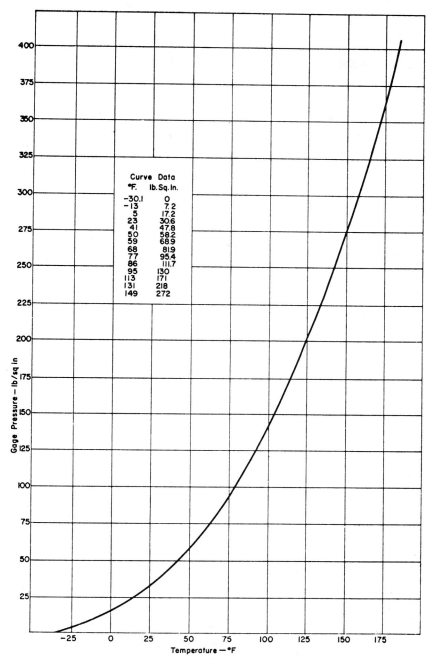

Curve Data

°F.	lb. Sq. In.
-30.1	0
-13	7.2
5	17.2
23	30.6
41	47.8
50	58.2
59	68.9
68	81.9
77	95.4
86	111.7
95	130
113	171
131	218
149	272

Figure 13.5 Relationship of temperature to pressure in chlorine

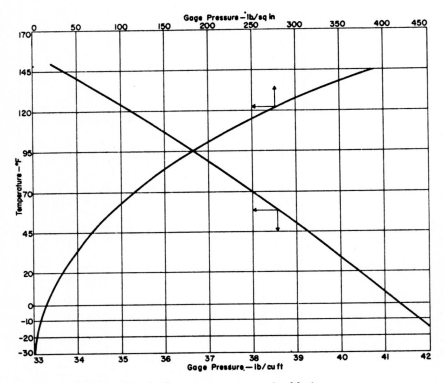

Figure 13.6   Relationship of volume to temperature in chlorine

pressed gases (such as anhydrous ammonia), and kept apart from turpentine, ether, finely divided metals, and hydrocarbons or other flammable materials. A typical chemical feed schematic for chlorine is shown in Fig. 13.7.

Chlorine dioxide

Under atmospheric conditions, chlorine dioxide is a yellow to red, unpleasant-smelling, irritating, unstable gas. It is produced by the action of a chlorine solution on a solution of sodium chlorite.

Usually the chlorine solution from the chlorinator is introduced into a ceramic-packed glass column along with the sodium chlorite solution. To obtain a complete reaction, the ratio of chlorine to sodium chlorite should be at least 50 percent above the theoretical amount.

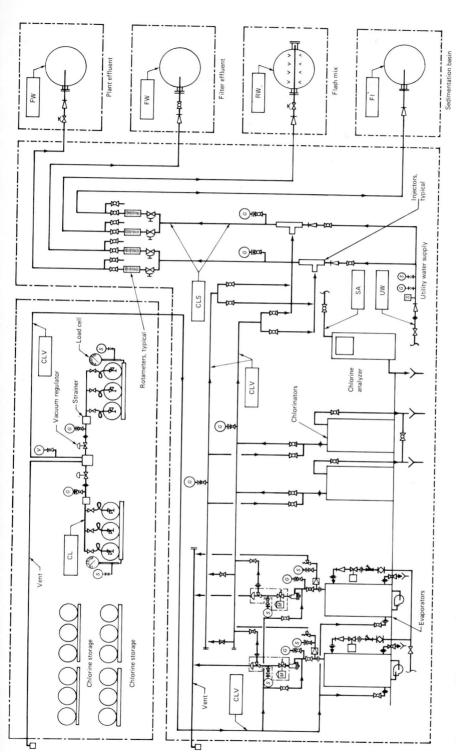

Figure 13.7 Chlorine system. (*J. M. Montgomery Consulting Engineers.*)

This ratio is 1 part chlorine to 3.1 parts of technical-grade sodium chlorite. The recommended ratio then would be not less than 1:2, and preferably 1:1. This material is primarily used in improving tastes and odors; it is considered by some to be more effective than chlorine in disinfecting water supplies. Because chlorine dioxide decomposes very quickly in water, the mixing is usually located just ahead of the point of application.

Copper sulfate (AWWA Standard B602)

Copper sulfate is available in blue crystalline granules or powder. It is used to control algae in impounding reservoirs. It is sometimes applied as a powder, distributed by dusting on the surface of the water through a suitable mechanism. Another technique is to drag burlap bags of copper sulfate crystals through the water, effecting solution and distribution in one stroke. Another method of application is to meter the copper sulfate solution into a narrow control channel at the entrance to the impounding reservoir. This chemical and its solution are poisonous and corrosive.

Ferric chloride

This material is primarily used in the coagulation of sewage and industrial wastes. For further information, a manufacturer should be consulted. A typical chemical schematic for both ferric chloride and aluminum sulfate appears in Fig. 13.2.

Ferric sulfate (AWWA Standard B406)

Ferric sulfate is produced to some degree when ferrous sulfate is chlorinated. It is available on the chemical market as a reddish brown deliquescent solid. Ferric sulfate is soluble in water, producing a somewhat acidic solution.

Ferrous sulfate (AWWA Standard B402)

The combination of ferrous sulfate and lime forms an effective coagulant for the clarification of turbid water. Ferrous sulfate itself is a greenish white crystalline solid that is obtained as a by-product of other chemical processes.

The AWWA standard for ferrous sulfate gives size standards for both its granular and lump forms. The standard-size granular ferrous sulfate has a tendency to cake and arch in dry feeder hoppers or storage bins. Material of a finer crystal size may be obtained which contains only five molecules of water crystallization ($FeSO_4 \cdot 5H_2O$). This material has less tendency to cake or arch. Ferrous sulfate is also available in a liquid form.

Fluorspar

Fluorspar is the principal and most economical source of the commercially available fluoride compounds. Pure fluorspar is a lustrous, glasslike material, almost always translucent or transparent, which may be colorless or range in color from blue to red. Fluorspar may be used as a direct source of fluoride for water fluoridation; an alum solution is used to dissolve it. It is available in three general grades of purity. The best grade for fluoridating purposes should contain at least 85 percent CaF_2 and less than 5 percent silica.

Hydrated lime

See Lime.

Hydrochloric acid

Hydrochloric acid is a clear or slightly yellow fuming, pungent liquid. It is poisonous, and may also contain iron or arsenic. If it is to be used in a potable water supply, care should be taken to obtain the purified form (USP). To reduce the fuming characteristics, it should be diluted (by adding the acid to water) to approximately 20 percent HCl. It is not often used in the treating of potable water supplies because it increases the chlorine content of the water.

Hydrofluosilicic acid (AWWA Standard B703)

Hydrofluosilicic acid is a 20 to 30 percent water solution of H_2SiF_6. It is a colorless, transparent, fuming, corrosive liquid, with a pungent odor and an irritating action on the skin. When vaporized, the acid decomposes to hydrofluoric acid and silicon tetrafluoride. The commercial product (23 to 30 percent H_2SiF_6) may have a straw or slightly reddish color owing to dissolved iron. In the amounts used in water fluoridation, this presents no problem.

Hypochlorites

For this discussion, hypochlorites can be classified as either dry or liquid, in accordance with commercial availability. Calcium hypochlorite is the predominant dry bleach in use in North America and Europe. It has been widely used for treatment of potable and swimming pool water since its introduction in the late 1920s; lithium hypochlorite was introduced in the early 1960s as a competitive product for the swimming pool market, but is little used today. Sodium hypochlorite, of which there are several grades and proprietary forms, is the only liquid hypochlorite disinfectant of note in current use. (See also Calcium hypochlorite and Sodium hypochlorite.)

Ion-exchange resins

The synthetic resins are sometimes used as dechlorinating agents, but usually on a small scale. The resin for this purpose must be very carefully selected, as only certain types have a marked degree of efficiency. The suppliers of these materials are usually well acquainted with which type of resin would be the most effective in absorbing chlorine from water.

Lime, quicklime, hydrated lime, and others (AWWA Standard B202)

Quicklime (CaO) results from the calcination of limestone or an equivalent, such as dried water-softening sludge of suitable analysis, and consists essentially of calcium oxide in natural association with a lesser amount of magnesium oxide. Hydrated lime is a very finely divided powder resulting from the hydration of quicklime with enough water to satisfy its chemical affinity. Commercial hydrated lime consists essentially of calcium hydroxide or a mixture of calcium hydroxide and magnesium hydroxide, depending on the type of quicklime slaked. The revised AWWA standard for quicklime and hydrated lime gives detailed recommendations on impurities and particle sizes. For quicklime, it recommends the minimum of 90 percent available calcium oxide content. Quicklime is available in any particle size required by a given installation, and size is usually specified in each contract. Hydrated lime is a powder that should be uniform in size and should have a minimum available calcium oxide content of 68.0 percent or more.

Quicklime has some tendency to air-slake, so exposure to outside air should be kept to a minimum. Hydrated lime tends to absorb carbon dioxide from the atmosphere even in the slurry form; thus its exposure to outside air should also be carefully controlled.

Thin milk-of-lime suspensions are liable to deposit calcium carbonate on the walls of the transmitting pipe or trough. It should be emphasized again that care is necessary to avoid mixtures of alum and quicklime. This is because there is a tendency for the water of crystallization from the alum to partially slake the lime. In a closed container, this may lead to a violent explosion. Equal care should be taken to avoid mixtures of ferric sulfate and lime.

Other forms of lime may also be found in specific areas.

Dolomitic lime. Dolomitic lime contains from 35 to 40 percent magnesium oxide. When the magnesium content exceeds the calcium content, the chemical is termed dolomitic magnesite. If the magnesium oxide content is greater than 5 percent but less than 35 percent, it is called magnesia quicklime.

Carbide lime. Carbide lime, which is also termed chemical lime, is a by-product from the manufacture of acetylene from calcium carbide. When the manufacturing process is dry, a dry hydrated lime is produced. If the process is wet, then the by-product is a slurry of 30 to 35 percent hydrated lime. Both wet and dry forms have a faint acetylene odor.

Dolomitic hydrated lime. This lime is produced by hydrating dolomitic quicklime. When normal hydrating conditions are present, only the calcium oxide is hydrated; the magnesium oxide remains unchanged. This is called monohydration.

Unburned lime. Calcium carbonate (limestone, calcite, whiting, chalk) is sometimes termed unburned lime. It is widely used as an agricultural lime and is also used in neutralization, stabilization, or corrosives prevention in water treatment.

Dolomite. Dolomitic limestone, which is essentially calcium and magnesium carbonate, is used in acid neutralization in wastewater treatment.

Ozone

Ozone is a faintly blue gas with a pungent odor. It is an unstable form of oxygen composed of three-atom molecules that break down readily to normal oxygen and nascent oxygen. The latter is a powerful oxidizing agent and has germicidal action. Ozone is usually produced by passing high-voltage electricity through dry atmospheric air between stationary electrodes. This process converts a small percentage of the oxygen in the air into ozone. It is usually injected into the water to be treated in a highly baffled mixing chamber. The ozone residual is determined by use of the orthotolidine test (0.1 ppm ozone equals 0.15 ppm Cl_2).

Potassium permanganate

This material is in the form of black or purple crystals or pellets with a blue metallic sheen and a sweetish, astringent taste; it is odorless. It is highly soluble in water, which allows easy application.

It is usually made up in dilute solution (1 to 4 percent) as needed for application. A typical chemical feed system for potassium permanganate appears in Fig. 13.8.

Quicklime

See Lime.

Soda ash

See Sodium carbonate.

Sodium aluminate (AWWA Standard B405)

Sodium aluminate is sometimes used as an auxiliary coagulant for the removal of fine turbidity and color bodies in soft, low-pH water. The solid form is a white or brown powder containing 70 to 80 percent $Na_2Al_2O_4$. The solution form is a concentrated solution containing approximately 32 percent $Na_2Al_2O_4$. This material is readily soluble in water, producing a noncorrosive solution.

Sodium bisulfate

The principal constituent is sodium pyrosulfite, or sodium metabisulfite ($Na_2S_2O_5$). These white, crystalline powders are readily soluble in water.

Sodium carbonate (soda ash) (AWWA Standard B201)

Soda ash used in the softening of water is a grayish white powder containing at least 98 percent sodium carbonate.

Sodium chloride (AWWA Standard B200)

The AWWA standard for sodium chloride requires that the materials be homogenous and in a dry granular form, white, grayish white, pink, brown, or brownish white in color. The size requirements state

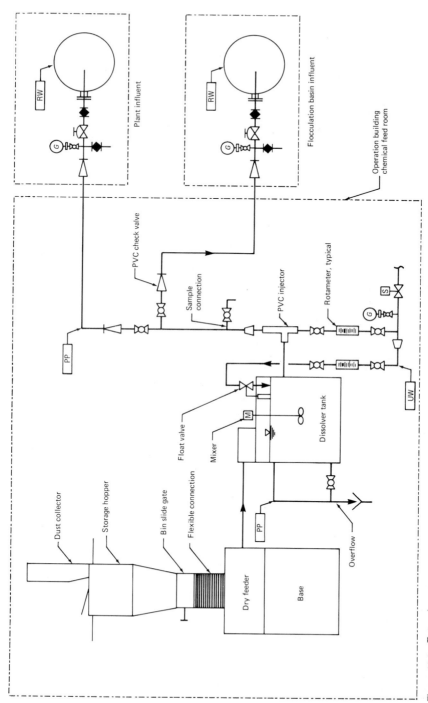

Figure 13.8 Potassium permanganate system. (*J. M. Montgomery Consulting Engineers.*)

that rock salt shall be of such fineness that it shall pass a No. 3 sieve, and 95 percent of it shall be retained on a No. 7 sieve. Evaporated salt shall be of such fineness that at least 85 percent shall be retained on a No. 7 sieve. The material shall dissolve rapidly without packing. The solution formed by dissolving the salt in distilled water shall have a phenolphthalein alkalinity of zero, and a hydrogen-ion concentration (pH) no higher than 8.0.

Sodium chlorite

Sodium chlorite is a dry, flaked salt with a powerfully oxidizing nature. It is stable when sealed or in solution, but is very combustible in the presence of organic material. Technical-grade sodium chlorite (approximately 80 percent dry weight $NaClO_2$) is an orange-colored flaked salt, with a density of approximately 56 lb/ft^3. It is a very powerful oxidizing agent.

Sodium chlorite in contact with acid will react rapidly to evolve chlorine dioxide gas. When heated above 347°F, sodium chlorite will decompose rapidly, liberating oxygen and evolving sufficient heat to make the decomposition self-sustaining. If this decomposition is confined, as in a closed container, the effect is explosive. Therefore, it should be protected at all times from exposure to heat.

Sodium chlorite dissolves easily in water at ordinary temperatures to form an orange-brown solution. This solution is chemically stable under ordinary conditions of temperature and pressure. Sodium chlorite is available from suppliers in dry form or liquid solutions. Because of the hazardous nature of dry sodium chlorite, liquid solutions are the preferred chemical form. For most applications, sodium chlorite solutions of 25 percent by weight should be used. This concentration has been selected by the industry because it has the lowest freezing point of sodium chlorite solutions, $-15°C$ (5°F). If dry sodium chlorite is to be used, special precautions are required for storage, handling, dust control, and worker safety.

For most chlorine dioxide generation systems, a low-alkalinity (< 10 g/L as $CaCO_3$) sodium chlorite should be used.

Sodium fluoride (AWWA Standard B701)

Sodium fluoride is produced by neutralizing hydrofluoric acid with either sodium carbonate or sodium hydroxide. It is available as crystals or white powder. It is highly soluble in water, which enhances its use in the fluoridation of water supplies.

Sodium hexametaphosphate

This is one of several forms of what are known as glassy phosphates. It is used in water softening and in boiler water treatment and is available from any number of manufacturers in both powdered and granular form. It is also used as a sequestering agent in municipal water supplies and is infinitely soluble in water.

Sodium hydroxide

Sodium hydroxide, also known as caustic soda, is available in the liquid form in two concentrations: 50 percent NaOH and 73 percent NaOH. The 50 percent caustic soda begins to crystallize at approximately 54°F, and the 73 percent concentration at about 145°F. It is also available as solid (pellet) or flake caustic soda, containing 98.06 percent NaOH. A typical chemical feed schematic for sodium hydroxide appears in Fig. 13.9.

Sodium hypochlorite

Commercial sodium hypochlorite or liquid bleach, manufactured by hundreds of companies in the United States, usually contains 12 to 15 percent available chlorine at the time of manufacture, and is available only in liquid form. Its use is generally limited to smaller potable water treatment installations and for swimming pool water disinfection.

All NaOCl solutions are unstable to some degree and deteriorate more rapidly than calcium hypochlorite. The effect can be minimized by care in the manufacturing processes and by controlling the alkalinity of the solution. Greatest stability is attained with a pH close to 11.0, and with the absence of heavy metal cations.

Sodium silicate

Sodium silicate in the form known as activated silica is called a coagulant aid. The chief advantage of activated silica is its ability to toughen the floc. Activated silica may be prepared in a number of ways.

Sodium silicate solution is available as a 40° Baumé liquid containing approximately 30 percent SiO_2.

Sodium silicofluoride (AWWA Standard B702)

This material is a white, free-flowing, odorless, crystalline powder. It is produced by neutralizing hydrofluosilicic acid with soda ash (Na_2CO_3) or sodium hydroxide (NaOH) and evaporating the resulting solution. Sodium silicofluoride is by far the most extensively used compound in the fluoridation of water supplies because of its availability and low cost. Its disadvantages lie in its very low solubility, 60 gal of water being required to dissolve 1 lb of sodium silicofluoride.

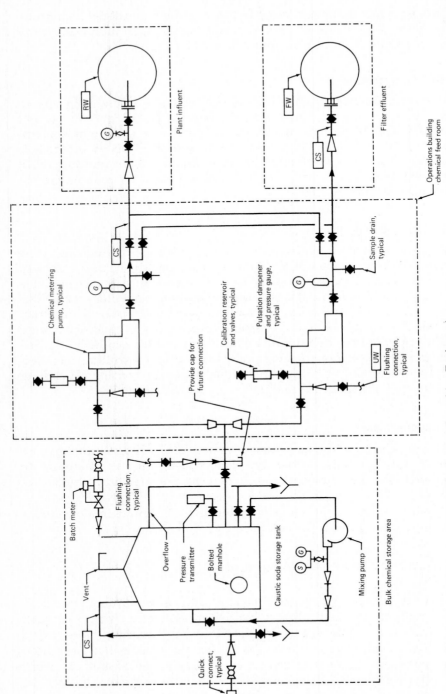

Figure 13.9 Caustic soda system. (*J. M. Montgomery Consulting Engineers.*)

378

Sodium sulfite

Sodium sulfite is similar in appearance and use to sodium bisulfate.

Sulfur dioxide

Sulfur dioxide is produced in North America either by the combustion of sulfur in special burners, by burning pyrites, or as a by-product of smelting operations. In the gaseous state, sulfur dioxide is colorless and about 2.26 times as heavy as air. The liquid, also colorless, is about 1.44 times as heavy as water. Unconfined liquid sulfur dioxide rapidly vaporizes to gas.

Sulfur dioxide is slightly soluble in water (however, it is about 20 times as soluble as chlorine). At 32°F, up to 20 percent by weight will dissolve to form a weak solution of sulfurous acid. Because its vapor pressure increases with increasing temperature, its solubility decreases with increasing temperature; at 80°F, it is soluble to less than 10 percent.

Sulfuric acid

Sulfuric acid (H_2SO_4) is a strong, corrosive, dense, oily liquid, colored or dark brown, depending on purity. For use in water treatment it should be of the USP grade and free of heavy metals. It is available in a number of grades, containing from 60 to 90 percent H_2SO_4.

Inventories and Delivery Requirements

Inventories

An appropriate inventory of chemicals is based on factors that vary from plant to plant, even within the same system. Once a basic decision has been made as to the number of days' supply desired, based on anticipated maximum daily requirements, additional factors must be considered. These include the type of container (if other than bulk), normal delivery time, potential delays resulting from emergencies (either natural or caused by human agency) that could affect delivery, and other such factors.

In larger plants where use levels justify bulk delivery of certain chemicals, the quantity stored will be dictated more by the size of the bulk shipping containers in use in the area than by the desired number of days' supply. Obviously, excess inventory is undesirable from both an economical and a physical standpoint.

Chemicals such as soda ash and quicklime which possess either hydroscopic properties or are otherwise affected by moisture can become difficult to handle after several months in bulk storage unless precautions are taken to control the environment. Chemicals furnished in returnable containers, such as chlorine cylinders or ton containers, may be subject to demurrage charges unless these are waived by agreement in the purchase contract.

Delivery

Normally, all chemicals will be delivered to the plant at grade level. Subsequent vertical or horizontal movement from the unloading point will be accomplished by various means, depending upon the type of material, its packaging, and the form of transportation employed. Possible modes of transport are railroad tank cars, trucks, and, in rare instances, barges.

Truck transportation appears today to be the preferred method of delivery of both containerized and bulk chemicals to both small and large treatment plants. Modern air-slide and pneumatic unloading equipment on these vehicles permits delivery of bulk loads below grade as well as to overhead silos with minimal human involvement.

Chlorine tank barges have either four or six tanks, each with a capacity of from 85 to 185 tons. These must comply with Coast Guard regulations. The valves are similar to those on tank cars, but the arrangement is not standard, and on some barges the valves are larger.

Unlike single-unit railroad tank cars, which are trip-leased and are often used as storage tanks, unloading directly to the consuming process, chlorine trucks and barges (which are not trip-leased) are unloaded into a storage tank that supplies the process requirements.

In general, requirements for emptying tank trucks and barges are similar to those discussed below for tank cars. Suitable chlorine bulk-storage facilities are required. In the case of barges, piping, loading, and unloading arrangements must be approved by the Coast Guard in the United States.

Tank trucks consist of cargo tanks for chlorine permanently attached to a motor vehicle; the tanks are loaded and unloaded without being removed from the vehicle. U. S. Department of Transportation (DOT) regulations are explicit as to tank and appurtenance design and maintenance, marking, and emergency handling. Only a few chlorine tank trucks are currently being operated in the United States.

Rail car deliveries are practical only for the largest plants, and even then they are subject to the economic feasibility of constructing a siding from the nearest service line. It appears, however, that large consumers of chlorine are best served by single-unit tank cars of 16.30 or 55 net tons. Refer to Table 13.3 for dimensions and weights.

DOT regulations permit shipment of chlorine cylinders by rail in ei-

TABLE 13.3 Dimensions and Weights of Chlorine Tank Cars

Car	Length over strikers*	Overall height†	Height to valve outlet†	Extreme width‡	Weight empty, lb§	Weight loaded, lb
TMU	42'4"–47'0"	6'8"–7'6"	—	9'6"–10'1"	54,500–59,000§	84,500–89,000
16-ton	32'2"–33'3"	10'5"–12'0"	9'3¼"–10'0"	9'2"–9'6½"	42,000–51,000	74,000–83,000
30-ton	33'10"–35'11½"	12'4½"–13'7"	11'3"–11'9"	9'3"–9'10"	55,000–65,000	115,000–125,000
55-ton	38'9½"–43'0"	14'3"–14'10½"	12'6"–13'1½"	9'3"–10'7½"	76,000–94,000	187,000–204,000

*Add 2'6" for length over centerline of coupler knuckles.
†Heights are for empty cars and are measured from top of rail; heights of loaded cars may be as much as 4" less.
‡Width over grab irons.
§Weight for car with empty containers; underframe only weighs about 34,000 to 46,000 lb.

381

ther carload or partial-carload lots. Freight tariffs specify minimum carload weights of 36,000 lb for full and 30,000 lb for empty cylinders. Any number of cylinders can be shipped by truck. Shipments via motor vehicles may be made in less than carload lots or in truckload quantities of various minimum weights, depending on the motor carrier and area of transportation.

Ton containers of chlorine are authorized for rail shipment, but only on a special tank-car frame known as a multiunit tank car (TMU); this car is designed to hold 15 containers. The initial rail shipment of these containers is unloaded from the car for use at the consumer's plant. In subsequent shipments, the full containers are exchanged for empties to be returned for refilling. No freight is charged on the return carload of empty containers because tank cars are entitled to free return movement. It is impractical to ship less than 15 containers because the transportation fee is figured for 15 full containers at prevailing carload rates. TMU cars must be consigned for delivery and unloading on a private track. Where a private track is not available, the containers may be removed from the car frame on carrier tracks if written permission is first obtained. Regulations also provide that one or more ton containers may be transported on trucks or semitrailers under special conditions.

Interstate Commerce Commission (ICC) regulations require that single-unit tank cars, which are trip-leased, be unloaded on a private track, a dead-end siding used only for chlorine transfer or unloading operations. Two parallel tracks are recommended to facilitate handling of cars and to permit continuous operation while cars are being switched. Regulations also stipulate that cars be attended throughout the entire unloading period.

Single-unit chlorine tank cars have 4-in corkboard or self-extinguishing foam insulation and are designed to withstand pressures of either 300 or 500 psig. The manway, at the center of the car on top, is the only opening permitted by regulations. Five valves are mounted in the manway. Four are operating angle valves, and one is a spring-loaded safety relief valve. Two of the angle valves are gas-discharge valves and two are liquid-discharge valves. Under each liquid valve is an eduction pipe extending to the bottom of the tank. At the top of each eduction line, immediately below the angle valve, is a rising-ball excess flow valve designed to close when the discharge rate is about 7000 lb/h. The safety valve is designed to start to discharge at 225 psig for the 300-lb cars, and at 375 psig for the 500-lb cars. Unlike cylinders and ton containers, single-unit tank cars are designed for the discharge of chlorine gas directly to the chlorinator. Dimensions and weights of chlorine tank cars are given in Table 13.3.

Elements of Design and Design Practice—Receiving and Storage of Process Chemicals

Receiving

Unloading platforms or docks must be provided in all but the smallest plants to accommodate truck deliveries of containerized chemicals, including bagged material, drums, small gas cylinders, and the like. Horizontal transport of nonbulk chemicals from the unloading dock is normally accomplished by the use of hand or power trucks, conveyors, or a monorail system. Storage in areas above or below the unloading area requires the installation of an inclined conveyor, hoist, or elevator designed for the maximum loads anticipated.

Unloading containers

Various mechanical devices, such as skids, troughs, or upending cradles, should be provided to facilitate the safe unloading of chlorine cylinders. Specially designed cradles or carrying platforms are recommended if it is necessary to lift the cylinders by crane or derrick. Chains, lifting magnets, and rope slings that encircle cylinders are unsafe. Handtrucks are preferred for lateral movement.

Provision should be made for the lifting of ton chlorine containers from a multiunit tank car or truck by means of hooks designed to fit on a chain sling or lifting clamp in combination with a hoist or crane with at least a 2-ton capacity. The containers may be moved to point of storage or use by truck, by a monorail system, or by rolling.

Receiving and unloading areas and safety precautions applicable to the handling of single-unit cars, cargo trucks, and barges are subject to DOT, Coast Guard, and other regulations.

Emptying of tank cars should be accomplished through a suitable metal flexible connection that can accommodate the rise of the car as its springs decompress. Tank cars are almost invariably emptied by discharging liquid. Liquefied gases may be unloaded by their own vapor pressure. Cold weather usually decreases the unloading rate; in extremely cold climates it may be helpful to unload cars in a shed maintained at about 70°F. Sometimes it is desirable to provide an air pad over the chlorine vapor in the car to facilitate unloading. This may be provided by the chlorine supplier or at the point of use. A reliable means must be provided for determining tank contents. Weight-measuring devices are preferred; gauge glasses should not be used.

Where night operations are contemplated, adequate lighting, including auxiliary power sources, should be provided.

Unloading bulk chemicals

The type of facilities provided will depend on the physical state of the chemical (solid or liquid) and the form in which it will be fed to the process; the type of carrier (rail or truck); and the location and type of storage silo, tank, or other storage facility. Whether the chemical is liquid or solid, truck delivery seems to be preferred because of its simplicity, maneuverability, and generally prompt and predictable delivery. In contrast to rail shipments, truck delivery makes more load-size options available while still preserving the economics of bulk purchasing.

Obviously, more mechanical equipment is necessary to unload solid-form chemicals than liquid, which can be handled by gravity flow or transfer pumping. Solids unloading is usually accomplished with pneumatic equipment (blower or vacuum), air slides, or mechanical screw conveyors and/or bucket elevators. The latter equipment is satisfactory for unloading lumpy or coarse material where excessive dust is not a problem.

Pneumatic truck unloading of dry bulk chemicals is done through the user's pipe conveying system, consisting of a truck inlet panel, interconnecting piping to silos or storage bins, safety release valve, and dust collector mounted on top of the storage bin. The diameter of the piping is usually standardized at 4 in, with bends having a minimum radius of 4 ft. The maximum length of piping between the inlet panel and storage depends on the nature of the material being transported. Pebble lime, for instance, may be blown as much as 100 ft vertically, providing the total length of run does not exceed 150 ft. Lightweight powdery material can easily be transported up to 300 ft over a combined vertical and horizontal distance. Pneumatic trucks are generally available in capacities of from 700 to 1300 ft^3. They are equipped with air compressors.

Rail-car delivery of dry bulk chemicals may involve covered hopper-type cars with capacities up to about 3700 ft^3. These cars are constructed with two to four compartments, each provided with its own bottom discharge gate. Material is withdrawn through these gates, which have been spotted over undertrack hoppers; air vibrators are used where necessary to facilitate the movement of fine, powdery material through the hopper. A more widely used type of rail car permits a method of pneumatic unloading similar to that used on pneumatic trucks. Others employ air-slide conveyors to move the material out to the truck hopper. Canvas connectors, or stockings, are generally used to connect to the truck hopper which feeds the conveying system. The user must provide air compressors for pressurizing the cars and/or the vibrators and air slides; they are not part of the car equipment, as is the case with pneumatic trucks. Hopper cars may also be unloaded using a vacuum system consisting of suction pump, filter receiver, and discharge air lock or rotary gate at the top of the silo or storage bin.

Liquid chemicals, such as caustic soda, liquid alum, acids, or corrosion inhibitors, will most likely be delivered by tank truck. To facilitate safe unloading, it is the user's responsibility to provide appropriate fill-pipe connections, clearly labeled and equipped with protective caps. A concrete drip sump protected with a chemically resistant coating should be provided beneath all fill-pipe connections. Storage tank vent pipes should terminate above the sump with screened elbows facing downward. As with any chemical, but particularly with liquids, the user must be certain that the quantity ordered can be accommodated in storage at the time of delivery. To further guard against overfilling a storage tank, it is recommended that a high-level audible alarm be provided as part of the in-plant chemical tank-level indicating system; this alarm should be mounted outside the unloading station to alert the vehicle operator. Usually the alarm can be common to all tanks served by the particular unloading station.

Dust collection

Any unloading or transfer of dry chemicals will create dust, especially when air-flow equipment is used to unload the material. Operation of this type of equipment requires the discharge of dust-free conveying air to the atmosphere, a job for which a bag-type filter is best suited. Since these filters collect chemical dust which can be returned to the process, it is common practice to mount the collector on top of the silo during the cleaning cycle. Operation of the dust collector is remotely controlled from the unloading point or truck inlet panel. It is possible to have one dust collector serve more than one storage receiver, provided the same chemical is being handled; under no circumstances should a mixture of different chemical dusts be allowed to accumulate within one collector. The size of a dust collector depends on the volume of air to be handled. The air blowers mounted on pneumatic trucks frequently have the capability of producing up to 750 ft^3/min of air.

Storage

Cylinders and ton containers

Cylinders should be stored upright in a manner that will permit ready access and removal, and secured. Ton containers should be stored horizontally, slightly elevated from ground or floor level, and blocked to prevent rolling; a convenient storage rack is obtained by supporting both ends of containers on rails or I-beams. Ton containers should not be stacked or racked unless special design provisions are made for easy access and removal. Storage areas should be clean, cool, well ventilated, and protected from corrosive vapors or continual dampness. Cylinders and ton containers should preferably be stored indoors, in a fire-resistant building, and away from heat sources, other compressed gases, and flammable substances. If they are stored outdoors, the area should be shielded from direct sunlight and accumulations of rain and snow. Subsurface areas should be avoided. If natural ventilation is inadequate, storage and use areas should be equipped with suitable mechanical ventilators.

All storage areas should be designed so that personnel can quickly escape in emergencies. Not less than two means of exit should be provided from each separate room or building in which chlorine and other gases are stored, handled, or used.

Bulk storage, bins, silos, tanks

Bulk storage of chemicals is indicated when large quantities of the product are consumed and high inventory levels are desired not only for the economic benefits but also to guard against supply shortages and transportation difficulties. Obviously, the type of storage facilities provided will vary with the chemical involved.

Chlorine used in the water industry is seldom stored in on-site receivers; the preference is to use the shipping container for storage. Where bulk storage is indicated (when chlorine is shipped by tank truck or, in some cases, by barge), a sufficient pressure differential must be maintained between the shipping container and the storage container. Facilities must be provided to vent chlorine gas or chlorine and air mixtures from the storage tank to the consuming process or other disposal system; venting may be required during the entire unloading period. When transferring chlorine from the storage tank to the consuming process, air padding may be necessary. The procedure is essentially the same as that required for emptying tank cars.

The location, design, maintenance, and operation of chlorine bulk storage tanks may be subject to local or state regulations and to insurance requirements. The number and capacity of the storage tanks should be consistent with the size of shipments received and the rate of consumption.

Powdered activated carbon, a finely ground, low-density material, is capable of producing copious quantities of black dust with the least disturbance. As a result, large users of this material who can accept air-slide truck or rail bulk shipments will prefer to have the carbon unloaded directly into slurry tanks. In this way, further handling of the powder into and out of storage is avoided, and dust problems are minimized. Activated carbon can be stored in bins and extension hoppers supplying dry feeders; this type of installation is quite appropriate in smaller plants and in plants where carbon usage is intermittent and the carbon is received and stored in paper bags.

Quicklime and hydrated limes are abrasive but not corrosive. Therefore, steel or concrete bins and silos can be used for storage. It is imperative that the storage units be airtight as well as watertight in order to reduce the effect of air slaking; this includes relief valves, access hatches, dust collector mechanism, and so on, all of which are normally exposed to the weather. Bins and silos can be designed with rectangular, square, hexagonal, or circular cross sections; the first three make optimum use of plant space, but the circular silo is less susceptible to sidewall hangups, which tend to occur in corners of bins of other shapes. Regardless of the cross-sectional configuration of the vertical storage unit, the bottom is always designed with a hopper or conical base right up to the discharge gate. The design volume of any silo or bin should be based on the average bulk density of the chemical, with an allowance for 50 to 100 percent extra capacity beyond that required to accommodate a normal-sized delivery.

Flow is the key word in bulk chemical handling. Generally, the flow of material increases with particle size, uniformity, hardness, smoothness, absence of fines, and lower moisture content. These physical parameters can be controlled to some degree by purchase specification. Once the desired material is delivered, proper bin or silo capability can maintain flow with vibrating or pulsating devices, live bin bottoms, and internal devices to control packing and arching. It is generally believed that the height of bins or silos can be approximately 2½ to 4 times the diameter, with the discharge area as large as possible. Hopper bottoms should slope at least 60° from the horizontal; an even greater slope is desirable for hydrated lime storage. Offset hopper sections are frequently recommended, with the outlet off to one side of the vertical bin axis. The distortion produced by the varying slope angles tends to prevent arching in the conveying section. The use of vibrators to maintain flow requires caution and consideration of the type of material being handled; the worst possible situation occurs when fine materials (such as hydrated lime) are overvibrated, and packing results. Such material can only be vibrated intermittently—for instance, by a 2- to 4-s pulse repeated several times a minute. By contrast, lumpy material like pebble lime can be vibrated continuously during discharge. The interruptor unit used to control the vibrator must be interlocked electrically with the process feeder so that vibration can occur only during discharge.

Air jets and pulsating air pads are frequently used to fluidize light materials like hydrated lime. Numerous other devices are available, the most popular being the live bin bottom. These units operate continuously during discharge and utilize gyrating forces or upward-thrusting baffles within the hopper to eliminate bridging and ratholing. Other less sophisticated devices include double-ended cones supported centrally within the hopper, rotating chains or paddles, and horizontal rods run from wall to wall.

Storage tanks for liquid chemicals are designed and fabricated of materials suitable for the service intended. Common construction materials include steel and fiberglass-reinforced plastic. The choice of tank material or lining, in addition to its chemical resistance, will also depend upon pressure and temperature conditions. Open-top tanks can be used for stable, nonvolatile liquids, but their use is restricted. Buried tanks must be strapped to anchor blocks with sufficient mass to prevent flotation when empty, and must meet EPA leak prevention criteria. These criteria mandate the use of double-wall tanks with leak detection alarms. Covered tanks must be provided with manholes and vent lines. Where possible, vent lines should be run along the route of the fill lines and should terminate outside at the unloading drip sump. Both lines must be run without traps. Overflow lines may interconnect covered tanks containing the same material but should not be allowed to terminate in the open air alongside the tank; such a line would become the primary vent and permit a dangerous spill to occur in the event of an overfill. Accidental overflows are best prevented by providing dependable level indicators and alarms on all tanks.

Numerous electrical and pneumatic systems are available with local or remote indicating and/or recording and alarm capability. Level sensors using bubble pipes are effective and accurate, but before they are used, it must first be determined that air bubbles will not deteriorate the chemical whose level is being measured.

The majority of storage tanks will be located in the lower or basement areas of buildings, where the air is naturally cooler. As a result, heating and insulation may be required for those tanks that contain chemicals subject to crystallization. The installation of thermostatically controlled hot water or steam coils within the tank will assure positive protection against slushing or freezing. If the problem is marginal or only occurs during severe seasonal weather, the application of electrical heating tape on the tank exterior will usually be sufficient.

Bags and drums

Areas used for dry chemical storage of bagged material, drums, and other such containers must be fireproof, dry, and well ventilated. Compressed gases in cylinders should be stored separately in an area provided with positive mechanical ventilation or exhaust fans. Bagged material and chemicals in small drums may be stored on pallets for easier handling and to economize on storage space. A few of the more widely used bagged or containerized chemicals, and specific problems relative to their storage and handling, are described below.

Powdered activated carbon.   Reports from the National Board of Fire Underwriters state that the activated carbons normally used in water treatment present no dust explosion hazard and are not subject to spontaneous combustion when configured in bags, drums, or storage bins. The carbons are combustible, however, and will burn when ignited. The ignition point of the activated carbons will vary from 600 to 800°F. After ignition, activated carbon will not burn with a flame, but will glow or smoulder until all the carbon material is oxidized. Storage of carbon in paper bags presents a hazard in that the paper will burn more rapidly. Bags of powdered carbon should be stacked in rows with aisles between in such a manner that each bag is accessible for removal in case of fire.

In the event of an activated carbon fire, the safest procedure, if possible, is to place the smoldering material in a metal container and haul it outside the building. A smoldering carbon fire may be smothered by means of a very fine spray or mist of water from a hose or by a foam-type chemical extinguisher. Do not attempt to extinguish the carbon by a direct stream of water, as this will cause the light smoldering particles to fly into the air and spread the fire. Installing an overhead sprinkler system in the storage and feeding rooms is a practical precautionary measure. Activated carbon should not be stored where it can come into contact with gasoline, mineral oils, or vegetable oils. These materials, when mixed with carbon, will slowly oxidize until the ignition temperature is reached. Never mix or store carbon with such materials as chlorine, lime hypochlorites, sodium chlorite, or potassium permanganate. Such mixtures are known to be spontaneously combustible.

Activated carbon is an electrical conductor and should not be allowed to accumulate as dust near or on open electric circuits. Some activated carbons are subject to deterioration in storage, so carbon storage areas should be relatively free of such air contaminants as sulfur dioxide, chlorine, hydrogen sulfide, and organic vapors. Normal safety equipment, such as protective clothing, respirators, neck cloths, gloves, and goggles, should be provided for workers handling powdered activated carbon.

Sodium chlorite. Sodium chlorite is a dry, flaked salt, which, because of its powerful oxidizing nature, is shipped in steel drums bearing an ICC "yellow" label classification. It is stable when sealed or in solution, but is very combustible in the presence of organic material. For this reason, the solution should not be allowed to dry out on floors, but should be hosed down with minimum splashing. Technical-grade sodium chlorite is an orange-colored flaked salt, with a density of approximately 56 lb/ft^3.

Sodium chlorite should be stored in an enclosed space specially prepared for the purpose and removed from the storage room only as needed for immediate use. Empty containers should be returned to the storage room immediately after each use unless they are shipping containers, in which case they should be thoroughly flushed with water (to the sewer) as soon as they are empty and should be immediately disposed of at some point well away from any building. Shipping containers should never be used for any other purpose after they are empty.

Calcium hypochlorite. Although calcium hypochlorite is a stable, nonflammable material that cannot be ignited, contact with heat, acids, or combustible, organic, or oxidizable materials may cause fire.

Calcium hypochlorite is readily soluble in water, varying from about 21.5 g/100 mL at 0°C to 23.4 g/100 mL at 40°C. Tablet forms dissolve more slowly than the granular materials, and provide a fairly steady source of available chlorine over an 18- to 24-h period.

Granular forms usually are shipped in 35- or 100-lb drums, cartons containing 3¾-lb resealable cans, or cases containing nine 5-lb resealable cans. Tablet forms are shipped in 35- and 100-lb drums, and in cases containing twelve 3¾-lb or 4-lb resealable plastic containers.

Because of its strong oxidizing powers and reactivity with organic materials, calcium hypochlorite should be segregated from other chemicals or material with which it can react or stored in a separate location. To minimize the loss in available chlorine content that occurs with elevated temperature, cool storage areas should be provided. Containers should be kept dry and located in a darkened area unless the containers themselves shield out excessive light. Their size should be consistent with use requirements. Stored containers should be so arranged that they can be easily moved from the storage area in the event of leaks.

Sodium hypochlorite. Commercial sodium hypochlorite, or liquid bleach, is manufactured by hundreds of companies in the United States. It usually contains 12 to 15 percent available chlorine at the time of manufacture, and is available only in liquid form. Its use is generally limited to smaller potable water treatment installations and for swimming pool water disinfection. It is marketed in carboys and rubber-lined drums of up to 50-gal volume, and in trucks. Household products, containing from 3 to 5.25 percent available chlorine, are packaged in brown or amber-colored glass or polyethylene bottles.

All NaOCl solutions are unstable to some degree and deteriorate more rapidly than calcium hypochlorite. The effect can be minimized by care in the manufacturing processes and by controlling the alkalinity of the solution. Greatest stability is attained with a pH close to 11.0 and with the absence of heavy metal cations. Storage temperatures should not exceed about 85°F; above that level, the rate of decomposition increases rapidly. While storage in a cool, darkened area very greatly limits the deterioration rate, most large manufacturers recommend a maximum shelf life of 60 to 90 days.

All hypochlorite solutions are corrosive to some degree and can affect the skin, eyes, and other body tissues. Accordingly, rubber gloves, aprons, goggles, and similar suitable protective apparel should be provided for preparing and handling hypochlorite solutions. Areas of skin contact should be promptly flushed with copious quantities of water. Every precaution should be observed to protect containers against physical damage, to prevent container breakage, and to minimize accidental splashing.

Sodium chloride. Sodium chloride has a tendency to absorb moisture and to cake under certain conditions. Care should be taken to protect it from moisture in storage. (It is best stored in concrete bins.) It is highly soluble in water, may be readily made up to a desired concentration, and may be fed by a standard liquid chemical metering device. The solution may be transmitted through rubber or bronze lines. Exposure of the skin to large amounts of the dry salt would have a tendency to cause the skin to dehydrate. Protective clothing and devices such as gloves and face shields should be provided. Large users of brine solution prefer to receive delivered salt directly into a saturator tank and avoid problems of dry storage.

Sodium carbonate (soda ash) (AWWA Standard B201). Soda ash used in the softening of water is a grayish white powder containing at least 98 percent sodium carbonate. It may be shipped in bulk, in bags, or in barrels. It is noncorrosive and may be stored in ordinary steel or concrete bins or silos. It may be fed using a conventional chemical dry

feeder. Its solution may be transmitted through conventional pipelines or troughs. Its hazards are primarily those of a chemical dust.
Protective clothing and devices such as gloves, respirators, and goggles should be provided.

Slurries

As used in water treatment, a slurry can be described as a suspension
of a relatively insoluble chemical in water. Powdered activated carbon
and lime (calcium hydroxide) are the most common slurries handled
in water treatment, and concern with them mainly involves questions
of handling and mixing. Once a slurry (carbon or lime) has been prepared, a pumping and piping system is needed to convey the material
to the point or points of application. Different techniques are required
for the handling of carbon and lime slurries.

Carbon slurries.   Numerous tests have demonstrated that there is no
loss of adsorptive activity when carbon is held in water as a slurry
over long periods of time (up to 1 year). Mixing equipment that is used
to wet and slurry activated carbon operates with the agitator revolving at 60 to 70 rpm. It is preferable that the agitator motor be dual
speed, providing about 80 rpm for initial wetting and 40 rpm to maintain suspension. Agitators normally consist of two sets of stainless
steel paddles, one set near the bottom of the tank and one set placed
approximately 18 in from the top. With such an arrangement the activated carbon can be slurried almost as rapidly as it is discharged
from the hopper car. With the proper equipment, tests have shown
that an air-slide car containing 21 tons of carbon can be unloaded in
less than 1 h. Water plants purchasing less than carload quantities of
powdered activated carbon may also find a slurry system very desirable.

The tank size required to slurry less than carload or truckload shipments can easily be determined: a 1000-lb carbon shipment would require a tank that had a usable capacity of 1200 gal when a slurry concentration of 1 lb/gal is used. It is common practice to size the tank to
have a total volume equal in gallons to the maximum load (in pounds)
of carbon to be received plus 20 percent for freeboard.

Carbon slurry tanks are usually square concrete structures with a
bitumastic or epoxy lining. If steel tanks are used, the surface must be
cleaned to bare metal prior to lining. The mixture agitator shaft, impeller, assembly bolts, pump suction piping, and other such parts must
be made of stainless steel or be rubber covered. Sufficient horsepower
should be available to handle carbon slurry concentrations up to 1.5 to

1.0 lb/gal. Mechanical failure of the mixing equipment will render the slurry system inoperative. For this reason, those installations that are critically dependent upon uninterrupted carbon feed will frequently elect to install an air-agitation system for backup. Although not as efficient as mechanical mixing, adequate suspension can usually be maintained until mixer repairs are made. Obviously, large plants that use carbon routinely should consider the feasibility of installing duplicate slurry tanks, not only for mechanical standby but because it is almost impossible to maintain a constant-strength slurry during the recharge and wetting period following a new delivery of carbon.

Accessories to be incorporated into a well-designed slurry storage system will include a dust collector to permit venting the tank during loading. An isolating gate is required to prevent tank moisture from entering the collector when it is not in use. It is desirable that the collector be equipped with a blower to maintain slight negative pressure on the slurry tank during unloading, thereby controlling dusting from vents, manhole covers, and mixer shaft seals. Tank level readings are best accomplished using an air bubbler system with a stainless steel bubble pipe. Strength of slurry is controlled by measuring makeup water to the tank through a water meter of sufficient capacity to fill the tank within a reasonable number of hours.

Most water plants using reasonably large quantities of activated carbon convert it to slurry form when it is received. It is even quite feasible to dump bag carbon into a tank equipped with a turbine mixer, from which point it can be fed through the usual slurry feeding devices.

Carbon, unlike lime, does not react chemically when it is diluted in water; therefore, problems with scaling and salt precipitation are not experienced. On the other hand, construction materials for piping, pumps, and valves must be resistant to the corrosive nature of powdered carbon slurries. Suitable materials for this service include Type 316 stainless steel, rubber, silicon bronze, monel, Hastelloy C, Saran, and fiberglass-reinforced plastic. On smaller installations, where feed control is achieved by regulating the flow of dry carbon through a dry feeder equipped with a slurry pot, the feed line carrying the carbon suspension from the machine should be of ample size to handle the volume of water required for dilution. If possible, the line should be installed with a continuous downgrade to the point of application. Provision should be made for cleaning out any carbon that may settle in the line and cause clogging. Whenever the feeding is stopped for any reason, the line should be flushed with clear water. In many smaller plants, a rubber hose has been used for the entire feed line, so that stoppages may be easily eliminated by manipulation. Ample volume of flushing water is important; if it is not available through the slurry pot, it should be added to the line by means of rotometer and air break.

Larger installations using agitated slurry storage of constant strength employ metering pumps for feed control. These pumps should discharge to a dilution box located at an appropriate elevation to permit gravity feed. Dilution water is added through a rotometer to maintain adequate velocity (at least 1½ fps) to prevent settling. The point of application should be above the water surface, and unavoidable high spots in the line must be vented.

Carbon slurry concentrations generated by dry feeder–slurry pot systems will naturally vary, since the dry carbon feed is variable. On the other hand, agitated slurry storage systems are commonly adjusted to contain 1 lb of carbon per gallon of water. Heavier or lighter slurries can be handled, but since metering pumps are calibrated in gallons per minute or gallons per hour, a shift operator can readily convert the pounds of carbon fed. For this reason, it is necessary that additional dilution water be added after the metering pump.

Lime slurries.   The formation and handling of lime slurries involves chemical as well as mechanical considerations. Lime slurries result from adding controlled amounts of water to either slaked quicklime or hydrated lime. A slurry of reasonable purity is not corrosive and is relatively easy to keep in suspension provided that the slurry has been stabilized; that is, all chemical reactions between the water used and the calcium hydroxide have been completed. This essentially is a softening reaction. If slurries are transported before stabilization is complete, dissolved solids contained in the dilution water will be precipitated upon piping, valves, and pumps as a scale. A detention time of 15 min in an agitated slurry-storage tank is usually sufficient for maximum development of salt crystals, which tend to grow upon themselves. By maintaining suspension, these crystallized scale-forming compounds can be pumped and transported to the process with a minimum of problems. Conversely, attempts to pump directly from hydrated lime-wetting tanks or from slaker sumps can produce intolerable maintenance problems.

Agitated detention or stabilization of lime slurry does not resolve all problems. Quicklime slaked on-site will contain fine settleable impurities which can be very abrasive. This material is usually too fine for removal by slaker grit-removal systems; the best that can be done is to rely upon purchase specifications that emphasize or reward purity of product. The quality of the water used for slaking and slurry dilution is also very important, particularly with respect to the amount and type of dissolved solids present.

Water of medium and high hardness, containing sulfates, is particularly objectionable in that it is likely to interfere with the hydration process itself. In such cases it may be feasible to consider the installation of water-softening equipment of ample capacity to satisfy slaking and slurry-dilution requirements. In less severe cases, the addition of 5 to 10 mg/L of hexametaphosphate to the supply line will sequester the mineral hardness present, provided 2- or 3-min detention time is available before reaching the slaker.

Once the quicklime has been slaked or the hydrate wetted to form the slurry, it is essential that it be discharged as directly as possible into an agitated storage tank where mixing and stabilization occur. Mixers must be designed to maintain the impurities and precipitated salts as well as the lime in suspension. As a general rule, about ½ to 1 hp per 1000 gal of tank capacity is required for cylindrical tanks of less than 3000-gal capacity and slurry concentration not exceeding 1 lb/gal. Smaller tanks are usually equipped with propeller agitators, while tanks above 2000-gal capacity resort to turbine-type mixers. Speeds will vary from approximately 350 rpm for propeller mixers to 100 rpm or less on the larger turbine units.

Since most slurry storage tanks are agitated continuously, care must be taken to position the mixing impellers in the lower portion of the tank when slaker operations are automatically controlled by level controls within the tank. Under no circumstances should the impeller be located so that exposure above the liquid surface is possible. Tanks should be equipped with peripheral baffles set 90° or 120° apart to control vortex formation; these should terminate above the bottom and be attached to the sides with intermittent spaces so as to prevent lime buildup in corners. Level sensors for slaker control and alarms are usually required; these can be probes or sonic devices. Float-actuated controls are usually impractical, even with stilling wells, as a result of heavy solids buildup.

One of the principal problems encountered with small systems using gravity feed lines with unstabilized slurry is the periodic clogging of the line as a result of low velocity. As a result, a compromise solution to the problem is to design the line for easy cleanout, removal, and/or flushing. Other measures frequently used include:

Use of polyphosphates in dilution water

Use of open troughs or channels to convey slurry

Installation of duplicate lines and passage of chlorine solution through these lines on an alternating schedule

On larger installations it is preferable to employ pumps which circulate the slurry to the point or points of application and back to storage. A properly designed system will size the pump and piping so as to produce a minimum velocity of 3 to 4 fps in the return line. At each application point several methods can be used to control the flow of slurry to process:

Control valve, manually or auto-modulated by an external controller analyzer.

Discharge into a local day tank equipped with agitator and metering pump. Tank refills through control valve actuated by level sensors.

It is essential that the recirculating line be run as close as possible to the point(s) of application so as to minimize the additional length of piping in which optimum velocities cannot be maintained. Takeoffs that are periodically closed, as in refilling day tanks, must be tapped and valved off the top of the pipe so as to prevent settling in the static line behind the closed valve. Throttling valves in continuous service may be tapped from the side or bottom of the line. Flow stability through these diversion valves requires some back pressure in the recirculating line; this is normally accomplished by installing a throttling valve in the line as it returns to storage.

While ball valves and plug-type valves perform reasonably well in open-close service, they are not recommended for throttling service. Similarly, diaphragm valves tend to collect compacted sludge behind their weirs. Pinch valves appear to be capable of operating well in throttling service, provided they are properly sized and not subject to a vacuum. These valves are available with manual, electric, hydraulic, or pneumatic operators. Flow modulation is possible with each type of power operator.

Mild steel piping is satisfactory for most slurry lines where rigid piping is preferred. Tees and crosses should be used as elbows to facilitate cleaning. A fresh-water flushing system should be installed to flush out piping, pumps, and valves when the system is shut down for any reason. Reduction of line size diameter must not be so abrupt as to cause a violent hydraulic disturbance; this can result in dewatering and compaction of the lime. Pipeline designers frequently use a coefficient of $C = 100$ for slurry lines carrying up to 3 lb/gal of hydrated lime. Piping should not be excessively oversized initially to accommodate estimated future system capacity. The penalty will usually be increased maintenance problems during the early years. As a final recommendation relating to piping layout, it must be remembered that there is a tendency for dissolved solids to be precipitated out of the process water where the slurry or any other alkaline substance is applied. For this reason, an air gap is preferable between the end of the feed line and the surface of the water being treated. If application without submergence is impractical, some means must be provided for periodic cleaning of the end of the slurry pipe to break up the precipitated mass which will eventually plug the feed line.

Lime suspensions are commonly referred to in three categories of concentration:

Paste   A wet, puttylike mass, with sufficient body to exhibit some angle of repose.

Slurry   A creamy suspension, pourable and pumpable. Contains about 50 percent more water than paste.

Milk-of lime   Waterlike consistency; may contain up to 1.8 lb/gal hydrated lime. Readily pumpable. The final diluted product from paste and slurry slakers and dry feeder slurry pots.

The concentration of slurry suspension is frequently expressed as pounds of CaO or Ca(OH)$_2$ per gallon of water. Others prefer to express it as percent lime solids, although some confusion can arise unless the dry weight basis (oxide or hydroxide) is specified. A typical waterworks milk of lime ready for application contains between 1 and 1½ lb/gal of hydrated lime (10.7 to 15.2 percent). At 15°C these suspensions would exhibit specific gravity readings of 1.07 and 1.11, respectively. Lime concentration can readily be checked using a hygrometer and specific gravity tables.[1]

Slurry feeders

Slurry pumps generally fall into two categories: centrifugal pumps and controlled-volume pumps. Centrifugal pumps are generally employed for low-head transfer or recirculating service. With proper selection of casing and impeller material and an appropriate shaft seal, satisfactory service can usually be attained at a reasonable cost. Replaceable liners and semi-open impellers are preferred. It is important that the design of the pump permit easy dismantling for cleanout and repair. Lime slurry will require the lowest speed of rotation (1725 rpm or less) consistent with hydraulic requirements in order to control impeller plating. The use of water-flushed seals on centrifugal lime slurry pumps is not recommended, as this will usually result in localized scaling.

Controlled-volume pumps are typically used where metering or positive control of slurry flow is required, as at the point of application to the process. Several types are available for slurry service.

Diaphragm pumps. These provide good accuracy, and their capacity range is dependent upon stroking speed as well as length of stroke. Drives are usually mechanical, either directly connected to the diaphragm or indirectly through a hydraulic fluid. Air-operated diaphragm pumps are also frequently used, the discharge rate being controlled by regulated air admission and exhaust to the power side of the diaphragm.

Progressive cavity pumps. These pumps, with their unique rotor and stator elements, are capable of pumping thick pastes, gritty slurries, or viscous shear-sensitive fluids. Wear can occur somewhat more rapidly than with other pumps handling slurry under similar conditions unless care is exercised in selecting proper construction materials. These are specialized service pumps with a relatively high initial cost, but given preventive maintenance they can be expected to give trouble-free service.

Dipper-wheel feeders. The rotating dipper feed has been a long-time favorite for feeding slurries where gravity feed is possible between the feeder and the point of application. The feeder consists of a tank in which the slurry level is maintained by a float valve (or overflow weir if gravity return to slurry storage is practical), a dipper wheel with variable-speed drive, and a totalizer to register wheel revolutions. The dipper wheel is usually divided into eight segments or dippers, each containing about 500 mL of slurry liquid. As the wheel rotates, an agitator bar maintains the slurry in suspension. The inlet float valve to the tank must be routinely cleaned, particularly if it is connected to a pressurized slurry recirculating system. An overflow connection must be provided when a float valve is used, and the selection of an appropriate discharge point for this overflow requires consideration on each project. Discharging the overflow to the process is not recommended. The overflow line is not required where gravity return of excess slurry to storage is possible using an overflow weir instead of the float valve.

Others. Piston-type pumps where the slurry is in direct contact with the cylinder walls are not recommended for slurry service because of uncontrolled wear and abrasion. Similarly, peristaltic or squeeze-type pumps are subject to wear and excessive tubing replacement and are not normally used for slurry pumping.

Dry chemical feeders

These may be classified as gravimetric (accuracy range ½ to 1 percent of set rate) and volumetric (accuracy range 1 to 5 percent of set range depending upon material being fed). Gravimetric feeders are preferred for accurate feeding of those chemicals whose bulk density is variable as a result of moisture, lack of uniformity, and other factors.

Loss-in-weight gravimetric

These feeders utilize a feeder hopper suspended from scale levers, a material feed-control mechanism, and a scale beam with motorized counterpoise. The rate of loss in weight of the hopper will equal the weight loss equivalency of a traveling counterpoise when the feeder is in balance. If it does not, the scale beam deflects, and the feed mechanism increases or decreases the feed accordingly.

These feeders are quite accurate, but their capacity is usually less than 1000 lb/h. The total amount of material fed may be recorded or read directly off the weight beam at any time.

Belt-type gravimetric

These feeders are available in numerous forms and are frequently constructed to handle specific types of material. Weight belts can be of the pivoted type for heavy feed rates (250 tons/h and up) or the rigid belt-type passing over a live or weigh-deck scale section, with a feed hopper at one end of the belt and a control gate to regulate the flow and depth of material placed on the belt. A scale counterpoise is adjusted to establish the desired belt loading, and the control gate is automatically repositioned in proportion to the error signal. Various gate-control systems are available depending upon the material to be handled, response time desired, feed range, and capacity. Normally the belt speed is varied to produce the desired flow of material. Total quantity of material fed can be read directly on a totalizer or similar device.

Volumetric feeders

Although more than a dozen types of volumetric feeders are available, all operate on the principal of feed-rate control by volume instead of weight. Some advantages of volumetric feeders include low initial cost, good overall performance at low feed rates, and acceptable accuracy for materials with stable density and uniformity. Some disadvantages include unresponsiveness to density changes, fixed orifices or openings subject to clogging, and calibration by manual sampling (which must be done regularly).

The many types of volumetric feeders available permit a good choice based on capacity requirements and the nature of the material to be fed. The roll feeder forms a smooth ribbon of material of adjustable thickness and width; this feeder is unique in its ability to handle low feed rates, down to 0.00016 ft³/h of fine ground materials such as hydrated lime. It cannot be used for coarse granular material. The screw feeder is a popular unit employing rotating and/or reciprocating feed screws which can handle most dry chemicals. Most of these require hopper agitation or vibration to maintain screw loading. The range of feed is good (at least 20 to 1), with capacities up to 600 ft³/h using 6-in helical screws. Minimum feeds on certain models are as low as 0.001 ft³/h when using fine powdery material through a small-diameter screw. On belt feeders the material is deposited on a moving belt from an overhead hopper and passes beneath an adjustable vertical gate. The speed of the belt and the position of the gate establish the volume of material passing through the feeder. These are high-capacity feeders that can handle anything from powder to 1½-in lump materials at rates from 600 to 3600 ft³/h, depending upon belt width. Rotary paddle feeders consist of a paddle or series of compartments revolving within an enclosure that receives material from the hopper and releases it through a discharge chute as rotation proceeds. Feed-rate control is normally achieved by using a sliding gate or varying the speed of the paddle shaft. These feeders have a unique application in that they can deliver into vacuum or pressure systems because they form an airlock. They are also frequently used to feed chemicals that tend to flow or gush out of control through a fixed orifice.

Vibrating feeders employ a vibrating mechanism attached to a slightly inclined feed trough. Flow is controlled by regulating the depth of material and the intensity of vibration. These feeders are used only on dry, nonhygroscopic, free-flowing materials. They are generally used in smaller installations, and their accuracy is acceptable as long as the material is of consistent quality and large voltage fluctuations that would affect the amplitude of the vibration do not occur. An oscillating hopper consists of a main hopper fitted with an oscillating apex section that discharges onto a stationary tray or plate. Oscillation of the hopper pushes previously deposited material off the tray in one or more directions. Capacity is controlled by adjusting the depth of chemical deposited and regulating the length of stroke. Since these feeders can handle a variety of chemicals, from powder to pebble lime, they are popular in smaller plants.

Virtually all feeders, gravimetric or volumetric, can be equipped to operate automatically in proportion to a flow or other process signal. The means for accomplishing this will vary depending upon the nature of the feeder's control mechanism. In its simplest form, time-duration control using a resettling time can provide proportional feed using a manually adjusted feeder, providing a flow-proportional pulse or contact signal is available from the flow metering system.

Solution feeders

This category includes feeders for chemicals in a true state of solution (nonslurry), in which suspended solids are absent or minimal. Practically all the slurry feeders described previously can handle clear solutions; descriptions of the diaphragm, progressive cavity, and dipper-wheel feeders need not be repeated here.

The majority of solution feeders handling liquid chemical solutions of alum, caustic soda, acids, silicates, and other chemicals are of the controlled-volume (CV) diaphragm or plunger type except on the very largest installations, where capacities in excess of 25 gpm may be required. A good controlled-volume pump functions to displace a predetermined quantity of liquid within a specified time, and does this with an accuracy of 1 percent or better of its rated capacity. CV pumps possessing these characteristics are essential in process-control systems, as they combine the functions of a pump, meter, and control valve, and they may be adapted to flow proportional or analyzer output control.

An almost infinite variety of materials are available for construction of the liquid end of these pumps. Check valves, pistons, or diaphragms and the pumping head are frequently fabricated of proprietary materials such as Viton, Derakane, Tyril, and others. The designer is well advised to avoid confusion in using these names since not all manufacturers use the same material for a given surface.

It is best to consult with potential suppliers and to specify the nature and strength of the material to be pumped, the capacity and range desired, and the hydraulic conditions of suction and discharge.

Transfer pumps

Transfer pumps are used to recirculate prepared chemical solutions or to move them from storage to day tanks. They are generally of the low-head centrifugal type, with a capacity several times greater than the maximum application rate to the process. Progressive cavity or controlled-volume units are sometimes used for transfer pumping where liquid polymers or other shear-sensitive liquids are being handled. The following criteria may be applied to transfer pipes.

Materials of construction.   Materials for fabrication of pump liners, body, impeller, and shaft depend upon the corrosive and/or abrasive nature of the material being pumped. In some instances, temperature can be a factor if nonmetallic parts are involved. As mentioned previously, the current trend of manufacturers to describe materials of construction by trade name can lead to misunderstanding and the use of "almost equal" materials. When ordering a pump for chemical service, it is best to consult with the pump supplier and cross-check with the chemical manufacturer. Total reliance on published tables of corrosion- or abrasion-resistant materials for various chemicals can be misleading.

Speed.   In itself, speed is not a major design factor where true solutions are being handled. However, slurries, viscous liquids, and shear-sensitive polymer solutions require special handling and use of low-rpm pumps. In no case should a centrifugal-type slurry pump operate in excess of 1750 rpm. Liquid, undiluted polymers may be transferred using a 1750-rpm pump; however, once dilution and aging have taken place, the product is subject to molecular shearing if it is transferred in a centrifugal pump operating at any speed. Screw-type progressive cavity pumps are recommended for this service.

Sealing water.   Generally speaking, pumps designed to use flushing water on shaft seals should not be used for chemical transfer. Chemical dilution, scaling in lime slurries, and the expense of furnishing a non-cross-connected seal water system are some of the problems encountered. Pumping of carbon slurry is one of the few exceptions.

Modern technology has made available a variety of dry-mechanical-shaft seals to handle most types of liquids and slurries. In addition, indirect magnetic drives are available for smaller pumps where the shaft seal has been entirely eliminated.

Other feed methods

Numerous other methods and devices, some of which date back to the nineteenth century, are employed to feed chemicals. Many of these devices are still in operation at smaller plants throughout the country, in testimony to their simplicity and adequacy for the job at hand. Some of the more common devices include the following.

Dissolving tanks.   The chemical to be dissolved is weighed and placed in a perforated wooden or metal basket which is hung in the upper part of a water-filled tank. Mechanical mixers can be installed to assist the dissolving of the chemical. When all material is dissolved, the batch is ready for use; it is applied using pumps or other flow-control devices. This method is popular for handling glassy polyphosphates in smaller installations and for other lumpy materials that do not handle well through a dry feeder.

Pot feeders. These are normally used with coarse chemicals, such as lump alum. The pot is charged manually through a pressure-tight cover. An orifice plate or gate valve in the pressure line to be treated generates a differential pressure, which is tapped off the line and permitted to flow through the pot via a flow-control valve. In theory, a quantity of chemical is dissolved and displayed in proportion to the flow, but the system is subject to clogging with chemical impurities.

Gravity orifice feeders. These generally consist of a constant-head supply tank and a fixed or adjustable orifice to deliver the desired rate of flow. While these devices can be started and stopped remotely, they do not lend themselves to slurry feeding or to proportional feed control.

Displacement or decanting feeder. A prepared batch of chemical is contained in a tank equipped with an overhead mechanism that lowers a displacement cylinder or decanting pipe arm into the liquid. The rate of feed flowing over the overflow weir or through the decanting pipe is related to the speed at which the cylinder or pipe is lowered. Mixers can be used if slurries are to be fed.

Rotometers. These devices are not feeders, but are used as flow indicators in conjunction with flow-control valves, and thereby become a part of a feed-control system. Modern rotometers can be equipped with rotor-position transmitters to permit remote recording of flow rates. Several types of local indication are possible. Visual rotometers, where the float position can be seen relative to a calibrated scale, are practical for use on clear liquids that are free of iron or other impurities that will obscure scale calibrations. Where the liquids will not allow visual indication, magnetically actuated indicators may be used.

Modulating control valves. These are sensitive valves capable of being positioned or modulated by an external control signal. The valve functions to control the flow of chemical to the process in proportion to the signal output analyzer, usually a pH meter. For this type of feed system to operate satisfactorily, it is essential that the chemical be supplied to the valve under reasonably constant head, free of suspended material that could clog the valve. Since this constitutes what is referred to as a closed-loop system, it is imperative that the response and sample detention time of the overall control loop be properly designed to prevent cyclic over- and underfeeding.

Pipelines. Suction lines between the pump and the supply tank must be kept as short as possible, and the entire system should be located as close as possible to the application point. Where possible, it is important to avoid a layout that permits siphoning by simultaneous existence of positive suction pressure and low or negative discharge pressure on the pump. Back-pressure valves installed on the discharge line will prevent this, but they should never be used on slurry lines. All positive-displacement pumps should have a suitable pressure relief valve installed in the discharge piping. In some cases these valves are integral with the pump. Calibration chambers, if used, should be teed and valved off the suction piping so that measurement can be made with the pump operating against normal discharge conditions.

Table 13.4 is a condensed listing of common waterworks chemicals and the corrosion resistance of various types of piping materials at normal temperatures (up to 40°C). It is important to remember that temperature and operating pressures are equally important parameters in the selection of piping material, particularly when using plastic material; in these cases temperatures in excess of 40°C generally reduce the maximum safe-working-pressure rating of the pipe. Consult manufacturers' data for special plastics good for temperatures up to 80°C. All chemical piping should be Schedule 80 thickness, particularly if threaded joints are to be used.

Unions or flanges together with suitable isolation valves must be provided at each pump or feed-controlling device to permit removal for routine maintenance. Plastic pipe fittings sized 3 in and smaller are preferably of the solvent-welded type. Larger sizes of plastic pipe fittings (4 in and up) are similar, except that pipe joints may use solvent-welded flanges instead of sleeves. The use of threaded plastic fittings is not recommended.

Valves used for open-close service should be of the straight-through pattern, maintaining full-line size. Plug, ball, and diaphragm-type valves fabricated of appropriate material are normally used for solutions that are free of suspended matter. Pinch valves are capable of handling slurries in both shutoff and modulating-control service. The relatively complicated internal parts of globe and gate valves would be exposed to the chemical flow; thus their use is not recommended.

It is good practice to support rigid plastic piping on hangers at intervals of 4 ft or less. The piping must not be clamped by the hanger, as movement resulting from expansion and contraction must not be restricted. Flexible plastic and rubber tubing is best supported by channel troughs or sections of steel piping supported on hangers or brackets. In these cases, gaps should be left in the support piping at bends and changes of direction to facilitate installation and removal of the tubing. Where rigid metallic piping is used for the solution line, support hangers or brackets should be provided at such intervals as will prevent sagging for the particular size of pipe used. In any case, support should be provided at least every 10 ft.

TABLE 13.4 Piping Applications

	Piping material								
Chemical	Iron or steel	Type 316 stainless	Type 304 stainless	Copper	PVC—type 1	Fiberglass-reinforced polyester (FRP)	Polypropylene	Rubber tubing	Glass
Activated carbon (slurry)	NR	X				X			
Alum	S	S	NR		S	X	X	X	X
Ammonia, aqua		X							
Calcium hydroxide (slurry)	S	X	X						
Calcium hypochlorite		X	X		X		X	X	
Carbon dioxide (dry)	S	X	X	X	X	X	X		X
Chlorinated copperas				X	X	X	X	X	
Chlorine (dry gas)	S			X	X			X	
Chlorine solution	S	NR	NR		NR	X	NR	X	
Chlorine dioxide (3% soln.)	NR				S	X		X	
Coagulant aids			Consult manufacturer—generally not corrosive		X				X
Copper sulfate		X			S	X	X	X	
Dolomitic lime (slurry)						X	X		
Ferric chloride	X	X	X		X	X	X	X	
Fluosilicic acid	NR	NR	NR	NR	S	X	X	X	X
Hydrochloric acid	NR	NR	NR	NR	X	X	X	X	NR
Potassium permanganate (2% soln.)	X	X			X	X	X		

TABLE 13.4 Piping Applications (Continued)

Chemical	Iron or steel	Type 316 stainless	Type 304 stainless	Copper	PVC—type 1	Fiberglass-reinforced polyester (FRP)	Polypropylene	Rubber tubing	Glass
Sodium carbonate (soln.)	S							X	
Sodium chloride		X			X	X	X		X
Sodium chlorite					X	X	X		X
Sodium fluoride (1 to 5% soln.)		X			X	X	X	X	
Sodium hexametaphosphate (soln.)		X			X	X		X	
Sodium hydroxide (to 50% soln.)	X	X	X		X	X	X	X	
Sodium hypochlorite (to 16% soln.)					S				X
Sodium silicate	S	X	X		X	X	X	X	
Sodium silicofluoride		X			X		X	X	
Sulfur dioxide (dry gas)	X	X	X						
Sulfur dioxide (soln.)		X							X
Sulfuric acid (conc.)	S				S	X	X	X	X
Sulfuric acid	NR								X

Key: S = Industrial standard or excellent for handling
X = Suitable for handling
NR = Not recommended

Design and Process Criteria

Safety equipment and procedures

Safety requirements and suggested protective measurements for handling various chemicals and chemical forms are presented in Table 13.5. Suggested protective measures shown in the table apply to the various chemicals used whether they are in the dry, liquid, or gaseous state.

With all safety procedures, a written program should be developed and reviewed regularly with all personnel. This will establish what should be done in emergency situations before they occur. Every new employee who may be expected to use the equipment should be instructed in safety equipment procedures. Periodic review and training sessions are recommended.

Personal safety

Safety equipment may be used by many people and must be capable of being disinfected and easily cleaned. A regular inspection and maintenance program will assure that all protective equipment is kept clean and in good repair. Protective clothing must include foot protection to prevent injury from falling objects. This is especially important in receiving and transferring inventory. Safety shoes should conform to the National Standard for Men's Safety Toe Footwear, Z41.1.

Protective clothing should be of the impervious type, covering exposed areas of the body, including arms and legs. Where gloves are used, they must be appropriate to the exposure. They may be standard work gloves of heavy canvas or leather construction or rubber gloves that are impervious to various liquid chemicals. Generally, gloves should protect the hands and forearms. Hard hats are normally required where workers may be subject to injury from falling or flying objects.

Eye protection is generally provided through the use of protective goggles, which should be fitted to each individual worker. Where skin exposure is a concern, the face should be protected by an 8- to 10-in high face shield normally covering the full face, with an appropriate head piece.

Wearing contact lenses with a respirator in a contaminated atmosphere is not advisable. Individuals wearing corrective glasses may find that they cannot achieve a proper seal with a gas mask or full-face mask. In such cases, corrective lenses should be provided in full-face pieces and should be clearly identified.

Respirators and masks

Respirators or gas masks should be provided as indicated in Table 13.5. Respirators may be of the particulate filter type, commonly re-

Protective Measures for Water Treatment Chemicals

Chemical (Dry = dry; L = liquid; G = gas)	Positive ventilation	Protective clothing	Neck cloths	Gloves	Rubber boots	Rubber gloves	Goggles	Face shields	Rubber aprons	Respirator	Gas mask	Avoid skin contact	Safety shower and eye baths	General
Activated alumina (D)	■	■		■		■	■			■			■	Store away from gasoline, minerl or vegetable oils, HTH, lime, sodium chlorite, or potassium permanganate
Activated carbon Powder (D)	■	■	■	■										
Activated carbon Granulate (D)	■	■	■											
Alum sulfate (D)	■									■		■		Similar to other acid
Alum sulfate (L)												■		
Ammonium hydroxide (L)	■							■	■			■	■	Moist NH_3 reacts with many metals and alloys—liquid contact produces burns
Ammonium sulfate (D)	■	■	■	■			■			■		■	■	See alum sulfate above
Anhydrous ammonia (G)	■	■	■			■		■		■	■	■	■	Fire sprinklers and water hoses effective in removing gas
Bauxite (D)	■		■	■										
Bentonite (D)	■													
Calcium Carbonate (D)	■													
Calcium hypochlorite (D)	■		■	■						■		■		Avoid contact with hydrogen or organic compounds or other flammable materials
Carbon dioxide (G)	■			■						■		■		
Chlorine (G)	■							■		■	■	■		

Chlorine dioxide (G) — Solution is corrosive
Copper sulfate (D)
Ferric chloride (D) — Very corrosive
Ferric sulfate (D) — Very corrosive

Ferrous sulfate (D)
Ferrous sulfate (L)

Fluorspar (D) — Etches glass when moist
Hydrated lime (D) — Can burn eyes or skin
Hydrochloric acid (L)
Hydrofluosilicic acid (L) — Have lime slurry on hand

Iron-exchange resins (D) — Hydrogen cation resins acid
Ozone (G)
Potassium permanganate (D) — Large quantities present fire hazard

Quicklime (D) — Can burn eyes or skin
Sodium aluminate (D)
Sodium aluminate (L)
Sodium bisulfate (D)

Sodium carbonate (D)
Sodium chloride (D)
Sodium chlorite (D)

Sodium fluoride (D)
Sodium polyphosphate, Glassy (D)
Sodium hydroxide (D) — Can dehydrate skin
Sodium hydroxide (L) — Rinse any spills immediately with water
Sodium hypochlorite (L)

Sodium silicate (D)
Sodium silicofluoride (D)
Sodium sulfite (D)
Sodium dioxide (G)
Sulfuric acid (L)

ferred to as dust-filter respirators. These should be properly fitted. They are generally used for short intermittent or occasional dust exposures. Respirators must be approved for protection against the specific type of dust encountered. Proper selection of respirators should be made in accordance with American National Standard Practices for Respiratory Protection, Z88.2. Normally, respirators are used as a protection from particulate matter, dust, or mist. Breathing air can be supplied to the airline-type respirator from cylinders or air compressors. The compressed air, compressed oxygen, or liquid oxygen used for respiration must be of high purity. Oxygen must meet U.S. requirements for medical use or breathing. Breathing air must meet, at a minimum, the specifications for Grade D breathing as described in the Compressed Gas Association Commodity Specifications, B-7.1. Compressed oxygen must not be used in supplied air respirators or in open-circuit self-contained breathing apparatus that have previously contained compressed air. Oxygen must never be used with airline-type respirators.

Normally, with gas or gas and particulate matter that is not immediately dangerous to life, the airline-type respirator is satisfactory. This can be a hose mask without a blower, or it can be a chemical-cartridge respirator provided with a special filter for the specific contaminant present in the atmosphere. Chemical cartridges for a specific gas may be used, provided 16 percent oxygen is available. When greater concentrations are experienced, it is preferable that gas masks with front- or back-mounted chest-type canisters or a Type C supplied-air respirator demand (negative pressure) with full-face piece be used. With extremely high concentrations, self-contained breathing apparatus and the pressure-demand-mode positive pressure should be employed.

With gas or gas and particulate matter that is immediately dangerous to life, a self-contained respirator or gas mask should be used. A hose mask with blower or a gas mask with a special filter can also be used.

Where gas masks are used, identification of the gas-mask canister by properly worded labels is required. Secondarily, the canisters are identified by color code. The full color code is listed in the proposed OSHA rules on page 62-800A, paragraph 1910.135. Each canister should have a label warning that such gas masks must be used in an atmosphere containing sufficient oxygen to support life (at least 16 percent by volume), since gas mask canisters are designed to neutralize or remove contaminants from the air and *do not* supply oxygen.

Personnel using respirators should be certain that they experience minimum face mask leakage and that the respirator is fitted properly. A semiquantitative fit test should be set up annually for each user of a nonpowered particulate filter respirator. Whenever an increase in breathing resistance is detected, the filter elements should be changed. A replacement supply of filter elements should be available.

Safety showers and eye baths

Where indicated for specific chemicals, suitable facilities for quick drenching or flushing of the eyes through the use of an eye bath, or quick washing the total body, *must* be provided within the work area when a person may be exposed to injurious or corrosive chemicals.

Ventilation

Positive ventilation indicated for specific chemicals is essential to remove gases or dust that may develop in the handling of the material. The contaminated area must be isolated from the rest of the plant, and the exhaust systems must be run for a sufficient period of time to remove all the contaminated air before that area is reopened. The rate of exhaust must be sufficient to provide prompt clearance of the laden air from the contaminated area. Doors to the area should be flanged and sealed tightly when closed. The construction, installation, inspection, and maintenance of the exhaust system should conform to requirements set forth in ASHRAE, *Ten State Standards,*[2] together with state and local codes governing design and operation of exhaust systems.

The static pressure in exhaust ducts leading from the ventilation equipment should be periodically checked to assure continuing satisfactory operation. If there is an appreciable change in pressure drop, the system should be cleaned.

It is normally good procedure in handling dust-laden air to have the ventilation equipment discharged through dust-collecting equipment. This equipment must be set up so that accumulated dust can be removed without contaminating other working areas.

References

1. National Lime Association, *Lime Handling, Application, and Storage,* Bulletin 213, May 1976, Table 8.
2. "Recommended Standards for Water Works," *Report of the Great Lakes–Upper Mississippi River Board of State Sanitary Engineers,* Health Education Services, Albany, N.Y., 1982.

Instrumentation and Control

Introduction

The treatment plant must be looked upon as a total system for the design of instrumentation and control. The design and selection of equipment will then be a natural consequence of the requirements of the individual plant processes and their interaction and interdependence in the overall system. The degree of instrumentation is directly related to the requirements for monitoring, i.e., the gathering and presentation of operational information essential to efficient, cost-effective plant control.

Instrumentation and control systems are used in water treatment plants to ensure consistently good quality, to optimize process reliability, and to minimize costs. Users and designers should be seeking the proper number and combination of instruments and controls to provide optimum results for the least input. Appropriate instruments, properly used, will provide an important source of operational data— essential to management of the utility. This chapter discusses some of the factors to be considered in designing instrumentation and control systems.

Information collected by instruments can generally be placed into one or more of three broad categories:

- Process data, to keep the plant operating within limits and alert plant personnel of out-of-limit conditions
- Technical information, to provide management with cost and efficiency figures
- Historical data, to identify long-term trends in water quality and plant performance for future planning, such as expansion and upgrading

The design engineer must attempt to satisfy these needs by defining all end uses of the data collected. For each unit process, he or she must decide:

What parameters to sense or measure

What parameters to control

The control system

What instrumentation and control equipment to employ

The physical location of the primary sensors and controlled elements

The engineering team for the design of a water treatment plant must therefore include instrumentation and control (I&C) engineering as well as treatment process engineering. The role of the I&C engineer will be to provide instrumentation and control designs within the defined constraints of the process requirements and interrelationships, plant size, cost limitations, and level of operating and maintenance personnel. An important design tool available to the engineer is the process and instrumentation diagram (P&ID), the standardized schematic format used to define the requirements for instrumentation and controls. These documents provide an effective, easily understood definition of instrumentation requirements that is suitable for review and modification. They are discussed in more detail later in this chapter.

Theoretical Review

Types of instrumentation

Many variations of measurement and control instruments can be used, ranging from the simplest panel indicator to complex, multi-component, computer-controlled interactive systems. The design of instrument systems is a specialized field, with its own descriptive language which defines the terms used and enables the nonspecialist to follow system descriptions.[1,2,3] A brief description of the characteristics and limitations of the principal types of instrument systems will broaden the view of the engineer responsible for the plant design.

An instrument system contains, at the very least, a primary sensor and a "signal conditioner" or "transmitter" which converts the output of the sensor into a usable form. These elements, which are usually in close proximity, are connected to an indicator, a recorder, or a controller (or to all three). If the system is being used solely as a monitor, such as a pressure gauge or thermometer, these two elements are sufficient. If the sensor signal is being used to control some other function, as when a level-sensing meter is used to set a valve position, there is a feedback link to the controlled function. The signal conditioner or transmitter may be so simple as to be virtually invisible, or it may be a complex piece of equipment which accepts the sensor signal and emits another, entirely different signal. Similarly, the indicator, recorder, or controller may be a simple or a complex mechanism, standing alone or interacting with other system elements (see Fig. 14.1). It may even be a computer which operates and controls the entire treatment plant.

Signal transmission.   The data signal is transmitted from the primary sensor via the signal conditioner to the controller and then back to the controlled element by mechanical linkage, pneumatic or hydraulic pressure or flow, or electric current or voltage. These methods may be used alone or in combination. Each has advantages and limitations.

A wholly mechanical system is completely self-contained and uses no outside power. Any change in the environment experienced by the primary sensor results in direct physical movement of some transmission linkage. This could be movement of a wire attached to a float, motion of the fluid in a capillary attached to a temperature bulb, or distortion of a bimetal strip. The other end of the linkage is attached to a readout device, or in some cases to a feedback linkage. In general, mechanical systems are simple and are used only for local indication or

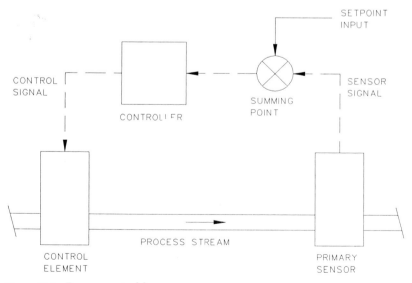

Figure 14.1 Process control loop.

recording in noncritical situations. They are rarely, if ever, used directly as controllers, as the amount of power available from the primary sensor is usually far too small to be effective.

In a logical development of such systems, a mechanical linkage can adjust a control mechanism which uses external power to move a controlled element. The power source can be pneumatic or hydraulic pressure or electricity; which one is used will depend on such specific circumstances as the availability of the power source in the plant, location of the instrumentation, and local safety considerations.

It was common in the past to use clean, dry air at 80 to 100 psi as the pneumatic power source. This is usually available in the plant, is easy to handle, and does not cause any pollution problems. When, by the nature or dispersion of the plant, it is not possible to supply air to a location, a local hydraulic power source can be used. This may be plant water or a special oil that is pressurized with a small electric pump. While quite effective, the piping and components for a hydraulic power system require relatively high maintenance and can be difficult to repair if leaks develop. Under some circumstances, it may be advantageous to use an electronic speed control or remote starter to control an electric motor directly.

There may be considerable physical distance between the primary sensor, the signal conditioner, and the controlled element—for example, when process control is centralized or when the primary sensor and controlled element are in different parts of the plant. This creates problems in the transmission of signals between the elements of the system. Friction and lost motion make wholly mechanical devices ineffective at distances greater than a few yards, while variations in temperature along the line rapidly cause degeneration of the signal in capillary transmissions. Mounting the signal conditioner close to or actually integral with the primary sensor is a partial solution, but the question of signal transmission to and from a centrally located controller is still a problem. The solution may be a pneumatic or hydraulic line, an electric or electronic circuit, or even a fiber optic link. The choice depends on many factors, including the nature of the signal and the transmission distance.

It is rarely realized that the theoretical maximum speed of a signal in a pneumatic or hydraulic line is no greater than the speed of sound in the medium. This fact introduces an irreducible time lag, which may be critical. In addition, there is an attenuation of the signal amplitude caused by friction, pipeline discontinuities, and minor leakage. The overall result is that extensive runs between the signal conditioner and the controller (of approximately 1000 ft) can severely compromise the accurate transmission of data, even to the point where no output is obtained for a given input. In addition, the planning, installation, and maintenance of multiple piping systems is expensive and may not be practical in some plant layout situations.

Although electrical or electronic data acquisition and transmission have their own unique problems, there is a growing body of technology devoted to this field. It evolved in other engineering disciplines, but is rapidly becoming accepted in large-scale continuous-process systems, particularly with the advent of computer control. Data can be transmitted over long distances virtually instantaneously, with almost no degeneration. Major operations can be performed on signals at low cost and in very little space, and local translation from electronic to pneumatic or hydraulic signals (e.g., when a valve is to be moved by a pneumatic actuator) can easily be done. If quantities of data have to be moved over a considerable distance (such as from a remote plant site), the use of telephone links, radio, or fiber optics may prove to be a cost-effective solution.

In the foregoing discussion it has been assumed that a change in environment results in physical movement of the primary sensor. Some parameters, such as pH and dissolved oxygen (DO), are measured by sensors which produce electrical signals. These signals require rather more elaborate conditioners and more careful system design, as the magnitude of the primary signal is very small and is susceptible to degradation by external electrical noise. Here again, a great deal of specialized technology exists to help the engineer in the selection and design of the control system.

The standard format for signal transmission of continuous (analog) variables, such as flow, level, pressure, and temperature, in the process control industry is the 4- to 20-milliampere (mA) direct current (dc) loop. The wide variety of transducers used to transform the initial measurement and energy conversion of dynamic variables into electrical analogs produces an equally wide variety of resultant signal characteristics. These must all be converted by signal conditioning to a form suitable for interfacing with other elements in a process control loop. The other elements may include indicators, recorders, and computer input. Thus, calibration of the basic variable converts the range—for example, a 0- to 100-mgd flow—to the corresponding analog, 4- to 20-mA dc, as the transmitted signal.

While the standard 4- to 20-mA dc analog signal accommodates electrical signal transmission for all continuous variables, plant monitoring must also include the detection of discrete states: equipment on or off, valves open or closed, above-upper-limit alarm, below-lower-limit alarms, and status changes. Simple two-state devices such as switches and relay contacts provide open and closed circuits to create the presence or absence of current flow to indicate a state, for example, by energizing or deenergizing a lamp on a panel.

Methods of control. Regardless of the drive medium selected, the end point at the controlled element is an actuator which physically moves the valve, gate, or other device, in response to the change in environment experienced by the primary sensor. There are well-developed theories and a great body of practical experience which the engineer can use to define the system transfer function (i.e., the relationship between environmental changes at the primary sensor and the effect on the system of the consequent change in the process stream at the location of the controlled element).

There are several methods by which the connection between the primary sensor and the controlled element can be made, requiring a greater or lesser degree of human intervention.

In the manual method, the controller is the human operator, who reads the environmental status of the primary sensor on a monitor and alters the controlled element to maintain or correct any status change. This has advantages in that an experienced operator can frequently sense changes and correct for them rapidly, but has much more serious disadvantages in that, over a period, the real degree of control will vary unpredictably and can become marginal when a number of interactive parameters are involved.

In the first step away from a completely manual system, a controller carries out a predetermined sequence of operations upon manual initiation. The operations are usually of the on-off variety. The controller may be required only to confirm that one action has been accomplished before initiating the next one in sequence. This form of control is known as "semiautomatic" or, in its more elaborate forms, "supervisory." It relieves the human operator of the need to coordinate sequential actions, but does not maintain any continuous monitor or control function.

The final step in automation occurs when the controller keeps a continuous watch on one or more process parameters and makes continuous adjustments to one or several control functions or controlled elements in order to hold the process within predefined limits. Although in the overall picture this is a major step in reducing the importance of the human operator, it really consists of a sequence of small jumps, each one of which increases the degree of sophistication and adds to the tightness of control over the process.

It is beyond the scope of this book to go deeply into the theoretical analysis of control systems. The following is a brief explanation of the more commonly encountered methods of automatic process control. Those definitions that will enable the non-instrumentation-oriented engineer to understand the specialized terminology are included.

Two-position control

The simplest form of control is two-position, or on-off control. The controlled element is moved from one extreme to the other when the variable detected by the primary sensor deviates from the desired value. Some examples are the opening or closing of a valve when a pressure switch opens or closes, turning a pump on or off to maintain a tank level, or turning heat on or off to maintain a temperature. The sensor must have some hysteresis, that is, some lag in returning to the preferred value, built into its operating characteristics. Otherwise, the situation can arise where the controlled element is continually jumping between its two stable states, which can result in its destruction. Two-position control is the simplest form of automatic control; it is used where close control is not critical.

Floating control

The floating mode of control, sometimes called "single-speed proportional control," is a variant of the two-position mode. The primary sensor provides an analog signal. When this changes by a preset amount, the controlled element moves at a constant speed in a direction which will reduce the sensor signal deviation to zero, such as a valve opening. Here again a measure of hysteresis is required to avoid continual "hunting" of the system. Floating control provides a tighter control than two-position control, and usually causes less cycling.

Proportional control

In the next stage of control development, called "proportional control," the amount of movement of the controlled element is proportional to the magnitude of the deviation of the sensed parameter from a fixed value. This control mode is inherently self-balancing, but has the serious deficiency that it will not compensate for changes in process load requirements. Suppose, for instance, that the input valve to a water tank is controlled by a level sensor. If the tank outflow is increased, the level will drop, and this will cause the input valve to open until the level restabilizes. At this point there will be a change in water level in the tank, called "offset," which will not be recognized by the proportional controller even though the level is not at the set point. In some cases this offset will not be important, but under other circumstances the phenomenon could have serious effects on the process.

Proportional-integral control

In order to compensate for offset, the integral mode (also called reset) is added. In essence, the integral function samples the difference between the fixed set point of the controller and the point at which the sensor stabilizes, and adjusts the controlled element in such a way as to return the parameter value to the set point. Applied to the above example, this means that the input valve will be opened wider than would be required by the proportional deviation only to stabilize the condition and will then be closed slowly as the tank level rises, until the level returns to its initial position.

Proportional-integral-differential control

Generally referred to by the initials PID, the proportional-integral-differential control mode adds the differential (or rate) function. The purpose of the rate function is to modify the position of the controlled element in terms of the rate at which the parameter signal deviates from the fixed set point. The consequence of the differential mode is to minimize the time required for the process to return to the defined set point. However, derivative action is seldom used in water treatment plants.

A PID controller is perhaps the most elaborate single means of automatic process control that can be used. When properly adjusted and maintained, it can be relied upon to hold the process within its defined limits. Unfortunately, there are no specific rules for adjusting or "tuning" a controlled process loop; each such loop is subject to its own unique characteristic sensitivities, which can be compensated for only by empirical trial-and-error methods. For tuning, the manufacturers' recommendations should be followed.

Control loops

In all the above discussion, it is assumed that any change in the process caused by alteration of the controlled element or a disturbance is sensed by the parameter sensor, and the signal (or deviation from the desired value) is used as input to the controller. This is known as a *closed-loop* or *feedback* control system.

The *open-loop* control system, on the other hand, has no operational coupling between the controlled element and the parameter sensor. A common example of open-loop control is the time-cycle-controlled opening and closing of a valve, or an operational sequence which is commanded by the timer with no reference to the conditions existing in the process controlled by the valve.

The third variant of basic control—the *feedforward* mode—is found when the sensor is upstream from the controlled element. An example of this is the control of prechlorination feed rate by intake flow volume. It is a partial control technique in that one parameter (flow volume) is sensed, but other parameters (such as water quality) are assumed to be invariant. While a feedforward control loop is, by its very nature, open-loop, the reverse is not necessarily true. An open-loop control need not be related in any immediate way to the specific process.

The control requirements of processes will vary widely, and it is economically wise to use as few different types of controllers as possible in order to minimize the variety of spare parts which must be carried. Thus, if one standard control mechanism is used, it must be adjustable to satisfy the different requirements of individual control loops. The adjustments fall into two groups: the ones that are made while tuning the system, and the ones that can be changed at any time during operation.

Essentially, the first group of adjustments sets up the transfer function of the loop, or the relationship between the sensed parameter and the controlled element. The proportional band or "span" adjusts the loop sensitivity, expressed as the percentage of parameter change required to move the controlled element over its full range. The "offset" biases the parameter range relative to the controlled element range and compensates for zero-level effects. The "reset rate" controls the repetition frequency of the integral mode and thus controls the rate of change of the controlled element. The first and last of these adjustments are interactive, so that it is necessary to adjust them alternately in small increments during tuning until the desired characteristics are obtained.

The second group of adjustments, which can usually be made at any time from the front of the controller, consists of the positioning of the set point, which is the desired control level, and the setting of any alarm limits. Unlike the transfer function adjustment, the setting of this group is normally visible on the dial or other indicator of the control unit, which may in addition have controlled-element position indicators, status and alarm indicators, and other displays to enable the human operator to keep an overview of process conditions.

Control errors

The aim of automatic process control is to keep a constant watch on the essential parameters of a particular process and to adjust the appropriate controls in such a way as to compensate for any changes. In theory this is possible, but in practice there are many uncontrollable variables which make the control less than perfect, such as:

The ability of the sensor to obtain continuous completely representative data

The accumulation of tolerance errors in the elements of the control loop

The necessary simplification of the transfer function equation by the controller

The presence of unknown process factors at the sensor or controlled element

If all these variables are lumped together, they become definable deviations of the control loop and can be altered to some extent by careful system design to optimize the control. *Static error* is the difference between the true and sensed values of a parameter. It can be negated by the offset control. *Deadband* is the amount of deviation from the set point of the sensed parameter which occurs before any corrective movement of the controlled element is made. With a multimode controller, the deadband is usually a fraction of 1 percent of the span and can be ignored. With a floating control mode, the deadband is incorporated to avoid excessive hunting. In such cases it may be renamed the "neutral zone." *Process lag* is the time delay between movement of the controlled element and the observation by the sensor of the consequent change in the parameter. It is a function of the physical separation of the two components. *Control lag* is the time delay between the receipt at the controller of a change in the sensor signal and the generation of a signal at the controlled element. It is evident only in multimode controllers and is caused by the inherent mathematics of the integral control mode. In a continuous dynamic control system, a PID controller can be adjusted so that the output "leads" the input, making it possible to balance out process lag and have a system with zero reaction time. Decisions of this nature, however, must be treated individually, as the requirements and problems of each case dictate.

The two most important element tolerance errors are *repeatability* and *stability*. They can both be defined as the ability of the element to maintain a constant output when subjected to a constant input. Repeatability, however, defines how closely the output returns to its initial value when the input is cycled, whereas stability defines the time-related change in output with constant input. Each element will have its own tolerance band of these factors, which have to be combined to obtain the total loop error band. Obviously it is desirable to keep the band as narrow as possible, since it affects the size of the deadband and also the ability of the control loop to hold to its set point.

Cascade control

In the foregoing it was tacitly assumed that each control loop was complete in itself and operated largely independently. There are times when adjustment of a controlled element depends on some function of the changes occurring in a number of sensed parameters. In such cases, a *cascade* control may be used, in which each parameter signal is operated on by its own controller or by a signal conditioner, and the resulting modified signals are combined and used to position the set point of the controller which is connected to the controlled element. Such control systems can become very complex and require a high degree of specific expertise. However, the increased use of computers has enabled the complexities of control to be transferred to computer programming. This opens the possibility of more sophisticated control philosophies and reduces the amount of control hardware required.

Elements of Design

Analog process control

Analog process control involves the use of equipment assembled into a panel which presents process information for operators and permits control activation. Figure 14.2 shows typical analog process control equipment in a flow control loop. Plant process signals comprising the typical continuous variables of flow, level, pressure, turbidity, and others, and discrete signals from contacts and switches for equipment on/off, valve open/close, above or below a limit, and others, are all wired into the panel. The values of the continuous (analog) variables are presented on calibrated meters, indicators, and/or recorders, and the discrete signals, providing alarm and status indications, are presented in annunciator windows and panel lights. The panel is labeled to identify all front face indicating equipment, generally grouped by process.

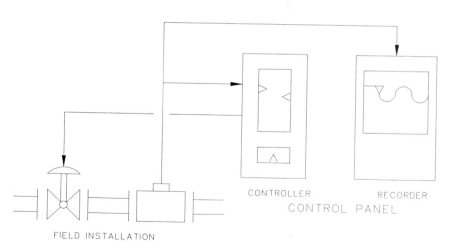

Figure 14.2   Analog process control loop.

Controls are initiated from the analog panel by pushbuttons, switches, and potentiometers. A critical analog panel instrument is the controller, described earlier (Fig. 14.1). The controller allows the operator to "dial in" the desired value or set point of a plant variable, such as a flow, which will then be maintained via feedback based on the deviation of the controlled variable from the desired set point. The set point and the measured value of the variable are displayed on the panel.

Analog panels may be small, containing a few indicators and controls, and limited to local equipment instrumentation, or very large and centrally located, encompassing an entire process or multiple processes. The instrumentation layout of a panel may be graphic, where the mounting pattern follows the process flow and sequence of operations, or nongraphic, mounted in groupings that are convenient for operator monitoring and control.

In recent years the expansion and microminiaturization of digital electronics have made inroads into the analog panel. Circular analog indicators have yielded to LED digital readouts; the PID circuits of controllers are printed circuit boards with digital equation equivalents of the PID calculations. Panels may now contain miniature digital devices which can be programmed to display plant variables and operational control sequences.

In general, analog panels are based on hard-wired instrumentation loops. Changes are expensive and not very flexible, generally requiring rewiring and panel hardware modifications. This has led to the advent of the digital presentation of the same information on computer-based video display terminals. The inherent flexibility of the digital computer allows a more compact and versatile presentation of any data displayed on an analog panel.

Computer monitoring and process control

The digital computer is a tool, and like any tool it can be described in terms of what it does and how it is made. A piece of electronic equipment whose circuits are designed to treat electrical signals as numbers, the computer must follow a sequence of instructions dealing with the processes from which these numbers are obtained. The hardware of a computer system has dormant capability and can do nothing without software, the program of application instructions. Similarly, the software is merely a documentation of procedures without the computer hardware to house and execute the instructions.[4]

Designing a computer into a water treatment plant application requires the design of both hardware and software as an integrated system. The engineer must have a comprehensive understanding of what the computer is to do; then he or she can define the most suitable configuration for optimum application.

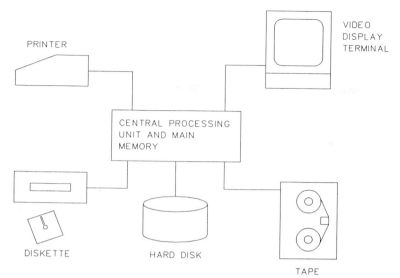

Figure 14.3 Typical digital computer structure.

For many years the computer stood alone, turned on only when needed to solve a scientific or business problem and fed its instructions and data by an operator or programmer. Figure 14.3 shows the organization of a basic computer divided into several modules, each of which is assigned a specific set of functions:

The *central processing unit* controls the sequencing and execution of the software instructions, that is, the arithmetic and logic processes applied to the stored data.

Main memory stores the instructions and data as they are processed by the central processing unit.

Secondary memory, such as the hard disc, magnetic tape, and diskette, is significantly slower in response time than the main memory. It stores more instructions and data that are available for transfer to main memory and execution by the central processing unit.

Human interface with the computer is accomplished through input/output devices and associated media which contain coded data and instructions for their interpretation by the computer:

1. A video display terminal (VDT) and keyboard allow the operator to type in data and call for information displays on a television-type screen.
2. A printer allows the operator to receive data on paper as hard copy.

3. Diskettes are convenient, cheap, popular portable storage devices for program entries and data input or output.
4. A magnetic tape unit allows the operator to use magnetically coded tapes for input, output, and information storage.

The computer of Fig. 14.3 is used successfully by water departments for their engineering and business requirements, such as billing, payroll, report preparation, process design, maintenance and inventory management, and statistical evaluation of operational data. Hardware can be added to convert the system to a process computer with direct links to the plant instrumentation, operating as a data logger, shown in Fig. 14.4. For example, in the preparation of a summary report of 24-h operational data, it would not be necessary for the operator to note instrument readings on a clipboard for subsequent computer entry. Instead, selected process measurements can be wired to and read by the computer at fixed time intervals and stored in memory. The field instrument readings are available not only for report preparation but also for immediate display of plant alarms and status. This process input/output capability integrates the computer into plant operational monitoring on a 24-h basis.

Taking the next logical step after data logging, we can add com-

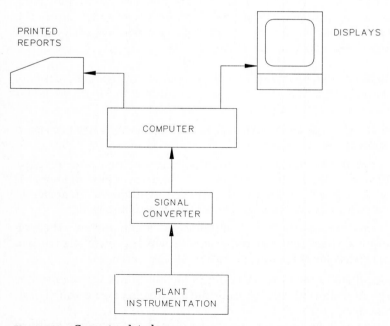

Figure 14.4   Computer data logger.

puter output signals to the existing computer input signals to build plant control as well as monitoring into the digital process computer. This is illustrated in Fig. 14.5. A popular term for computer monitoring and control, which has come into widespread use, is SCADA, which is an acronym for *Supervisory Control and Data Acquisition*.

The advent of integrated circuits and high-density microminiaturized electronic technology has inaugurated new designs in computer systems. In process control applications, the central computer is giving way to distributed computers and data highways. Instead of one central computer with a data-collection network, we have a set of dedicated microcomputers performing monitoring and control functions for local processes, for example, filter operation and backwash, chemical dosing, or plant intake control. The central computer serves as an operator interface to all plant data, allows manual control at a VDT keyboard, and provides overall central storage of the data base of plant information and backup software. An example of a distributed computer network is shown in Fig. 14.6.

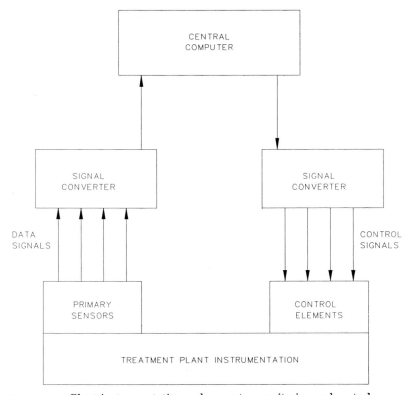

Figure 14.5 Plant instrumentation and computer monitoring and control.

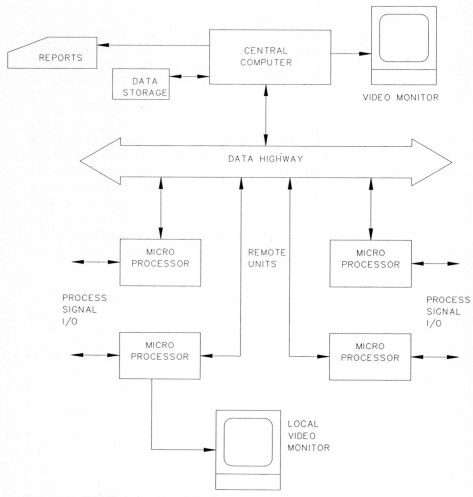

Figure 14.6   Distributed process control.

While each local computer installation is essentially independent, they all communicate with the central computer over a data highway hard-wired network to deliver information for operator displays and logs, as well as to accept operator control from the central console keyboard. The distributed computer system divides the computation load so that the central computer can respond more rapidly to operator requests. Any one computer may fail without affecting the others. Hence, with more units, each failure is far less catastrophic than the failure of a central system.

Data acquisition and processing

Connecting a computer directly to plant signals provides the power of digital data computing to process information. At a central location, the operator can have access to comprehensive, organized, and rapidly presented plant intelligence. Priority information displays, such as alarms, will alert the operator immediately to problems by displaying brief, relevant alarm statements. The operator can also be informed of plant status changes (pump on/off, valve open/close, chemical feed start/stop) as they occur. Plant information can be made available to the operator on paper generated by a printer or as a display on a VDT.

These two output media can replace indicators and recorders. The VDT provides a continuously updated display of plant data in the form of tables, charts, time-based graphs, treatment process graphics, and other arbitrary data configurations. For example, Fig. 14.7 is a bar-graph display of selected plant data. The picture remains fixed, but as changes occur, the bars and numerical values vary in proportion to the signals received by the computer.

Permanent reports of plant data are provided by printers. While the VDT is effective at providing instantaneous, "live" plant data, the printer is more suited for periodic operational summary reporting, as is shown in Fig. 14.8.

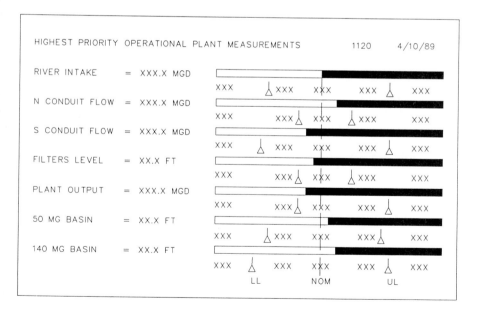

Figure 14.7   Video display of plant overview bar graph.

MAJOR PLANT FLOWS

DATE	TOTAL INFLUENT PUMPED MGD	GRAVITY EFFLUENT MGD	HIGH SERVICE EFFLUENT MGD	TOTAL EFFLUENT MGD
1	73.1	12.8	60.5	73.3
2	82.5	12.5	64.5	77.0
3	88.5	12.7	73.5	86.2
4	90.0	12.6	71.3	83.9
5	81.4	12.6	68.5	81.1
6	81.0	12.5	63.0	75.5
7	83.6	12.5	63.0	75.5
8	87.4	12.5	74.9	99.9
9	85.8	12.7	60.0	72.7
10	84.6	12.7	68.5	81.2
11	85.5	12.5	68.5	81.0
12	80.1	12.6	63.0	75.6
13	69.8	12.7	58.0	70.7
14	79.1	12.5	60.3	72.8
15	85.8	12.6	72.5	85.1
16	88.8	12.6	72.3	84.9
17	83.5	12.5	62.5	75.0
18	77.8	12.5	63.5	76.0
19	83.2	12.5	62.5	75.0
20	74.0	12.5	61.5	74.0
21	71.3	12.5	67.5	70.0
22	77.9	12.5	57.5	70.0
23	75.5	12.5	62.5	75.0
24	69.0	12.7	57.5	70.2
25	69.5	12.5	53.1	65.6
26	69.5	12.6	51.6	64.2
27	74.0	12.5	53.2	65.7
28	64.4	12.5	50.4	62.9
29	78.3	12.5	60.1	72.6
30	87.8	12.5	70.0	82.5
31	81.6	12.5	60.0	72.5
AVG	79.4	12.6	63.0	75.7
MAX	90.0	12.8	74.9	99.9
MIN	64.4	12.5	50.4	62.9
SD	6.8	0.1	6.4	7.4

Figure 14.8 Periodic report (monthly summary).

The full data-processing power of a digital computer can be applied to plant intelligence reporting for management and engineers as well as operators. Data can be processed into such display, logs, and reports as:

Process graphic (mimic) displays

Alarms

Trend logs—present and past

Historic logs

Status change logs

Demand logs

Periodic and long-term reports

Preventive maintenance reports

One type of display which merits special consideration is the process graphic. In this display on a VDT, sensed real-time data from a specific process are superimposed on a schematic diagram of the process. As equipment changes status and process variables change values, these are reflected on the diagram almost instantaneously. Computer storage can retain many process graphic displays, making them available for presentation upon selection by the operator. Figure 14.9 is a plant overview diagram showing selected important variables.

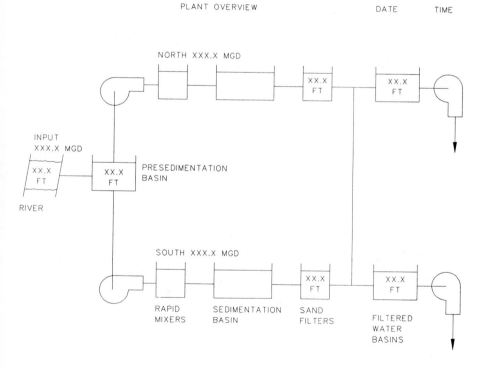

Figure 14.9 Video display of plant graphic overview.

Data acquisition systems with logging and displays clearly assist the operator by organizing and centralizing plant information more conveniently. Such systems are relatively inexpensive, as a considerable amount of standardized software is available. Detailed descriptions of data acquisition and logging systems and much additional information can be found in textbooks, technical journals, and manufacturers' literature.

Computer control

Computer control is inherently more complex and controversial than data acquisition and display. By allowing the computer to store a composite picture of plant status on a continuous basis, data acquisition and display form an essential prerequisite to control. Simultaneously with data sampling, the computer examines plant status according to internally stored rules to determine whether the status is acceptable or needs adjustment. The rules are part of the software prepared to reflect the control approaches of the plant operators. Programs can be prepared to control the various phases of plant processes, such as maintaining flows and levels, filter operation and backwash, chemical dosage, flocculation, clarification, and chemical sludge disposal. In closed-loop procedures, the computer will deliver control signals to plant equipment, such as:

Pumps—start, stop, speed adjustment, and sequencing

Valves—open, close, position adjustment, and sequencing

Screens—operation and cleaning

Conveyors—start, stop, and speed adjustment

Mixers—start, stop, and speed adjustment

The control procedures are automatic and proceed without operator intervention. However, the operator does have the ability to inhibit the delivery of control signals from the computer and to override internally stored control logic with arbitrary commands from the keyboard of the control console. Inhibiting controls does not inhibit data sampling and evaluation, so that if an operator inadvertently causes an alarm, it will be recognized and annunciated.

Designing for digital computer control

The specifications for a digital computer control system should minimally include:

Application software definition

Process signal list

Hardware configuration

System (packaged) configuration

The most important point in preparing specifications for a system is to define the role of the computer in plant monitoring and control. The specifications for the application are based upon the treatment process designs and operational procedures. The plant processes are divided into sequential and regulatory procedures, status changes, contingencies and alarm conditions, information requirements, and displays. These are the bases for the development of application software.

Of equal importance to the application is the list of process signals for both monitoring and control which comprise the information interface between the computer and plant. These signals are described in terms of source, type, scanning frequency, and other parameters required by computer system suppliers.

Having documented the computer system application and the signal list, the designer has a basis for defining the hardware and system software requirements. These should be general-purpose production items checked out in previous similar installations of state-of-the-art design. The technology of computer process control is changing so rapidly that the designer must be able to assess the technical literature to be sure that the specifications reflect the state of the art.

The PC. The personal computer (PC) has made tremendous inroads into the overall computer marketplace, with a continuous parade of new and innovative hardware and software. Spreadsheet and database software packages have significantly facilitated the organization and processing of data into custom logs and reports. Many product houses offer industrialized microcomputers in modular assemblies, tolerant to heat and humidity, with air filtration systems and heavy-duty power supplies. The PC in a network with programmable logic controllers (PLC) specifically dedicated to process monitoring and control of local areas is becoming a reliable, acceptable combination. This combination utilizes the data processing capability of the PC and the longstanding reputation of the PLC in dedicated control functions.

There is no question that PCs have captured a large sector of the data acquisition marketplace. A wide variety of support devices have been developed to enhance PC capability. As system houses move rapidly into assembling PC-based process control systems with the necessary multitasking, this approach should provide a low-cost system built on standardized hardware and software. This sounds very attractive, but the buyer cannot assume that all the plant needs will be met.

To safeguard the plant management interests, a specification for the process computer system must be prepared, explicitly reflecting the needs of plant operations management. If the specifications clearly identify the technical expectations of the plant process control system, manufacturers can compete to match the requirements at the least cost.

Design Principles and Practices

Processes monitored and controlled

There are monitoring requirements that apply to most water treatment plants with chemical treatment, such as raw-water flow rate, filter flow rate and control, and clearwell level. Several standard monitoring requirements may be used as starting points for control system design. Frequently, process equipment manufacturers will provide valuable suggestions for consideration by the design engineer. However, as water treatment becomes more complex, the design engineer would do well to become familiar with chemical engineering process control theory.

In general, raw data parameters can be divided into a number of distinct classes:

Composition, such as pH, turbidity

Physical, such as flow, level

Mechanical, such as pump speed, valve status

Chemical, such as dosage rate

Efficiency, such as power usage

When designing the process control system, the needs of each of these classes must be considered, and control modes, sampling techniques, and physical location decided.

Primary sensors

The primary sensors are the devices which are in contact with the process media being measured and which respond to changes in the media. These changes, which may be mechanical, chemical, or electrical, and are typically of small magnitude, are converted through signal conditioning to the standard 4- to 20-mA dc analog signal format. The standard signal can be transmitted in a loop to indicators, recorders, and totalizers as well as to a computer. Thus the sensor detects plant operational information for presentation where the data will serve plant monitoring and control needs.

Sensors may be *on-line*, connected to the process media and providing unattended continuous measurement, or *off-line* in a laboratory, providing a measurement only when in contact with a sample. Off-line laboratory sensing equipment is used because (1) no acceptable on-line sensor is available, or (2) off-line measurements are required to calibrate the on-line sensors.

Care must be taken in the selection of sensors to ensure that they are suitably matched to the environment. They may have to be hardened to the anticipated environment, such as high humidity, temperature, vibration, and dust. While standard, field-proven equipment should be selected, the specifications should also reflect the constraints imposed by the process media and environment. Primary sensors should be considered fragile, and the manufacturers' recommendations for installation and maintenance should be rigorously followed.

The major primary sensors used in water treatment are summarized below.

Flow.   Flow is the most important variable measured in a water treatment plant, and there is a variety of flow-measuring techniques from which to choose for the required plant applications. It is therefore essential to understand and properly define the application, and to acquire the basic knowledge of the flowmeter types available to effect the best match.

Meters in water treatment plants include:

Differential-pressure types
    Venturi
    Orifice plate
    Flow tube
Propeller or turbine meters
Magnetic flowmeter
Ultrasonic (acoustic) flowmeter
Vortex meter
Variable-area (rotameter)
Flumes and weirs

Some general criteria are provided for those flowmeters for which the entire flow must fill the pipe (therefore flumes and weirs are excluded).

- Two factors are common to the mathematical model of the meter: cross-sectional area, and a means of measuring the fluid velocity; the product yields the flow rate (volume per unit time).

- Approach piping and discharge piping configurations must be considered in terms of manufacturers' recommendations for the extent of straight pipe lengths to assure uniform flow through the meter.

■ Where the requirements for extensive straight lengths cannot be met in a particular installation, especially upstream of the meter, flow straighteners may be installed, also following manufacturers' recommendations.

■ Virtually all meters can be fitted with electronic circuits to convert the sensed signal to the standard 4- to 20-mA dc.

Extensive manufacturers' literature is available to provide detailed information about the physical and mathematical theory of the meters, configuration, recommended application, structure, installation, calibration, maintenance, and diagrams.

Differential pressure. Differential-pressure (also called "head loss") meters are the most widely used. They are based upon the creation of a constriction in the flow to force increased velocity and therefore decreased pressure. The change in pressure (differential) is measured and this value used to calculate flow rate, which is proportional to the square root of the differential pressure. The square root factor restricts the range of flow to at most 4 to 1. While the orifice plate is the least expensive, it causes the highest energy loss. By conical geometry the Venturi brings about the restriction in flow cross section gradually and therefore causes significantly less energy (head) loss through the tube. However, the Venturi is much more costly. The flow tube is a more compact form of the Venturi; it has lower energy loss, but is also expensive compared with the orifice plate. These meters have no moving parts and require little maintenance.

Propeller and turbine meters. Flow in a propeller or turbine meter is measured by the fluid impinging on the blades of a rotor suspended on bearings in the flow stream. As the rotor spins, the speed is sensed through a magnetic coupling, which causes one or more pulses per rotation. At rated values, the flow is linear with the rotation and maintains good accuracy. The range of flow is 10 to 1 with very little head loss. The meter parts are subject to wear and are vulnerable to particles in the flow stream. The meters are relatively inexpensive.

Magnetic flowmeter. The magnetic flowmeter is based on Faraday's law of electromagnetic induction: A conductor moving in a magnetic field causes a voltage proportional to the velocity of relative motion. The flowing liquid is the moving conductor; fixed electromagnetic coils around the pipe produce the magnetic field perpendicular to the flow; the resulting induced voltage is detected by two electrodes embedded in the pipe in a line perpendicular to both the flow and the magnetic field.

Essentially the magnetic flow tube is empty, thereby causing the minimal head loss of the pipe itself. Magnetic flowmeters are costly, but the accuracy is high. Nevertheless, calibration is necessary because the signal may drift. The range of flow is 10 to 1.

Ultrasonic flowmeter.   Ultrasonic flowmeters are based upon measurement of the time required for an ultrasonic pulse to travel diagonally across a pipe with and against the flow. The type of ultrasonic meter used in clean-water flow is called "time of flight" or "transit time." The velocity of the liquid flow is proportional to the difference in the time of traverse of the two pulses. The meter has built-in electronics to make the measurements, calculate the velocity signal, and convert it to the standard 4- to 20-mA dc. The meter can very conveniently be strapped to the outside of a pipe, making for an easy and inexpensive installation. Changes in fluid composition affect meter sensitivity, and air bubbles or particles in the fluid interfere with pulse travel. The range of flow exceeds that of the turbine meter.

The transit time ultrasonic meter must be distinguished from the Doppler type, which depends upon the reflection of a pulse from a particle or air bubble and hence would not be used for clear water.

Vortex meter.   When a liquid flows past an unstreamlined or bluff body, the flow cannot follow the contour of the obstacle, and the separated layers roll into eddies or vortices. The frequency at which the vortices are generated is proportional to the velocity of the flowing liquid. The resulting pressure changes are detected by probes mounted on the bluff body, and are then converted to the standard 4- to 20-mA dc signal proportional to the flow. The range of flow is a high 12 to 1. The meter does not have any moving parts, simplifying maintenance.

Variable-area meters (rotameters).   The typical rotameter is composed of a vertically oriented tapered glass tube (widest at the top) with a freely moving float inside. Upward-flowing liquid keeps the float up. The float balances between the weight downward and the upward buoyant force and upward hydraulic force of the flow. Where the float reaches an equilibrium position provides a linear indication of the rate of flow. Since the vertical position of the float indicates the flow rate, a reading scale etched into the tube can be calibrated to provide the flow rate. The range of flow is 10 to 1, and the rotameter is suitable for very low flow rates. Proper operation is based upon and requires the vertical mounting. The rotameter is not affected by upstream piping effects, and can be installed with almost any configuration of piping before the meter entrance.

Parshall flume. The Parshall and other flumes are used to measure open-channel flow, especially very large flows. The geometry of the flume provides a direct relation between the water level at a specific point in the flume and the rate of flow. The level measurement may be performed by a bubbler system or a float installed in a stilling well adjacent to the flume. The stilling well reduces the variations in level resulting from flow turbulence in the flume itself. Level may also be measured by an ultrasonic level detector mounted above the flume. The relatively high velocities tend to flush away any solids deposits which may have accumulated. Range of flow may go as high as 35 to 1.

Weir. The weir is also a suitable device for measuring large open-channel flows. Essentially, the weir is a dam with apertures at the top, such as V-notch, rectangular, trapezoidal, and other configurations. The flow is a function of the water level or head, that is, the difference in level from some steady value at a point upstream from the weir to the crest at the weir. It may be constructed of concrete or steel. The level may be measured by the common methods of the float, the bubbler, or the acoustic meter mounted above the weir. The practical range of flow is 20 to 1. Accuracy is limited, in particular, because silt and other solids which may be in the water tend to build up at the weir.

Level. Level is an important measurement in a water treatment plant. Three of the most commonly used measurement methods include the float type, the bubbler unit, and the ultrasonic type.

Float type. The float-type level detector is a buoyancy device that makes contact with the liquid via a float. The float may be directly on the surface or in a stilling well. Floats are used in tanks, reservoirs, and flumes, and can indicate level in many different ways. The float may be cable-connected to a counterweight sliding along a direct-reading gauge and providing level indication on the site of a tank. In another mechanical approach, the float cable may wind or unwind on a drum rim as the water level rises and falls. The drum may also be connected to a transmitter that converts the measurement to an electrical signal.

While the advantage of float devices is their simplicity, they require periodic mechanical maintenance to keep them relatively friction-free, and they are not practical where ice may form. To ensure steady measurement, a stilling well must frequently be used.

Liquid head.   A pressure-sensing device open to the atmosphere that is located near the base of a tank can be calibrated to read water level directly, based on the pressure or head produced by the weight (height) of the liquid above the pressure transducer. The pressure sensor may be a Bourdon tube, a manometer, or a differential-pressure transducer with the low-pressure side open to the atmosphere.

Bubbler.   The bubbler tube offers a satisfactory alternative to liquid-head-type level measurement in clean water where access to the bottom of a tank is inconvenient or impossible. The bubbler tube is also called a dip tube or air-purge level system. The system utilizes a tube installed inside, down the height of a tank and open about 3 in from the bottom. Compressed air is introduced into the tube from the top so that the air bubbles just escape from the bottom, and therefore the air pressure in the tube equals the hydrostatic head of the liquid in the tank. With this equilibrium maintained, the air pressure in the tube correspondingly changes as the liquid level changes. The pressure is detected by a gauge or manometer suitably calibrated to indicate tank level.

Ultrasonic level detector.   Another convenient level-sensing device for tanks that are open to the atmosphere is the ultrasonic level detector. The height of the water is measured on the basis of an acoustic pulse transmitted by an ultrasonic transmitter/receiver located above the highest anticipated tank level. The transmitter generates a pulse down perpendicular to the water level, and detects how long it takes to receive the reflected pulse energy, based on the speed of sound in air. Utilizing tank geometry and the distance from the top of the tank, the device converts the pulse travel time to a calibrated water level. Accuracy is improved if a temperature detector is added to adjust the speed of sound value as temperature changes.

Pressure.   Pressure is a most important variable on its own, notably with respect to pump operation, compressors, and blowers. A pressure gauge is mechanically activated by the pressure detector and can indicate the pressure in suction and discharge pipes. In flow detection, differential pressure is used to find the velocity of the liquid.

Measured pressure may be

- Gauge pressure, referenced to the ambient atmospheric pressure
- Absolute pressure, referenced to absolute vacuum
- Differential pressure, referenced to another pressure

Therefore all pressure measurements are essentially differential pressure measurements, and the transducers are working against a second pressure, usually atmospheric.

There are common mechanical devices that are designed to distort their shape when subjected to pressure. These are called elastic deformation pressure elements. They include the diaphragm, the bellows, the capsule, the Bourdon tube, the spiral, and the helix. Each is responsive to a differing range of pressure. In a pressure gauge, the deformation is interconnected directly or through gears or springs to a pointer that is calibrated and scaled to indicate the source pressure.

For signal transmission the pressure-induced motion is converted to an electrical signal using a motion-to-electrical-signal transducer. For example, the pressure change may be converted to a resistance or a capacitance change. The transduced changes are then subjected to signal conditioning to generate a standard 4- to 20-mA dc signal proportional to pressure for transmission to an analog panel indicator, recorder, or controller, as well as to a computer.

In selection of a pressure sensor device for an application, the required pressure range must be known. Consideration must also be given to the potential for adverse environmental conditions, potential vibration, and flow conditions at the location of the instrument.

Temperature.   Temperature measurements are important in water treatment, applicable both to the water and to equipment, such as pump bearings and motor windings. There are many ways to measure temperature:

- Thermometer
- Thermocouple (T/C)
- Resistance temperature detector (RTD)
- Thermistor
- Bimetallic strip

The familiar mercury thermometer can be used for arbitrary local readings.

The thermocouple uses a wire pair of different metals joined at the two ends. If the two joined ends are at different temperatures, a voltage will develop dependent on the temperature difference and type of wires. If one end is kept at a constant known reference temperature, the voltage will be proportional to the temperature at the other end as the measuring junction. The voltage generated is small and may drift; hence the reading is subject to inaccuracy if not kept in calibration.

Resistance temperature detectors use the variation of metal wire resistance with temperature changes to provide an indication of the temperature. Resistance varies directly, but not necessarily linearly, with temperature.

The thermistor is a semiconductor whose resistance varies inversely with temperature.

The bimetallic strip consists of two different metals with different expansion versus temperature properties. Therefore, as temperature changes, the different expansion will cause the strip to bend. The motion can be used to provide a temperature indication, or on/off control of temperature.

Turbidity. Turbidity measurement is an indication of the amount of solids in suspension in a flow, and is therefore a major indicator of water treatment effectiveness. The measurement depends upon the scattering of a light beam projected into a sample fluid. The extent of light scattering or attenuation, as a result of the solids in suspension, is a function of the turbidity of the sample. In a turbidity meter, a fixed-candlepower lamp provides a light beam for measurement, and photocells are located to detect transmitted or scattered light and convert it to an electrical signal proportional to the turbidity.

The names for turbidity measurement units have varied over the years because of the changing criteria for measurement. Units have been called:

JTU—Jackson turbidity unit

FTU—Formazin turbidity unit

NTU—Nephelometric turbidity unit

JCU—Jackson candle unit

It is important, therefore, to read the manufacturer's instructions on what the unit will read. Accuracy is impaired by deposits on optical windows and dissolved colors in the sample. Air bubbles will also reduce the accuracy of a reading.

Chlorine residual. As one of the most prevalent means of disinfection, chlorine is among the most widely used chemicals in water treatment. Application of chlorine is typically paced with flow in feedforward control. Use of the residual chlorine analyzer in closed-loop feedback control has improved the effectiveness of chlorination in water treatment plants. The methods of on-line residual chlorine analysis are colorimetric or amperometric.

Colorimetric analysis is based on chlorine mixing with a reagent and creating a characteristic color, whose intensity is proportional to the amount of chlorine present. A photocell converts the light to an output signal. In amperometric analysis, the chlorine sample is buffered for pH, if necessary, before electrodes are used to generate a direct current proportional to the chlorine present in the sample. The analyzer may be associated with alarm actuation and external control functions.

Turbidity and color will influence the colorimetric analysis, but are generally not a problem in amperometric analysis. Both methods require periodic parts cleaning and the use of external chemicals. The amperometric analyzer is more expensive.

pH.   The pH measurement provides a value of the acidity or alkalinity of a solution on a scale of 1 to 14. The pH number is the negative logarithm of the hydrogen-ion concentration in a solution. The instrument utilizes two electrodes and a temperature sensor:

pH electrode

Reference electrode

Temperature compensation sensor

The three electrodes develop a temperature-compensated electric potential based on the hydrogen-ion activity. Mounted in an electrode chamber, the three electrodes may be installed in a tank, reservoir, or channel. pH control is important in coagulation and corrosion control.

Electric power monitoring.   Electricity is distributed throughout a water treatment plant as the prime source of power for virtually all equipment. Sensors for electric power variables, watts, voltage, and current, are simple, reliable, and a source of important operational data. Electric energy costs are high, but there are many ways to economize on the use of electricity in the plant, based on comprehensive monitoring.

Billing is generally based upon demand (watts, power), energy (watthours), and power factor (ratio of watts to voltamperes). The power company monitors the plant's cumulative total kilowatthours of energy use over a demand interval, typically 15 min or ½ h. Should the energy quantity used during the demand interval exceed some specified upper limit, the power company may increase the unit kilowatthour charge over a subsequent extended period, such as a year. This increased charge is levied to pay for the necessity of adding extra electric power generation to the system, according to power company claims.

It would therefore be wise for the plant monitoring system to include close tracking of cumulative kilowatthour usage synchronized with the demand interval period of the power company, with alarm signals alerting operators whenever the energy usage limit is approached. The operator would then have an opportunity to shed preselected low-priority loads that would not disturb the treatment processes. This could be done on a temporary basis until the next demand interval was initiated.

There may be other factors in the electric power bill that could be monitored and controlled, especially with a computer. It would be valuable for plant operations management to discuss the economics of power billing with local power company engineers for recommendations on power monitoring specifically to reduce cost.

Process and instrumentation diagrams

The process and instrumentation diagram, usually referred to by its initials P&ID, is to the instrumentation engineer what the circuit diagram is to the electronics engineer. It consists essentially of a formalized picture of a process, to which has been added a network of lines and symbols representing the elements of the instrumentation monitoring and control system. It is the starting point of the detailed control system design, and is used to develop and check out on paper the various control strategies. The diagrams indicate process functions— monitoring, control, recording, and interfacing with a computer.

Because it provides a common language for those involved in instrumentation design and specifications for process monitoring and control systems, the P&ID has come into widespread use. As a universal standard, the documentation of instrumentation systems via the P&ID enables contractors and equipment manufacturers to easily interpret specifications written by instrumentation designers. Process and instrumentation diagrams provide a uniform means of diagraming instrumentation systems, using standard equipment symbols and identification codes for functions, signal lines, and process flow lines, examples of which are depicted in Table 14.1.

So that a P&ID can be read and clearly understood by many people, conventions have been developed which define the majority of the symbols and labels,[1] but some process control elements which are unique to a particular industry may have to be invented. Before developing a new symbol, it is worthwhile to check pertinent literature, including papers delivered at symposia, to be sure that an appropriate symbol does not already exist.[5] A chart of the letters used in a typical P&ID with their definitions is presented in Table 14.2, excerpted from the ISA Standard S5.1.

In the preparation of a P&ID, it is first necessary to examine the process flow diagram and edit it to delete the nonpertinent parts, while retaining those aspects of the process which have an effect on

TABLE 14.1   Process and Instrumentation Diagrams

Process and instrumentation diagrams most common symbols:

— — — — — — — — —   Electric signal

—— // —— // —— // ——   Pneumatic signal

——————————————   Process

◯   Balloon for the instrument containing:

FC   Code for device represented

201   Process loop number

(FC / 201)   Locally mounted

(FC / 201)   Control room-board mounted

(FC / 201)   Contol room-mounted behind board

(FE / 145)
—▷◁—   Venturi flowmeter:
         flow element in loop 145

—▷◁—   Control valve

◯   Pilot light

◇   Generalized interlock

—⟲—   Pump

the control of the system. This presupposes that the designer has a reasonably comprehensive knowledge of the process.

In parallel with the reduction of the flow diagram to its pertinent essentials, it is necessary to define the process control philosophy. This includes such items as the degree of manual, automatic, and computer control; the depth of detail of control structures; and the level of accuracy desired. While some of these factors may not in themselves

TABLE 14.2 Meanings of Identification Letters*

	FIRST-LETTER (4)		SUCCEEDING-LETTERS (3)		
	MEASURED OR INITIATING VARIABLE	MODIFIER	READOUT OR PASSIVE FUNCTION	OUTPUT FUNCTION	MODIFIER
A	Analysis(5,19)		Alarm		
B	Burner, Combustion		User's Choice(1)	User's Choice(1)	User's Choice(1)
C	User's Choice(1)			Control(13)	
D	User's Choice(1)	Differential(4)			
E	Voltage		Sensor (Primary Element)		
F	Flow Rate	Ratio (Fraction)(4)			
G	User's Choice(1)		Glass, Viewing Device(9)		
H	Hand				High(7,15,16)
I	Current (Electrical)		Indicate(10)		
J	Power	Scan(7)			
K	Time, Time Schedule	Time Rate of Change(4,21)		Control Station (22)	
L	Level		Light(11)		Low(7,15,16)
M	User's Choice(1)	Momentary(4)			Middle, Intermediate(7,15)
N	User's Choice(1)		User's Choice(1)	User's Choice(1)	User's Choice(1)
O	User's Choice(1)		Orifice, Restriction		
P	Pressure, Vacuum		Point (Test) Connection		
Q	Quantity	Integrate, Totalize(4)			
R	Radiation		Record(17)		
S	Speed, Frequency	Safety(8)		Switch(13)	
T	Temperature			Transmit(18)	
U	Multivariable(6)		Multifunction(12)	Multifunction(12)	Multifunction(12)
V	Vibration, Mechanical Analysis(19)			Valve, Damper, Louver(13)	
W	Weight, Force		Well		
X	Unclassified(2)	X Axis	Unclassified(2)	Unclassified(2)	Unclassified(2)
Y	Event, State or Presence(20)	Y Axis		Relay, Compute, Convert(13,14,18)	
Z	Position, Dimension	Z Axis		Driver, Actuator, Unclassified Final Control Element	

*Reprinted by permission. Copyright © 1984 Instrument Society of America. From ISA Standard S5.1, *Instrument Symbols and Identification*. Numbers in parentheses refer to specific explanatory notes from ISA Standard S5.1 as follows: (1) A "user's choice" letter is intended to cover unlisted meanings that will be used repetitively in a particular project. If used, the letter may have one meaning as a first letter and another meaning as a succeeding letter. The meanings need to be defined only once in a legend, or other place, for that project. For example, the letter N may be defined as "modulus of elasticity" as a first letter and "oscilloscope" as a succeeding letter. (2) The unclassified letter X is intended to cover unlisted meanings that will be used only once or to a limited extent. If used, the letter may have any number of meanings as a first letter and any number of meanings as a succeeding letter. Except for its use with distinctive symbols, it is expected that the meanings will be defined outside a tagging bubble on a flow diagram. For example, *XR-2* may be a stress recorder and *XX-4* may be a stress oscilloscope. (3) The grammatical form of the succeeding-letter meanings may be modified as required. For example, "indicate" may be applied as "indicator" or "indicating," "transmit" as "transmitter" or "transmitting," and so forth. (4) Any first letter, if used in combination with modifying letters D (differential), F (ratio), M (momentary), K (time rate of change), Q (integrate or totalize), or any combination of these, is intended to represent a new and separate measured variable, and the combination is treated as a first-letter entity. Thus, instruments *TDI* and *TI* indicate two different variables, namely, differential temperature and temperature. Modifying letters are used when applicable. (5) First-letter A (analysis) covers all analyses not described by a "user's choice" letter. It is expected that the type of analysis will be defined outside a tagging bubble. (6) Use of first-letter U for "multivariable" in lieu of a combination of first letters is optional. It is recommended that nonspecific variable designators, such as U, be used sparingly. (7) The use of modifying terms "high," "low," "middle" or "intermediate," and "scan" is optional. (8) The term "safety" applies to emergency protective primary elements and emergency protective final-control elements only. Thus, a self-actuated valve that prevents operation of a fluid system at a higher-than-desired pressure by bleeding fluid from the system is a back-pressure-type *PCV*, even if the valve is not intended to be used normally. However, this valve is designated as a PSV if it is intended to protect against emergency conditions, i.e., conditions that are hazardous to personnel and/or equipment and that are not expected to arise normally. The designation *PSV* applies to all valves intended to protect against emergency pressure conditions regardless of whether the valve construction and mode of operation place them in the category of the safety valve, relief valve, or safety relief valve. A rupture disk is designated *PSE*. (9) The passive function G applies to instruments or devices that provide an uncalibrated view, such as sight glasses and television monitors. (10) "Indicate" normally applies to the readout—analog or digital—of an actual measurement. In the case of a manual loader, it may be used for the dial or setting indication, i.e., for the value of the initiating variable. (11) A pilot light that is part of an instrument loop should be designated by a first letter followed by the succeeding-letter L. For example, a pilot light that indicates an expired time period should be tagged *KQL*. If it is desired to tag a pilot light that is not part of an instrument loop, the light is designated in the same way. For example, a running light for an electric motor may be tagged *EL*, assuming voltage to be the appropriate measured variable, or *YL*, assuming the operating status is being monitored. The unclassified variable X should be used only for applications which are limited in extent. The designation *XL* should not be used for motor running lights, as these are commonly numerous. It is permissible to use the user's choice letters M, N, or O for a motor running light when the meaning is previously defined. If M is used, it must be clear that the letter does not stand for the word "motor," but for a monitored state. (12) Use of a succeeding-letter U for "multifunction" instead of a combination of other functional letters is optional. This nonspecific function designator should be used sparingly. (13) A device that connects, disconnects, or transfers one or more circuits may be either a switch, a relay, an ON-OFF controller, or a control valve, depending on the application. If the device manipulates a fluid process stream and is not a hand-actuated ON-OFF block valve, it is designated as a control valve. It is incorrect to use the succeeding-letters *CV* for anything other than a self-actuated control valve. For all applications other than fluid process streams, the device is designated as follows: A switch, if it is actuated by hand; a switch or an ON-OFF controller, if it is automatic and is the first such device in a loop. The term "switch" is generally used if the device is used for alarm, pilot light, selection, interlock, or safety. The term "controller" is generally used if the device is used for normal operating control. A relay, if it is automatic and is not the first such device in a loop, i.e., it is actuated by a switch or an ON-OFF controller. (14) It is expected that the functions associated with the use of succeeding-letter Y will be defined outside a bubble on a diagram when further definition is considered necessary. This definition need not be made when the function is self-evident, as for a solenoid valve in a fluid signal line. (15) The modifying terms "high," and "low," and "middle" or "intermediate" correspond to values of the measured variable, not to values of the signal, unless otherwise noted. For example, a high-level alarm derived from a reverse-acting level transmitter signal should be an *LAH*, even though the alarm is actuated when the signal falls to a low value. The terms may be used in combinations as appropriate. (16) The terms "high" and "low," when applied to positions of valves and other open-closed devices, are defined as follows: "high" denotes that the valve is in or approaching the fully open position, and "low" denotes that it is in or approaching the fully closed position. (17) The word "record" applies to any form of permanent storage of information that permits retrieval by any means. (18) For use of the term "transmitter" versus "converter," refer to Section 3, Definitions, in ISA Standard S5.1. (19) First-letter V, "vibration or mechanical analysis," is intended to perform the duties in machinery monitoring that the letter A performs in more general analyses. Except for vibration, it is expected that the variable of interest will be defined outside the tagging bubble. (20) First-letter Y is intended for use when control or monitoring responses are event driven as opposed to time or time-schedule driven. The letter Y, in this position, can also signify presence or state. (21) Modifying-letter K, in combination with a first letter such as L, T, or W, signifies a time rate of change of the measured or initiating variable. The variable $WKIC$, for instance, may represent a rate-of-weight-loss controller. (22) Succeeding-letter K is a user's option for designating a control station, while the succeeding-letter C is used for describing automatic or manual controllers.

appear in the P&ID, they may very well define the form and location of primary sensors and control elements.

Once the details of the control philosophy have been defined, it can be translated to hardware on the flow diagram, starting with the elementary control loops and adding the loop and process interaction links.

The control loops and elements must be identified with some code. This can be a simple start-to-finish sequential numbering system or a more elaborate multidigit group which identifies the main process, the subprocess, signal format, and so on. Derivation of a coding system of this form must be approached with caution, as it is very easy to end up with a system which is too unwieldy to be practical.

A completed and proven P&ID is the basis for the specification of the instrumentation and control system and is an essential element in the detailed design of the plant, since it has an effect on such items as the electrical wiring layout and the physical placement of sensors. It is the controlling document in the derivation of the process computer program and is, from the instrumentation engineer's point of view, one of the most essential documents connected with the design and operation of the plant. Typical P&I diagrams are shown in Figs. 14.10 and 14.11.

Plant processes

Raw water. Raw-water flow rate is a major variable in plant control because it can be used to pace downstream unit processes (feedforward). Monitoring and control of raw-water pumping can include scheduling and minimizing of pump starts in order to reduce peak electrical demands. Table 14.3 shows many of the common parameters associated with raw-water pumping and other operations.

The list of parameters given in Table 14.3 is not intended to be all-inclusive. Many others can be monitored and controlled. The design engineer should make a detailed analysis of what data to collect and which parameters to control.

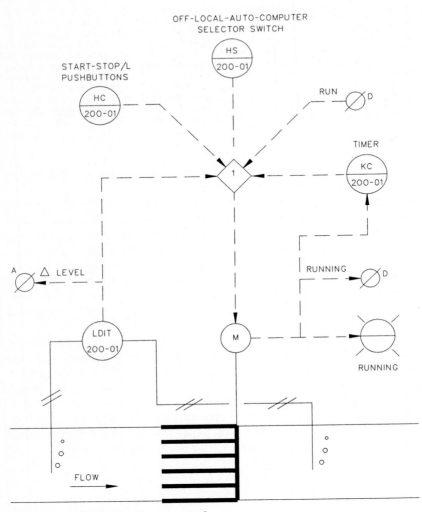

Figure 14.10   P&ID of bar screen control.

Flash mixing.   Parameters to be monitored and controlled in the flash-mixing process will depend upon plant hydraulics, type of downstream treatment processes, and other factors. For example, if flash mixing is to be conducted in a chamber which has a short detention time, there is much more danger of hydraulic overflow than with a clarifier or other long-detention-time basin. This means that instrumentation to monitor and control the water level in a flash-mix chamber must have very rapid response in its ability to control flow. Chemical feed control is generally flow-paced.

Control algorithms can be used to calculate a coagulant dosage (for

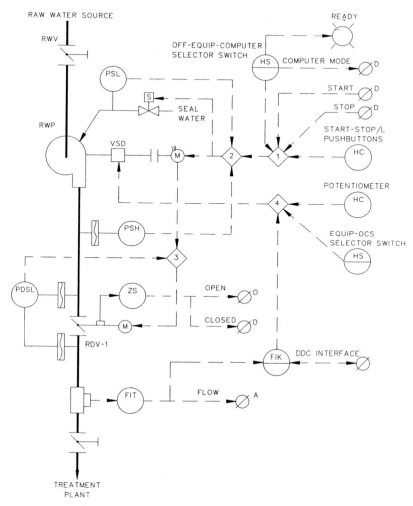

Figure 14.11 P&ID of raw-water pumping.

instance) which will be a function of raw-water pH, turbidity, temperature, or some combination of these and other parameters.

Flocculation. If flocculation is carried out in a tank which is hydraulically separated from sedimentation, water level monitoring will be necessary to maintain hydraulic balance through the plant. Speed of flocculators can be monitored and controlled as a variable.

Settling. Level instrumentation used during the settling process basically serves the same purpose as that used during flocculation. In addition, sludge-density detectors and controls can be used for auto-

TABLE 14.3 Raw Water

Class of parameter	Parameter	Parameters monitored or controlled		Comment
		Measure	Control	
Composition	Conductivity	X		For softening plants
	pH	X		
	Turbidity	X		
	Temperature	X		
	Disinfectant (prior to treatment)	X	X	
Physical	Flow rate	X	X	
	Pump discharge head	X	X	May or may not be controlled
	Pump suction head	X		
Mechanical	Pump speed(s)	X	X	
	Pump status	X	X	
	Valve status	X	X	
	Drive motor status	X		Alarms and auto-shutdown of system can be included
Efficiency	Power supply status	X		
	Electric power usage	X	X	May be easily controlled with digital algorithms
	Electric power peak demand	X	X	
Chemical	Addition of disinfectant or other chemical	X	X	

matic sludge drawoff, giving improved basin operation. A slow-acting controlled element should be used to keep disturbance of the solids to a minimum.

Solids-contact clarifiers require more gradual flow-rate changes than gravity clarifiers. This factor should be considered when designing the flow-rate control system. Sludge-blanket level detectors can also be used.

Filtration. The filtration portion of any modern plant requires the most carefully designed instrumentation and control applications. While the key variables encountered are effluent rate of flow and loss of head, it is important that the total operating concept designed into the filter determine the degree, type, and mode of instrumentation applied. Three basic operating philosophies can be considered in the instrumentation design analysis for a filter.

1. *Manual operation.* Control of all major valves is accomplished using individual switch action. Effluent rate is directly controlled from an operating console. All filter operations—filtering drawdown, surface and backwash, rewash, and return to line—are operator directed.

2. *Manual-sequenced operation.* Valve control has been designed into a single manually operated programming switch. Effluent rate is controlled in a closed loop, with the rate set at the control panel or console. Filter operations require operator direction but less rigid supervision.

3. *Automatic operation.* Control of all operations is on an automatic programmed basis.

Measuring effluent or interface turbidity during backwashing with measurement of bed expansion for each filter allows determination of the completeness of the wash cycle.[6] Pilot filter effluent can be monitored for high turbidity.

There are four basic systems for control of filter rate of flow that are applicable to municipal water treatment:

Constant rate

Constant level

Declining rate

Constant level, variable declining rate

These systems are detailed in the Filtration chapter.

Details of the control instrumentation are discussed by Shinsky[7] as well as in manufacturers' literature.

In all control strategies, filter flow-rate changes must be made gradually to avoid the surges which can occur when one filter is taken out of service for backwashing and the remaining filters must take up the slack. Filter backwashing can be controlled by systems ranging from fully manual to total computer control, including control of each individual filter by a microcomputer.

Wash water and clearwell storage. Level instrumentation with high- and low-level alarm functions is necessary when wash-water storage tanks are used to provide wash water to the filter by gravity. Control of the wash-water rate of flow can be accomplished by the use of a master control valve in the main supply line or by individual valves at each filter.

Instrumentation and control applied to the clearwell can serve many important functions and is an important factor in maintaining balanced plant operation. Level control can act as a a master set point or rate adjustment for the pacing of filters, thereby maintaining a balance between filtering and pumping to the distribution system. Each plant will have a different hydraulic relationship between clearwell levels, rates of increase for filter flow rates, and raw-water pumping rates, which must be considered by the design engineer.

Quality determinations are, of course, mandatory. In lieu of sampling and laboratory analysis, the use of continuous measurements enables quality data to play the dual roles of recording a specific value and controlling it within established limits. For example, disinfectant residual measurement can act as a set point adjustment for control systems; turbidity checks can aid filter performance and make backwash programming more effective; pH and polarization meters can be critical in developing application procedures for posttreatment chemicals, including corrosion inhibitors.

Softening and ion exchange. The softening portion of a water treatment plant can make use of the quality instrumentation and control. In addition, an automatic hardness titrator and recorder installed in the filter effluent will provide important performance data.

Chlorides can be measured by a conductivity sensor. This is an important measurement in an ion-exchange treatment process because excessive chlorides must be prevented from entering the distribution system. Conductivity sensors in the ion-exchange medium can be used to indicate the need for ion-exchange bed recharge.

Maintenance and training. For a process control system to be effective, it has to be implicitly trusted by the operators. All too often, a system is designed and installed, only to be bypassed little by little when it proves to be incapable of fulfilling expectations. When such cases are investigated, it is often found that the fault lies not with the system but with failure of the designer, the engineer, and the operator to communicate with one another and to understand the scope and limitations of the system. The answer to this is to train everyone concerned and to make sure that effective channels of communication are established.

Once a system is operating, a scheme of preventive maintenance should be set up and the technicians concerned should be trained in the overhaul and adjustment of the instruments and controls. Most major instrument manufacturers have training schools, and local community colleges offer courses oriented toward the instrument technician. It is recommended that both operating and maintenance training be regarded as a necessary part of the plant process control design.

Costs and benefits

Throughout the design process it is desirable to maintain a comparative analysis of the costs incurred and the benefits obtained. Although it is well established that automation is cost-effective, a point will be reached where the advantages are overwhelmed by the price. Each design case must be treated on its own merits. Harrison[8] gives a checklist of factors to be considered, while Barnes et al.[9] details the analysis of a typical installation.

A look to the future

Making definite statements about future trends is a dangerous practice and one which, as often as not, leads to frustration. Therefore, what follows should be regarded not so much as an exposition of what *will* happen, as some thoughts on what *could* happen in the field of water treatment process control.

The one sequence of events whose occurrence is highly probable starts with a radical increase in mandatory potable water quality standards, complete with enforcement legislation. It continues with a reassessment of treatment requirements, processes, energy efficiencies, and control philosophies, and culminates in the evolution of more sophisticated continuous process control systems. It is practically certain that the systems will be computer-oriented with a broadening role for the user-friendly microcomputer. What is much more speculative is the scope and nature of the additions.

One of the areas in which major advances are possible is continuous on-line chemical monitoring. Although many parameters are now measured, the increase in quality requirements will make it necessary to keep constant watch over the presence of other biological, organic, and inorganic contaminants, some in trace quantities. This need will trigger the emergence of sensing systems from the current intermittent laboratory environment to the process stream. It is, of course, not possible at this stage to predict either the nature or the requirements of the measurements, but it seems probable that many of them will be indirect, that is, they will be derived from other independent data.

The water treatment industry is still digesting the advent and implications of the process computer. As its acceptance increases through microcomputer applications, the technology inherent in the medium- and large-scale central computer in the data acquisition and processing fields will expand. Packaged software will become more relevant to water treatment process control. Competition among hardware and software suppliers will continue to improve the capability and capacity of microcomputers as costs decrease.

It may well be that the trend toward distributed computer control systems will penetrate so far up the data stream as to become virtually integral with the primary elements. The implication in this is that the data signals will tend more and more toward a digital format.

As regards the primary sensors, there will be an increase in the use of noncontacting and indirect devices. These will use ultrasonic, laser, nuclear, and electromagnetic techniques and will be more stable and less environmentally sensitive than those now in use. The demand for on-line chemical monitoring will lead to the development of such devices as laser-powered spectrophotometers, continuous gas chromatographs, and nuclear resonance chambers.

One of the big problems currently facing computer-oriented process control systems is data transmission quality and security. Techniques now used are almost exclusively electronic and consequently suffer from all the problems of noise, common mode, and distortion associated with such systems.

With the general use of digital data formats, it will be possible to use photonic techniques which will be totally unaffected by extraneous electromagnetic environments and will have almost total security.

It may seem at first sight that much of the above is fantasy. Remember, however, that a lot of the hardware has already been proven in service, and most of the rest is even now in an advanced state of development. In answer to the argument that it has not been proven in water utility service, it should be pointed out that its proving grounds have involved far harsher environments than would ever be experienced in a treatment plant—such places as deep-sea mining vessels, offshore oil drilling rigs, planetary probes, and so on. Fiber optics have been demonstrated over several miles, infrared lasers have replaced microwaves, and solar-generated power operates irrigation systems.

Regardless of any predictions, the advance of automation and instrumentation in the water treatment industry will ultimately depend on nonmaterial factors. The most important of these are:

Recognition of the critical importance of process control

Recognition of instrumentation as a technological discipline in its own right

Willingness of plant owners to be pioneers

Imagination of the plant design and operating engineers

References

1. Instrument Society of America, Standard S5.1, "Instrumentation Symbols and Identification," ISA, Research Triangle Park, N.C., 1984.
2. *Ibid.*, Standard S51.5, "Process Instrumentation Terminology," ISA, Research Triangle Park, N.C., 1979.
3. C. D. Johnson, *Process Control Instrumentation Technology*, Wiley, New York, 1977.
4. A. W. Manning, "Digital Control of Water Treatment Plants and Distribution Systems," *Proc. AWWA Seminar—Water Plant Instrumentation and Automation*, No. 20143, June 1976.
5. B. W. Lawler, "Instrument Diagramming for the Water Industry: A Committee Update," *Journal AWWA*, vol. 70, no. 4, 1978, p. 209.
6. W. J. Stephenson, "Multi-media Filters and Control," *Proc. AWWA Seminar—Water Plant Instrumentation and Automation,* no. 20143, June 1976.
7. F. G. Shinsky, "Process Control Strategies Combining Digital and Analog Systems," *Proc. AWWA Seminar—Water Plant Instrumentation and Automation,* no. 20143, June 1976.
8. T. J. Harrison, *Minicomputers in Industrial Control,* Instrument Society of America, Research Triangle Park, N.C., 1978.
9. S. Barnes, R. Graupman, and C. Moore, "Selection of a Digital Control System for the Parsons Avenue Water Plant," *Instrument Society of America National Conference,* no. 714, 1978.

Trace Organics

Introduction

Aesthetic problems of taste, odor, and color are recognized effects of organics that occur naturally in very small or trace concentrations in drinking water. In addition, the use of man-made (synthetic) organics is rapidly expanding, and as toxicological and epidemiological evidence mounts, controlling these compounds in drinking water is becoming increasingly important.

Trace organics may enter a water supply from one or several of the following sources: intentional or accidental wastewater discharges, rainfall and direct or indirect runoff, chemical spills, and air transport. The materials used to treat, store, and distribute water, such as pipe liners, reservoir liners, and joint solvents, can sometimes be the source of organic contamination. Petroleum distillates that have percolated into soil can weaken and sometimes penetrate the walls of plastic pipe, thus contaminating the water being conveyed. Certain halogenated organics are created or introduced by the chlorination process in water treatment. For these reasons, any design for controlling trace organics should assess both treatment and nontreatment techniques. The factors included in water supply source management and protection of finished drinking water will be mentioned, but not discussed in as much detail as the processes designed to prevent, remove, or reduce trace organic concentrations.

Definitions

With the exception of a few customary exclusions (e.g., cyanides and carbonates), organics are chemical compounds containing the element carbon. Symons[1] suggested five general categories for grouping organics of interest in water treatment. They are:

Class I: Organic compounds that cause odor problems (geosmin, 2-methylisoborneol, and so forth).

Class II: Synthetic organic chemicals (several hundred have been identified in drinking water).[2]

Class III: Precursors that react with disinfectants to produce "disinfection byproducts" (acetone, resorcinol, humic and fulvic acids). These are measured indirectly by trihalomethane formation potential analysis.

Class IV: Disinfection by-products (trihalomethanes plus other halogenated organics produced by the reaction of disinfectants such as chlorine with Class III organics).

Class V: Natural (non-Class II) organic compounds not suspected of being of toxicological importance.

Occurrence and measurement

In general, surface water is more prone to contamination by a variety of trace organics than is groundwater. Groundwater in several locations across the United States has, however, become contaminated by solvents such as trichloroethylene, tetrachloroethylene, and 1,1,1-trichloroethane. Likely sources of this contamination are leaking storage tanks, improper or careless waste disposal, inappropriate pump bearing lubricants, and septic tank degreasers. Additionally, in some farming areas pesticides such as 1,2-dibromo-3-chloropropane (DBCP) and 1,2-dibromoethane (EDB) have been detected in deep wells, indicating that organics can travel great distances within an aquifer or in some cases may possibly be backsiphoned into a well as a result of a cross connection.

Total organics in drinking water, or more accurately the carbon content, can be measured with sensitive instruments. This measurement is usually referred to as total organic carbon (TOC). TOC provides general, but useful, quality information. For example, in one study of 39 U.S. water utilities, the TOC concentrations in finished water ranged from less than 0.5 mg/L to 12.2 mg/L, with a median concentration of 1.5 mg/L.[3] Some highly colored ground- or surface water can have a TOC as high as 20 to 30 mg/L. This parameter, although general, can sometimes be correlated with disinfectant demand as well as with concentration of certain specific organics. The presence of many organic pollutants can be detected by taste, odor, or color. Several analytical techniques (total organic carbon; organic halogen; carbon-chloroform extract; closed-loop stripping; ultraviolet absorbance; fluorescence; and gas-thin-layer, high-performance liquid, or paper chromatography) exist for the detection of organic compounds. Detectors such as the mass spectrometer, and ancillary computer capabilities, have greatly improved the ability to identify specific organic compounds, but *no single test gives a complete organic analysis.*

Total organic carbon concentrations are usually reported in milligrams per liter (mg/L) or parts per million (ppm), whereas specific organics are generally reported in micrograms per liter (μg/L) or parts per billion (ppb) [or even nanograms per liter (ng/L) or parts per trillion (ppt)]. This exemplifies the multitude of specific organics comprised in TOC.

Overview of Pretreatment Options

The importance of controlling the quality of water selected for treatment cannot be overemphasized. Quality management of a surface source may include multiple ports on intakes (see Chaps. 3 and 9). This allows some flexibility in selecting raw water to maintain high-quality drinking water. Legislated constraints such as limited public access to watersheds, controlled recreation, and zoning all have some positive effect on water quality. Discharge permits issued to industries give an indication as to the type, quantity, and frequency of occurrence of Class II organics above the intake. Improvements in analytical procedures, particularly chromatographic analyses, allow monitoring for specific organic contaminants; this alone can have a favorable effect on water quality. The following example illustrates how this technique is being used by the Ohio River Valley Water Sanitation Commission (ORSANCO). Water quality monitoring stations along the Ohio River can detect minute concentrations of certain synthetic organics. Detection of these pollutants alerts the analyst to potential problems, and warnings are transmitted to water utilities downstream. Knowing river flow conditions, water purveyors can close their intakes until the contaminant passes.

Persistent contamination in surface water should be traced to the source and stopped. Isolating the source of groundwater contamination is more difficult and often impractical because of hydrogeological conditions. To further complicate the investigation, some solvents undergo biological or abiotic transformations within the soil; thus, the organic detected in the well water may be different from what was originally discharged or spilled.

Relying totally on monitoring to control organic contaminants in drinking water, however, has two obvious shortcomings. First, even the most sophisticated analytical procedures can detect only a small fraction of the potential number of organics present. Second, if the contamination in the source persists, the utility must have a vast amount of offstream storage or an alternative source. Wintertime organic concentrations can be unusually high because an ice cover can prevent trace organics from volatilizing to the atmosphere or degrading through biological action. Because of limitations on nontreatment controls, a second barrier, treatment, is necessary at utilities that are vulnerable to synthetic organics.

Treatment Options for Controlling Trace Organics

Source control

The option of artificial destratification has been shown to improve water quality in lakes and reservoirs and prevent the occurrence of nuisance organisms. This can lessen problems from Class I and Class II organics. Details of this process are covered in *Water Quality Behavior in Reservoirs.*[4] The following discussion of other treatment options is intended to supplement the previous chapters in this book on process design.

Precipitation and filtration

The addition of a metal coagulant for the removal of particulates or raising the pH for removal of calcium and magnesium (i.e., softening) results in the removal of some organic matter. This can be measured both by the reduction in the organic carbon concentration (up to 50 percent in some water) and by color. Although it is partially effective for the removal of disinfection by-product precursors (Class III organics) and some specific organics, such as polychlorinated biphenyls (PCB), which are generally associated with particulates, this process does little to remove the other classes of organic compounds that are in true solution. For some water, iron salts such as ferric sulfate and ferric chloride are more effective than aluminum sulfate (alum) for removing TOC, and laboratory investigations using different coagulants are warranted to optimize the removal of both turbidity and trace organics by precipitation.

Direct filtration

This process is effective for turbidity and color removal and shows some effectiveness for removing Class III organics. Polyelectrolytes or polymers used as coagulant or filter aids are complex organics, and some are haloform precursors. The use of polymers should be encouraged so that sludge production will be minimized; however, any proposed use of treatment aids should include some analysis for trihalomethane formation potential in addition to evaluating the product for

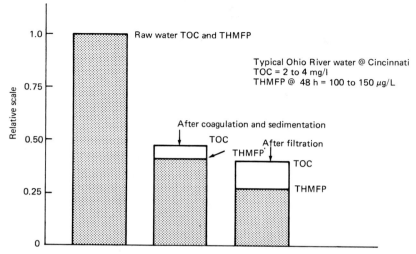

Figure 15.1 Relative organic carbon and trihalomethane precursor removal during water treatment.

particulate removal. Figure 15.1 shows the relative amounts of organic carbon and certain Class IV organics removed by conventional treatment of one specific water.

Aeration

The fundamentals of aeration are discussed in detail in Chap. 4. The advantage of aeration as an organics removal process is that the contaminants are actually removed from the water without the formation of by-products. The disadvantages are that the contaminants are transferred to the air phase, possibly causing another problem, and that only organic substances with certain characteristics are removable even with excessive quantities of air.

Several factors influence the effectiveness of aeration for stripping organic compounds from water. Among these are contact time, ratio of air to water, water temperature, vapor pressure, and solubility of the contaminant(s). The last two variables can be useful for estimating the feasibility of aeration. To illustrate, Henry's law states that when dissolved, the partial pressure of a compound varies directly with its concentration in the liquid phase.

$$P = C \qquad (15.1)$$

where P = partial pressure
$\quad C$ = concentration in the liquid phase

Therefore

$$P = HC \qquad (15.2)$$

where H = Henry's law coefficient

Rearranging,

$$H = \frac{P}{C} \qquad (15.3)$$

The units used for Henry's coefficient are atm (m^3 water/m^3 air), and all air volume units are at standard temperature (273 K) and pressure (1 atm). The units used to express Henry's coefficient differ among professional disciplines. For example, the chemical engineering discipline generally expresses both air- and liquid-phase contaminant concentrations as mole fractions. In this form, the units for Henry's coefficient become atm (mole water/mole air). In physical chemistry, the air-phase concentration is generally expressed as partial pressure of the contaminant and the liquid-phase concentration as molar concentration, resulting in units for Henry's coefficient. The conversion factors are as follows:

Multiply	By	To obtain
atm (mole/mole)	0.000804	atm (m^3/m^3)
atm (L/m)	0.0445	atm (m^3/m^3)

Henry's coefficient can be determined experimentally by placing a volume of contaminated water in a partially filled, closed container and allowing the contaminant concentration to come to equilibrium with the air and water phases. Alternatively, as an approximation, Henry's coefficient can be estimated by dividing vapor pressure solubility and converting to the appropriate units.

$$H = \frac{P}{S} \times \frac{M \times 1000 \text{ mg/g}}{760 \text{ mm Hg/atm} \times 22.4 \text{ L/}M} \times \frac{\text{atm air mole}}{\text{atm mole air}} \qquad (15.4)$$

where H = Henry's coefficient, atm (m^3 water/m^3 air)
$\quad\;\; P$ = vapor pressure, mm Hg
$\quad\;\; S$ = solubility, mg/L
$\quad\;\; M$ = molecular weight, g/mole

This gives an estimate for Henry's coefficient at the temperature of the vapor pressure and solubility measurements. However, it is necessary to be aware that site-specific Henry's coefficients may be significantly lower than those estimated by vapor pressure and solubility. Estimated Henry's coefficients should be used only in preliminary evaluations, feasibility studies, preparation for field evaluations, and so on. Full-scale equipment should be based on site-specific Henry's coefficients.

Presented in Table 15.1 are estimated Henry's coefficients that were used to estimate the size and cost of the equipment needed to remove various compounds from contaminated water supplies. The equipment size and cost estimates were prepared to support Safe Drinking Water Act regulations.[5]

The reciprocal of H $(1/H)$ is called the *partition coefficient*. This parameter gives the theoretical minimum air-to-water ratio for removing a volatile compound.[6]

The efficiency of aeration increases as the Henry's coefficient increases (see Fig. 15.2); therefore, it is logical to consider aeration for treating water contaminated by low-molecular-weight volatile organ-

TABLE 15.1 **Estimated Henry's Coefficient at 12°C**

Compound	Henry's coefficient (1)		
	atm (m^3/m^3)	atm (mol/mol)	
Alachlor	0.0043	5	(3)
Benzene	0.060	80	(2)
Carbon tetrachloride	0.21	260	(3)
Chlorobenzene	0.06	75	(2)
Dibromochloropropane	0.005	6	(3)
o-Dichlorobenzene	0.031	40	(2)
1,2-Dichloroethane	0.027	34	(2)
1,1-Dichloroethylene	0.40	500	(2)
cis-1,2-Dichloroethylene	0.067	80	(2)
trans-1,2-Dichloroethylene	0.10	130	(3)
1,2-Dichloropropane	0.043	50	(2)
Ethylbenzene	0.14	180	(3)
Ethylene dibromide	0.014	17	(2)
Heptachlor	0.06	70	(3)
PCB	0.01	12	(3)
Styrene	0.05	60	(3)
Tetrachloroethylene	0.22	280	(2)
Toluene	0.13	160	(2)
Toxaphene	0.11	140	(3)
1,1,1-Trichloroethane	0.23	290	(2)
Trichloroethylene	0.125	155	(2)
Vinyl chloride	2.4	3000	(2)
m-Xylene	0.11	140	(2)
o-Xylene	0.10	130	(2)
p-Xylene	0.12	150	(2)

Note: (1) These estimated Henry's coefficients were used to estimate equipment size and cost to remove the compounds from contaminated water supplies. The estimates were prepared to support Safe Drinking Water Act regulations.[7] (2) Henry's coefficient based on field evaluation. The indicated value gave the best fit between predicted and observed performance. (3) Henry's coefficient based on vapor pressure and solubility, with a safety factor of 2 to account for temperature and field effects.

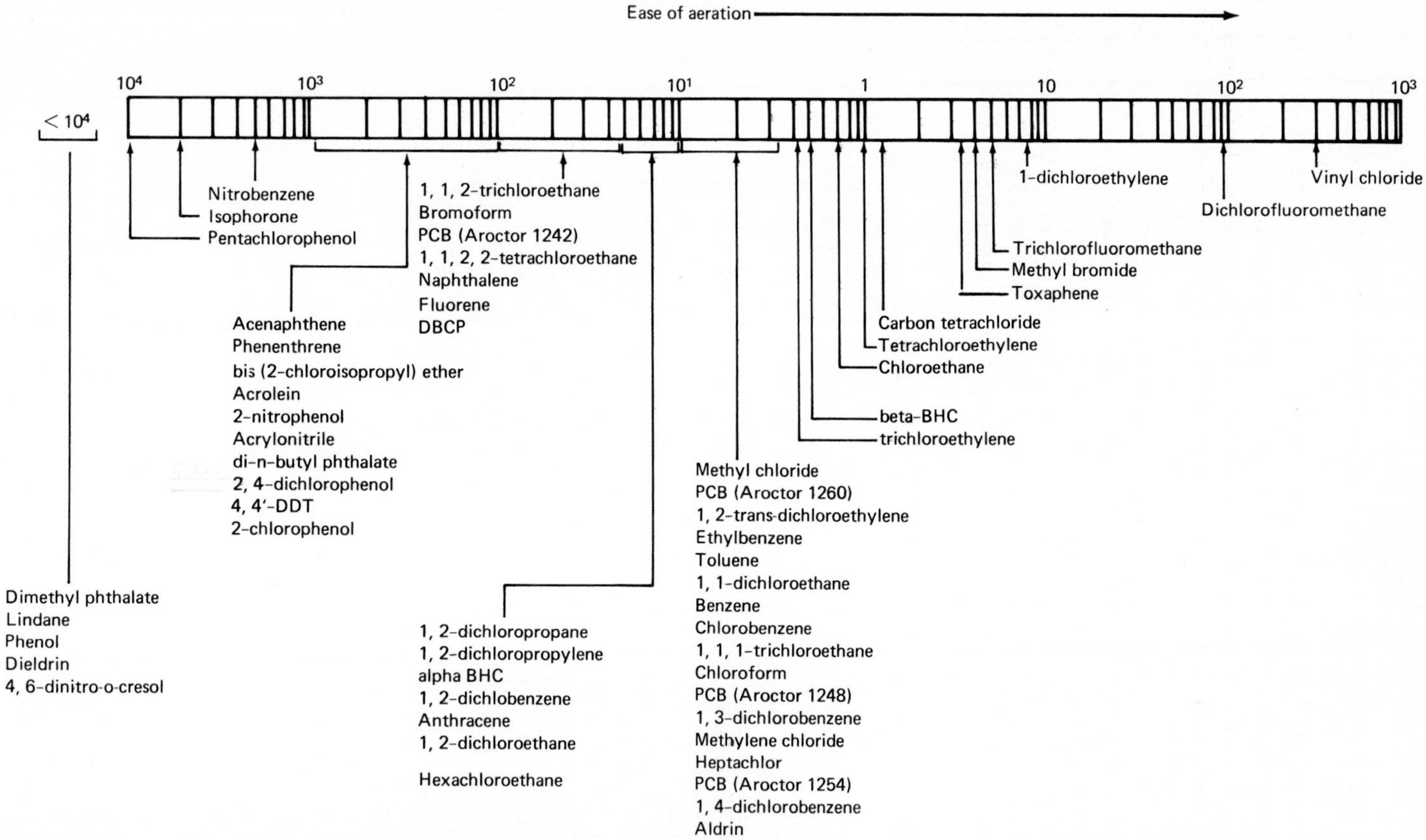

Figure 15.2 Henry's coefficients for selected organics.

ics, such as vinyl chloride, tri- and tetrachloroethylene, and 1,1,1-trichloroethane. Of the aeration options available (diffused air, spray, mechanical aerators, or packed towers), packed towers are most widely used.[7]

Packed-tower aeration theory.   A schematic drawing of a packed-tower aerator is shown in Fig. 15.3. The object is to contact a small volume of organic-contaminated water with a large volume of contaminant-free air. Mass transfer theory in a packed column has been well developed in the chemical engineering literature for processes in chemical manufacturing that exhibit a wide range of concentrations, viscosities, and specific gravities. In contrast, air stripping of trace concentrations of volatile organic compounds from water allows the following assumptions that simplify the general theory.

1. Liquid and air volumes do not change as a result of organic compound between air and water phases.

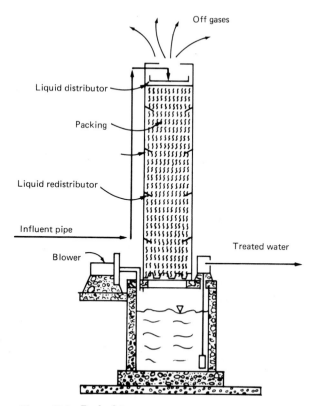

Figure 15.3   Packed-tower aerator.

2. Organic compound equilibrium concentration can be described using Henry's law.

3. Influent air does not contain organic contaminants.

A general equation relating packing height to mass transfer coefficient, removal efficiency, Henry's coefficient, air loading, and liquid loading can be found in an excellent article by Kavanaugh and Trussell.[8]

$$Zt = \frac{L}{KLa} \times \frac{R}{R-1} \times \ln \frac{(Xt/Xb) \times (R-1) + 1}{R} \qquad (15.5)$$

where Zt = packing height, m
$\quad L$ = liquid loading, $m^3/(m^2 \cdot s)$
$\quad KLa$ = mass transfer coefficient, 1/s
$\quad Xt$ = top of packing contaminant concentration, $\mu g/L$
$\quad R$ = stripping factor (dimensionless)

$$R = \frac{G}{L} \times \frac{H}{Pt} \qquad (15.6)$$

where G = air loading, $m^3/(m^2 \cdot s)$
$\quad H$ = Henry's coefficient, atm $\cdot m^3$ water/m^3 air
$\quad Pt$ = atmospheric pressure, atm

Process design criteria

When designing a packed-column aeration system, the following parameters must be known:

1. Total water flow

2. Water temperature

3. Chemical properties of organic contaminant

4. Required organic-contaminant removal efficiency

From this general information and a few system design parameters assumed or obtained from the literature, the size of an aeration system can be estimated. Additional system design parameters include safety factors and engineering economic design parameters. Because iron and manganese and high background concentrations of heterotrophic plate count can foul an aerator, the designer needs inorganic and microbiological data as well as organic characterization of the water to be aerated.

The preliminary design procedure utilizes the following steps. An example illustrating these steps is shown in Ref. 9.

Step 1: Determine system requirements: These include the amount of water to be treated, the treatment efficiency required, and the characteristics of the contaminants to be treated.

Step 2: Select packing material: Many different packing materials are available in today's market, and the properties of the packing are available from packing material vendors.

Step 3: Obtain properties of air and water: The required properties of air and water are molecular weight, density, and viscosity at the temperatures to be encountered with treatment.

Step 4: Estimate properties of the organic contaminants: Diffusion coefficients of the organic contaminants through both air and water are required for estimation of the mass transfer coefficient. The diffusion coefficients can be estimated using an empirical correlation developed by Wilke and Chang and recommended by Treybal.[10] Henry's coefficient for the organic contaminant(s) should be adjusted by a safety factor. The factor 1.2 is commonly used to reduce the Henry's coefficient.

Step 5: Compute air-to-water ratio: The air-to-water ratio is computed from Henry's law constant and the stripping factor by rearranging Eq. (15.6) and including the safety factor *Sf*.

$$\text{Air-to-water ratio} = \frac{R \times Pt}{H/Sf} \qquad (15.7)$$

R, the stripping factor, ranges from 2 to 6 in typical designs.

Step 6: Estimate air and liquid loadings: The air and liquid loadings are estimated from the air-to-water ratio and the air pressure drop gradient. As air flows up through a bed of packing material, air pressure loss will occur. The air pressure loss is related to air loading, liquid loading, and the friction factor of the packing material. This relationship between the air pressure drop gradient and the above three parameters is generally available from packing material vendors.

Step 7: Estimate mass transfer coefficient: The liquid- and gas-phase mass transfer coefficients are estimated using a correlation developed by Onda et al. and presented in *Chemical Engineers' Handbook*.[11] The Onda correlation estimates, separately, the liquid-phase mass transfer coefficient, the gas-phase mass transfer coefficient, and the wetted surface area.

Step 8: Estimate equipment size: The equipment size can now be estimated using Eq. (15.5) and the information obtained in steps 1 through 7. Although sizes vary, packed towers are typically 7 to 8 m in height and less than 5 m in diameter.

It should be noted that a Henry's coefficient for an organic compound in contaminated water assumed using data from clean water and a mass transfer coefficient assumed from an empirical correlation are only estimates. Both the Henry's coefficient and the mass transfer coefficient should be verified at the field site using the actual water and a pilot system. Given a design objective, this preliminary design procedure can be used to select a range of air and liquid loadings for evaluation. Generally, the loading range should be selected using stripping factors and air pressure drop gradients ranging from 2 to 6 and 50 to 200 N/m^2, respectively. After Henry's coefficient and the mass transfer coefficients are obtained from pilot data, full-scale equipment size can be determined for a number of different air and liquid loading combinations. The most economical size can then be selected from the range of loadings.

Generally, good agreement between site-specific and predicted mass transfer coefficients has been obtained using the Onda correlation; however, significant deviations have occasionally been observed. Also, aeration is not without secondary environmental effects. In addition to organics being transferred from the water into the air (which may require off-gas control), the aerated water needs to be properly disinfected and assessed for corrosivity.

Adsorption

The effectiveness of adsorption within a water treatment plant is influenced by the temperature and pH of the water, but adsorption also depends on:

- Characteristics and concentrations of adsorbents and adsorbates
- Contact or residence time
- Competition for available adsorption sites

For controlling organics, the adsorbent can be passed through the water, or the water can be passed through the adsorbent. In practice, powdered activated carbon and granular activated carbon are the most common examples of each respective method.

Granular activated carbon.   A fixed-bed adsorber provides intimate contact between adsorbent and adsorbate. In effect, a small amount of adsorbate is in contact with a large amount of adsorbent, and this permits a granular activated carbon column to produce water containing very low concentrations of organic matter. The effective size and uniformity coefficient for granular activated carbon (see Table 15.2) allow it to be used as a filtering medium as well as an adsorbent. This mode of operation is generally referred to as sand replacement, as con-

TABLE 15.2 Properties of Granular Activated Carbon Produced in the United States*

	The Carborundum Company	Calgon Corporation	NICIT Hydrodarco®	NICIT Hydrodarco®	Witco Chemical
Product name	GAC 40	Filtrasorb® F-400	HD-1030	83 Plus	Witcarb® 950
Base material	Western bituminous coal	Bituminous coal	Lignite	Bituminous coal	Petroleum coke
U.S. standard sieve size	12 × 40	12 × 40	10 × 30	8 × 30	12 × 40
Effective size, mm	0.6	0.8–0.9	0.8–0.9	0.8–0.9	0.8–0.9
Uniformity coefficient	≤ 1.9	≤ 1.9	≤ 1.7	≤ 1.9	≤ 1.7
Apparent (or vibrating feed) density, g/cm^3	0.47	0.4–0.5	0.40–0.50	0.47	0.46–0.53
Washed density, lb/ft^3	25	25	23.5	26	29–33
Iodine number, mg/g	1050	1050	600	900	1050
Surface area, m^2/g	1000–1100	1050	650	1000	1000
Available in:	60-lb bags, bulk	60-lb bags, bulk	40-lb bags, bulk	50-lb bags, bulk	50-lb bags, 200-lb drums, hopper trucks, tote bins

*"AWWA Standard for Granular Activated Carbon" (AWWA B604-74, *Journal AWWA*, vol. 66, no. 11, p. 672) provides minimum specifications on the properties of granular activated carbon used as an adsorption medium for treating drinking water.

trasted with post-filter adsorption, in which separate contactors are constructed following the granular media filters.

The sand-replacement mode is common in the United States for taste and odor control because granular activated carbon is as effective as sand as a filtration medium. Because it is a single medium, granular activated carbon provides surface rather than depth filtration; consequently, filter runs are likely to be shorter than dual-media filter runs, but similar to those for sand filters.

One problem with the sand-replacement mode in existing filter plants is that the size of the filter box is fixed, thus limiting flexibility in contact times and activated carbon handling. A graded gravel base (or an equivalent means of providing a uniformly distributed backwash) along with a surface scrubber (or air scourer) are necessary for proper filter cleansing (see Chap. 7). Some state regulatory agencies require that 6 to 12 in (15 to 30 cm) of sand be left in the bottom of the filter to prevent floc penetration. Other states, however, believe that this is an unnecessary safeguard, as long as at least 24 in of granular activated carbon with an effective size of between 0.5 and 0.9 mm and a uniformity coefficient of 1.9 or less is used.

The filter box should have freeboard adequate for 30 to 50 percent bed expansion during backwash. Activated carbon, when wetted, can become very corrosive, so construction materials should be concrete, 316 stainless steel (304 stainless steel can corrode in the presence of activated carbon), or materials coated with paints or liners that have been approved by the appropriate water supply regulatory agency. If concrete is used, the reinforcing steel should be covered by at least 2 in (5 cm) of concrete. Also vulnerable to corrosion are valves, pipes, pumps, backwash launders, surface scrubbers, and storage bins that are directly in contact with wet granular carbon. These must be protected.

Backwashing granular activated carbon is not difficult, but requires close operator attention. As with other granular media, a rise rate of 24 to 26 in/min (60 to 66 cm/min), equivalent to a backwash application rate of 14 to 16 gal/(min)(ft)^2 (35 to 90 m/h), has been successful for expanding the bed 30 to 50 percent. Abrupt increases in backwash rates or poor attention by the operator can cause attrition from abrasion and direct losses in the overflow troughs. Granular activated carbon is less dense than sand (1.4 g/cm^3 versus 2.6 g/cm^3), so backwash water should be applied slowly, then the rate gradually increased until the bed is expanded properly. The operator must be particularly careful to prevent the entire bed from lifting as a block and shearing off fixed appurtenances within the filter box. Surface scrubbing and attentive operation will help prevent mishaps.

When the granular activated carbon is first installed, as many as 10 backwashes may be necessary before the filter effluent is void of activated carbon fines. Membrane filters are useful for monitoring the decline of activated carbon particulates in the effluent. Some engineers believe that filtering the waste for a few minutes after backwashing will prevent building of activated carbon fines in the distribution system and thereby lessen potential bacteriological problems.

Separate adsorbers following filtration offer the most flexibility for handling granular activated carbon and for varying the adsorption conditions (e.g., contact time, upflow versus downflow, series or parallel operation). Post-filter adsorbers (or contactors, as they are sometimes called) are usually designed with an adsorbent depth-to-diameter ratio of 1.5 or more to effect good distribution of flow. The contactor should be designed to include backwashing, and some engineers recommend both water and air for this purpose. The bottom support may be a perforated plate or a flat plate of 316 stainless steel (with an inert coating for additional protection) with nozzles. Porous ceramic tiles covered with gravel and sand can be used, but separating the media might be a problem if the activated carbon has to be reactivated frequently. Regardless of the bottom type selected, care must be taken to ensure that the system is secure and can withstand the hydraulic forces from backwashing.

Reactivation

During use, the large surface area of the internal pore structure of granular activated carbon eventually becomes saturated with adsorbate. The adsorbent is then said to be spent, or exhausted, and must be either replaced or reactivated. If virgin activated carbon is available for replacement, the exhausted carbon may have some salvage value to either the activated carbon suppliers or an advanced wastewater treatment plant for reactivation and reuse. Disposal of the material by landfill is another alternative.

Although several factors must be considered, an economic analysis may show that reactivation is less expensive than replacement if the granular activated carbon is exhausted within 6 to 12 months. Reactivation is the process of removing adsorbed organics and restoring the adsorptive characteristics of the adsorbent. Often, the terms "reactivation" and "regeneration" are used interchangeably.

Granular activated carbon can be reactivated chemically or thermally. Biological reactivation (aside from that which may occur naturally within an adsorber) has been suggested, but is untried technology. Chemical (or solvent) reactivation is used in some industrial waste treatment schemes where recovery of the adsorbate is of concern, but it has had very limited applicability in water treatment. Thermal reactivation services are offered by suppliers of activated carbon; however, some state regulatory agencies will not permit off-site reactivation because the opportunity to mix activated carbon used in water and wastewater treatment exists. If reactivation is done on-site, a typical scheme would be as follows:

1. The exhausted granular carbon is backwashed and scoured with air.
2. The washed granular carbon is fed into a furnace and subjected to a controlled atmosphere of steam and oxygen at temperatures approaching 1000°C. Off gases must comply with local air quality requirements.
3. The reactivated carbon is quenched with water and hydraulically transported back to the contactor (or to storage).
4. Virgin activated carbon (makeup) is added to replace attrition losses.

The distance that exhausted or reactivated carbon has to be hydraulically transported should be as short, and the route as free of bends, as possible. Stainless steel (316 grade) is a suitable construction material where activated carbon is stored, and also where pipe bends cannot be avoided. For straight sections of pipe, however, polyvinyl chloride (PVC) or other synthetic materials are adequate. All piping should be easily accessible and have several cleanouts because clogging of the lines can and does occasionally occur. According to Strack,[12] the velocity of the water-carbon mixture should be between 5 and 10 fps (1.5 and 3 m/s) to minimize deposition and abrasion and wear. High water-to-activated-carbon ratios also help prevent attrition losses.

Types of furnaces available

Multiple hearth. The multiple-hearth or Herschoff furnace (see Fig. 15.4a) is the most popular unit for both activating and reactivating granular carbon. These generally have four to eight hearths, with drying occurring on the upper hearth. Rabble arms move the adsorbent alternately in and out across the hearth. Steam is introduced near the bottom of the furnace, and off gases are passed through a scrubber or an afterburner followed by a scrubber. This type of furnace was used in the water treatment plant in Nitro, W. Va., and examples are currently in use at the Wilne Treatment Works in Nottingham, U.K., and at a plant in Gothenburg, Sweden.

Rotary kiln. The rotary kiln consists of a cylindrical drum that is slightly inclined and rotated on its horizontal axis (see Fig. 15.4b). The speed of rotation determines the residence time for the adsorbent.

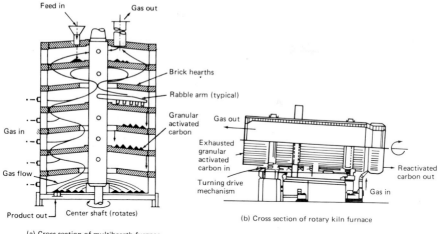

(a) Cross section of multihearth furnace

(b) Cross section of rotary kiln furnace

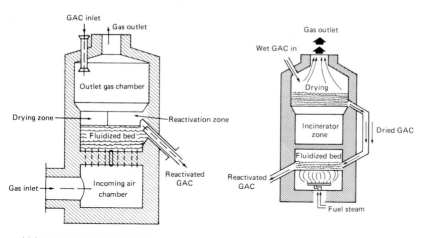

(c) Cross section of one-stage fluidized-bed furnace

(d) Cross section of two-stage fluidized-bed furnace

Figure 15.4 Furnaces available for reactivating granular carbon.

Exhausted carbon

Dryer

Off gas

Reactivated carbon

(e) Cross section fo fluidized-bed furnace
with external dryer

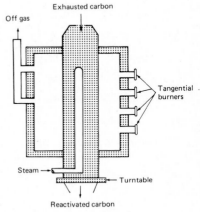

Exhausted carbon

Off gas

Tangential
burners

Steam →

Turntable

Reactivated carbon

(f) Cross section of indirect heated vertical
moving-bed furnace

Remote control panel

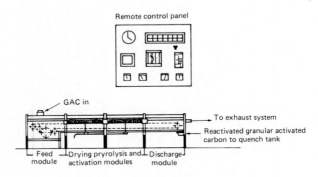

GAC in

To exhaust system

Reactivated granular activated
carbon to quench tank

Feed
module

Drying pryrolysis and
activation modules

Discharge
module

(g) Cross section of infra-red tunnel furnace

Figure 15.4   *(Continued)*

Fluidized bed.   Three variations of the fluid or fluidized bed furnace are available. Figure 15.4c shows a *one-stage* unit in which drying occurs near the inlet. This type of furnace is used at the Benrath Water Treatment Plant, Wuppertal, Federal Republic of Germany. Figure 15.4d shows a *two-stage* fluid bed. Here, drying is achieved by routing waste heat through the upper chamber. The Stadtwerke, Dusseldorf, Federal Republic of Germany, has a two-stage furnace, as do the water works serving Manchester, N.H., and Cincinnati, Ohio. The third type of fluid bed employs remote drying (see Fig. 15.4e); one example of this furnace is on site at the Zurich Waterworks, Zurich, Switzerland.

Indirect heated vertical moving bed.   Figure 15.4f shows a simplified schematic of a furnace in use in Japan. The exhausted granular carbon travels downward through the inner core and never directly contacts the tangential burners. Steam is introduced countercurrently and exits through ports (not shown in Fig. 15.4f) on the inner core. This type of furnace is sometimes called a shaft kiln.

Infrared tunnel furnace.   This unit is electric and, unlike the other furnaces, uses no external steam source. The activated carbon is transported on a conveyor belt through drying followed by an activation zone (see Fig. 15.4g). This type of furnace was used by the Passaic Valley Water Commission at their Little Falls, N.J., water filtration plants and the Jefferson Parrish, La., pilot water treatment plant to study on-site reactivation.

Steaming.   Steam alone is effective for removing certain halogenated organics from granular activated carbon and is being used in the soft drink industry to remove adsorbed trihalomethanes. Steam is applied at 1 gal/(min)(ft)^2 (2.4 m/h) condensate in an upflow fashion, and the process takes from 18 to 24 h (70 to 100 bed volumes).[13]

Monitors of reactivation efficiency

Iodine number and apparent density.   Several analyses can be used to determine furnace conditions for reactivating. The simplest and most economical tests are the iodine number and the apparent density. The iodine number, that is, the amount of $0.02N$ I_2 in milligrams adsorbed by 1 g of activated carbon at equilibrium, reportedly provides three general pieces of information: (1) it correlates well with the ability of the activated carbon to adsorb low-molecular-weight organics; (2) it relates to the distribution of pores with diameters down to 1 nm; and (3) the iodine number (neglecting units of measure) coincidentally compares closely with the surface area of the activated carbon. Typically, a granular activated carbon with a surface area of 1000 m^2/g will also have an iodine number of approximately 1000 mg/g (refer to Table 15.2).

The apparent density analysis is often performed by the furnace operators, as it is a rapid test and requires only a balance, a graduated cylinder, and some type of vibrator to assure a homogeneous mixture of the activated carbon. As an activated carbon becomes exhausted, the iodine number decreases and the apparent density increases. Several replicates of each of these tests are required to get a meaningful average value.

Pore-size distribution.   More complicated and therefore more expensive tests are required to determine surface area, pore volumes, and pore diameters on activated carbon. The test for pore size distribution usually involves a combination of nitrogen adsorption (measured by a porosimeter) for large pores. A good example of evaluating these process parameters is given in Ref. 14.

Adsorption isotherms.   Another means of comparing virgin and reactivated granular carbon is by examining their relative adsorptive capacities. Traditionally, this is done by pulverizing the granular carbon (95 percent $\leq$ 325 mesh), contacting it with some adsorbate (such as TOC, color, or a specific organic), and using the Freundlich isotherm plot to calculate the capacity. The Freundlich equation has the form:

$$\frac{X}{M} = KC_f^{1/n} \tag{15.8}$$

where X = amount of contaminant adsorbed (difference between initial and final concentrations)
M = weight of activated carbon
C_f = final concentration of contaminant
$1/n$ = the slope of the isotherm (from a log-log plot)
K = the intercept

Both K and $1/n$ are specific to the test conditions.

Figure 15.5 illustrates how virgin and reactivated carbon can be compared for relative efficiency from their TOC adsorption isotherms. For a residual TOC concentration of 0.3 mg/L, both adsorbents have a capacity of approximately 5 mg/g. The adsorption isotherm is a useful empirical approach to comparing adsorbents, but the results are *capacities at equilibrium* and subject to the test conditions. An adsorption isotherm does not give the rate of adsorption or the time to exhaustion or breakthrough. This must be determined in a dynamic system, and the prudent engineer conducts pilot-scale adsorption tests on the water to be treated.

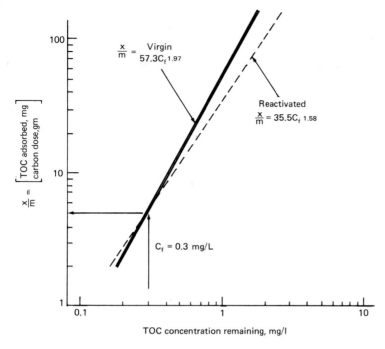

Figure 15.5 Comparison of TOC isotherms for virgin and reactivated granular carbon.

Pilot-scale adsorption studies

Whether designing a new water treatment plant or updating an old one to include adsorption, the engineer must conduct some pilot-plant studies. The purpose of this is to investigate the efficacy of a small, manageable system before expending large sums of money on a process design that may give marginal performance. Other chapters in this book contain sections describing studies that give guidance on determining optimum coagulant doses for particulate removal, disinfectant demands, filtration rates, and so forth. This section explains one approach to gathering similar design information on adsorption of trace organics.

Treatment efficiency varies with the organic character of the water, and because this differs between locations, experimentation must be done with the actual water, preferably on-site. At a minimum, pilot-scale columns are required to study adsorption. These columns should have an internal diameter of 1 in (2.5 cm) or more. This will minimize anomalous effects from column walls by maintaining a large ratio between the amount of adsorbent in a cross-sectional area to bacteria, floc particles, bubbles, and other things that cannot be scaled down. In studies in which water flow is less than 10 gpm (38 L/min), equipment should be constructed from stainless steel, Teflon$^{©}$, or glass whenever possible to minimize contamination from structural materials.

Two aspects of adsorption, the critical depth and the rate of contaminant movement, must be considered in adsorber design, whether it be pilot or modular scale. The critical depth (sometimes called the mass transfer zone) is the depth of adsorbent necessary to contain the contaminant wavefront. Once contained, the wavefront then moves through the remaining adsorbent until the contaminant breaks through. Eventually exhaustion results. A very simple illustration of the complicated chain of events is given in Fig. 15.6. The critical depth and rate of movement vary among specific organics and are influenced by the approach velocity, the type of adsorbent, and the competition for the adsorption sites.

In practice the approach velocity and the amount of adsorbent are often combined and expressed as contact time. The term "empty-bed contact time" (EBCT) is calculated by dividing the volume of media V

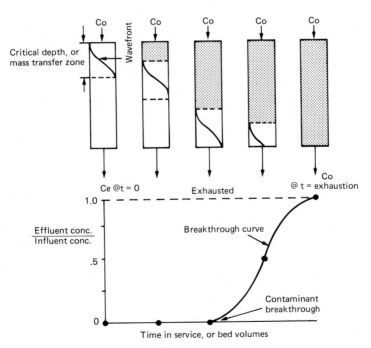

Figure 15.6 Simplified illustration of contaminant movement through a granular activated carbon column.

by the hydraulic loading Q (i.e., EBCT = V/Q). Some granular activated carbon contactors are designed with an EBCT as high as 40 min; however, most designs range from 17 to 20 min. Sometimes the term "apparent contact time" is used. This is the EBCT multiplied by the porosity of the adsorbent. A pilot-scale adsorption study should incorporate several empty-bed contact times so that an optimum can be selected. Examples of the effect of contact time are shown in Ref. 1.

Figure 15.7 shows a schematic of an experimental system that can be used to evaluate both the sand-replacement mode and the post-filtration adsorption mode simultaneously. Granular activated carbon is placed in one column to the depth allowable in the existing filter boxes at the water treatment plant. Approximately 6 in (15 cm) of graded gravel is placed in the bottom of the column as an aid in distributing backwash water. Some type of surface scrubbing (air or water scour) should be incorporated because when granular activated

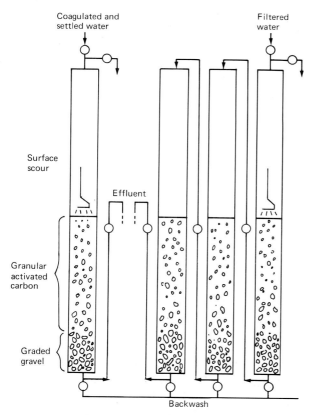

Figure 15.7   Pilot granular activated carbon columns.

carbon, like sand, is used, most of the filtration occurs in the upper few centimenters of the bed, and scouring assures adequate cleansing.

The series of columns shown in Fig. 15.7 can be operated concurrently in a postfiltration adsorption mode to examine the effects of longer empty-bed contact times. For example, the columns can be charged with granular activated carbon, exposed to filtered rather than settled water, and sampled sequentially to monitor the breakthrough (wavefront) of specific organics and the total organic carbon. On the other hand, an investigator may want to use one column as a sand filter receiving coagulated and settled water, and the remaining columns as adsorbers. Additional columns and the appropriate plumbing modifications would allow one to investigate in parallel, rather than in sequence, the performance of different brands of commercially available granular activated carbon, should that be desirable. The engineer should experiment with several options so that the most satisfactory adsorption design can be selected.

Pilot-plant operation. Granular activated carbon must be backwashed before it is put into service. Gently tapping or bumping the columns might be necessary to ensure that the media are wetted. Sufficient freeboard should exist to permit 30 to 50 percent bed expansion during backwash. The frequency of backwashing during the experimental study will vary, depending upon the same factors that influence full-scale filtration (e.g., head loss, turbidity, and floc carried over from settling). Details on monitoring the system are given in Ref. 1; however, a routine operation schedule would include that shown in Table 15.3.

Data interpretation and decision making. Variability in source water quality will determine how long a system should be operated before selecting a conceptual design. If historical trace organic data are lack-

TABLE 15.3   Routine Schedule for Pilot-Plant Operation

Parameter	Frequency
Flow adjustment Q	Daily
Temperature, pH, turbidity, threshold odor number, color	Investigator's discretion (based on variability of applied water)
Low-molecular-weight halogenated organic carbon compounds	Weekly
Organic carbon (TOC)	Weekly
Trihalomethane formation potential or maybe organic halogen analysis (TOX)	Biweekly

ing, the design engineer may want the system operated over a period of several months or even a year to determine seasonal effects. Breakthrough curves should be developed for total organic carbon or specific organics, or both. Concepts such as the "bed depth service time"[15] can be useful in optimizing an adsorption system.

Powdered activated carbon.   This adsorbent is commercially prepared from base products such as bituminous coal, lignite, wood, bark, coconut husks, and petroleum. Particle sizes range from 5 to 100 μm, and it weighs approximately 25 to 30 lb/ft^3 (400 to 480 kg/m^3). Powdered activated carbon is most effective when injected at multiple locations between the intake and filters. If chlorination is practiced, the chlorine and the adsorbent should never be added together, as chlorine is readily reduced by powdered activated carbon, and therefore will not be available for disinfection. This not only wastes disinfectant, but some of the adsorbent may be oxidized. Jar tests similar to those used to determine coagulant dosage can be helpful in estimating optimum powdered activated carbon doses.

The National Interim Primary Drinking Water Regulations[16] established maximum contaminant levels for endrine, lindane, Toxaphene, methoxychlor, 2,4-D, and 2,4,5-TP (Silvex). With the exception of Toxaphene, unreasonably high doses of powdered activated carbon are needed to effect removal of the Class II contaminants listed in these regulations. Toxaphene, however, is well removed by powdered activated carbon at doses of about 10 mg/L. Figure 15.8 is a compilation of the effectiveness of powdered activated carbon for removing several specific Class II compounds in single-solute systems (i.e., no competition exists for the adsorptive sites).[17]

The idea of adding an adsorbent only when needed is appealing from a cost and sludge-handling standpoint, but for this concept of organic control to be successful for other Class I compounds, a very sophisticated and reliable organics monitoring program must exist.

Synthetic resins.   Synthetic resins of the Amherlite XAD* type (a class of divinylbenzene-styrene or acrylic copolymers) have a limited capacity for a spectrum of adsorbates. A carbonaceous adsorbent, Ambersorb XE-340,* has a high adsorption capacity for low-molecular-weight halogenated organic compounds such as chloroform, 1,1,1-trichloroethane, and carbon tetrachloride, but it has little capacity for removing TOC. The potential of these materials in water treatment has not yet been fully evaluated, but they are likely to have a role,

---

*Rohm and Haas, Philadelphia, Pa. Mention of commercial products does not constitute an endorsement or approval.

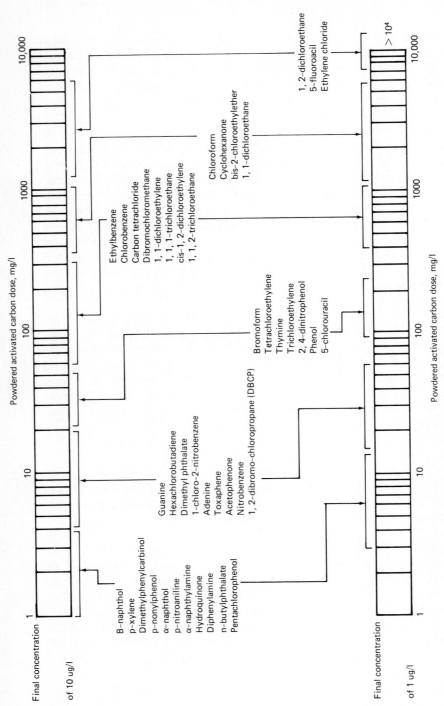

Figure 15.8 Powdered activated carbon dose (mg/L) necessary to reduce contaminant concentration of 100 μg/L to 10 μg/L or 1 μg/L. (*After Dobbs et al., "Carbon Adsorption Isotherms for Toxic Organics," U.S. Environmental Protection Agency, Office of Research and Development, MERL, Cincinnati, Ohio, May 1978.*)

perhaps in treating solvent-contaminated groundwater.[18] Figure 15.9 shows a scanning electron photomicrograph (40X) of both granular activated carbon and Amersorb XE-340. The resin is designed for a specific group of contaminants, and the activated carbon can remove a spectrum of adsorbates.

Other organic control processes

Combination of oxidation and adsorption. Ozone plus granular activated carbon (sand replacement) or ozone plus filtration followed by granular activated carbon (postfilter adsorber) can produce water with a lower total organic carbon and trihalomethane formation potential than either ozone alone or granular activated carbon alone. Oxygen applied at equivalent doses does not produce similar improved treatment. Although the process is not well understood, ozone apparently oxidizes certain biorefractory organics, making them a source of nutrition for a select bacterial population which propagates on granular media (sand, coal, or activated carbon) following ozonation. This concept is being used at a few water utilities in the Federal Republic of Germany. The ozone dose necessary to effect changes has been found to range between 0.5 and 3 mg/L ozone per mg/L TOC. From a cost standpoint, the combination of ozone and granular activated carbon may become an attractive consideration when the activated carbon alone is exhausted in 3 months or less.[19]

Boiling. For short-term situations, such as emergencies, boiling can be effective for removing some of the more volatile organics from drinking water. Predicting the effectiveness of boiling is difficult because the behavior of trace contaminants can follow the principles of simple distillation, steam distillation, or azeotropic distillation. These principles are too involved for this discussion; suffice it to say that some organic contaminants in water can be removed by boiling even though their boiling point in a pure solution is above the boiling point of water. Tetrachloroethylene (boiling point = 121°C) is a good example of an organic in that category.

In a situation in which a few hundred micrograms per liter of an "insoluble" solvent have contaminated a drinking water, boiling can be effective (see Table 15.4) but very energy-intensive as a treatment method. When advised to boil their water, homeowners should be instructed not to directly breathe the vapors and, if possible, to use range hoods that are vented to the outside or that have activated carbon or some equivalent type of adsorbent on the exhaust. The water must be brought to a vigorous boil. Also, organic contaminants are more efficiently removed from a shallow pan with an inch or two of

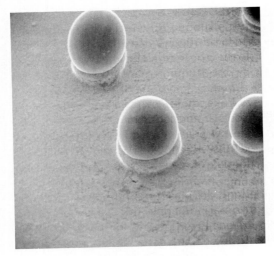

Ambersorb XE-340
(resin)

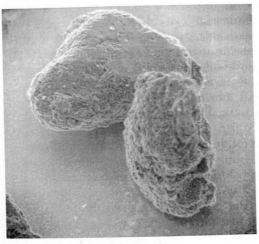

Filtrasorb 400
(granular activated carbon)

Figure 15.9 Scanning electron photomicrograph
(40 ×) of the surface on synthetic resin and activated carbon granules.

TABLE 15.4   Effects of Boiling on Several Trace Organics
Found in Drinking Water

Time of boil, min	Average percent remaining				
	A	B	C	D	E
3	2	14	13	7	—
5	<1	7	7	3	<1
10	<1	1	1	<1	<1

A, tetrachloroethylene; B, trichloroethylene; C, *cis*-1,2-dichloro-
ethylene; D, chloroform; E, carbon tetrachloride.

water than from a deep vessel with several inches of water that has to
boil. Inorganic constituents may be concentrated on boiling, so water
that is marginal in inorganic quality might be rendered unsuitable.

Summary

Just as there is no single technique for measuring all organics, there
is no single technique for controlling them. A combination of source
control, monitoring, and treatment is necessary to minimize their occurrence in finished drinking water. Granular activated carbon is the
most effective broad-spectrum adsorbent; however, oxidation, aeration, precipitation, or combinations of these may be necessary to com-
bat a particular problem. The National Academy of Sciences[20] com-
piled published literature on the efficacy of granular activated carbon,
and their report should be reviewed by the design engineers for a more
detailed explanation of the adsorption process and potential operational problems.

Figure 15.10, similar to diagrams presented by Symons et al.,[21]
demonstrates the variability of the different unit processes for the removal of various classes of organic contaminants. The first bar (A)
shows the five classes of organics found in drinking water. The second
bar (B) represents those organic contaminants adsorbed by granular
activated carbon. This unit process removes a wide range of organic
contaminant types, measured typically as total organic carbon (V) and
trihalomethane precursors (III), synthetic organic chemicals (IIb) such
as polychlorinated biphenyls, and pesticides, and taste- and odor-
producing compounds (I). Further, unsaturated chlorinated solvents
(IIa) such as trichloroethylene and tetrachloroethylene are well removed by granular activated carbon adsorption. Saturated chlorinated solvents (IV) such as chloroform are removed when the adsorbent is fresh, but in general it has a short life for these kinds of
compounds. Trihalomethanes are best controlled by preventing their
formation through improved coagulation and changes in disinfectants
or disinfection practices. Care must be exercised if changes are made

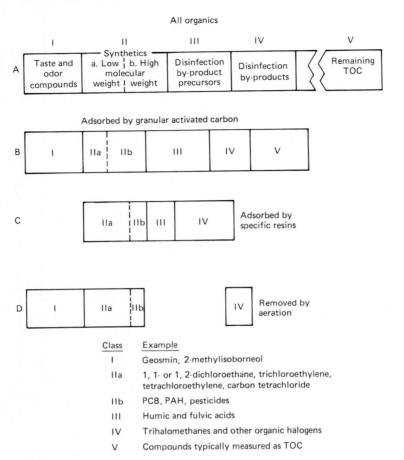

Class	Example
I	Geosmin, 2-methylisoborneol
IIa	1, 1- or 1, 2-dichloroethane, trichloroethylene, tetrachloroethylene, carbon tetrachloride
IIb	PCB, PAH, pesticides
III	Humic and fulvic acids
IV	Trihalomethanes and other organic halogens
V	Compounds typically measured as TOC

Figure 15.10 Summary of treatment efficiencies for controlling trace organics in drinking water.

in disinfection practices so as not to compromise the bacteriological quality of finished water.

Bar C shows that synthetic resins can remove some of the same materials that are reasonably well adsorbed by granular activated carbon (IIb) but are not effective for all compounds presented by IIb (smaller than in Bar B) and are not effective for organic compounds measured as TOC (V). Also, area III is smaller in Bar C, indicating that less trihalomethane precursor material is adsorbed by synthetic resins than by granular activated carbon. On the other hand, resins may be very effective for removing compounds represented by IIa, such as 1,1- and 1,2-dichloroethane, which are poorly adsorbed by granular activated carbon.

Aeration can remove compounds such as vinyl chloride that cannot be well removed by adsorption. In addition, aeration removes some compounds that are well adsorbed on synthetic resins (II & IV), some that are adsorbed by both resins and granular activated carbon (IIb), and some taste and odor compounds (I).

Combined oxidation and adsorption on granular activated carbon as compared with granular activated carbon adsorption alone is not shown. Evidence is accumulating that this combination treatment is more effective for contaminants in classes III and V. An economic analysis must be made, however, to determine whether or not the increase is great enough to justify the expense of the oxidant. These and other biological processes, such as riverbank filtration and slow sand filters, are options available to include with source protection and monitoring for controlling against organic contamination. Finally, the distribution system must be protected against contamination from open reservoirs, and the utility should have an active cross-connection program. Controlling organics in potable water requires a combination of source protection, treatment, and distribution surveillance.

Acknowledgments

The authors appreciate the assistance, suggestions, and comments received from Mr. Gordon Robeck, Dr. James Symons, Mr. Alan Stevens, and Mr. James Westrick, who reviewed this material. Their help, and that of Mrs. Margaret Oldham, who typed the manuscript, was excellent and valuable to the usefulness of this information.

References

1. J. M. Symons, "Interim Treatment Guide for Controlling Organic Contaminants in Drinking Water Using Granular Activated Carbon," U.S. Environmental Protection Agency, Office of Research and Development, MERL, Cincinnati, Ohio, January 1978.
2. U.S. Environmental Protection Agency, "Interim Primary Drinking Water Regulations: Control of Organic Chemical Contaminants in Drinking Water," *Federal Register,* vol. 43, no. 28, part II, February 9, 1978, pp. 5756–5780.
3. J. M. Symons, T. A. Bellar, J. K. Carswell, J. DeMarco, K. L. Kropp, D. R. Seeger, C. J. Slocum, B. L. Smith, and A. A. Stevens, "National Organics Reconnaissance Survey for Halogenated Organics," *Journal AWWA,* vol. 67, no. 11, 1975, pp. 634–648.
4. J. M. Symons (ed.), *Water Quality Behavior in Reservoirs,* U.S. Department of Health, Education, and Welfare, PHS, Cincinnati, Ohio, 1969.
5. U.S. Environmental Protection Agency, "Innovative and Alternative Technology Assessment Manual," Office of Research and Development, MERL, EPA-430/9-78-009, Cincinnati, Ohio, 1978.
6. J. M. Symons, A. A. Stevens, R. M. Clark, E. E. Geldreich, O. T. Love, Jr., and J. DeMarco, "Treatment Techniques for Controlling Trihalomethanes in Drinking Water," U.S. Environmental Protection Agency, EPA 600/2-81-156, Cincinnati, Ohio, September 1981.
7. U.S. Environmental Protection Agency, "National Primary Drinking Water Regu-

lations," Part III, Volatile Synthetic Organic Chemicals, *Federal Register,* vol. 50, no. 219, November 13, 1985.

8. M. C. Kavanaugh and R. R. Trussell, "Design of Aeration Towers to Strip Contaminants from Drinking Water," *Journal AWWA,* vol. 72, no. 12, 1980, p. 684.

9. M. Cummins and J. Westerick, "Packed Column Air Stripping Preliminary Design Procedure," *Proceedings,* Post-Conference Workshop, Water Pollution Control Federation Conference, 1986.

10. R. E. Treybal, *Mass Transfer Operations,* McGraw-Hill, New York, 1980.

11. R. H. Perry and C. H. Chilton, *Chemical Engineers' Handbook,* McGraw-Hill, New York, 1973.

12. B. Strack, "Operation, Problems and Economy of Activated Carbon Regeneration," Translation of Reports on Special Problems of Water Technology, vol. 9, Adsorption, U. S. Environmental Protection Agency, Drinking Water Research Division, EPA 600/9-76-030, Cincinnati, Ohio, December 1976.

13. D. Dalsis, "Controlling Trihalomethane Concentration in Ingredient Water," *Proc. 26th Annual Meeting Soc. Soft Drink Technologists,* Orlando, Fla., April 1979.

14. S. B. Smith, "Techniques of Activated Carbon Regeneration," *Water—1975,* American Institute of Chemical Engineers Symposium Series, vol. 71, no. 151, 1975.

15. R. A. Hutchins, "New Method Simplifies Design of Activated Carbon System," *Chemical Engineering,* vol. 80, August 1973, pp. 133–138.

16. U.S. Environmental Protection Agency, "National Interim Primary Drinking Water Regulations," Office of Drinking Water, Washington, D.C., EPA-570/9-76-003, plus "Amendment to the NIPDWR on Trihalomethanes," *Federal Register,* vol. 44, no. 231, November 29, 1979.

17. R. A. Dobbs, R. J. Middendorf, and J. M. Cohen, "Carbon Adsorption Isotherms for Toxic Organics," U.S. Environmental Protection Agency, Office of Research and Development, MERL, Cincinnati, Ohio, May 1978.

18. J. W. Neely and E. G. Isacoff, *Carbonaceous Adsorbents for the Treatment of Ground and Surface Waters,* Marcel Dekker, New York, 1982.

19. R. M. Clark and P. Dorsey, "Influence of Operating Variable on the Cost of Treatment by GAC Adsorption," in *Practical Application of Adsorption Techniques in Drinking Water,* EPA/NATO Committee for Challenges of Modern Society, Reston, Va., EPA 570/9-84-005, 1984.

20. National Academy of Sciences, "An Evaluation of Activated Carbon for Drinking Water Treatment," prepared for the U.S. Environmental Protection Agency by the Safe Drinking Water Committee, Washington, D.C., 1979.

21. J. M. Symons, J. K. Carswell, J. DeMarco, and O. T. Love, Jr., "Removal of Organic Contaminants from Drinking Water Using Techniques Other than Granular Activated Carbon Alone—A Progress Report," in *Practical Application of Adsorption Techniques in Drinking Water,* EPA/NATO Committee for Challenges of Modern Society, Reston, Va., EPA 570/9-84-005, 1984.

Special Water Treatment Processes

Introduction

As we pointed out in Chap. 1, the National Interim Primary Drinking Water Regulations (NIPDWRs) establish maximum contamination levels (MCLs) for several inorganic chemicals and for several radioactive contaminants.[1,2] The National Secondary Drinking Water Regulations (NSDWRs),[3] based primarily on aesthetic considerations related to public acceptance of drinking water, established secondary MCLs for a number of parameters, including chloride, color, copper, corrosivity, foaming agents, iron, manganese, odor, pH, sulfate, total dissolved solids, and zinc. The 1986 Amendments to the Safe Drinking Water Act added many inorganic contaminants to the list of those that have been or will be regulated. This chapter discusses removal technology for many of the inorganic contaminants and methods applicable to achieving a noncorrosive water supply.

Inorganic contaminants may be present in potable water supplies as naturally occurring minerals in ground- or surface water, from industrial or agricultural pollution, or as by-products of corrosion in water distribution systems. No single method of treatment short of demineralization is effective for removing all the inorganic or radioactive contaminants, and that process generally exacerbates the corrosivity of the water. Conventional treatment methods, such as chemical coagulation or lime softening, are effective for removing many of the heavy metals and radium. Removal of nitrate and fluoride may require unit processes such as ion exchange or adsorption on activated alumina or bone char.

The safest and surest method of safeguarding the consuming public, of course, is to select a potable water source that is free of contaminants. But while many of the nation's water supplies have this luxury, others do not. Existing water supplies which are discovered to contain elevated levels of inorganic contaminants can be rendered safe without further treatment by blending the existing source with water from an alternative source that is relatively free from contamination. Although source selection or blending may seem a simplistic solution, it is often possible and should always be considered before deciding to treat a potable water source specifically for removal of inorganic contaminants.

Several of the metal ions included in the primary and secondary regulations are not present in the water leaving the utility at the point of entry into the distribution system, but enter as a result of the reaction between the water and the conveying structures, either the transmission mains or the customer's piping. A study of Boston's distribution system by Craun and McCabe[4] showed that 19 percent of standing water samples exceeded the MCL for copper, 9 percent the limit for iron, and 65 percent the limit for lead.

Contaminants such as cadmium, copper, lead, and zinc occur almost entirely as a result of reactions subsequent to the treatment facilities. Concentrations of any of these seldom, if ever, occur at levels above the MCL in either raw or treated water. Therefore, the problem of treatment of the water supply rarely involves processes for removing these contaminants, but rather treatment to prevent their appearance as a result of reactions with metal surfaces with which the water comes in contact. Since this process is commonly termed corrosion, the relevant control systems will be discussed under that topic later in this chapter.

Theoretical Review

Incidence

The NIPDWR defines a community system as one which serves at least 15 service connections used by year-round residents, or regularly serves 25 year-round residents. Under this definition there are approximately 60,000 community water systems in the United States. Noncommunity systems, defined as all systems which are not community systems, are estimated to number about 200,000. The primary MCLs for all inorganic contaminants are applicable to community systems only, with the exception of the nitrate MCL, which is also applicable to noncommunity systems. In 1970, the EPA conducted the Community Water Supply Study,[5] which evaluated 969 community water supply systems throughout the country. Table 16.1 shows the percent

TABLE 16.1   Percent of Samples in the Community Water Supply with Value Exceeding 75 Percent of Each Limit in the 1962 Public Health Service Drinking Water Standards[5]

Constituent	DWS limit, mg/L	DWS limit 75%, mg/L	Percent of samples exceeding
Arsenic	0.05	0.0375	1.24
Barium	1	0.75	1.08
Cadmium	0.010	0.0075	1.45
Chloride	250	187.5	1.56
Chromium	0.05	0.0375	1.43
Color (color units)	15	11.25	3.54
Copper	1	0.75	2.47
Cyanide	0.2	0.15	0.00
Foaming agents	0.5	0.375	0.08
Iron	0.3	0.225	15.81
Lead	0.05	0.0375	3.32
Manganese	0.05	0.0375	11.91
Nitrate	45	33.75	3.46
Selenium	0.01	0.0075	8.35
Silver	0.05	0.0375	0.00
Sulfate	250	187.5	3.37
Zinc	5	3.75	0.35

of the community systems which exceeded 75 percent of the 1962 United States Public Health Service Drinking Water Standards in effect at the time. More recent data from monitoring required by the NIPDWR show that the most common problems are occurrences of nitrate, fluoride, arsenic, radium-226, selenium, and barium. All of these contaminants occur naturally.

Inorganic contaminants in water sources may occur in cationic or anionic form, in various states of chemical oxidation (valence states), or in chemical complexes formed with organic compounds. The ionic form and the valence state of the inorganic contaminants are important, as they often influence solubility as well as treatability by various treatment techniques. Many of the heavy metals which exist as cations form hydroxide or carbonate complexes of low solubility, and are therefore readily removed by conventional treatment techniques. The anionic forms of metals such as arsenic and selenium are more difficult to treat, and their removal is strongly dependent upon the valance state in which the anions occur. Table 16.2 lists the major ionic forms, valences, principal sources, and probable occurrences of the inorganic contaminants.[6]

TABLE 16.2   Principal Form and Sources of Inorganic Contaminants (Sorg[6])

Contaminant	Valence	Principal forms in water	Sources	Probable occurrence
Arsenic	+3 (arsenite) +5 (arsenate)	Anion AsO_2^- Anion AsO_4^{3-}	Mineral, industry	Groundwater, surface water
Barium	+2	Cation Ba^{2+}	Mineral	Groundwater
Cadmium	+2	Cation Cd^{2+}	Corrosion by-product, industry	Distribution system, surface water
Chromium	+3 +5 (chromate) +5 (dichromate)	Cation Cr^{3+} Anion CrO_4^{3-} Anion $Cr_2O_7^{4-}$	Industry	Surface water
Copper	+2	Cation Cu^{2+}	Corrosion by-product, industry	Distribution system, surface water
Fluoride	−1	Anion F^-	Mineral	Groundwater
Lead	+3	Cation Pb^{3+}	Corrosion by-product, industry	Distribution system, surface water
Mercury	+2 (inorganic) +2 (organic)	Cation Hg^{2+} Cation CH_3Hg^+	Industry	Surface water
Nitrate	+1	Anion NO_3^-	Agricultural	Groundwater
Radium[226]	+2	Cation Ra^{2+}	Mineral	Groundwater
Selenium	+4 (selenite) +6 (selenate)	Anion SeO_3^{2-} Anion SeO_4^{2-}	Mineral	Groundwater
Silver	+1	Cation Ag^{1+}	Industry, water treatment	Surface water, water treated with silver bactericide
Zinc	+2	Cation Zn^{2+}	Corrosion by-product	Distribution system

Design Principles and Practices—Treatment Processes for Inorganics

Except for distillation and other demineralization processes, which are not commonly used to treat potable water in the United States, no single treatment process is effective for all inorganic contaminants. But fortunately, many can be removed from water by coagulation or lime softening, the effectiveness of which frequently depends on pH, coagulant chemical and dose, the initial concentration of the contaminant, and the form and valence state of the contaminant. Of these variables, the pH of the treated water is the most important.

Ion exchange may be effective in cases where a contaminant cannot be removed by conventional coagulation or lime softening. Membrane processes, such as reverse osmosis and electrodialysis, although relatively expensive, are effective for removing inorganic contaminants.

Table 16.3 summarizes the treatment processes known to be effective for removal of inorganic and radioactive contaminants. It is intended as a guide to allow the process designer to select a treatment process or processes for further site-specific evaluation. Removal of inorganic contaminants from a potable source can vary considerably from water to water, and any treatment process should always be tested on a laboratory- or pilot-scale basis, using the actual raw-water source, before final process design. Table 16.4 lists the applicable processes and the contaminants amenable to removal by that process.

Conventional treatment

For purposes of this discussion, conventional treatment is defined as chemical coagulation using aluminum or iron salts, and lime or lime-soda softening. The unit operations involved in conventional treatment—mixing, flocculation, sedimentation, and filtration—have been discussed in detail in previous chapters; this discussion focuses on the removal of inorganic contaminants in conventional treatment systems.

The mechanism of removal for inorganic contaminants in conventional treatment may be either precipitation of insoluble metal hydroxides or carbonates, coprecipitation with iron or aluminum hydroxides, or adsorption with natural turbidity or on floc particles formed by hydrolyzing metal salts with the water.

Precipitation of cadmium, lead, and silver occurs readily during conventional treatment. Since the solubilities of these precipitates are pH-dependent, close control of pH is essential.

Coprecipitation occurs when the inorganic contaminant forms an insoluble complex with the iron or aluminum salt used as a coagulant. Iron salts are generally more effective coagulants than alum for inorganic contaminant removal, perhaps because of the higher reactivity of iron and its tendency to form iron–metal-ion complexes. Both the valence of the inorganic contaminant in the solution and the pH of the solution are important in determining removal by coprecipitation. Arsenic, for example, can be removed effectively at one valence state ($+5$ or arsenate), but exhibits considerably lower removals at another valence state ($+3$ or arsenite).

Metals such as lead, silver, and mercury adsorb easily on turbidity particles in raw water or on floc particles produced as a result of coagulation. The removal of these metals is dependent on the level of turbidity in the raw water, the nature of the floc formed in the coag-

TABLE 16.3 Summary of Treatment Processes for Inorganic Contaminants[11]

Contaminant	Process	pH range	Comments
Arsenic +5	Ferric sulfate coagulation	6–8	—
	Alum coagulation	6–7	—
	Lime softening	>10.5	—
Arsenic +3	Ferric sulfate coagulation	6–8	Oxidation to As^{5+} by chlorination required prior to coagulation
	Alum coagulation	6–7	
	Lime softening	>10.5	
Barium	Lime softening	10–11	—
	Ion exchange	—	Normal cationic exchange resins effective
Cadmium	Ferric sulfate coagulation	7–8	Effective over full lime-softening range
	Lime softening	—	
Copper	Stabilization and corrosion control	Site-specific	—
Chromium +3	Ferric sulfate coagulation	6–9	—
	Alum coagulation	7–9	—
	Lime softening	>10.5	—
Chromium +6	Ferric sulfate coagulation	7–9.5	—
Fluoride	Ion exchange	Neutral pH recommended	Ion-exchange media: activated alumina or bone char
	Lime softening	>11	Fluoride coprecipitates with magnesium hydroxide, high magnesium required
Lead	Ferric sulfate coagulation	6–9	—
	Alum coagulation	6–9	—
	Lime softening	—	Effective over full lime-softening range
Inorganic mercury	Stabilization & corrosion control/ferric sulfate coagulation	Site-specific 7–8	—
Organic mercury	Activated carbon	—	Powdered and granular carbon effective
Nitrate	Ion exchange	—	Ion-exchange media: strong base resin
Radium	Lime softening	—	Effective throughout entire softening range
	Ion exchange	—	Normal cationic exchange media effective
	Reverse osmosis	—	—
Selenium +4	Ferric sulfate coagulation	6–7	—
	Ion exchange	—	Ion-exchange media: strong base resin or activated alumina
	Reverse osmosis	—	
Selenium +6	Reverse osmosis	—	—
Silver	Ferric sulfate coagulation	7–9	—
	Alum coagulation	6–8	—
	Lime softening	—	Effective over full lime-softening range
Zinc	Stabilization and corrosion control	Site-specific	—

494

TABLE 16.4 Applicable Treatment Technologies for Removal of Inorganic Contaminants

Treatment technology applicable to removal of listed contaminants					
Coagulation with ferric or aluminum salts	Lime or lime-soda softening	Ion exchange	Reverse osmosis	Corrosion control	Activated carbon
As	As	Ba	Significant removal of all inorganics parameters, including radionuclides	Cu	Hg (organically complexed)
Cd (ferric salts)	Ba	Ra		Pb	
Cr^{3+}	Cd	F^-		Zn	
Cr^{6+} (ferric salts)	Pb	NO_3^-		Cd	
Pb	Ra	Se^{+4}			
Hg (inorganic form—ferric salts)	Ag				
Se					
Ag					

ulation process, and overall turbidity removal. Figures 16.1 through 16.3 present a summary of inorganic contaminant removal efficiencies using iron coagulation, alum coagulation, and lime softening. These data have been summarized by the U.S. Environmental Protection Agency (USEPA) from jar tests and pilot-scale experiments presented in the literature.

Arsenic. Laboratory jar tests and pilot-scale tests have been conducted by several investigators to study the removal of arsenic from potable water by coagulation. Doses of 30 mg/L of alum and ferric sulfate were shown by Gulledge and O'Connor[7] to remove more than 90 percent of the arsenic +5 (arsenate) originally present at 0.05 mg/L. Ferric sulfate was effective over a wider pH range (5 to 8) than alum (5 to 7). Significant removal of arsenic +3 (arsenite) occurred only after it was oxidized to arsenic +5 with chlorine. Logsdon et al.[10] corroborated the results of Gulledge and O'Connor by demonstrating that 30-mg/L coagulant doses were capable of accomplishing high removals of arsenic +5 and chlorine-oxidized arsenic +3 from samples containing initial arsenic concentrations up to about 1.5 mg/L. Increased coagulant doses were shown to be effective in maintaining high removals when the initial arsenic concentration was increased. Ferric sulfate was shown to achieve greater increases in removals than alum at the same incremental dosage increase. Logsdon et al.[8] also demonstrated that lime softening is effective for achieving greater than 90 percent removals of arsenic +5 and chlorine-oxidized arsenic +3 if the softening reaction is carried out at a pH above 10.5. When the initial arsenic +3 concentration was less than 0.1 mg/L, preoxidation was not required to achieve concentration less than the

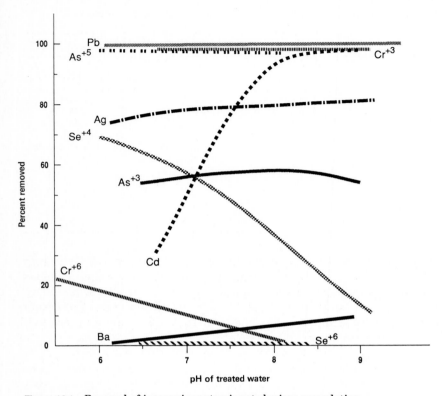

Figure 16.1   Removal of inorganic contaminants by iron coagulation.

MCL of 0.05 mg/L when the softening was performed at a pH of 10.7 or above.

Barium.   Barium, an alkaline earth metal chemically similar to calcium, has been shown to be removed very effectively by lime softening.[8–10] Greater than 90 percent removals have been demonstrated in the 10 to 11 pH range on well water containing 7 to 8.5 mg/L of naturally occurring barium. Barium removal decreased below and above this pH range. Coagulation using alum or iron salts was not found to be effective for barium.

Cadmium.   Laboratory experiments and pilot-scale studies have shown[11] that cadmium can be removed by lime softening throughout the normal softening pH range. Greater than 98 percent removal has been demonstrated in the 8.5 to 11.3 pH range for samples with an initial cadmium concentration of 0.3 mg/L. Cadmium removal by ferric sulfate or alum coagulation is less effective than that achieved by

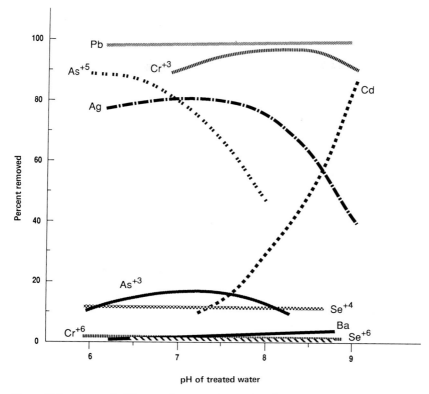

Figure 16.2   Removal of inorganic contaminants by alum coagulation.

lime softening, and dosage is more pH-dependent. A pH of above 8 was required to achieve removals of greater than 90 percent from an initial concentration of 0.3 mg/L cadmium.[11] Coagulation with alum or iron salts is relatively ineffective at this high pH, since 90 percent removal does not produce water which meets the MCL of 0.01 mg/L.

Chromium.   Chromium $+3$ is easily removed from water using alum or iron salts, and by lime softening. Laboratory studies have shown that chromium $+3$ removal by lime softening is pH-dependent, whereas pH has significantly less effect on removal by iron or alum coagulation. Chromium $+3$ removals of 98 percent have been demonstrated throughout the pH range of 6.7 to 8.5 with alum. These coagulants were effective even at high initial chromium concentrations. Lime softening achieved 98 percent removal in the pH range of 10.6 to 11.3. Below pH 10.6, removals decreased.

Neither alum, iron coagulation, nor lime softening is effective for removing chromium $+6$ from water, and care must be taken that chro-

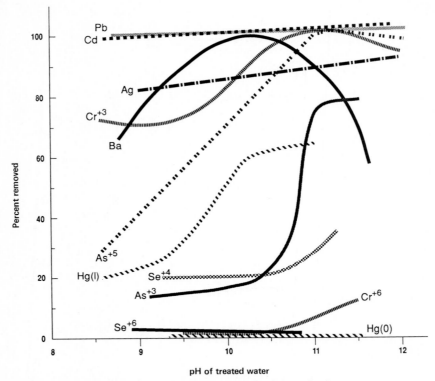

Figure 16.3   Removal of inorganic contaminants by lime softening.

mium +3 is not oxidized to chromium +6 by prechlorination. Ferrous sulfate has been shown to be effective because of its ability to reduce chromium +6 to chromium +3. Studies[12] conducted on ferrous sulfate coagulation demonstrated 98 percent removal of chromium +6 within the pH range of 6.5 to 9.3 from an initial concentration of 0.15 mg/L. If a water supply containing chromium +3 must be prechlorinated, ferrous sulfate should be the coagulant of choice in order that chromium +6 produced by the chlorine be reduced by the coagulant and thus removed.

Fluoride.   According to studies by Scott,[13] fluoride can be removed by lime softening of high-magnesium water. The removal mechanism is coprecipitation of magnesium fluoride with magnesium hydroxide; therefore, the pH must be maintained sufficiently high to ensure maximum magnesium removal. Culp and Stoltenberg[14] showed that fluoride could also be removed by alum coagulation; however, extremely high coagulant doses were required, and the process was not considered to be economical.

Lead.   Lead can be removed from water both by coagulation and by lime softening. Laboratory studies[15] of the removal of lead using alum and ferric sulfate coagulation showed greater than 97 percent removal of 0.15 mg/L lead within the wide pH range of 6 to 10. In the same studies, lime-softening experiments demonstrated greater than 98 percent removal from samples containing an initial concentration of 0.15 mg/L lead throughout the entire normal softening range of 8.5 to 11.3. One study[11] reported 85 to 90 percent removal of lead by sedimentation of a turbid river water without the use of a coagulant, which is indicative of the very low solubility of lead in natural water.

Mercury.   Mercury may occur in water in either the inorganic or organic form. Organic mercury is usually present as the methyl[1] mercury ion, CH_3Hg^+, and is the more prevalent and toxic of the two forms. Laboratory studies[16] of organic mercury removal during conventional treatment indicated that less than 40 percent removal can be expected with iron or alum coagulation, but that higher removals occur when a high raw-water turbidity is present, indicating an adsorption effect. Lime softening was found to be ineffective for organic mercury removal. Inorganic mercury removal was shown to depend on pH and the raw-water turbidity. Ferric sulfate coagulation at pH 8 was capable of 97 percent removal from samples containing 0.05 mg/L inorganic mercury, but only 66 percent removal at pH 7. Alum coagulation was found to be much less effective, demonstrating 47 percent removal at pH 7 from samples with a 0.05 mg/L initial concentration and 38 percent removal at pH 8. High raw-water turbidity somewhat increased the removal of inorganic mercury when alum was used as a coagulant.

Nitrate.   Nitrate is relatively unaffected by conventional treatment. Ion exchange or a demineralization process is required to reduce nitrate concentrations.

Radium.   Radium, an alkaline earth metal chemically similar to calcium and barium, is generally unaffected by coagulation but is removed during lime-softening treatment. Removals of 70 to 95 percent have been reported[17] in full-scale treatment systems, with greater removals occurring in conjunction with increased hardness removals; the latter relationship is shown in Fig. 16.4. Since hardness removal in a lime-softening system increases with increasing pH, provided

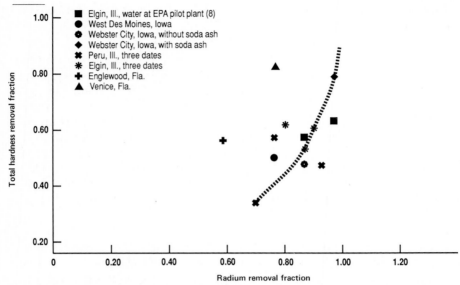

Figure 16.4   Lime-soda process: total hardness removal fraction versus radium removal fraction.

sufficient alkalinity is present in the raw water or added in the forms of soda ash, so does radium removal.

Selenium.   Of the two valence forms of selenium commonly found in water supplies, only selenium +4 (selenite) demonstrates significant removal using conventional treatment. Ferric sulfate laboratory studies[8–12] have demonstrated 85 percent removal of selenium +4 from river water containing 0.03 mg/L selenite. Removal was best at a pH of 5.5 and decreased with increasing pH. Alum coagulation was much less effective. Lime softening removed up to 45 percent of the selenium +4 from well water containing 0.03 mg/L selenite.

Silver.   Laboratory tests[11] have demonstrated that silver is easily removed from water by coagulation and lime softening. Greater than 70 percent removal has been achieved using both alum and ferric sulfate to treat river water containing 0.15 mg/L silver. The effective pH range was 6 to 8. Lime-softening experiments demonstrated silver removal ranging from 70 percent at pH 9 to 90 percent at pH 11.5 from the same water.

Design considerations.   An obvious factor in design of a system is the process selection, which may be specific to the contaminant of concern. The effectiveness of the process must be compared with the desired performance in terms of the initial and final concentrations. Figure 16.5 shows the percent removal required to achieve compliance with a given MCL based upon the expected raw-water concentration. In designing a conventional treatment system for removal of inorganic contaminants, particular attention must be given to ensuring maximum flexibility in chemical feed systems and in pH control. Provisions should be made in the initial design for adding treatment chemicals and chlorine (or other oxidants) in each unit process.

pH recording and controlling systems should also be designed with the maximum possible flexibility. Chemical feed systems should be provided to handle various treatment chemicals in case changes should become necessary as a result of changes in the nature of the inorganic contaminants in the raw water. It is considerably easier and cheaper to modify the treatment scheme at a plant designed for such flexibility than to retrofit a plant that was not.

Ion exchange

The ion-exchange process depends on the ability of a solid substance (exchange medium) to exchange ions bound to the medium with ions

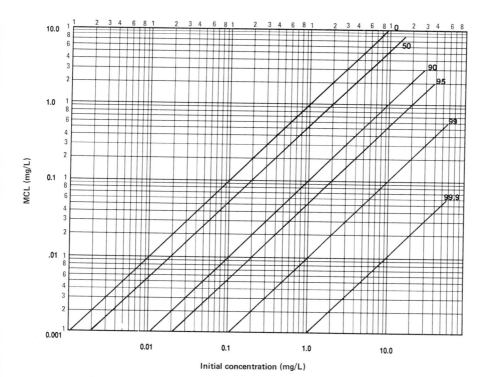

Figure 16.5   Percent removal required to meet a given MCL.

of another species dissolved in water. Ion exchange, to be effective, must be both selective for the ions to be removed and reversible. Once all the readily exchangeable ions on the medium have been replaced by dissolved ions, the exhausted medium is regenerated with a solution which provides a concentrated supply of the originally bound ions. Although various naturally occurring materials exhibit ion-exchange properties, most ion-exchange media now in use are synthetically produced. Materials which exchange cations are called cationic or base exchangers; materials which exchange anions are called anionic or acid exchangers.

An example of a modern cationic exchange medium commonly used for water softening is a synthetically manufactured sulfonated polystyrene-divinylbenzene copolymeric resin. Sodium ions, which are bound to the resin, will exchange with calcium and magnesium cations dissolved in water. Once exhausted, the resin is normally regenerated with a sodium chloride brine, then rinsed to remove the excess brine before being placed back in service.

Cationic exchangers may be produced to specifically favor one or more cations; however, in general, multivalent ions are removed preferentially over monovalent ions. Since most of the cationic inorganic contaminants of concern in water are multivalent, cationic exchange is quite effective in removing these.

Anionic exchange media may also be produced from synthetic polymers. Several inorganic materials, such as bone char (calcium phosphate) and activated alumina (calcined granules of hydrated alumina), also exhibit important anionic exchange properties for inorganic contaminants such as fluoride.

Ion exchange is an excellent process for small utilities because it can be installed on an individual well or group of wells and it is easily automated.

Ion-exchange operation can be cocurrent (the service and regenerant flows moving in the same direction) or countercurrent (the service and regenerant flows moving in opposite directions). Although the former configuration is easier and less expensive to install, contaminant ions left in the effluent end of the column following regeneration result in high leakage levels unless excess regenerant is used. With countercurrent operation, the less exhausted end of the column is exposed to the fresh regenerant, resulting in minimum leakage and more efficient regenerant utilization.

Continuous countercurrent ion exchangers (pulsed-bed exchangers) have been developed in which the resin, the regenerant, and the service move continuously in a large loop. By this means, the benefits of a long countercurrent column can be achieved with a smaller resin volume. Operation of a such a system, however, is more difficult than operation of a simple cocurrent or countercurrent column. Figure 16.6 depicts a diagram of a typical cocurrent ion-exchange column.

Ion exchange is an important process for removing nitrate, fluoride, barium, radium, and selenium +4 from drinking water. Although few data are available on the removal of heavy metal cations such as cadmium, silver, inorganic mercury, and lead, these cations should be removed easily by typical cationic exchange media. These metals, however, are rarely a problem of sufficient scope to warrant such treatment.

Fluoride is the inorganic contaminant for which there is the most

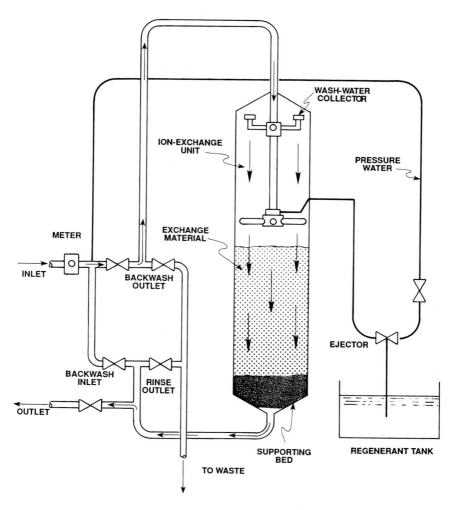

Figure 16.6 Diagram of typical ion-exchange unit.

full-scale ion-exchange process experience. Full-scale plants are currently operating in California and Arizona, and a fluoride-removal plant in Bartlett, Tex., was operated from 1952 through 1977.[18,19] All these plants treat source water with an initial fluoride concentration of from 5 to 8 mg/L and produce water with a concentration of less than 1 mg/L using an activated alumina exchange medium with sodium hydroxide as the regenerant. Sodium hydroxide is also used as a regenerant for bone-char media and for strong-base anionic exchange resins.

Activated alumina is the exchange medium of choice for fluoride removal because of its low cost compared with bone char or synthetic resins and its greater ion-exchange capacity. Activated alumina is somewhat specific for fluoride, and its capacity, unlike that of synthetic resins, is not affected by the sulfate or chloride concentrations of the water.[20] The lower the pH, the more effectively fluoride is removed by the medium. Since activated alumina is dissolved in acid solution, however, a pH of slightly more than 7 is the best choice for operation.

Laboratory studies[21] have shown that while arsenic can interfere with fluoride removal by bone char, it can itself be removed readily from water by both bone char and activated alumina. The investigations showed that arsenic sorption on bone char results in irreversible change of the char and ultimately renders it useless for fluoride removal. On the other hand, activated alumina is readily regenerated when both fluoride and arsenic are removed, although a recent investigation[22] determined that a stronger sodium hydroxide solution (4 percent) is required during regeneration to remove the arsenic than would be required to remove fluoride alone (1 percent). Pilot studies[22] indicate that the preferred method of treating water with the combined contaminants arsenic and fluoride is the use of two activated alumina columns in series. Table 16.5 presents typical design data for an ion-exchange system using an activated alumina medium.[23] Site-specific testing should always be conducted prior to designing a system for fluoride removal.

TABLE 16.5   Flouride Removal by Activated Alumina—Typical Design Data[23]

Exchange capacity	1500 to 2000 grains/ft^3 as F
Regenerant amount	0.75 to 1 lb NaOH/ft^3
Regenerant concentration	0.5 to 1 percent NaOH
	4 percent if arsenic is present
Regenerant flow rate	0.5 gpm/ft^2
Leakage	1 mg/L
Service rates	4 to 5 gpm/ft^2
	1 gpm/ft^3

Ion exchange is the only process currently in use that removes nitrate from water. Laboratory studies[24-27] have shown that some strong-base and weak-base ion-exchange resins are nitrate-selective and can reduce the nitrate concentration from as high as 50 mg/L as N to 0.5 mg/L.

At the present time, one full-scale nitrate removal installation has been operated in the United States. The 1200-gpm continuous countercurrent ion-exchange plant of the Garden City Park Water District, Long Island, N.Y., which began operating in 1974, used a strong-base resin and sodium chloride regenerant, and achieved a finished-water nitrate concentration of 0.5 mg/L with 20 to 30 mg/L in the raw water. This plant is not now in operation, but recent studies have developed adequate design criteria for construction of other full-scale plants.

Sulfates, and to some extent other ions, compete with nitrate for exchange sites on the resin. High sulfate and high TDS levels, in general, can therefore adversely affect cost. Another caution regarding this process is that, because every resin tested to date is more selective for sulfate than for nitrate, at the end of the exhaustion cycle the nitrate ion concentration rises rather suddenly to levels exceeding those in the influent. This phenomenon suggests that regeneration should be undertaken prior to completion of the exhaustion cycle.

Table 16.6 represents typical design data for nitrate removal by ion exchange. This process should always be thoroughly evaluated on a pilot scale prior to system design.

Laboratory studies[28] have demonstrated greater than 97 percent removal of selenium +4 and +6 from a solution containing 0.1 mg/L using an exchange with synthetic anionic resins. A recent study[29] of selenium removal using ion exchange with activated alumina indicated that selenium +4 was removed at a rate 12 times greater than selenium +6. Bicarbonate and sulfate were found to be exchanged preferentially over selenium +6, and regeneration with sodium hydroxide required much longer contact times for selenium +6 than for selenium +4. Because of the limited amount of information available for sele-

TABLE 16.6   Nitrate Removal by Ion Exchange—Typical Design Data[24]

Media	Strong base type II
Exchange capacity	5000 to 15,000 grains/ft^3 (as N)
Regenerant amount	15 to 20 lb/ft^3
Regenerant concentration	10 to 12 percent
Regenerant flow rate	0.5 gpm/ft^3
Leakage	Often less than 1 mg/L as N
Service rates	8 to 12 gpm/ft^2
	1 to 5 gpm/ft^3

nium removal using ion exchange, this process should always be evaluated on a site-specific basis.

Field data[30] from two midwestern full-scale ion-exchange softening plants indicated that barium removal was comparable to hardness removal for well water containing 11 to 19 mg/L of barium and 225 to 230 mg/L of hardness as $CaCO_3$. Barium was removed almost completely in these plants, as was the hardness; the barium breakthrough occurred at about the same time as the hardness breakthrough. This similarity in behavior of hardness and barium in ion-exchange treatment allows the hardness test to be used as a practical method of monitoring barium during treatment.

If barium is present in the raw water at very high concentrations, ion exchange may not be a practical treatment method for removal, since raw-water blending—a normal step used to provide finished water with a reasonable amount of hardness—may not be possible while maintaining a finished-water barium concentration below the MCL.

Radium is similarly removed almost completely along with the hardness in full-scale ion-exchange softening plants. Unlike barium, radium exhaustion does not occur simultaneously with hardness exhaustion, but continues for a period of time. Regeneration to achieve good hardness removal is sufficient, however, to achieve good radium removal.

As with barium, blending raw water containing very high radium levels with finished water may cause the radium level in the blended water to exceed the MCL. Blending must be given careful study before it is used with water containing radium.

Design considerations. Any water to be treated using the ion-exchange process must be relatively free of particulate matter in order to prevent plugging of the medium and subsequent operational problems. If the raw water contains high turbidity, pretreatment using sedimentation, coagulation, and filtration may be necessary. The ability of the medium to withstand a chlorine residual must also be investigated, since high chlorine residuals may oxidize some types of media and render them useless. Iron, manganese, or other heavy metals, if present at high levels, may cause problems with cation-exchange resins by binding permanently to the medium, thereby reducing the exchange capacity over time. All materials used in the construction of an ion-exchange plant must be selected for corrosion-resistant properties.

Ion-exchange brine disposal. One of the problems created by sodium-cycle ion exchange is the disposal of spent brine from the regeneration cycle. In view of the increasing water pollution control requirements, severe limits may be placed on discharge of this high-salinity or alkaline water. The problem becomes even more sensitive when the waste contains elevated levels of radium. The total solids in a composite sample of waste regenerant can vary from a typical average concentration of 50,000 to 100,000 mg/L to a maximum of 70,000 to 200,000 mg/L.

Disposal techniques may be limited by salinity rather than by radium concentration. A list of potential alternatives for handling the wastewater streams follows.

Discharge
    To sanitary sewer
    To local receiving water
Storage
    Evaporation lagoons
    Land spreading
Use recovery
Disposal
    In deep aquifers
    In oil-well fields
    As nuclear wastes

Reverse osmosis treatment

Osmosis is the spontaneous passage of liquid from a dilute to a more concentrated solution across a semipermeable membrane that allows passage of the liquid but not of dissolved solids. Reverse osmosis is a process in which the natural osmotic flow is reversed by the application to the concentrated solution of sufficient pressure to overcome the natural osmotic pressure of the less concentrated (dilute) solution. When the amounts of water passing in both directions are equal, the applied pressure can be defined as the osmotic pressure of the dilute solution with that particular concentration of solutes.

In practical applications, pumps are used to supply the necessary pressure, and the water flow rate through the membrane is dependent principally upon the net driving pressure. The solute flow rate through the membrane, or bleed, is dependent almost solely upon the solute concentration of the feedwater.

Figure 16.7 illustrates a typical reverse-osmosis installation. A single pressure vessel containing the membrane is shown, but normally there would be a number of pressure vessels arranged in a series-parallel array. A pump continuously feeds the pressure vessel, and a backpressure valve on the concentrate stream controls the pressure within the vessel and against the membrane. Increased pressure increases the transport rate to the permeate (the product water). Cur-

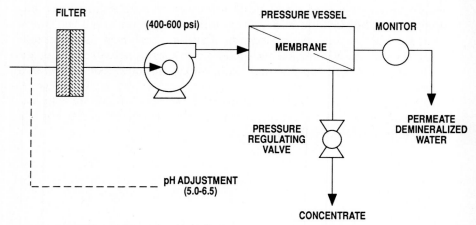

Figure 16.7   Typical reverse-osmosis system.

TABLE 16.7   Rejection and Removal of Various Ions by Reverse Osmosis[32,33]

	Average rejection, %
Constituent	
Borates	60–80
Ammonia, cyanide, nitrate	
perchlorate, thiocyanate	90–96
Nonelectrolytes	92–95
Monovalent ions	94–98
Divalent ions	98–99.5
Trivalent ions	99.0–99.9
Molecular weight greater than 180	98–100
Specifics	
Arsenic	99.5
Cadmium	99.0
Copper	99.1
Fluoride	96.5
Lead	98.5
Molybdates	99.2
Radionuclides:	
Gross alpha	85–96
Gross beta	95–99
Selenium	99.1
Total dissolved solids	95–97
Vanadium	97.2
Zinc	98.8

rently, there are two predominant membrane configurations: the spiral-wound module and hollow fine fiber.

The primary advantage of reverse osmosis is its high percentage of rejection of dissolved solids from the raw water. The rejection allows contaminated, brackish, and saline water to be desalted for potable use. Reverse osmosis has also been shown to be extremely effective for removal of radium from water. Data from two full-scale systems containing initial radium concentrations from 14 to 22 mg/L demonstrated 96 percent radium removal.[31] Table 16.7 summarizes the rejection and removal of various ions by reverse osmosis under ideal laboratory conditions and gives a good idea of the usefulness of reverse osmosis for removing inorganic contaminants; however, few data are available to confirm these rejection percentages for full-scale plants.[32,33]

Reverse osmosis has several disadvantages:

- High initial and operating costs.

- Need for pretreatment or turbid-raw-water treatment with acid and other chemicals to prevent fouling of the membranes by slimes, suspended solids, iron, manganese, and precipitates of calcium carbonate and magnesium hydroxide.

- Need to stabilize finished water with lime or other chemicals to prevent corrosion in distribution systems.

- Disposal of the reject waste stream. Because the strength of the reject waste stream from reverse osmosis units is lower than that of the regenerant brine from ion-exchange plants, disposal of this continuous stream presents somewhat less of a problem.

Other treatment processes

Powdered and granular activated carbon adsorption have been investigated[16] for organic mercury removal, and both were found effective. These studies showed that about 1 μg/L of powdered activated carbon was needed to remove each 0.1 μg/L of mercury in order to reach a level of 2 μg/L. Removal by granular activated carbon depends on contact time and the amount of water treated by the carbon. At a contact time of 3.5 min, mercury removals of 80 percent or more were achieved for 25,000 bed volumes of water containing 20 to 29 μg/L of organic mercury. Results for inorganic mercury were very similar. Figures 16.8 and 16.9 depict mercury removal by granular activated carbon columns for organic and inorganic mercury, respectively.

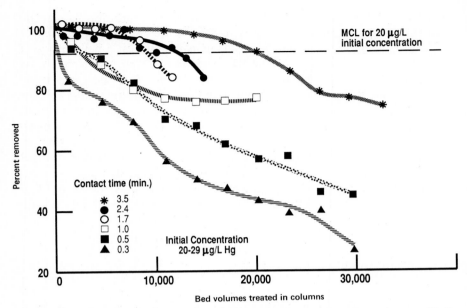

Figure 16.8 Organic mercury removal by granular activated carbon columns. (*G. S. Logsdon and J. M. Symons, "Mercury Removed by Conventional Water Treatment Techniques," Journal AWWA, vol. 65, no. 8, August 1973, p. 554.*)

Design Criteria

Stabilization and corrosion control

When water comes into contact with any metallic surface, the metal corrodes, i.e., metal is oxidized to the ionic form and passes into the liquid phase. In order to prevent this from occurring, it is necessary to separate the two reactants—to provide a physical barrier between them. This barrier can be applied by the pipe manufacturer—cement, plastic, or zinc—or by allowing the water to deposit a coating of calcium carbonate (by precipitation from the solution) or various metal complexes (such as metallic phosphates or silicates resulting from reaction of the metallic surface with some constituent in the water) to provide an unreactive surface coating.

Red coloration in water from soluble iron, blue from copper, and black from manganese, and the potential toxicity of water containing lead and cadmium, most frequently result from the leaching of these metals from the surfaces with which water comes into contact after it leaves the treatment plant. Control of this corrosion is the responsibility of the water purveyor, since the water quality regulations must be met at the consumer's tap.

Another problem, particularly in hard water areas, is the excessive

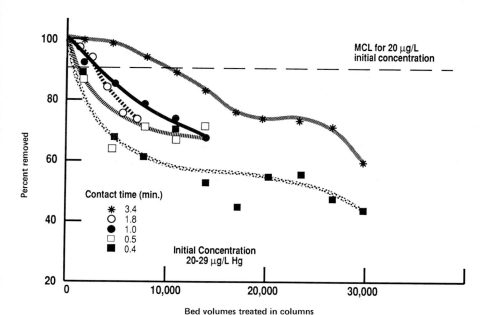

Figure 16.9 Inorganic mercury removal by granular activated carbon columns. *(G. S. Logsdon and J. M. Symons, "Mercury Removed by Conventional Water Treatment Techniques," Journal AWWA, vol. 65, no. 8, August 1973, p. 554.)*

precipitation of coatings on the distribution pipes or within household plumbing. This is due to supersaturated water which enters the system from the utility reaching equilibrium while in the distribution system. The major precipitates under such conditions are calcium carbonate and aluminum hydroxide. This problem, too, is within the control of the utility.

The system and the consumer can be protected from the effects of corrosion or excessive deposits by modifying the water quality prior to distribution. The two major options are addition of a substance that will react with the surface of the pipes to form a protective coating, such as phosphates or silicates; and precipitating a coating of calcium carbonate onto the pipe surfaces.

The first, phosphate or silicate feed, is site-specific and requires evaluation of the available formulations by the utility. Dosages required are usually in the 0.5- to 2-mg/L range, with higher dosages required initially in order to establish an effective coating. Among the factors that are important in maintenance of the protective coating are a constant feed and adequate flow in order to provide a continuous supply of the reactant to the surface. A physical barrier of calcium carbonate can be laid down for protection by supersaturating the water with calcium carbonate. Overzealous use, though, can lead to excessive precipitation and consequent loss of carrying capacity.

Determination of the exact point of saturation is based upon the work of Langelier in 1936, when he developed the well-known Langelier index, which relates the relevant calcium carbonate solubility parameters through the control of pH.[34] It is referred to as the pH of saturation pH_s and can be expressed as

$$pH_s = -\log \frac{K_2}{K_{so}}[Ca^{2+}][Alk]$$

where K_2 = second ionization constant for H_2CO_3
  K_{so} = solubility product constant for $CaCO_3$
  [Alk] = alkalinity
  [Ca^{2+}] = calcium-ion concentration

This relationship has been used in many modified forms since that time. Among the most common expressions are:

1. Saturation index = pH_a − pH_s, where pH_a is the actual pH. The values obtained for the saturation index are interpreted as:

   Positive: Water supersaturated, tends to precipitate calcium carbonate
   Negative: Water undersaturated, tends to dissolve calcium carbonate
   Zero: Water exactly saturated with calcium carbonate, neither deposits nor removes a coating

2. Ryznar index, defined in 1944 by Ryznar[35] as a "stability index." The definition was $2pH_s$ − pH_a. Ryznar generated a curve based on field results showing encrustation or corrosion as a function of this index.

   This use of the word "corrosive" points out one of the major errors in the use of any of the modifications of the solubility equations for calcium carbonate. The undersaturation of a water with respect to calcium carbonate does not make it corrosive, but only defines its state with respect to solid calcium carbonate. If a protective coating of calcium carbonate is not present, none of these indices relate to corrosion.

3. The aggressive index[36] is the only exception to this statement because it relates to the effect of the water on an in-place calcium-containing material. It is used for estimating the leaching of the cement matrix for asbestos-cement pipe. The aggressive index (AI) for such cases is defined as

$$AI = pH + \log AH$$

where A is the alkalinity and H is the calcium hardness, both expressed in terms of calcium carbonate.

This calculation has been shown to give a preliminary approximation of the attack on the cement matrix and subsequent release of asbestos fibers in some cases. It may be applicable to the cement lining in steel pipes.

The establishment of a protective coating of calcium carbonate is an art. It can be accomplished if the concentrations are controlled so that an eggshell coating is laid down uniformly throughout the parts of the system that needs such protection. The coating should be preserved by maintaining the quality of the water so that it is in equilibrium with the solid calcium carbonate.[37] Because of the many variables that influence this process, it is always necessary to monitor the system carefully in order to assure the continued presence of the coating. Water quality degradation can be established from customer complaints and from scheduled physical examinations.

A parallel problem exists as a result of precipitation of supersaturated aluminum hydroxide from treated water. This occurs when the aluminum-ion concentration entering the system exceeds that which can exist in equilibrium with solid aluminum hydroxide. The hydrolysis of the aluminum ion in the system leads to the presence of white deposits in rippled layers, dramatically reducing the carrying capacity. In order to avoid this problem, it is necessary to reduce the aluminum-ion concentration. Since the problem almost always results in plants that coagulate with alum, the pH should be adjusted to the pH of minimum aluminum hydroxide solubility ahead of the filters. The exact pH must be determined on a case-by-case basis, but it is normally within the pH range of 5.5 to 7.

References

1. U.S. Environmental Protection Agency, "National Interim Primary Drinking Water Regulations," *Federal Register,* vol. 40, no. 248, December 24, 1975.
2. U.S. Environmental Protection Agency, "Drinking Water Regulations, Radionuclides," *Federal Register,* vol. 41, no. 133, July 19, 1976.
3. U.S. Environmental Protection Agency, "National Secondary Drinking Water Regulations," *Federal Register,* vol. 44, no. 140, July 19, 1979.
4. G. F. Craun and L. J. McCabe, "Problems Associated with Metals in Drinking Water," *Journal AWWA,* vol. 67, no. 11, 1975, p. 593.
5. Bureau of Water Hygiene, Environmental Health Service, PHS, *Community Water Supply Study: Analysis of National Survey Findings,* U.S. Department of Health, Education, and Welfare, Washington, D.C., July 1970.
6. T. J. Sorg, "Treatment Technology to Meet the Interim Primary Drinking Water Regulations for Inorganics," *Journal AWWA,* vol. 70, no. 2, 1978, p. 105.
7. J. H. Gulledge and J. T. O'Connor, "Removal of Arsenic (V) from Water by Adsorption on Aluminum and Ferric Hydroxide," *Journal AWWA,* vol. 65, no. 8, August 1973, p. 548.

8. G. S. Logsdon, T. J. Sorg, and J. M. Symons, "Removal of Heavy Metals by Conventional Treatment," *Proc. 16th Water Quality Conference—Trace Metals in Water Supplies: Occurrence, Significance, and Control,* University of Illinois Bull. No. 71, Urbana-Champaign, 1974.
9. G. L. Logsdon and J. M. Symons, "Removal of Heavy Metals by Conventional Treatment," *Proceedings of a Symposium on Trace Metals in Water Removal Processes and Monitoring,* U.S. Environmental Protection Agency, New York, 1973.
10. G. S. Logsdon and J. M. Symons, "Removal of Trace Inorganics by Drinking Water Treatment Unit Processes," *AICE Symposium Series,* vol. 70, 1974, p. 136.
11. U.S. Environmental Protection Agency, Office of Research and Development, *Manual of Treatment Techniques for Meeting the Interim Primary Drinking Water Regulations,* EPA-600/8-77-005, May 1977.
12. J. T. O'Connor, "Removal of Trace Inorganic Constituents by Conventional Water Treatment Processes," *Proc. 16th Water Quality Conference—Trace Metals in Water Supplies: Occurrence, Significance and Control,* University of Illinois Bull. no. 71, Urbana-Champaign, 1974.
13. R. D. Scott et al., "Fluoride in Ohio Water Supplies," *Journal AWWA,* vol. 29, no. 1, 1937, p. 9.
14. R. L. Culp and H. A. Stoltenberg, "Fluoride Reduction at LaCrosse, Kansas," *Journal AWWA,* vol. 29, no. 1, 1937.
15. L. M. Naylor and R. R. Dague, "Simulation of Lead Removal by Chemical Treatment," *Journal AWWA,* vol. 67, no. 10, 1975, p. 560.
16. G. S. Logsdon and J. M. Symons, "Mercury Removal by Conventional Water Treatment Techniques," *Journal AWWA,* vol. 65, no. 8, 1973, p. 554.
17. J. E. Singley et al., *Costs of Radium Removal from Potable Water Supplies,* U.S. Environmental Protection Agency, Cincinnati, Ohio, EPA-600/2-77-073, February 1977.
18. F. J. Maier, "Defluoridation of Municipal Water Supplies," *Journal AWWA,* vol. 45, no. 8, 1953, p. 879.
19. F. J. Maier, "Partial Defluoridation of Water," *Public Works,* vol. 91, 1960, pp. 90–92.
20. E. A. Savinelli and A. P. Black, "Defluoridation of Water with Activated Alumina," *Journal AWWA,* vol. 50, no. 1, 1958, p. 33.
21. E. Bellack, "Arsenic Removal from Potable Water," *Journal AWWA,* vol. 63, no. 7, 1971, p. 454.
22. F. Rubel, Jr., and F. S. Williams, *Pilot Study of Fluoride and Arsenic Removal from Potable Water,* U.S. Environmental Protection Agency, EPA-600/2/80-110, February 1980.
23. R. R. Trussell, "Application of Treatment Technology," *Technology Transfer Seminar on Designing and Upgrading Drinking Water Systems,* U.S. Environmental Protection Agency Research Center, June 1977.
24. R. B. Gauntlett, "Nitrate Removal from Water by Ion Exchange," *Water Treat. Exam,* vol. 24, no. 3, 1975.
25. J. C. Gregg, "Nitrate Removal at Water Treatment Plant," *Civil Eng.,* vol. 43, no. 4, 1973.
26. E. Korngold, "Removal of Nitrates from Potable Water by Ion Exchange," *Water, Air, Soil Pollut.,* vol. 2, 1973, pp. 15–22.
27. R. W. Beulow et al, "Nitrate Removal by Anion-Exchange Resins," *Journal AWWA,* vol. 67, no. 9, 1975, p. 528.
28. T. J. Sorg and G. S. Logsdon, "Removal of Selenium from Water—State-of-the-Art," *Proc. 1976 Industrial Health Foundation, Inc. Symposium on Selenium-Tellurium,* University of Notre Dame, South Bend, Ind., May 1976.
29. R. R. Trussell et al., *Selenium Removal from Ground Water Using Activated Alumina,* U.S. Environmental Protection Agency, EPA-600/2-80-153, February 1980.
30. *Manual of Treatment Techniques for Meeting the Interim Primary Drinking Water Regulations,* U.S. Environmental Protection Agency, Office of Research and Development, EPA-600/8-77-005, May 1973.
31. J. E. Fingley et al., *Costs of Radium Removal from Potable Water Supplies,* U.S.

Environmental Protection Agency, Cincinnati, Ohio, USEPA-600/2-77-073, February 1977.

32. *Groundwater Elements of In-Situ Leach Mining of Uranium,* Nuclear Regulatory Commission, NUREG/CR-0311, 1978.

33. S. E. Smith and K. H. Garrett, "Some Recent Developments in the Extraction of Uranium and Its Ores," *The Chemical Engineer,* vol. 268, p. 440.

34. W. F. Langelier, "The Analytical Control of Anti-Corrosion Water Treatment," *Journal AWWA,* vol. 28, no. 10, 1936, p. 1500; *ibid.,* vol. 38, no. 2, 1946, p. 169.

35. J. W. Ryznar, "A New Index for Determining Amount of Calcium Carbonate Formed by a Water," *Journal AWWA,* vol. 36, no. 4, 1944, p. 472.

36. *AWWA Standard for Asbestos-Cement Pressure Pipe, 4 in. Through 24 in. for Water and Other Liquids,.* AWWA C400-77, Denver, Colo., 1977.

37. D. T. Merrill and R. L. Sanks, "Corrosion Control by Deposition of $CaCO_3$ Films: A Practical Approach for Plant Operators," *Journal AWWA,* vol. 69, no. 11, 1978, p. 592; vol. 69, no. 12, 1978, p. 634; vol. 70, no. 1, 1979, p. 12.

17

Design Considerations

Introduction

This chapter identifies and describes a number of design considerations (other than the treatment process) that are important to any
treatment plant design. The importance of ancillary facilities is described, followed by design considerations in the civil, architectural,
mechanical, electrical, security, and safety areas. While the reader
should find the information presented in this chapter helpful and
practical, it is not intended to be complete or all-inclusive.

Ancillary facilities

Ancillary facilities do not treat water but are necessary either to enable the various process units to operate or to house the people who
supervise, operate, and maintain the plant. These include the electric
power system and other utilities such as water, gas, and waste disposal; administrative offices, meeting rooms, laboratories, and maintenance facilities; and also those items which are related to site work
and may be necessary to make the plant habitable. Frequently, space
to receive the public in small or large groups is required. A plant, being a source of municipal or company pride, is often required to receive groups of school children, college students, or professionals. In
all, the ancillary facilities may amount to 15 to 35 percent of the total
cost of a water treatment plant.

Ancillary facilities may perform functions that are not directly involved with the treatment of water. The laboratory may be planned to
perform analyses of distribution system samples or physical testing of
construction materials. The control room may operate remote pumping stations as well as those at the treatment plant. A garage may be
constructed to house vehicles used by field or nonplant personnel. In

many cases, experience has shown the value of allowing space for additional functions.

The sizes of the ancillary structures are generally proportional to the treatment capacity of the plant. For instance, a small plant may have a single room housing the superintendent's desk, the control panel, record cabinets, and a small laboratory capable of a half-dozen analyses. Conversely, a large plant might have several separate administrative offices, multiple rooms for laboratories, a separate control room, and a record-storage room. Similarly, maintenance facilities can vary from a few wall cabinets for tools to a number of fully equipped specialized maintenance shops.

Very often the public judges a water treatment plant by its ancillary facilities, not by its primary elements, the treatment units which process water. This is partially because the treatment units cannot be fully observed as they operate. For example, most of the essential parts of a filter cannot be seen by a visitor. However, a laboratory, a control room, or an entrance lobby is easily inspected. Deficiencies in the design of ancillary facilities can be much more visible than deficiencies in process design and, unfortunately, can be more readily understood by the public and those people who authorize the expenditure of operating and capital funds. Even small details which may not interfere with operation can create a bad impression. As insignificant as floor drainage may seem to some, a tiny stream of water running across the floor to a puddle may be a considerable source of aggravation to someone who gets his shoes wet. Well-designed and functional ancillary facilities are important to enhance the public's image of, and confidence in, a water treatment installation.

Civil

In addition to an efficient plant layout with adequate room for expansion, the design engineer should provide sufficient paved areas for parking and access.

Parking

Plant design should include adequate space for visitor, employee, and delivery parking. It is preferable that employee parking be isolated from the main entrance, near access to showers, lockers, and other similar facilities. This will reduce traffic near administrative and public areas and enhance the aesthetic value of the plant. If possible, administrative areas should be nearest the main entrance, not only for the convenience of visitors, but for control of visitor access.

Access

The road network at any plant must serve both light passenger vehicles and trucks, such as cranes, chemical delivery trucks, and snow removal vehicles (where applicable). Road grades should be planned for heavy truck access. Radii of curves should be large enough to allow trucks to stay on paved areas under all circumstances. Other considerations include fire trucks, hydrant locations, fencing, gates, and intercoms.

Architectural

Administrative facilities

The size and kind of administrative facilities required will vary widely from plant to plant. Though larger plants may require proportionately larger administrative areas, the needs and special circumstances of the individual plant will determine the size of these facilities.

Office space, for example, can vary from a superintendent's or operator's utility desk in a nonoffice area to a large and populous office requiring special design considerations. Any provisions for offices must include space for storage of plant records. These records include contract and shop design drawings of the plant, operating manuals, and personnel and purchasing records, as well as operating records, including recorded charts and logs.

Additional spaces which may be required, depending on individual plant circumstances, may include:

A *lobby* or *reception area* for use on occasions when the public visits the plant. Visits by groups of school children, scouts, or civic groups are not uncommon, especially in larger facilities.

A *public room* with seating which can be used for large-scale ceremonies or instructional or other public occasions. This room might be as elaborate as a small civic auditorium, equipped with stage, lighting and sound equipment, a podium for speakers, and equipment for audiovisual displays; or it might simply be a multipurpose room, such as a lunchroom with a collapsible stage platform and folding seats and tables. Such rooms can function during working shifts as employee lunchrooms or rest areas, and also for receptions or other occasions.

A *classroom*. The need for a special instructional area would depend on the individual needs of the plant in question. A new or greatly expanded facility might require training space for a large number of personnel. The general-purpose spaces mentioned above might be adapted as classrooms in certain circumstances. (See also "Personnel facilities" below.)

Handicapped access. Many states have laws requiring public buildings to provide facilities for handicapped persons. In any case, it may be desirable to hire available and qualified handicapped persons. Facilities may then include wheelchair ramps, specialized elevators, and larger than normal toilet stalls, as a few examples.

Laboratory

Laboratory testing is usually required for applications affecting process control, cost control, historical data, or requirements of regulatory agencies. Sampling lines are best brought directly to the analytical laboratory where the samples are to be analyzed. Frequently, a sampling sink is installed in the laboratory, with sample water from various parts of the process running continuously (to waste) for immediate sampling access. Inasmuch as the treatment plant laboratory may be in charge of performing analyses for the entire water system, adequate space for receiving samples and preparation of containers must be provided.

Estimating laboratory needs. The main factors in estimating needs for the treatment plant laboratory are estimated requirements for staffing, space, equipment, supplies, and chemicals.[1] An efficient layout and adequate materials are the most important considerations.

In calculating staffing requirements, it is advisable to list the analyses to be performed and their frequency. Experience, judgment, or information obtained from existing treatment plants allow the annual number of person-hours required for the facility under consideration to be computed. Special attention must be paid to certain factors which affect the staffing requirements, such as

- The type of laboratory equipment to be used
- The extent of automatic monitoring and recording instruments
- The amount of laboratory work to be done by outside laboratories
- The level of training of laboratory personnel

Once the annual number of person-hours has been estimated, the number of persons involved can be determined by considering the actual on-the-job hours per person.

Planning of laboratory space includes the estimation of laboratory floor area, bench surface area, and cabinet volume. Initial estimates of floor space may be between 200 and 300 ft^2 (18.6 to 27.9 m^2) per staff member. The estimates can be checked once the layout is made and equipment requirements are known.

Bench-top working surface may be assumed to be between 30 and 40 percent of the total floor space. Cabinet volume may be initially estimated at between 200 and 250 ft^3 (5.7 to 7.1 m^3) per staff member. One sink should be provided for every 25 to 30 ft (7.6 to 9.1 m) of bench length. Electrical receptacles should be spaced at 1½-ft (0.5-m) intervals along benches used for laboratory tests. In large labs compressed air and vacuum lines should be provided in bench tops, but in small labs a portable air/vacuum pump is adequate.

Equipment and supplies should be selected based on the frequency of tests, the sophistication of the unit processes, cost-effectiveness, and the desire to achieve optimum plant efficiency. The selection of major equipment items can be made from the equipment requirements suggested by the American Public Health Association in *Standard Methods*[2] and AWWA Manual M15.[3] Minor equipment for general laboratory use should be sufficient to assure suitable operation of the laboratory. Chemical needs should be based on the amounts required for analyses during a given period of time. Packaging policies of chemical manufacturers and known shelving times should serve as a guide for selection of minimum amounts of chemicals.

Laboratory operation.   Efficient laboratory operation depends largely on the layout of the laboratory. Flexibility, adaptability, and expandability should be considered in planning the physical layout. A northerly location should be preferred in order to obtain a better exposure to natural light. The laboratory should be located away from any vibrating machines or equipment which might affect the performance of laboratory instruments. In the laboratory, sensitive instruments should be in a separate room or isolated from the main centers of activity. It is also desirable to locate equipment that gives off heat or that poses some minor hazard, such as furnaces and fume hoods, in a separate room or area.

Many laboratories are separated into chemical and biological functions, and sometimes physical testing functions as well. Others merely have separate work areas that can share common equipment.

Equipment arrangement should be carefully considered in the layout. Pieces of equipment used in common tests should be in close proximity in order to eliminate wasted motion in the laboratory. However, sink areas should not be adjacent to instruments.

Safety must be a prime consideration in the laboratory layout. First-aid kits, fire extinguishers, fire blankets, eye washes, and emergency showers should be located near the principal working areas. Minimum space between work benches should be 4 ft (1.2 m). Minimum ceiling height should be 8 ft 6 in (2.6 m). Hard-to-reach storage areas should be reserved for nonhazardous chemicals or materials. Strong acids and bases should be stored within convenient reach of laboratory personnel.

Maintenance facilities

Repair shops.   The size and number of repair shops is, again, related to the size of the plant. The repair shop should be accessible by wheeled vehicles, so that bulky and cumbersome apparatus may be easily moved. Doors should be made wide enough to permit this equipment to pass in and out. Ideally, the repair shop is located adjacent to the equipment most frequently repaired; this is usually the chemical feed equipment. Pumping equipment maintenance is usually done at the pumps, as is most electrical and instrument maintenance.

Where plant size and anticipated maintenance workloads warrant, a separate electrical repair shop and a paint shop are desirable. Electrical repair requires a high degree of cleanliness. Paint solvents are flammable, and prudence requires that this area be protected from sparks and open flames.

Adequate bench space is necessary in all shops. Benches should be sturdy and heavy, permitting rough work on top surfaces. Drawers installed in work benches to hold small, frequently used parts and hand tools are helpful. Tools used with vises should be stored adjacent to the vise. These tools in particular are taps and dies, pipe threaders, an electric drill motor and bits, and various components. Lighting directly over the tables should be strong without being intense. Other lighting may be needed to boost light intensity, and numerous electrical outlets should be included in the back board or the wall behind the bench for this purpose.

One item frequently overlooked in repair shops is the need to use water and to dispose of wastewater. Testing of solution tanks for feed machines, the injectors on chlorinators, or electric mixers frequently results in spilled water. It is valuable for a machine shop to have a drainage area, in a corner or an end of the room, set off by a 4-in (10-cm) concrete curb, in which such wet testing can be done. A floor drain should also be installed at the low point of the floor.

Tools.   A wide variety of tools will be required. For equipment repair and maintenance, heavy tools may include a drill press, a bench grinder, a portable hoist, a portable pump, a light welding rig, mobile light and power, and, if warranted, a portable valve operator. Light tools should include those for plumbing, automotive, electrical, painting, carpentry, sheet metal, and masonry work. These should include grease guns, oilers, and trouble lamps. For housekeeping, mops, pails, brooms, and vacuum cleaners are needed. For outside maintenance, wheelbarrows, rakes, shovels, hoses, lawn sprinklers, and a power lawn mower (sized according to grassed area) should be included. In cold climates, snow removal equipment is needed. Foul-weather gear should include rain clothes and storm boots. Safety equipment should include first-aid kits, portable gas indicators, goggles and other protective equipment, and a resuscitator and portable breathing equipment.

Spare parts.   Spare parts should be kept in a separate area that can be locked for inventory control, in plants large enough to warrant this. The storage room should include a section of drawers, a large amount of shelf space, and some peg racks on which roll material such as gasket stock, screen wire, and hardware cloth may be stored. Some designers prefer to keep spare parts near the point of use. For example, spare chlorinator parts are kept in a wall cabinet near or in the chlorinator room, along with special testing and protective equipment.

Personnel facilities

Locker facilities and showers are usually provided for each individual expected to be working at the plant. Showers are frequently located adjacent to lockers. If it is expected that handicapped employees will be at this plant, specialized restrooms, showers, and lockers should be included.

A lunchroom for plant personnel will not only benefit employee morale, but simplify housekeeping and help to eliminate mice, cockroaches, and other vermin. The lunchroom is often equipped with a small kitchen unit.

If there is a demonstrated need for in-plant training programs, suitable space should be provided for this, preferably in the administrative section of the plant. If a room large enough to serve as a lecture room is provided, it may be equipped with a projection screen, a blackboard, and possibly a chemical demonstration table. Provision might be made for note-taking, perhaps by providing classroom-type desk arms at seats.

Material selection

Finishes.   The finishes selected for plant interiors, subject to budget restrictions, should suit the function of each area and be easy to maintain. Typical finishes for administrative and control areas and the filter operating area might be plaster or ceramic tile walls, terrazzo tile or carpet floors and bases, suspended acoustical ceilings, all utilities concealed, and paint or wall covering on plaster finishes. Less expensive finishes could be used in places such as chemical feed areas or pumping stations where an attractive finish is desired. These finishes might be structural or glazed tile walls, terrazzo or tile floors and bases, utilities concealed in walls but exposed on ceilings, and paint on concrete and plaster. Finishes in areas where cleaning should be made easy but appearance is not important, such as filter galleries and pumping stations, might be concrete or concrete block walls with tooled joints, concrete floors with hardener, cement bases, utilities all exposed, openings through floor curbed to match base, and walls and metals painted. Other areas, such as basements, boiler rooms, and pipe galleries, need have no finishes nor bases.

There are no restrictions on color schemes except that care should be used in the laboratory. The determination of small concentrations of minerals in water is often done colorimetrically, and light reflected from various colored areas in the laboratory may interfere with these tests. Preferred laboratory colors are subdued colors such as off white, light grays, or light blues in the areas where any colorimetric work may be done.

To facilitate building maintenance, abundant electrical outlets should be provided in the hallways and in the various cubicles. There should be provision on each floor of the building for adequately sized mop and broom closets containing a slop sink and storage space for mop buckets and cleaning materials.

Painting.   Steel surfaces at a water treatment plant that require painting include clarifier mechanisms, piping railings, structural members, storage tanks, and miscellaneous ironwork. A number of different painting systems are possible.[4] Nontoxic paint should be used for painted surfaces that are in contact with both raw and potable water; these should be those systems specified as Inside Paint Systems.[4]

The durability of paint depends, to a large extent, on the way the surface is prepared. Surfaces may be prepared by removing rust, grease, oil, dirt, old paint films, and mill scale. Cleaning methods can be wire brushing, chipping and scraping, sand blasting, flame conditioning, and solvent cleaning. Hand and power steel wire brushing are the most common methods used.

For decorative painting of galvanized surfaces, special treatment is necessary to make paint coatings adhere. Smooth galvanizing must be roughened with a mild acid such as phosphoric acid.

Most painting work can be avoided by selecting finishes that do not require painting. Where painting is not needed for aesthetic purposes, concrete walls and slabs should be left in their natural state or materials such as glazed brick or tile or quarry tile should be used.

Mechanical

The mechanical design of a water treatment plant involves components of varying complexity. A number of mechanical design considerations, if overlooked by the design engineer, can create a nuisance in the operation and maintenance of a plant. These include space and maintenance requirements, in-plant drainage, color-coded piping, noise control, HVAC (heating, ventilation, and air conditioning), and plant utilities.

Space and maintenance requirements

There are a number of space and maintenance requirements that should be included throughout a water treatment plant, particularly for rooms containing machinery. There should be adequate space around pumps, motors, engines, and machinery to permit repair. Equipment placement should allow adequate space to get a wrench on all nuts. Rotating shafts and moving parts should have cages or guards, and long vertical shafts should have safeguards to prevent injury from "whipping" if a shaft breaks. Machinery or pump rooms should have fixed or portable hoists; lifting attachments, such as hooks in the ceiling, should be provided. Repair shops, tools, and spare parts are described under "Maintenance Facilities."

In-plant drainage

A water treatment plant has many potential sources of water leakage which, if not allowed for in the original design, can be extremely costly to remedy. A leaky pipe or valve that causes puddles to form or water to run across the floor to a drain, or that stains a wall, is a source of irritation to a plant operator. No plant can be designed to prevent all leaks. But if the designer does not consider appropriate drainage for possible leaks, this lack of thoroughness will be obvious to every visitor to the plant.

Concrete walls which contain water on one side may develop leaks and create a nuisance if proper drainage is not provided. Typically, this situation exists in the piping gallery between filters or a gallery between sedimentation basins. No matter how careful the construction inspection or how restrictive the specifications, it is almost impossible to guarantee absolute watertightness in a plain reinforced-concrete wall. It is best to provide a gutter at the bottom of the wall, with the floor sloping toward this gutter. The gutter may be open or covered with a grate, but should be accessible for cleaning. If the appearance of the wall is important, joints should be designed with waterstop and joint sealant, or a double wall should be constructed.

Piping and valves with packing on the stems are potential sources of leaks. Small piping should be grouped together and preferably placed next to a wall with a gutter drain below. It is wise to anticipate leaks from all valves and have drains below. Floors should slope toward floor drains or gutters about ¼ in/ft (2 percent), with the minimum slope being about ⅛ in/ft (1 percent). Gutters with removable grates are easier to maintain than round drains connected with soil pipe. Gutters, however, are usually more expensive to construct.

Most common types of pumps have shafts which extend through a packing gland or mechanical seal to the driving unit. Leakage at the glands is frequently necessary to allow for lubrication of the packing. Mechanical seals may leak slightly even when new. Drainage from pump bases is therefore a necessity. Water leaking from bases should not be allowed to run onto floors.

Means should be provided for draining every tank or process unit containing liquid. This may be accomplished by installing drain valves to gravity outlets or to sumps from which liquid can be removed by pumping. It may be more cost-effective not to provide drain valves and connecting pipelines, but instead to use a portable pump to empty the tank. This will depend on the frequency with which a structure is drained and the relative cost of drain lines. Disposal of wastes should always be considered when planning dewatering and drainage operations.

Color-coded piping

Color-coded plant piping is useful for safety reasons and educational purposes, and greatly assists in maintenance work. The color code should be consistent with any previously established color codes.

Where there are many different kinds of pipes to be identified, or where the color codes become too complicated, it may be desirable to stencil the name of the contents on each pipe. A metal tag can be used on small pipes. An arrow indicating direction of flow may also be useful.

Noise control

Noise control may be necessary either to reduce the noise level at adjacent properties or to avoid occupational health problems for plant personnel. An excessively noisy water treatment plant is a bad neighbor. In addition, economic damage could result from nuisance noise.

The majority of noise problems can be solved by careful design without the use of special acoustical methods or enclosures. All internal combustion engines and air compressors should be muffled. Insulation jackets should be specified for engines. These jackets have the additional function of protecting operating personnel from burns, as well as reducing noise. Large electric motors can be specified to be "extra quiet"; motor manufacturers should be consulted. Masonry building construction usually offers the greatest sound resistance. For a slight additional cost, ceilings and walls in noisy rooms can have sound-absorbing construction or finishes. The layout and arrangement of the structure can have considerable effect on the noise radiated, which can be further reduced by belts of trees. Noise level will decrease 6 dB for every doubling of distance from the source.

Damage to personnel from excessive noise varies with the length of time of exposure. Many designers find it more cost-effective to provide plant personnel with individual ear protection devices instead of reducing noise at the source.

HVAC

Ventilation requirements—that is, the number of air changes per hour in the various rooms of a building—are usually determined by state or local building codes. These codes can vary widely. The "10-State Standards"[5] require one air change per minute in chlorine rooms while they are occupied, and six air changes per hour in spaces below ground in pumping stations.

Internal combustion engines have an unusually high ventilation requirement even when the jacket water is cooled with a heat exchanger. In addition to combustion air, these engines radiate large amounts of heat from the engine block; in hot weather, substantial air circulation is needed to keep engine room temperatures within acceptable limits.

Administrative areas—offices, laboratories, lunchrooms, and public spaces—are usually air-conditioned. Computer rooms may require a special environment, and air-conditioning may be essential in this area. If so, a separate air-conditioning system is desirable, as these rooms must be cooled 24 h per day.

Dehumidification.   In highly humid areas, the dehumidification of circulated air in a plant is highly desirable, as paint, equipment, and instrumentation may deteriorate rapidly. Filter-piping galleries are particularly susceptible because the cool water flowing through the pipes causes pipes and valves to sweat, which accelerates corrosion and deterioration of paint films. Water dripping from pipes is also a nuisance. Lithium-type dehumidifiers are usually more economical for large areas than dehumidifiers of the refrigerant type. Some chemicals, such as dry polymers, are hydroscopic and should be stored in areas of lower humidity or in rooms that are specifically dehumidified.

Plant utilities

Plant water supply.   The use of water for various plant purposes is significant, and the design of this supply requires careful consideration. Backwashing and surface washing of filters take the largest fraction of plant water. Backwash water is required in large quantities at low pressure, but media-washing systems usually work best with a small quantity of water at high pressure (about 80 to 100 psi).

The next largest amount of water is used by the chemical feeding systems. Water may be required for chemical dilution, and if injectors are used, additional water is required. Chlorinators use a particularly large amount of water, as solution strength may be limited to 3500 mg/L, and water-operated injectors are used to create a vacuum for chlorine gas withdrawal. Consequently, injectors run continuously.

Other plant uses of water may include fire hydrants, fire sprinklers, washing of basins and filter walls, lawn sprinkling, washing of screens, backwashing of strainers, pump seal water, and hydraulically operated valves and sluice gates. Water may be used for sanitary purposes in lavatories, showers, toilets, urinals, sinks, laboratories, and drinking fountains.

Backflow-prevention devices are required to prevent cross-connections. Care should be used in piping chemical systems, as serious siphoning and backflows have occurred in this area. The plant water system is obtained from a high-pressure main, if available, or from a separate small pumping station. Surface washers may require a separate system (or a booster pump) because of their need for high-pressure water.

Gas service.   Natural gas can be an economical source of energy for internal combustion engines, boilers, and carbon regeneration furnaces. Gas has important advantages for internal combustion engines compared with gasoline or diesel oil. Combustion of gas is clean, with less gumming and less carbon buildup. Efficiency is greater because of higher compression ratios. In addition, fuel storage problems are minimized if the gas can be taken directly from a gas main. One disadvantage is possible service interruptions. In addition, future costs and availability should be considered. The National Electric Code requires on-site storage of fuel for emergency power systems. This may preclude the use of natural gas for standby generators. Gas service, when available, should be brought into the laboratory.

Electrical

Power systems

The design of a treatment plant electrical system must conform with applicable codes, local regulations, and the rules of the serving utility. Most such codes basically agree with the National Electrical Safety Code.[6] In the absence of detailed local requirements, these standards usually are the minimum safety design requirements. On completion of construction, the contractor is often required to obtain and furnish certification of inspection and approval from all required authorities and the underwriters.

The choice of power-supply voltages from a utility is limited by the types of service available from the utility in question. The distribution capability, policy, and system of an electric utility has a strong influence on the design of the power system.

Important electrical characteristics of a power company's distribution system are the power capacity, distribution voltage, and short-circuit capacity. The power capacity of the distribution system should obviously be at least equal to the load it is to supply.

A grounded neutral operation is highly desirable. Destructive transient overvoltages are eliminated in a grounded system. Grounded systems basically fall into three classifications: solidly grounded, resistance grounded, and reactance grounded. Small, low-voltage systems are usually solidly grounded; larger systems, including those where relay protection is used or generating equipment is employed, will require other grounding methods. System grounding should not be confused with equipment grounding. Equipment should always be grounded solidly, regardless of whether or not the system is grounded.

All systems should be protected from lightning and surges. Destructive overvoltage surges can occur on lines feeding a station even in the absence of a lightning storm. Generally, the greater the investment in station equipment, the greater should be the investment in lightning and overvoltage protection. Average-sized plants, especially those fed from overhead lines, should have lightning arrestors and surge capacitors connected between the main bus or lines and grounded for minimum protection. The use of more extensive protection should be considered for each individual installation.

Working around and operating electrical equipment could be hazardous as well, but fortunately, the National Electrical Code is comprehensive, is updated frequently, and is included in almost every building code. This safety code is essentially a minimum safety standard which should be fully complied with. Some major requirements are that all electrical switching gear shall be completely enclosed in explosionproof enclosures and that all electrical equipment shall be adequately grounded. All switchboards should have a "dead front" and a "dead rear." There should be a clearly labeled emergency shutoff switch at all machinery units.

Motors

Motors used should be properly sized to operate at a reasonably high power factor. Some state codes require a specific minimum power factor, and most utility companies apply charges if certain power-factor levels are exceeded. The use of energy-efficient motors should be considered.

A major cause of motor failure is breakdown of the winding insulation. Motor overloads cause excessive heat, which is damaging to the insulation; this effect is cumulative, as each occasion of excessive temperature adds to the deterioration. For this reason, the overload-protection device should disconnect the motor before excessive heat can be generated.

Instrumentation and controls

Electrical controls should be simple, direct, and reliable. Large plants increasingly employ centralized control systems that automatically start and stop the pump units and associated valves and auxiliaries after initiation by pushbutton stations or automatic sensory devices. Centralized control panels or consoles usually include indicating lights, control switches or pushbutton stations, and a line of instrumentation for operation and record purposes. Instrumentation may consist of pressure gauges, pressure or level controls and recorders, flow indicators and recorders, and electrical devices such as ammeters, wattmeters, and voltmeters. The outstanding success of local centralized control has led to the use of remote control, which is accomplished by adding interposing starting and stopping relays operated by supervisory equipment. Supervisory control equipment can operate over telephone lines. Telemetering equipment may be employed, in addition, to transmit instrument readings over the same or additional communication channels. This is discussed in greater detail in Chap. 14.

Electrical control equipment also includes apparatus and accessory devices for starting, stopping, regulating, and protecting motors and other equipment. Applications employing automatic and sequence controls based on liquid levels should be designed with sufficient well or reservoir capacity to prevent equipment from starting and stopping too often. If more than four to six parts per hour are necessary, special care should be taken in selecting both the motor and the controls.

Alternative power supply

Alternative power supplies may be required to maintain at least partial continuous plant operation. These systems usually employ diesel generators, which automatically start when power fails, and automatic switches, which automatically transfer power to preselected distribution zones.

Lighting

A good lighting system will promote safer and more efficient working conditions. For indoor lighting, the use of efficient fluorescent and high-intensity discharge lamps should be considered; however, when high-intensity discharge lamps are included in a design, their delay in developing light output must be remembered.

Emergency lighting units should be used throughout. These may be individual battery-powered units. If automatically started engine generators are used, separate emergency lighting circuits should be provided.

Lighting levels for general illumination should follow the Illumination Engineering Society recommendations.[7] Exterior lighting should generally utilize high-intensity discharge lamps.

Communications

Good communication throughout the plant is essential to good operation, and an absolute necessity when the plant occupies several acres. Intercoms should be located at each operating point and where operating equipment is stored. This will expedite repair work and save travel time. There are many types of intercom systems, ranging from systems installed by a telephone company to a common telephone system with calling codes on horns or buzzers. Systems with loudspeaker paging are very common. Paging systems should be selected with the noise level at each station in mind. Many types of equipment with remote control or indication can be properly serviced and maintained only with the aid of an intercom. If the initial budget for the plant does not include an intercom system, it would be wise to provide conduits for future installations.

Security

Water treatment plants, as well as accessible distribution facilities, are frequently targets for vandals. Sabotage may also occur. The facilities must be protected, not to mention the need to protect the safety of plant personnel. A strong argument in favor of such protection is the possibility of lawsuits based on lack of protection or negligence in upkeep of facilities. Installation and maintenance costs must be weighed against possible economic damages from lawsuits brought by employees, the general public, or even trespassers.

Fencing

The most common first line of protection consists of a fence around the facility coupled with proper lighting and gate protection, providing security along with ease of access for authorized personnel and visitors. The layout or size of some facilities may preclude appropriate perimeter fencing, in which case the individual buildings must be protected and equipment fenced separately or provided with housing.

The fencing should surround all pertinent operation facilities, with some clear area left between the fence and the nearest structure. The fence should be climb-proof, with barbed wire at the top; the bottom edge should be anchored to preclude undermining at the bottom of the fence. When chain-link fencing is used, a large wire must be passed through the bottom of the fencing, fastened to each fence post, and, depending on post spacing, staked into the earth between the posts. Otherwise, the fencing is elastic enough to be lifted and the plant entered. Care should be taken to secure points where utility lines and other such facilities cross the fencing.

Security lighting

Perimeter lighting that gives good illumination of the open areas between the fence and the plant structure should be provided in addition to the usual plant lighting. Floodlights should be efficient and allow lamp servicing without special equipment. Where large areas, such as the entire plant and/or a reservoir, are to be protected, sectionalized vibration-detecting equipment can be used for fences and for fence gates that are infrequently operated. When a disturbance is detected, this equipment can activate local floodlights and closed-circuit television (CCTV) cameras. Further action is then decided on at the central monitoring station.

Entry control

Many entry-control methods of varying degrees of sophistication are now available. While a simple single or double gate or door lock may suffice in many places, for large plants it is generally safer, less cumbersome, and more desirable to invest in more advanced systems. Such systems might include:

A gate house, manned either during the main shift or at all times.

Gate(s) with fully automated control, operated for entry and exit by key or badge cards, including automatic trestles to close the gate after cars or trucks pass through.

CCTV to allow observation of gates at all times; gates may be left open during day hours, and staff may operate them or present badges to enter at other hours and on weekends. CCTV cameras should be bulletproof, vandalproof, and provided with remotely adjustable zoom lenses for close viewing.

Telephone intercommunications between gates and a control room should be provided in any event, and *manual takeover* should be furnished for all automatic features.

With a badge system, it is also possible to utilize the system to supervise entry and exit of personnel, to search for personnel in the plant by review of a printout, and for payroll purposes. Badge reader systems will also protect equipment rooms, allowing only authorized personnel to enter and to use special equipment, and aid in supervision and protection during watchmen's rounds.

Visitors' hours and appropriate legal constraints, including possible penalties, should be prominently posted. Other methods for detecting intruders are on the market, including photocells, microwave or ultrasonic detectors in the form of beam-breaking or motion-detection devices, door- and/or window-mounted switches, vibration feelers on glass areas, foot-mat switches, and so on.

Control center

It is important that all these features be monitored from one central area. The operator can control and observe all events from this point and, if desired, maintain an automatic log of events for the entry system. Such a security center could be expanded to monitor fire and gas detection systems, heating and ventilation systems, or specialized environmental or fire-protection systems for special equipment such as a computer. The protective devices needed for the distribution systems should also be monitored at this point.

It is of great importance in plant security that the operating staff have the maximum amount of plant area under direct observation. Therefore, as part of the security measures, the operator's office should be located in an area that will not discourage him or her from giving attention to the plant grounds, especially at night.

All protective and allied equipment (telemetering) must be supplied from a steady power supply, with standby generator power or batteries in reserve. The need for protective devices may not be the most important consideration at times when the public power system is down; however, the installation must, in general, be safe in such emergencies as well as secure against disruption, sabotage, or vandalism.

The action to be taken in case of vandalism or other destructive forces may be left to the operator. He or she may call the police or investigate personally. In many cases, it may be simpler to provide contacts for alarms to the police or to a plant security officer in addition to local alarms in various areas of the plant. To avoid the cost of a special telephone line, call-up units may be used to call police or actuate alarms. Such units may also be used for outlying points on plant grounds.

Safety

Regulations

The occupational health and physical safety of working or operating personnel in a water treatment plant should be a major concern of the designer. Compliance with federal, state, and local regulations may be mandatory. Even if it is not, these regulations should be considered, as they frequently establish an industry standard.

The major safety regulations are those of the U.S. Department of Labor based on the Occupational Safety and Health Act (OSHA) of 1970. Suggestions for promoting safety are contained in the AWWA *Safety Practices for Water Utilities* manual.[8] Specific rules and practices such as those published by the Chlorine Institute[9] should also be considered.

Safety hazards

The major safety hazards at a water treatment plant are similar to those found at any sizable hydraulic processing plant. These include fire, explosions, falls, and drownings. Those hazards associated with electrical machinery are electric shock and injuries from rotating mechanisms. Chemical hazards include acid burns, poisoning, asphyxiation, and direct attack on body tissue by fumes, gases, vapor, and smoke.

One of the most hazardous areas in the water treatment plant is the area where chlorine gas is fed and stored. Chlorination equipment is discussed along with other chemical feed systems in Chap. 13.

Safety measures

As a water treatment plant may include pumping stations, storage basins, chemical handling areas, electrical equipment rooms, laboratories, storerooms, and offices, the hazards peculiar to each should be known and possible safety measures incorporated into the design as outlined below.

- Open process units or holes in floors or walls should be protected with railings—double railings where applicable.
- Chains should be provided at access gaps in railings.
- Ladders or manholes should be installed in wells or tanks.
- Ladders should have safety cages if they are more than one story high, and long ladders should have offset platforms.
- Hazardous structures, such as substations and open tanks, should be fenced to prevent unauthorized entry and mishaps.
- Emergency lighting should be provided throughout the plant, with particular attention to stairs.
- Fire alarms and automatic fire-fighting systems may be justified in some areas.
- Appropriate types of fire extinguishers should be provided.
- Laboratories and basements should have two exits.
- Stairs should have rests and nonslip treads, and the risers should be of equal heights and the treads uniform in width.
- Ramps should have slopes suitable for the material or equipment being transported.
- Design of chemical feed systems should minimize lifting of bags or drums.
- Interior doors in passages should swing both ways where possible and should have wired glass windows.
- Fixtures should be selected or means provided so that lamps can be replaced safely.
- Floors should be painted with light and dark areas to distinguish safe pedestrian areas from danger zones, where applicable.

References

1. *Estimating Laboratory Needs for Municipal Wastewater Treatment Facilities,* U.S. Environmental Protection Agency, Washington, D.C., 1973.
2. *Standard Methods for the Examination of Water and Wastewater,* American Water Works Association, Denver, Colo., 1985.
3. *Guidelines for the Selection of Laboratory Instruments,* Manual of Water Supply Practices no. M15, American Water Works Association, Denver, Colo., 1979.
4. *Painting Steel Water Storage Tanks,* ANSI/AWWA D102-78, American Water Works Association, Denver, Colo., 1978.
5. "Recommended Standards for Water Works," *Report of the Committee of the Great*

Lakes–Upper Mississippi River Board of State Sanitary Engineers, Health Education Services, Albany, N.Y., 1982.
6. *National Electric Code, An American National Standard,* ANSI/NFPA no. 70-1984, National Fire Protection Association, Quincy, Mass., 1984.
7. J. Kaufman, *Illuminating Engineering Society Lighting Handbook,* 2 vols., 6th ed., Illuminating Engineering Society, New York, 1981.
8. *Safety Practice for Water Utilities,* 4th ed., Manual of Water Supply Practices, no. M3, American Water Works Association, Denver, Colo., 1983.
9. *Chlorine Manual,* The Chlorine Institute, New York, 1969.

Water Treatment Plant Design Reliability

Introduction

Maintenance of a public water supply of adequate quantity and quality is essential to the health and welfare of the customers served. The overall reliability provisions in water treatment plant designs ensure an adequate water supply of high quality. This reliability must be dictated by the potential consequences of loss of the use of part or all of the plant for a time, or the production of water that does not meet drinking-water standards. The design of water treatment facilities should be based on the premise that failure of any single plant component must not prevent the plant from operating at the design flow or from meeting drinking-water standards. Furthermore, sufficient operational flexibility should be included in the design to handle a variety of water quality problems where raw-water quality is variable. Reserve or redundant capacity should be provided in each unit process, so that process efficiency can be maintained even when a single treatment unit within the unit process must be removed from service altogether.

Another important part of this design philosophy is accounting for recycle flows (i.e., filter wash-water recycling) and recycle solids streams in the overall plant process design. Some of these recycle streams may be significant in size, and the point at which they can most effectively be returned to the main process stream must be carefully determined.

Reliability and redundancy concepts

Reliability and redundancy, although related to each other in plant design, have entirely different meanings. In the context of treatment plant design, *reliability* refers to the inherent dependability of a piece of equipment, a unit process, or the overall treatment process in achieving the design objective. *Redundancy* refers to the provision of standby equipment or processes to improve reliability.

As a highly simplified example of the relationship between redundancy and reliability, assume that the reliability of a single rapid-mix basin (expressed as a fraction) is 0.9. Using the equation

$$R_s = 1 - (1 - r)^m$$

where R_s = system reliability
      r = unit reliability
      m = number of components in parallel

the provision of two rapid-mix basins in parallel increases the reliability of the unit process to 0.99, or 99 percent. Provision of three rapid-mix basins increases the process reliability to 0.999, or 99.9 percent.

Because system reliability increases exponentially with the number of components, it appears that providing two half-capacity basins might economically increase reliability by a factor of 10. However, in the strictest sense, providing an additional rapid-mix basin (assuming that the first provides the requisite capacity to meet the design requirements) increases reliability to a greater extent than using two half-capacity basins. A second full-sized basin provides sufficient reserve capacity to sustain process efficiency should an entire basin be lost for any reason.

Reserve capacity can also be provided in unit processes by using conservative design criteria. For example, three settling basins, each of 2 mgd (7.6 ML/day) capacity, but each sized for a maximum surface overflow rate equivalent to 3 mgd (11 ML/day), would still conservatively provide a capacity of 6 mgd (23 ML/day) even if one basin were lost. In effect, this is the same as providing a standby process unit. As a practical matter, however, such an approach is applicable only where at least three component units are provided.

Overall plant reliability may also be improved when more than one process in the system is able to perform a given function. Both sedimentation and filtration, in the simplest sense, remove particulate materials. Reliability in removing particulate materials is provided by providing sedimentation ahead of filtration. Complex plants may have two or more processes capable of several treatment functions, resulting in a very high overall reliability of the treatment system.

Overall treatment plant reliability is also influenced by the degree of flexibility of operation inherent in a given design. In particular, flexibility can have a dramatic effect on the plant's capability to produce high-quality finished water. For example, having the flexibility to add potassium permanganate, ozone, or chlorine dioxide, as well as powdered activated carbon, to the treatment process at the onset of a taste and odor problem will increase the capability to eliminate the problem in the finished water.

Whereas reliability obtained through the use of redundant units, conservative design, or functional unit arrangement presumes the use of the same treatment processes, reliability obtained through flexibility does not. A flexible system offers an operator a set of choices from which he or she may select those that are best suited to the needs of any particular time. Beyond this, flexibility can also offer an important element of redundancy. Redundancy does not always have to be "in kind," i.e., extra "carbon-copy" units. Often redundancy can be quite economically obtained with no sacrifice of reliability through multipurpose equipment. As an example, a backup wash-water supply for an elevated storage tank system may often be economically obtained through appropriate valving and orifice plates in the piping interconnected with high-service pumps.

Elements of Design

Unit process configuration

Unit processes that combine two or more process functions are inherently less reliable than single-purpose unit processes. For example, flocculation-clarifiers suffer from a deficiency known as the A–B syndrome, as illustrated in Fig. 18.1. If unit A must be removed from service because of malfunction of the flocculation equipment, and during this time unit B has a malfunction in the clarifier (e.g., the sludge col-

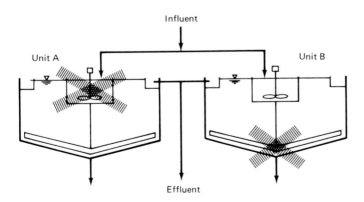

Figure 18.1 A–B syndrome—malfunction of two interrelated unit processes.

lector jams), then both units could conceivably be out of service at the same time. If the flocculation and clarification steps are built as separate units, then at most only one flocculator and one clarifier would be out of service under these same conditions.

Another example of the A–B syndrome exists in the plant with two production trains, A and B, each with several of the unit processes shown in Fig. 18.2 (note that there are no interties between the two trains). The trains operate in parallel and are totally independent of one another. If process A malfunctions in train A and process B malfunctions in train B, the entire plant may be out of service, or at least its efficiency would be impaired. Figure 18.3 illustrates an alternative design that is much more reliable, because parallel trains are interconnected between each unit process. This minimizes the impact of any single unit failure on plant performance, and eliminates the possibility of both trains being out of service simultaneously.

The inherent reliability characteristics of a particular unit process are only one consideration in the selection process. Certainly process efficiency, among other factors, is extremely important. However, as the number of separate component units provided to accomplish a specific function decreases, reliability becomes increasingly important. When only two units are provided, reliability is the prime consideration. Many states require a minimum of two component units for each of the unit processes that are primarily responsible for meeting drinking-water standards. For a surface supply, such processes might include rapid mix, flocculation, clarification, and filtration as a minimum. Processes that would not normally be required to have at least two components for reliability purposes could include aeration for carbon dioxide removal, waste wash-water handling facilities, and sludge processing, unless the size of the facility dictates otherwise. Other ex-

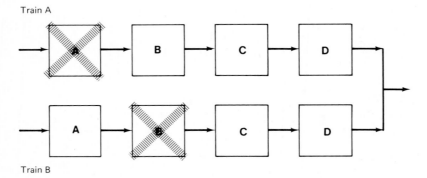

Figure 18.2   A–B syndrome—malfunction of two independent production trains.

Train A

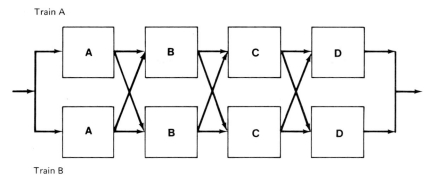

Train B

Figure 18.3   Interconnected parallel production trains minimize impact of single unit failure.

amples include certain chemical feeds, such as fluoride for fluoridation and hexametaphosphate for corrosion and scale control.

Gravity flow versus pumping

Perhaps nothing in this world is as reliable as gravity. At the outset of
design, maximum consideration should be given to the use of gravity
flow to minimize the amount of pumping needed. Where alternatives
exist in the layout of processes, priority should be given to gravity
flow in the unit processes that are critical to producing finished water.
For example, a plant layout that uses available gravity head to provide gravity flow through the rapid mix, flocculation, clarification,
and filtration processes, rather than using the same available head to
allow gravity flow from a wash-water recovery well, places the most
reliable head-producing system (gravity) in the most appropriate
plant unit processes. In this example, pumping is required in either
case, but the consequences of pump failure are dramatically different.
Capacity can be provided in the recovery well to absorb the loss of part
or all of the waste wash-water pump capacity for a time, or dirty filters can be taken off-line without backwash, which would, at worst,
only partially decrease output without affecting finished water quality while repairs are made. In contrast, malfunction of a valve in a
filter influent pump station header could halt the entire production of
finished water.

Likewise, location of chemical feed equipment so that gravity feed
to the process is possible may increase process reliability. Not all
chemicals can be gravity-fed, however. Chlorine gas, for instance,
must usually be dissolved in water prior to being fed to the process,
and the solution process requires pumping of the injector water. Other
chemicals, such as alum, lime, soda ash, and activated carbon, are of-

ten better controlled and fed through gravity systems, even though this requires elevated storage areas.

Design Principles and Practices

Disaster considerations

In planning for the location, design, and operation of reliable plant facilities, the potential for natural disasters—tornados, hurricanes, earthquakes, fires, and floods—should be considered. Such disasters may affect the location and structural design of the treatment plant, but, except for flooding and earthquakes, will usually not dictate specific design criteria. The effects of flooding can be minimized by choosing an appropriate design elevation for the plant facilities. The disastrous effects of earthquakes can be counteracted to some extent by choosing structural design criteria that are appropriate for the plant location.

Human-caused disasters can also affect plant design. Such disasters can originate either from outside the plant confines or from within. Examples of such disasters are strikes, civil disorders, sabotage, vandalism, explosions and fires, nuclear incidents, and airplane crashes. The occurrence of many of these events cannot be reckoned with in plant design, except from the standpoint of vulnerability. Nuclear incidents, sabotage, vandalism, aircraft accidents, and fires or explosions originating outside the plant can be assessed in this manner. Control of access to the plant and provision of plant security can alleviate, to some extent, the potential for acts of sabotage or vandalism. Locating the plant carefully or providing an alternative supply of drinking water can reduce the risk of being without a supply because of an airplane crash within the plant area or fallout from a nuclear incident. The impact of strikes and civil disorders, such as truck blockades, can be reduced by adequate storage of chemicals and other materials on the plant site. On-site generation of some critical chemicals, such as chlorine, also reduces a plant's dependence on truck or rail shipments. Although a supply of sodium chloride is still necessary, maintaining a large inventory of sodium chloride is simpler and safer than storing chlorine in liquid or gaseous form.

Vulnerability to explosions and fires within the plant can be reduced by establishing proper design safeguards with respect to the handling of hazardous materials. A thorough safety program established by the utility's management for the protection of operation and maintenance personnel is also a critical element in preventing in-plant accidents.

At the outset of the design process, a vulnerability analysis of the plant and the site should be performed. Its results can provide critical direction for the designers and the utility, and can certainly reduce the exposure of a plant to natural and human-caused disasters. AWWA's manual, *Emergency Planning for Water Utility Management*,[1] is an excellent guide to assessing the need for many of these contingencies.

Supply reliability

Undoubtedly, one of the primary concerns in system design is the adequacy of the water supply itself to deliver the flow needed to the plant. The available flow or yield of a river, impoundment, or well field must be sufficient to deliver the design flow of the plant plus estimated losses through the treatment process. Some larger utilities have two or more sources of supply—for example, a well field in addition to river intakes. This not only improves reliability, but also offers the possibility of improved performance in colder climates, where surface water becomes more difficult to treat as the temperature drops. Blending warmer groundwater with cold surface water generally will result in water that is easier to treat.

Another feature that can add to the reliability of the supply is multiple ports on intake structures. With a river supply, multiple ports can eliminate the problem of an intake structure becoming clogged with ice or debris. Multiple ports on an intake in an impounding reservoir make available waters of different quality, and thereby improve the capability for producing water of the best possible quality.

Reliability of the supply can also be enhanced by off-stream raw-water storage reservoirs. With a polluted river supply, off-stream storage with several hours capacity will allow a plant to reduce its exposure to chemical spills or toxic discharges upstream from the intake. This feature also allows the intake to be taken out of service for maintenance.

Process reliability

A complete discussion of individual process and equipment reliability characteristics would require a complete study and comparison. Such an effort is not undertaken here; however, a general overview of the subject can provide valuable insight.

Table 18.1 lists the minimum requirements for selected treatment processes, as set by the state of Virginia and the 10-state Great Lakes–Upper Mississippi River Board for surface-water supplies.

The exclusion from Table 18.1 of requirements for appurtenant parts or accessories to the processes is not meant to minimize the need for adequate reliability. Among these appurtenant parts are flowmeters, valves, chemical feed equipment, pumps, instrumentation and controls,

TABLE 18.1   Minimum Requirements for Surface Water

	10-state standards (1976)	Virginia (1974)
Rapid mix	2 units	Duplicate units or spare mixers
Flocculation	2 units	Multiple units for plants > 0.14 mgd
Clarification	2 units	Multiple units for plants > 0.14 mgd
Filtration	2 units (where more than 2 units are provided, add 1 redundant unit)	For $Q > 0.14$ mgd but < 2 mgd, provide 2 units. For $Q > 2$ mgd, provide $2.7\sqrt{Q}$ units
Chlorinators	Standby capacity equal to largest unit out of service	Standby capacity equal to largest unit out of service

liquid-level controls, piping, turbidity and other process-monitoring equipment, and the plant service water system. Fundamental to the design of water treatment facilities should be the philosophy that failure of any single structure, piece of mechanical or electrical equipment, element of pipe, or valve should not put the entire facility out of service.

An example of the importance of a single plant component to reliability is illustrated by the August 31, 1975, incident in Trenton, N.J. The inability to close a single cone valve led to a series of events that flooded the high-lift pump station. As a result, 211,000 people were without drinking water and many businesses were closed for a 10-day period. The monetary loss was estimated at between $5 and $10 million. Thus the importance to system reliability of each component of a plant facility cannot be overstated.

Reliability of plant utilities

The reliability of a water treatment plant is critically affected by the reliability of its power source. Without power, all mechanical and electrical equipment ceases to function. Most states require that each water treatment facility be served by two separate, independent sources of power. Often, standby power, such as gasoline- or diesel-engine-powered generators, is necessary to ensure the plant's ability to operate during a power outage. In addition to the power supply itself, dual transformer substations, duplicate primary feeders, and other duplicate components may also be necessary to maintain the integrity of the power-supply system. A standby source of power is of little value if failure of a primary substation transformer can prevent the power from being delivered to the equipment.

An adequate inventory of chemicals maintained on the plant site is also critical to reliability. The inventory should be sufficient to ensure the production of water at the design flow for a reasonable period of time. In some instances, access to the plant may dictate inventory needs. In others, the inventory may be dictated by the need to survive a truckers' strike. Location of the nearest source of the chemical may also affect the storage requirements.

On-site generation of a chemical may offer advantages in terms of reliability. The use of ozone for disinfection or taste and odor control does not depend on delivery of any chemicals to the plant. Except for power and air, the generation process is self-contained. As mentioned earlier, on-site generation of hypochlorite may also offer some advantages in terms of reliability, in that transport and storage of a hazardous chemical are eliminated. Again, as with power supply, system integrity is critical. An adequate supply of chemical on the plant site is of little benefit if a single conveyor, transfer pump, feeder, or other component can prevent the chemical from being applied.

Operation and maintenance

Proper operation and maintenance is crucial to plant reliability. Proper training of operators will prevent many process failures. Giving adequate attention to maintenance will aid in the prevention of equipment malfunction; inadequate maintenance will guarantee malfunction. In keeping with the often-quoted Murphy's law, "If anything can go wrong, it will go wrong, and given the potential for two or more malfunctions, that which is worse will occur first," inadequate maintenance will certainly increase the probability and severity of Murphy's syndrome events.

A safety program is a necessity at each water treatment facility. Safety practices of plant personnel are critical not only to their health, but also to the operation of the plant. Often, accidents that disable plant personnel also cause damage to machinery, equipment, or materials that may put part of the plant out of service. AWWA's manual, *Safety Practices for Water Utilities*,[2] offers information on the development of a safety program.

References

1. *Emergency Planning for Water Utility Management,* Manual of Water Supply Practices No. M19, American Water Works Association, Denver, Colo., 1973.
2. *Safety Practices for Water Utilities,* Manual of Water Supply Practices No. M3, American Water Works Association, Denver, Colo., 1983.

Behavior and Design of Water Treatment Plants Subjected to Earthquakes

Introduction

Water treatment plants must be capable of withstanding anticipated earthquake forces without impairment of any essential functions. This chapter outlines procedures for assessing vulnerability and risk from earthquakes at a particular site and suggests design methods and guidelines to resist the anticipated earthquake forces. Treatment plant components covered are:

- Basins, vaults, large conduits, and channels
- Buildings and superstructures
- Piping
- Equipment
- Instrumentation and controls
- Power supply

Discussion of damage to these components from past earthquakes is included to provide guidance in the design of new facilities or the upgrading and/or retrofitting of existing facilities. Treatment plant building structures are discussed only insofar as they affect the operation of the treatment system, as the design of buildings to resist earthquakes is extensively covered elsewhere in the literature.

Vulnerability and Risk

The discussion in Chap. 18 suggested an approach and procedures for estimating reliability and providing redundancy for water treatment facilities. These concepts apply particularly to facilities subject to earthquakes.

The necessity for an adequate geotechnical investigation and vulnerability assessment cannot be overemphasized. Once a preliminary site has been selected or is known, the geologic and seismic study and foundation investigation should give the design parameters for the site. The expected intensity and frequency of earthquakes are the basis for judgment regarding the extent to which mitigation measures should be implemented. Seismic studies are to some extent subjective, although actual numbers finally result. Judgment, experience, and common sense set the criteria resulting from the investigations. In areas that are less vulnerable to earthquake, the study may be relatively simple and involve only a general investigation of existing codes and concepts of the probability of risk.

Many facilities may be allowed to function at a reduced level of service during an emergency, such as following a damaging earthquake. Those processes, functions, structures, or facilities which can be dispensed with and the time such outage can be tolerated should be determined so that time, effort, and money are not spent in mitigating damage to nonessential portions of the facility.

Evaluating the acceptable level of service for treatment works may be complex. From the parameters developed by the seismic risk evaluation and soils and foundation investigation, the critical weak links in the system are identified by using the flow diagrams for the treatment facility. Those units of the process which become critical in terms of maintaining minimum serviceability after the earthquake are then established. Those unit processes which are not essential to short-term continuation of service by the facility can be identified, and the time frame established within which these nonessential functions may be out of service. Such facilities might include carbon regeneration, lime regeneration, sludge collection, sludge disposal, and similar functions which are not essential to producing a safe but not polished treated water for short periods.

Seismic-resistant design is not absolute. One unit of a pair with the same design may fail while the other remains intact. Therefore, it is desirable to provide redundancy and flexibility wherever practical and economical, to reduce loss of functions. For example, multiple pumps, separately supported and flexibly interconnected, can often be fitted with the normal demand variation to provide redundancy.

Scope

Each facility has its own special problems and must be treated individually, applying a degree of conservatism that depends on particular circumstances developed from the vulnerability and risk assessment study. The following discussion suggests the steps that may be taken to mitigate seismic hazards to water treatment works, including suggestions for analysis and design procedures and construction details. Observations of damage from previous earthquakes are summarized for each of the treatment plant components as a prelude to the discussion of design procedures and guidelines.

Geotechnical Considerations

It is essential to provide seismically stable foundations protected against liquefaction, settling, and other earthquake-related foundation failures. Often it is necessary to support structures on piles or otherwise stabilize the underlying soil. Treatment plants are typically sited in low areas, often on alluvial plains, to permit access to raw water or disposal channels. Siting of such facilities in areas of high liquefaction or densification potential can be a serious problem. If at all possible, no structure or system component should be placed on earth fill or on an existing stratum with a high potential for liquefaction or densification, or near the toe or shoulder of a slope susceptible to failure by earthquake.[1] If construction of the facility over a stratum with a liquefaction or densification potential is unavoidable, the designer may alter the soil characteristics or design the structure to overcome earthquake effects. Depending on the local topography, an effective drainage system may be constructed to prevent liquefaction. Sensitive clays may be removed and replaced with stable fill material, or structures may be supported on piles extending through the sensitive clay layer.

Basins, Vaults, Large Conduits, and Channels

Observation of damage

The most extensive earthquake damage to a water treatment system documented in the literature was sustained by the Joseph Jensen water filtration plant of the Metropolitan Water District of Southern California (Fig. 19.1). The Jensen treatment plant was under construction in decomposed granite soil and only 85 percent complete at the time of the 1971 San Fernando earthquake. It is estimated that the site was subjected to between 0.3 and 0.4 g horizontal acceleration. A major earth slide occurred at the plant site. Existing structures in the northeast section of the plant moved ½ to 1 ft, causing many expansion joints to open. Mixing and settling basins founded on com-

Figure 19.1 Joseph Jensen filtration plant. Reservoir overflow pipe, 96-in diameter. First pipe joint from east end, pipe separated about 2 ft and is offset (San Fernando, Calif, 1971). (*Advisory Notes on Lifeline Earthquake Engineering, American Society of Civil Engineers, New York, 1983.*)

pacted fill in the northwest section suffered uneven settlement directly proportional to the depth of fill on which they were supported; the maximum settlement experienced was 5 in. This led to the opening of expansion joints, accompanied by concrete spalling related to contact during shaking.

The most significant damage at the Jensen treatment plant was the failure of the finished-water reservoir, a concrete structure. The reservoir roof was to have been covered with 8 ft of fill to prevent potential flotation of the empty structure. The failure of the structure is purported to have resulted from the inertia effect of the soil overburden. An end wall failed in bending. The floor and walls underwent differential settlement of 3 to 6 in, although this is not believed to have been a significant cause of structural failure.[2] Most of the damage to open-top basins occurred at expansion joints, which pounded together and moved during the shaking action. Maximum joint opening was about 1 in, and in many cases the concrete spalled at the edges of the joint and the joint filler was squeezed out.

At the Jensen treatment plant, reinforced concrete box conduit structures varying from 8 to 12 ft in width and height and concrete-lined metal pipe up to 14 ft in diameter suffered major damage near the junctures with major structures. Spalling occurred near the bottom slab at the expansion joints of conduits. The joint sealant was stretched and ruptured or squeezed out in some cases, and in others joints were separated by as much as 2 in. Differential displacement occurred at most expansion joints, with transverse cracking between joints and longitudinal horizontal cracks. In some places, damage to the roof slab and spalling at the juncture with the structures on each end occurred.

Where large-diameter pipe was connected to massive structures in the Jensen plant, the concrete was shattered at the juncture and the joint immediately adjacent to the structure opened, sometimes as much as 1 ft, with the separated ends becoming misaligned by as much as 8 in. Smaller pipe joints opened as much as 2½ in, and the rubber gasket was partially pulled out. In some cases (not all) where pipe was cast into walls, the wall was shattered from the pounding action. A 14-ft-diameter concrete-steel cylinder pipe conduit suffered transverse cracks in the concrete encasement up to ½ in in width, and three joints in the steel cylinder opened.

Foundations for basins and vaults

Plant siting is particularly significant in the design of concrete basins and vaults, as these massive structures require stable bearing. If the site is vulnerable to soil densification or liquefaction, three courses of action are available: (1) an alternative site can be used if a more favorable one can be located; (2) the high densification and liquefaction vulnerability can be ignored if the probability of an earthquake occurring during the design period multiplied by the potential cost of damage is less than the cost of construction to resist seismic-induced conditions; and (3) the facility may be designed to resist the effects of densification or liquefaction, or the vulnerability may be reduced with corrective measures. Past studies have shown that the cost of soil stabilization for a complete facility is very high; therefore, proper siting can be critical in minimizing seismic damage.

The alternative method of mitigating earthquake-induced settlement is to attain bearing on a stable soil layer below the layer that is vulnerable to consolidation and liquefaction.

When a tank is constructed on fill, the fill materials should be of uniform thickness and compacted to a degree that will ensure comparatively high soil shear strengths, little future consolidation, and no differential settlement. If a tank is sited in an unstable soil area, the soil may be stabilized using vibroflotation or chemical or cement grouting. The tank could also be supported on piles. Basins or structures, or parts thereof, founded on different foundation materials should be separated by a flexible joint.

Ductility should be provided in piles for seismic-induced bending stresses. The tops of piles should be embedded in the structure as deeply as feasible in order to transfer forces. Individual pile caps and caissons of every building or structure should be interconnected by ties, as is normally done for buildings and as required in the Uniform Building Code.

Extreme caution should be used in the design of a structure that is supported partially by piling and partially by an alternative method. Continuity of the structure's response to earthquake motions can best be attained by using similar foundation supports throughout the structure. If a structure is supported on two unlike foundations, a flexible joint between the two sections may accommodate any differential movement between the two elements of the structure.[1]

Analysis of basins and vaults

Many treatment facility structures are rigid and box-shaped, possibly buried in the ground, sometimes with no superstructure. These very short period structures are designed using the appropriate percent of gravity applied to produce an equivalent static load.

The forces acting on basins containing water must include or account for the sloshing action caused by an earthquake. The analysis may involve the effective mass method as shown in *AWWA Standard for Welded Steel Tanks for Water Storage* (ANSI/AWWA D-100).[3]

Water holding basins in regions where strong earthquakes may occur may require greater than normal freeboard to prevent the contents from sloshing over the exterior walls and flooding adjacent areas of the plant site.

Structural design of basins and vaults for seismic forces is briefly discussed below. Refer to Haroun and Housner[4] for a more complete detailed analysis of earthquake-induced loadings on water holding basins.

Design guidelines for basins and vaults

Standards.   Recognized standards for construction of tanks include:

- The structural design of steel tanks (surface and elevated) should be in accordance with *AWWA Standard for Welded Steel Tanks for Water Storage* (ANSI/AWWA D100-84).[3]

- The structural design of concrete tanks should reflect the provisions of *ACI Concrete Sanitary Engineering Structures* (ACI-350).[5] This requires design on the basis of elastic distribution of stress.

- The structural design of prestressed concrete tanks should be in accordance with *AWWA Standard for Wire-Wound Circular Prestressed-Concrete Water Tanks* (ANSI/AWWA D110-86).[6]

- The structural design of the tank appurtenances should reflect the provisions of ATC 3-06, *Tentative Provisions for the Development of Seismic Regulations for Buildings,* Applied Technology Council, Washington, D.C., 1978,[7] or the most recent Uniform Building Code.

- The design should exceed local building and safety code minimums.

Surface basins and vaults.   Surface facilities are generally supported directly by the ground, with little or no burial that could provide lateral support.

A potential problem during earthquakes is tank foundation failure. One possible reason is the increased localized loading caused by the tank overturning moment. The earthquake motions may cause the soil structure to liquefy, lose shear strength, or simply consolidate (settle), depending on the soil conditions. This may allow the tank to tip or settle unevenly, causing the tank shell or roof to buckle and sometimes fail. Proper design includes provision for friction or other restraint of surface basins and vaults.

Buried basins and vaults.   Buried tanks are either cylindrical or rectangular. Their bottoms are supported directly by the ground, and their sides resist lateral earth pressure in a way similar to a retaining wall. The majority are constructed of reinforced and prestressed concrete. The design criteria should consider both the empty and full conditions, and provisions, such as drainage, should be made to prevent liquefaction of the foundation material.

Seismic design should consider at least these factors: settlement, earth-retaining forces, flotation, effect of the inertia and sloshing of the water, inertia of the tank structure and the soil it supports, and appurtenant items such as baffles, miners, sludge collectors, water troughs, and filter surface washers. Sloshing and the inertial effect are earthquake-induced forces only; the other items are normally considered in a nonseismic design, although they must now be considered in greater detail.

Specific design recommendations are as follows:

- Control the type of backfill used behind tank walls during construction. A noncohesive soil is normally used, as it is easier to attain a specified high compaction density with minimum effort. The higher the relative density of the backfill, the lower the liquefaction potential of the backfill material. Liquefaction of the backfill is the severe condition that must be resisted by a wall. Following liquefaction, the backfill becomes a very dense fluid which lacks the shear strength required to resist deformation of the wall.

- Allow for lateral forces acting on the tank structure, including any earth fill which may have been placed on top to prevent flotation and which may contribute substantially to the lateral forces during earthquakes.

- Consider that earthquake motion may cause liquefaction of backfill and natural ground immediately adjoining the tank structure, which may cause the tank to float, even if it has been designed to resist flotation from high groundwater. Buoyant forces causing flotation can be controlled in several ways:

  1. Providing a positive tie-down mechanism
  2. Tying the tank to supporting piles designed to resist uplift
  3. Increasing the weight of the structure by using mass concrete, using heavy aggregate concrete, adding to the overburden on top of the tank, or keeping the tank at least partially filled
  4. Providing a positive drainage system

- Avoid abrupt changes in structural configuration, including sharp interior angles.

- Provide for structural continuity in the construction of the floor-to-wall connection.

  Note: Most prestressed tanks use a hinge connection between the wall and the floor.

- Provide flexible, watertight joints with either embedded water stops or internal "diaper" seals.

- Consider flexible pipe joints outside the tank walls within inlet-outlet control valve vaults.

Other considerations for basins and vaults.   Flexible connections should be provided between the storage facility and its inlet-outlet pipeline. These connections or joints can be mechanical, restrained expansion, rubber, ball and socket, or gimbel restrained bellows-type couplings. AWWA D100-84[3] recommends a minimum of 50.8 mm (2 in) flexibility in all directions for all piping attached to the shell or bottom of storage tanks. If major movement greater than 50.8 mm (2 in) is expected, a more elaborate flexibility system should be designed. Shutoff valves, check valves, blow-off valves, and bypass facilities should have adequate flexibility or restraint to withstand movement.

All roof openings, hatches, ladders, and other appurtenances should be designed to resist or accommodate seismic forces. Provide breaks in ladders and catwalks spanning independently moving structures, construction joints, or expansion joints.

Locate air release valves outside vaults containing equipment which could be damaged if the valves are broken off or malfunction.

Design walls serving as shear walls or diaphragms with expansion and construction joints keyed to carry the shear forces. To maintain watertight integrity following an earthquake, use flexible joints including flexible waterstops. The flexibility of the joint will be dependent on the distance between the concrete faces and the flexibility of the waterstop. Flexible PVC waterstops are commercially available as wide as 9 in with mechanical elongation of as much as 1½ in. Wider stops with greater elongation capabilities can be manufactured if required.

Flexible joints in concrete basin walls and channels should be placed close enough together to limit wall material stresses to less than their design stresses. A maximum joint spacing of 30 ft has been suggested for channels.[8]

Collection troughs (launders) found in clarifiers and filters are subject to impulsive and convective forces from the surrounding water during an earthquake. The joints connecting these troughs to tank wall penetrations or other troughs should be flexible. They should be designed so that they will not damage the tank wall if they fail and so that they may be easily replaced.

Consider the cost of strengthening components such as baffles and collection troughs, which have a larger cross section and are relatively weak horizontally. Depending on the estimated earthquake recurrence during the facility's anticipated useful life, the designer may choose to allow these components to fail during an earthquake. If this is the case, the design should attempt to limit damage to the basic structure from component failure, and provision should be made for quick replacement of the components if they are damaged.

Buildings and Superstructures

Observation of damage

Superstructures and buildings associated with water treatment plants have fared better than equipment, tankage, and piping in recent earthquakes. In the Coalinga earthquake (California, 1982), while there was damage to electrical starting equipment and piping, there was no superstructure or building damage. Interior damage, such as fallen book and storage cases, occurred, but no structural damage. In the Morgan Hill earthquake (California, 1984), piping failed at screwed connections or at asbestos cement joints and feet, but no pumphouse damage occurred.

A landslide from an adjacent earth dam embankment caused Outlet Tower No. 1 in the Lower Van Norman Reservoir to topple during the 1971 San Fernando earthquake (Fig. 19.2). Sand, gravel, and rocks entered the distribution system through the broken intake, plugging some pipelines and causing extensive damage to pump bearings and seals and instrumentation and controls. Outlet Tower No. 2 in that same reservoir experienced slight cracking. Both of these towers, built in 1914–1915, were designed as unreinforced concrete gravity structures. The outfall line from the intake tower in the Upper Van

Figure 19.2 Outlet Tower No. 1 lies toppled in a north direction after earthquake, lower Van Norman Reservoir (San Fernando earthquake of 1971). (*Advisory Notes on Lifeline Earthquake Engineering, American Society of Civil Engineers, New York, 1983.*)

Norman Reservoir was damaged through either compression or extension of various joints.

Design guidelines for buildings and superstructures

Control buildings, buildings housing equipment, and other superstructures for treatment facilities are usually designed according to the local building code. Before using an existing building code, the level of importance of the building must be established. Any building structure housing essential facilities should be designed as an essential facility itself. Consideration should be given to what portions of water treatment facilities should be defined as essential.

The building and the enclosed facilities should be structurally compatible. A rigid design would provide adequate support to any attached facilities. A flexible or ductile building may not adequately support a rigid attached system. Either the building and the attached system should respond as a single unit, or flexibility should be designed into the attachment. Pipes penetrating walls exemplify this situation.

The design criteria developed as a result of the geotechnical investigation are used to determine structural response conditions. Under loading from these criteria, the facility would be designed to sustain the earthquake with repairable damage; structures, systems, and components vital to safety would remain functional. The degree of damage which would be acceptable should be based on the minimum level of service which would be acceptable after an earthquake.

A dynamic analysis is required for more complex structures with large masses, such as overhead cranes or heavy roofs. The severity of the earthquake hazard, developed as part of the design criteria, forms the basis for a judgment as to whether the structures have features which warrant dynamic analysis.

The design should be simple. Discontinuities where stresses may build up are to be avoided. Units or components should be single, continuous structures, or flexible connections between units or components should be provided. Symmetry is desirable in all three dimensions. The damage to the El Centro Public Works Building (Imperial Valley Earthquake, 1979) pointed out the need for symmetrical design. If nonsymmetrical structures are unavoidable and cannot be separated into balanced units, additional strengthening is called for at discontinuities.

The structural materials should have reserve ductility. When the material reaches its yield strength, it should be able to deform without significant loss of strength. Equipment structures should be designed to resist the "design" earthquake loading without yielding. However, because of the possibility of an earthquake which exceeds the "design" level, consideration should be given to motions greater than those produced by the "design" loading. This is done by providing ductile design and details. Connections of each structural member should be designed to be less highly stressed than the member itself.[9]

Piping

Analysis and design for buried piping

Flexibility and ductility in yard piping is essential, either through choice of material or in the pipe joints. Joint separation and crushing has often occurred at the junction between units of differing mass, such as between basins and the piping connected to them.

The type of analysis which is appropriate for pipelines depends on the anticipated type of ground motions. In cases where the pipeline is subjected to movements caused primarily by wave propagation, the analysis considers homogeneous ground strain and curvature to be the parameters of interest. In cases where the pipeline crosses a zone of faulting or ground rupture, the analysis recognizes that discontinuous relative displacement across the zone is the main parameter.

For continuous pipelines subjected to homogeneous ground strain induced by wave effects, it is assumed that the pipe has no stiffness or mass, and hence the strain and curvatures are the same as those induced in the soil.[10] The axial strain of the pipe, $\epsilon_{p,max}$ is the maximum free-field ground strain ϵ_{max} resulting from the earthquake:

$$\epsilon_p = \epsilon_{max} = \frac{V_{max}}{C_\epsilon} \qquad (19.1)$$

where V_{max} is the maximum ground velocity and C_ϵ is the apparent longitudinal propagation speed of the seismic waves with respect to the structure at the site. The upper bound for the maximum curvature of the pipeline $X_{p,max}$ is the maximum ground curvature X_{max}:

$$X_{p,max} = X_{max} = \frac{A_{max}}{(C_x)^2} \qquad (19.2)$$

where A_{max} represents the maximum ground acceleration and C_x is the apparent transverse propagation speed of the seismic waves with respect to the structure at the site.

If the pipe can withstand both strain and curvature criteria, it will be adequate against earthquakes producing ground velocities and accelerations less than the V_{max} and A_{max} used in the analysis. Strain governs more frequently than curvature.

For long, segmented pipelines which contain flexible joints spaced at a distance L, the maximum relative joint displacements and maximum joint rotations become important design parameters in addition to the pipe strains and curvatures. The analysis assumes that the pipeline consists of rigid segments which at the midpoints move with the ground exactly; it follows that the maximum relative motion/rotation between two points on the ground will be entirely accommodated by movement at the joints. Hence, the upper bounds of maximum joint displacement $U_{p,\max}$ and maximum joint rotation $\theta_{p,\max}$, can be conservatively expressed as

$$U_{p,\max} = \epsilon_{\max} L = \frac{V_{\max} L}{C_{\epsilon}} \qquad (19.3)$$

$$\theta_{p,\max} = x_{\max} L = \frac{A_{\max} L}{(C_x)^2} \qquad (19.4)$$

If a buried segmented piping system meets all four sets of upper bounds (pipe strain, pipe curvature, joint displacement, and rotation) specified in Eqs. (19.1) to (19.4) for a design earthquake, the pipeline is safe for that design earthquake or one of a lesser magnitude.

The apparent wave propagation speeds C_{ϵ} and C_x to be used in Eqs. (19.1) to (19.4), depend upon the wave type which results in the maximum ground velocity and acceleration. Wave types to be considered are dilatational, shear, and Rayleigh waves. The apparent wave propagation speeds to be used are indicated below.

Apparent wave propagation	Wave type		
	Dilatational	Shear	Rayleigh
C_{ϵ}	C_c	$2C_s$	C_R
C_x	$1.6C_c$	C_s	C_R

where C_c, C_s, and C_R are the effective dilatational, shear, and Rayleigh wave velocities, respectively. For important projects, the values of C_c, C_s, and C_R should be determined experimentally for the site. However, approximate values for these wave velocities can be found in Refs. 11 and 12.

Piping connections and joints

Observations of damage. Experience in Alaska (1964), Niigata (1969), San Fernando (1971), and Morgan Hill (1984) has shown that while welded, soldered, and brazed joints and mechanical couplings have survived earthquakes with relatively little damage, screwed joints have often failed at the joint threads.[13,14] In Alaska, stress was developed in screwed fittings from the vibration of a long pipe section connected to a shorter leg.[13]

Many earthquake-induced failures in flexible joints have also been observed where large ground movement has occurred. In Alaska, flexible joints in cast-iron pipe were pulled apart when the pipe was set in motion. Many bellows-type flexible pipe connections for thermal expansion failed as a result of lack of flexibility and the absence of stops to limit lateral movement.[13] Where flexible couplings were used between pumps and piping in a Los Angeles pumping station, no damage occurred in the 1971 San Fernando earthquake.[2]

The behavior of piping support systems in past earthquakes was varied. In Alaska, expansion loops in steam and hot water systems failed because of lack of bracing. As one pipe hanger failed, adjoining ones also failed because of the increased load.[13] The piping support system at the Managua (Nicaragua, 1972) Thermal Electric Power Plant, on the other hand, was designed for mechanical displacements with springs and snubbers, and the system functioned well.[15] It is significant to note that sprinkler systems installed in accordance with the National Fire Protection Code Standards performed well in Alaska.[13]

Secondary impacts of pipeline failure can be extremely damaging. Flooding from broken lines can severely damage electrical components, adjacent property, and structures. Shorted windings in motors require complete rebuilding of the motors. Instrumentation shorts can damage the complete system, requiring replacement of the electrical components resulting in loss of pump control.

Design guidelines for piping connections and joints.   The National Fire Protection Association (NFPA) has presented criteria for seismic-resistant piping configurations in NFPA Publication no. 13, *Installation of Sprinkler Systems.*[16] As NFPA systems have responded well to past earthquakes, fire protection systems should be designed, as a minimum, in accordance with NFPA no. 13.

Welded, screwed, and flange joints are rigid, adding no flexibility to the piping systems. Welded joints may have some advantage over flange joints, as they provide greater structural continuity across the joint, limiting stress concentration where failure may occur. If iron or steel pipe with screw fittings is used, great care should be taken in pipe restraint design and flexibility provisions, as screw fittings have had a poor record in resisting earthquake movement.

Both steel and ductile iron pipe have ductile properties that will allow some deformation before failure. In recent years, ductile iron has replaced cast-iron pipe. This is advantageous for seismic-resistant design, as cast-iron pipe is brittle and allows little differential movement before failure occurs. However, smaller pipe fittings and flanges of all sizes are still usually fabricated from cast iron unless otherwise specified. Care should be taken to provide freedom of action during shaking to compensate for lack of material ductility when cast-iron fittings must be used.

Clearances should be maintained between pipes and adjacent pipes or structures. Adjacent parallel pipes should be separated a minimum of 4 times the maximum displacement calculated from earthquake-induced forces unless spreaders are employed. A clearance of 3 times the maximum calculated pipe displacement from earthquake-induced forces should be allowed between pipes and walls or other rigid elements, with a 3-in maximum maintained.

Rigid pipeline systems with no flexible joints or allowance for flexure should be supported by a single structural system, one that will respond as a single structure, unless specific provisions are made for movement of supports attached to other structures. Where different structural systems are used for anchorage and relative displacement may occur, flexible joints that will allow relative movement should be provided in the piping systems. Examples include wall penetrations, anchorage to the floor with adjacent ceiling anchorage, and building joint crossings. Piping systems should have continuous response characteristics. Any discontinuities in the system should be separated from the system by flexible joints or other techniques. Discontinuities may include valves, meters, fittings in the line, or major changes in pipe size (e.g., branch lines off main lines) (see Fig. 19.3).

When large conduits or channels are connected to structures, expansion joints in the usual form will allow for reasonable amounts of

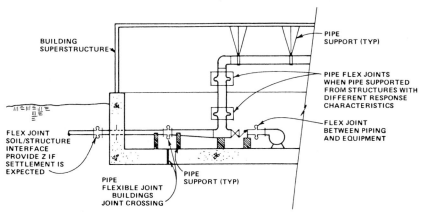

Figure 19.3 Flexible joint locations. (*Advisory Notes on Lifeline Earthquake Engineering, American Society of Civil Engineers, New York, 1983.*)

movement, but experience has indicated that they will be damaged during the shaking action of the earthquake. Some damage must be anticipated. The present state of the art, within reasonable economic limits, has not developed an adequate solution to this problem. At the connection of a channel to a structure, where the amount of movement is reasonably limited and an adequate plastic bulb-type waterstop through the joint is provided, it is probable that no serious leakage or failure of hydraulic capacity of the facility will occur.

Nonwatertight wall penetrations are typically used between adjacent "dry" areas in water facilities. In these areas, adequate clearance should be provided around the pipe to allow for expected movement. If a physical barrier is required between the two areas, an easily deformable material should be used.

Watertight penetrations are typically found in tank walls and below-grade vaults or basements. If the penetration is grouted in the wall and rigidly supported, flexible joints should be provided on both sides of the wall. If lateral displacement or shear is expected between the pipe and the wall, as may occur when a structure settles during an earthquake, two flexible joints should be provided on the side of the wall where the shear is expected.

Maximum flexibility for pipe is achieved with ball-and-socket joints. An allowable 6-in differential movement requires ball joints that can rotate $7\frac{1}{2}°$ in conjunction with a 4-ft pipe leg for each joint. Rubber bellows-type joints have limited angular flexibility, particularly in the larger pipe diameters. Some designs (e.g., multiple bellows) may, however, accommodate adequate flexibility. They must be restrained to avoid distortion (see Fig. 19.4).

Two sleeve-type couplings can be used to provide for an offset movement between the structure and the piping. The distance between the sleeve couplings is set to provide the desired amount of offset. The joints must be harnessed for axial stability. Thrust restraints must be provided for mechanical, sleeve, metal bellows, and rubber bellows flexible joints, as the internal water pressure attempts to force joints apart.

Adequate bracing must be provided for flexible joint connections. Pipe movement relative to the pipe supporting structure must be limited to the pipe section designed to move. Pipe guides must be provided to limit the relative motion of the flexible joint to the direction for which it was designed. Continuity should be maintained in the type of anchorage used. Flexible supports in combination with rigid supports may allow stress buildups and failure of the rigid supports. Long, continuous pipe runs are seldom critical structurally. Independently support piping appurtenances if they weigh enough to affect the response of the piping system. Independently support racks carry-

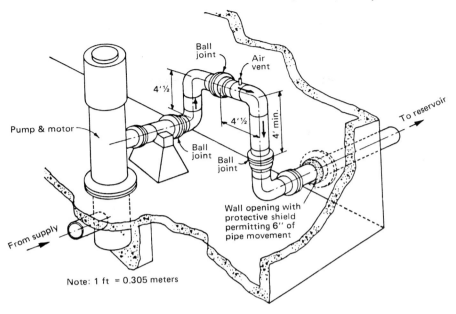

Note: 1 ft = 0.305 meters

Figure 19.4 Ball-joint-type connection. (*Advisory Notes on Lifeline Earthquake Engineering, American Society of Civil Engineers, New York, 1983.*)

ing industrial and control piping serving small tanks and equipment used in plant processes. Do not support racks on tanks of equipment which may themselves move.

Pipes should be rigidly supported to resist earthquake-induced loadings in addition to loads normally included in pipe support design. This requires not only an increased vertical loading resistance, including tie-downs to support blocks, but horizontal bracing, both perpendicular (resisting lateral displacement) and parallel (axial loading). Sway bracing should be provided to maintain a rigid system laterally, similar to vertical support systems. One axial brace for each run (straight length) of pipe is adequate unless extremely long runs are encountered.

Pipe supports should be provided at close enough intervals so that the pipe's natural response frequency will be greater than 20 cps. In many instances, pipe hanger design has been left up to the contractor. Because hanger design details are important in seismic-resistant design, the design engineer should provide hanger design details for each installation. A high level of quality control through inspection should be provided. All critical piping should be protected from building and facility elements which could become falling debris in an earthquake.

Valves, meters, backflow preventers, strainers, air filters, and blower silencers are commonly included in water facility piping systems. If these appurtenances affect the response of the piping system, they should be independently supported. If differential movement between the appurtenance and the piping system is expected, a flexible joint should be provided.

Automatic shutoff valves should be provided on all hazardous material piping systems. These systems may include those for natural gas, chlorine gas or solutions, and acid or caustic solutions. The valve should be located as close to the hazardous source as possible. The valve may be activated by pressure drop caused by pipe rupture, common for natural gas service, or it may be a seismically activated switch, which is currently available commercially. However, because seismically activated systems would shut off at a preset seismic acceleration, flow would be discontinued even if there were no damage to the piping system. The effect of possible interruption of flow should be considered.

Equipment

Observation of damage

The greatest damage to treatment plant equipment during earthquakes has historically occurred when earthquake-induced forces have not been taken into account during design and installation. Equipment is often secured from lateral movement by friction only, which may be reduced substantially during an earthquake as a result of vertical acceleration and horizontal forces on the equipment. When equipment moves or overturns, connections such as electrical conduit and piping can easily break. Horizontal circular tanks, although stable in the longitudinal direction, can easily roll in the other direction if they are not properly anchored. Equipment moving off its foundation can itself be damaged or can cause adjacent equipment or structures to break when they interact. For example, chlorine cylinders in Managua's water supply facility were not anchored, resulting in breakage of connecting lines. At the Sylmar Convertor Station, 31 power transformers and other electrical equipment toppled (San Fernando, 1971). Unanchored equipment movement caused secondary damage, such as breaking of piping and electrical connections (San Fernando, 1971). At Coalinga (California, 1982), chlorine tanks moved 6 in and wooden sedimentation baffles were wrenched loose, blocking coagulation paddles.

Equipment and tanks mounted on legs are susceptible to failure. The Managua industrial survey indicated that jack-type equipment legs moved, since they lacked provisions for anchorage[17] and were unable to transfer shear to the equipment. In the 1964 Alaska earthquake at Fort Richardson, four cast-iron legs supporting a sand filter, which were designed for static loading, failed.

Vibration isolation systems including spring and rubber mounts, when not designed for earthquakes, have a significantly higher failure rate than rigidly anchored systems. In the 1964 Alaska earthquake, motor/generator vibration isolation mounts permitted movement of the equipment, since they were not bolted to the floor.[13] A survey of Managua's industry after the earthquake showed that spring or rubber vibration isolation mountings failed in all cases except where pumps were mounted on inertia blocks keyed to the foundation, with springs underneath. Keying of the blocks to the foundation behaved as a snubber, limiting horizontal movement.[18]

In the 1971 San Fernando earthquake, systems without vibration isolation systems generally suffered less damage than those with isolation systems. Most damage occurred when vibration isolation systems were not bolted to both the equipment and the floor. Some isolators were torn apart. An emergency generator supported on a multispring vibration system collapsed. The isolators were destroyed when cast-iron spring guards failed, allowing the springs to pop out even though the system was "properly" mounted. It is interesting to note that molded neoprene isolators survived with no particular damage.

Secondary damage occurs when failure of one structure leads to damage of another. Even the most carefully seismically designed piece of equipment will be unable to survive an earthquake if, for example, a roof collapses on it; this occurred in a soft drink plant in Managua (Nicaragua, 1972), where a falling roof damaged otherwise intact equipment.[18] An overhead bridge crane in the Managua thermal electric plant fell off its rails onto generators below, and diesel generators used for standby power at the Managua thermal electric plant were inoperable because of damage to several support systems: the fuel tank overturned; the cooling-water lines to three units broke at pipe joints; compressed air for the backup starting system had not been stored, nor was there a way to generate it; and one exhaust system was crushed.[15,18] At the ENALUF power plant in Managua, the turbine support systems failed. Batteries used to supply backup power to the oil lubrication pumps and valve controls fell off their racks. The turbine was damaged extensively because lubricating oil for its bearings was not delivered as a result of damage to the lubricating oil system. An emergency generator at the Sendai sewage treatment plant moved 6 in during the Miyagi-Ken-Oki earthquake, breaking some electrical connections. Cooling water for the engine could not be supplied because its source, the public water supply system, had been rendered inoperable in that part of the city by the earthquake.

Design loadings for equipment

Equipment installed in treatment facilities should be capable of withstanding seismically induced forces. Refer to Uniform Building Code,[19] Applied Technology Councils, *Tentative Provisions for the Development of Seismic Regulations for Buildings* (ATC 3-06),[7] and Refs. 20 and 21 for detailed information on seismic-induced forces on equipment.

All equipment should be rigidly anchored in accordance with these design loadings. It is wise to require seismic calculations for anchor bolt design and to check seismic loadings on the equipment structure or foundation.

Foundations and supports for equipment

Heavy equipment is preferably supported on separate foundations designed to withstand the earthquake forces which may operate on the supported equipment and its foundation. When equipment must be located on upper floors (such as pump motors, conveyors, blowers, and hoists), the supporting structure must be rigid and the equipment rigidly attached so that the structure and equipment respond as a unit, with provision made to resist amplification of seismic loadings by the building structure. Where separate foundations are used, particular attention must be paid to overturning. Equipment on a separate foundation must also be separated from the structure and its floor slabs so they do not damage one another when responding to ground motion. If base isolation systems are used, they must be carefully designed so that rubber, steel, and restraint elements are adequate.

Massive sludge dewatering equipment such as filter belt presses and centrifuges is often mounted on the second floor of a structure to allow for loading of sludge into trucks by gravity. This equipment can be located on the ground level if a belt conveyor is used for loading trucks, but this may not be economically feasible.

Recent experience has indicated that earthquake forces can cause pull-out or shear failure of anchor bolts. These bolts must be carefully designed for the anticipated earthquake forces and properly spaced and located to avoid pull-out or other failure resulting in toppling of equipment.

Anchor-bolt embedments should be designed to resist the loadings calculated without yielding. However, because the design levels used in earthquake design are not the maximum that may be expected, the motions experienced may exceed those calculated. To accommodate these possible increased motions, the anchor-bolt steel should be ductile so that it can yield at a loading greater than the design load to absorb energy. The anchor bolts should be designed to yield prior to failure of the concrete embedment or critical equipment elements.

The American Concrete Institute has code requirements for design and anchorage of steel embedments as part of the *Code Requirements for Nuclear Safety Related Concrete Structures* (ACI-349-85).[22] Anchor-bolt and expansion-anchor spacing and side cover are included.

When expansion-type anchors are used, care should be taken in drilling the holes and installing anchors. Oversized holes, which may result from the use of worn bits, may not allow the specified strength of the connection to be developed. Self-drilling expansion anchors avoid this problem, but have the disadvantage that the shells are brittle. Pull-out tests to the design load of a random sample of installed expansion-type or epoxy cemented anchors are recommended. Pull-out tests to failure should also be made, and should demonstrate a minimum safety factor of 4.

Anchor-bolt embedments should be used in preference to expansion anchors when continuous dynamic loads are encountered (e.g., rotating equipment). Expansion anchors are acceptable for static loads and infrequent dynamic loads such as earthquakes (e.g., for pipe supports).

Pumps

Vertical turbine pumps in a wet well often hang free from a motor or supporting floor above, and will be subject to vibratory motion from the connection at the top, modified by the dynamic characteristics of the column and the water. The period of such a system should be checked and compared with the anticipated earthquake period of vibration. Vertical end suction pumps, often used for solids handling, may be tall, slim structures, so their bases and anchorages should be designed to resist overturning.

Where horizontal pumps are used, it is important to mount pump and motor on a single structure so that they respond together. This concept would also apply where a battery of pumps is connected to a single header. Pumps and piping should always be separated by a flexible connection to allow them to respond independently to earthquake movement.

Mechanical equipment

Equipment design and anchorage is often left up to the equipment manufacturer and contractor, with only superficial review by the designer. However, detailing of equipment and anchorage is critical for seismic-resistant design. It should, therefore, be specified by the system designer, and the construction or installation should be closely inspected.

Connections of piping and conduit between equipment and floor or ceiling should be designed with flexibility, as differential displacement may take place between the equipment and the structure. Out-of-phase vibration between two connected pieces of equipment can cause failure even if adequate anchoring has been provided. Banging between equipment and a wall or another piece of equipment that abuts it or is close to it has been known to occur. Minor differential movement between a motor and pump, for example, can cause extensive damage if the system is operating during an earthquake event.

Special care should be taken in locating equipment, storage tanks, and feed lines containing hazardous materials. Most regulatory agencies require that chlorination facilities be located in a separate, well-ventilated room away from the rest of the treatment facility, with chlorinators separated from chlorine tank rooms. Similar precautions should be taken with other types of systems containing caustic, acidic, or other hazardous materials. All gas bottles and containers of hazardous materials should be restrained in a carefully designed rack. Chlorine cylinders on scales must be provided with hold-down devices so that the cylinders move with the scales or are restrained.

All equipment should be positively anchored to resist earthquake-induced horizontal forces and overturning moments. Resilient anchorage using vibration isolation systems must be carefully designed. Spring or rubber block vibration isolation systems have historically not performed well when subjected to earthquake motion, but the more recently developed sandwich-type vibration isolation mounts made of alternating rubber and steel sheets have performed well in tests. Use snubbers (stops to limit movement) when vibration isolation systems are necessary. (See Fig. 19.5.)

When shims are used to level equipment, they should provide full vertical support to the equipment base. Failure to provide full support may allow bending of the base around the shim, allowing the structure to rock. Stiffening of equipment bases that are not fully supported should be provided so that vibration response will not be amplified by flexibility of the base. Shims should be positively restrained against displacement resulting from equipment vibration.

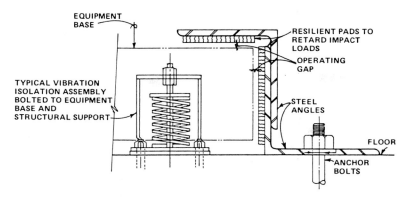

Figure 19.5 Restraining devices against lateral and vertical loads for equipment mounted on vibration isolators. (*Advisory Notes on Lifeline Earthquake Engineering, American Society of Civil Engineers, New York, 1983.*)

Hydraulic flow control and in-channel equipment such as valve controls, valve stands, hydraulic and pneumatic cylinders, sluice gates and operators, bar screens, comminutors, open-channel flow-measuring weirs, and flumes are typically required to maintain operating goals following an earthquake and should be carefully designed. Automated controls should have manual overrides. Equipment appendages (valve stands, cylinder operators, and so on) should be analyzed as cantilevers. Structures embedded in concrete (sluice-gate guide rails, bar screens, and so on) will respond as an integral part of the concrete structure; therefore, the surrounding concrete should be designed to prevent cracking and displacement so that clearances required for embedded equipment operation will be maintained.

Equipment systems often rely on secondary systems such as lubrication pumps, batteries for startup, and cooling or sealing water. While failure of one of these secondary systems may in itself be minor, the effect on the overall system could be very serious. Because these secondary systems are as critical as the primary piece of equipment they service, the same level of seismic-resistant design should be used.

Seismic qualification of equipment

Seismic design of the equipment itself is a relatively new field. Attempts to calculate the dynamic responses of equipment have met with limited success because of structural complexity, among other things. The nuclear industry requires that system components be highly reliable and requires assurance that these components will not fail when subjected to seismic motions. They have, therefore, turned to seismic qualification of the equipment for this assurance. This same concept should apply to equipment installed in water treatment facilities.

The system designer must determine which equipment should be seismically qualified. This qualification should be required for critical equipment necessary to meet immediate post-earthquake operation goals (see earlier discussion). In addition, because of possible limitations of availability of replacement equipment, consideration should be given to requiring a reasonable minimum level of seismic qualification for equipment that will be required to keep the system functioning up to 6 months after the earthquake.

Seismic qualification may be demonstrated by dynamic shake table tests, dynamic analysis, or system design team judgment based on past experience.[23] Shake table tests are designed to subject the equipment to the conditions that would be experienced during an earthquake. The equipment should be installed and operated on the shake table as it would be installed and operated in the facility, i.e., similar anchorage, connections, operating mode, and so on.

Electrical equipment

Heavy electrical equipment should be anchored to base pads or buildings, as indicated previously for mechanical equipment. Conductors and connections must be sized and sagged to allow for expected movement during an earthquake, avoiding breakage of insulators and contact between adjacent conductors. This usually means wider spacing between conductors and greater sag than in normal nonseismic design.

Flexible overhead power supplies in some facilities limited failure of electrical connections from movement of equipment during the Managua earthquake. A recommendation that adequate slack be allowed in electrical connections followed the earthquake in Kanto, Japan (1923).

The failure of electrical systems in treatment or pumping facilities can lead to severe operating problems. Secondary insulators in the main service transformers serving Managua's water supply system failed. Numerous internal electrical components were broken in Managua's industrial facilities. In the power plant at Fort Richardson, Alaska (1964), many motors were burned out, damaged by falling debris. Most burnouts probably resulted from the starting of motors under low-voltage conditions.[13]

Electrical safeguards such as the following are often provided:

- Low-voltage and single-phase protection for motors

- Pressure switches on the discharge piping to shut down pumps on low pressure (ruptured pipelines) or on high pressure (collapsed or blocked pipelines)

- Temperature switches to sense high-discharge piping temperature, as would occur from continuous water recirculation through a failed bypass pump control valve, a failed high-discharge-pressure switch, or a closed isolating valve

- Motor winding temperature detectors to sense overload motor conditions or severely unbalanced electric power phase and voltage conditions

Instrumentation and Control

Where the possibility of strong earthquakes is high, a means by which the facility can continue to operate in case of failure of the instrumentation and control system should be provided, but 100 percent redundancy for all instrumentation and control functions is not practical. Separate switching at each equipment, valve, or motor site, so that in case of damage or failure of the central control system, individual units can be manually operated if necessary, is highly desirable. This concept requires advance emergency training for operators.

This philosophy also calls for provision for manual or individual hydraulic operation of valves and gates so that loss of power does not require plant shutdown. Locally controlled hydraulic operators with accumulators are often used for this purpose.

Precision equipment, such as residual analyzers, recorders, indicators, meter electronic instrumentation, electronic switching gear, equipment instrumentation, and communications systems, should be mounted rigidly to avoid amplification of seismic accelerations. (This type of equipment is a prime candidate for shake table testing qualification because analysis usually cannot demonstrate that operating capability will survive shaking.) Positive locking devices should be used to hold circuit boards in place. All mechanical switching components, such as relays, should be tested for their seismic response characteristics. Mercury switches should be avoided.

Caution should be exercised in the use of gravity or light-duty spring-controlled switches. Relays often respond adequately in the energized position, but may fail in the nonenergized position. Caution should be exercised when using friction-restrained switches and components. Avoid mounting circuit boards on standoffs, as this may result in local resonance; additional strengthening such as welded supports should be provided. Communication equipment and instrumentation controlling critical equipment should be provided with a dedicated emergency power supply (possibly batteries) as well as the plant standby power supply and should be bolted down. All automatic control systems should have manual overrides (see discussion above). Critical installations that cannot be designed to withstand seismic motion may be supported on a floor vibration isolation system designed to attenuate seismic motions.

Laboratory and office equipment, such as stills, refrigerators, incubators, jar testing equipment, typewriters, analytical equipment (e.g., chromatographs and spectrographs) and shelving and cabinets should be anchored or restrained. Hot-water heaters should be secured against sliding or overturning and can usually be conveniently and securely strapped to adjacent walls or bulkheads. Shelving for chemicals and other stores should be provided with positive latch doors.

Power Supply

All plants require extensive electric power supplies. The ideal situation would be redundant, with power service to a facility from two sources of power so arranged that transmission lines and substation facilities come from different directions and separate sources. Where such redundancy cannot be obtained, it may be necessary to provide sufficient in-plant auxiliary power generation capability to operate the critical elements of the facility in case of a power outage. Within the plant, redundant power cables and transformers can be provided for the critical portions of the operation, with transfer switches so arranged that at least a portion of the critical facilities can continue to operate if one of the in-plant power supplies fails.

Batteries are commonly critical in disaster situations, as they may be required to provide emergency power to start generators, operate communication equipment, and operate control instrumentation. Batteries should be restrained to resist overturning, shear, and vertical forces.

Secondary power supplies should have no common components with the primary power supply, such as the main power transformer, electric poles, and feeders, and should be completely separated from the primary supply (i.e., they should have separate conduits, power panel, and similar vital elements).

If possible, standby generators should be rigidly anchored to the floor or base. The engine, generator, control panel, cooling system, and related appurtenances should all be mounted on a common base. If vibration isolation systems must be used, stops to limit movement should be employed (see Fig. 19.5). Flexible connections should be provided for the fuel, cooling water, exhaust, and electrical attachments to the generator set. Service lines should be kept short. Powered fuel-oil pumps serving the standby generator should have a backup system for filling the day tank (possibly a manual pump). Fuel lines should be protected from falling debris, and cooling-water systems should be independent of other water systems.

Maintenance practices should be adopted to minimize the possibility that sediment in the fuel supply system might be so disturbed by seismic shaking that fuel flow is obstructed.

The emergency power supply systems for elevator equipment should be given especially detailed treatment in seismic design.

Summary

The design of water treatment plants for earthquake forces is based on applied common sense and requires careful attention to detail. The first step is an assessment of vulnerability and risk, including an adequate geotechnical investigation to determine the foundation conditions and the earthquake intensity to be expected at the site. Foundations must be seismically stable. Basins and tanks are structurally designed according to recognized standards for the sloshing effect of the contained liquid, with stable foundations and backfill controlled for buried tanks. Buildings and superstructures should be simple and symmetrical, with reserve ductility and designed according to the applicable building code. Piping should be flexible. Continuous pipelines are analyzed for ground strain and designed accordingly. Connections are usually the weak link and require extensive flexibility, with particular attention to connections to structures. Equipment is vulnerable. All equipment should be anchored with carefully designed anchor bolts. Equipment on vibration isolation mounts needs to be provided with snubbers. Secondary systems serving critical equipment must also be made earthquake-resistant. Consideration should be given to seismically qualifying critical items of equipment. Hazardous materials are located in separate rooms with containers securely anchored or tied down. Electrical equipment must also be anchored, conductors well spaced and sagged, and low-voltage and temperature detectors provided. Instrumentation and control systems should be supplemented by manual on/off controls at the individual equipment sites and provided with emergency or standby operating capability. Alternative power from separate sources is desirable, and when standby power generation is called for, the generation equipment should be securely anchored and capable of fully independent operation.

Acknowledgment

The material for this chapter has been primarily taken from *Advisory Notes on Lifeline Earthquake Engineering,* a report prepared by the Technical Committees of the ASCE Technical Council on Lifeline

Earthquake Engineering, published by the American Society of Civil Engineers, New York, 1983. The text has been reviewed by the current Water and Sewage Committee of this council.

References

1. Japan Water Works Association, "Earthquake-Proof Measures for a Water Supply System," *Earthquake Resistant Design for Civil Engineering Structures, Earth Structures and Foundation in Japan,* The Japan Society of Civil Engineers, 1977, pp. 91–106.
2. NOAA/EERI Earthquake Investigation Committee, Subcommittee on Water and Sewerage Systems, "Earthquake Damage to Water and Sewerage Facilities," *San Fernando, California, Earthquake of February 9, 1971,* vol. II, U.S. Department of Commerce, National Oceanic and Atmospheric Administration, Environmental Research Laboratories, Washington, D.C., 1973, pp. 75–198.
3. American Water Works Association, *AWWA Standard for Welded Steel Tanks for Water Storage,* ANSI-AWWA D100-79, 1979.
4. M. A. Haroun and G. W. Housner, "Dynamic Analyses of Liquid Storage Tanks," *Report EERL 80-04,* California Institute of Technology, Earthquake Engineering Laboratory, Pasadena, Calif., February 1980.
5. American Concrete Institute, *Concrete Sanitary Engineering Structures,* Title no. 74-26, ACI Committee 350, Detroit, Mich., 1977.
6. *AWWA Standard for Wire-Wound Circular Prestressed-Concrete Water Tanks,* ANSI/AWWA D110-86, American Water Works Association, Denver, Colo., 1986.
7. Applied Technology Council, *Tentative Provisions for the Development of Seismic Regulations for Buildings, ATC 3-06,* Special Publication 510, National Bureau of Standards, Washington, D.C., 1978.
8. American Society of Civil Engineers, *Earthquake Damage Evaluation and Design Considerations for Underground Structures,* Los Angeles Section, Los Angeles, Calif., February 1974.
9. G. V. Berg, "Design Procedures, Structural Dynamics, and the Behavior of Structures in Earthquakes," *Proc. of U.S. National Conference on Earthquake Engineering—1975,* Earthquake Engineering Research Institute, Oakland, Calif., 1975, pp. 70–76.
10. L. R. L. Wang, "Some Aspects of Seismic Resistant Design of Buried Pipelines," *ASME 3d National Congress on Pressure Vessels and Piping,* Publication PVP-34, San Francisco, Calif., June 1979.
11. F. E. Richart, R. D. Woods, and J. R. Hall, *Vibrations of Soils and Foundations,* Prentice-Hall, Englewood Cliffs, N.J., 1970.
12. R. D. Wood, "Measurement of Dynamic Soil Properties," *Proceedings of the ASCE Specialty Conference on Earthquake Engineering and Soil Dynamics,* Pasadena, Calif., June 1978, pp. 91–178.
13. J. M. Ayers, T. Sun, and F. R. Brown, "Nonstructural Damage to Buildings," *The Great Alaska Earthquake of 1964: Engineering,* National Academy of Sciences, Washington, D.C., 1973, pp. 347–456.
14. J. M. Ayers and T. Sun, "Nonstructural Damage," *San Fernando, California, Earthquake of February 9, 1971,* vol. 1, part B, U.S. Department of Commerce, National Oceanic and Atmospheric Administration, Environmental Research Laboratories, Washington, D.C., 1973, pp. 735–776.
15. A. Klopfenstein and B. V. Palk, "Effects of the Managua Earthquake on the Electrical Power System," *Proc., Managua, Nicaragua Earthquake of December 23, 1972,* vol. II, Earthquake Engineering Institute, Oakland, Calif., November 1973, pp. 791–821.
16. *Installation of Sprinkler Systems,* NFPA Standard no. 13-78, National Fire Protection Association, Quincy, Mass., 1978.
17. P. I. Yanev, "Industrial Damage," *Proc., Managua, Nicaragua Earthquake of*

December 23, 1972, vol. II, Earthquake Engineering Research Institute, Oakland, Calif., November 1973, pp. 709–732.

18. G. W. Ferver, "Managua: Effects on Systems," *Proc., Managua, Nicaragua Earthquake of December 23, 1972,* vol. II, Earthquake Engineering Research Institute, Oakland, Calif., November 1973, pp. 885–912.

19. International Conference of Building Officials, *Uniform Building Code,* 1979 edition, Whittier, Calif., 1979.

20. D. B. Ballantyne, C. W. Pinkham, and L. W. Weinberge, "Seismic Induced Loadings on Sanitary Facilities," *Lifeline Earthquake Engineering, The Current State of Knowledge 1981,* American Society of Civil Engineers, New York, 1981, pp. 310–320.

21. Walter F. Anton, "Seismic Design of Pumping Plants," *Journal of the Technical Councils of ASCE,* American Society of Civil Engineers, New York, April 1981, pp. 1–12.

22. American Concrete Institute, *Code Requirements for Nuclear Safety Related Concrete Structures,* ACI-349-85, Detroit, Mich., 1985.

23. G. L. McGavin, "Seismic Qualification of Nonstructural Equipment in Essential Facilities," thesis presented to California State Polytechnic University, Pomona, Calif., in June 1978, in partial fulfillment of the requirements for the degree of Master of Architecture.

Bibliography

Adin, A., E. R. Bauman, and J. L. Cleasby: "The Application of Filtration Theory to Pilot-Plant Design," *Journal AWWA*, vol. 71, no. 1, January 1979, p. 17.

Alsaffar, Adnan M.: "Hydrodynamic Effects on Flow Through Screens at Intakes," *Water Research*, vol. 8, no. 9, September 1974, p. 617.

AWWA, *Handbook of Occupational Safety and Health Standards for Water Utilities*, no. 20104, American Water Works Association, Denver, Colo., August 1974.

————: *Water Fluoridation Principles and Practices*, Manual of Water Supply Practices no. M4, American Water Works Association, Denver, Colo., 1977.

Amirtharaja, A., and D. P. Wetstein: "Initial Degradation of Effluent Quality during Filtration," *Journal AWWA*, vol. 72, no. 9, September 1980, p. 518.

Anonymous: "South Carolina Water Treatment Plant—Unique Construction Approach Realizes Savings in Raw Water Intake Structure," *Water & Sewage Works*, vol. 117, no. 10, October 1971, p. 314.

Anonymous: "Water Collector Blends with the Environment," *The American City*, vol. 88, no. 3, March 1973, p. 82.

Anonymous: "System Protects Fish from Water Intake Structure," *Water & Sewage Works*, vol. 125, no. 3, March 1978, p. 63.

Argo, John W.: "Design and Installation of Intakes for Canadian Supplies," *Journal AWWA*, vol. 52, no. 1, January 1960, p. 88.

Austin, Garry H., Donald A. Gray, and Donald G. Swain: "Multilevel Outlet Works at Four Existing Reservoirs," *Journal of the Hydraulics Division (ASCE)*, vol. 95, no. HY6, November 1969, p. 1793.

Babbitt, Harold E., James J. Doland, and John L. Cleasby: *Water Supply Engineering*, 6th ed., McGraw-Hill, New York, 1962.

Bayliss, J. R.: "Experiences in Filtration," *Journal AWWA*, vol. 29, no. 7, July 1937, p. 1010.

————: "Filter Bed Troubles and Their Elimination," *Journal NEWWA*, vol. 51, no. 17, 1937.

————: "Experience with High-Rate Filtration," *Journal AWWA*, vol. 42, no. 7, July 1950, p. 687.

————: "Surges in the Flow of Water through Filters," *Pure Water*, Bureau of Water, City of Chicago, vol. 10, no. 5, May 1958.

————: "Nature and Effects of Filter Backwashing," *Journal AWWA*, vol. 51, no. 1, January 1959, p. 126.

————: "Variable Rate Filtration," *Pure Water*, Bureau of Water, City of Chicago, vol. 11, no. 5, May 1959.

————: "A Ten Year Test on High Rate Filtration," *Pure Water*, Bureau of Water, City of Chicago, vol. 29, no. 7, June 1959.

————: "Review of Filter Bed Design and Methods of Washing," *Journal AWWA*, vol. 51, no. 11, November 1959, p. 1433.

Benton, Walter B., William J. Wall, and Shelton R. McKeever: "Select Reservoir Withdrawal by Multilevel Intakes," *Journal of the Power Division (ASCE)*, vol. 96, no. PO1, January 1970, p. 109.

Bingham, George R.: "Better Water Supply for Wayne County. Development of the Metropolitan System," *Journal AWWA*, vol. 50, no. 5, May 1958, p. 665.

Carlock, Howard J.: "Design of Water Supply Structures," *Journal of the Sanitary Engineering Division (ASCE)*, paper 1682, SA 3, June 1958.

Cleasby, J. L: "Declining Rate Filtration," *Journal AWWA*, vol. 73, no. 9, September 1981, p. 484.

———: "Comparison of Alternative Systems for Controlling Flow through Filters," Committee Report, *Journal AWWA*, vol. 76, no. 1, January 1984, p. 91.

Conley, W. R., and R. W. Pitman: "Innovations in Water Clarification," *Journal AWWA*, vol. 52, no. 10, October 1960, p. 1319.

Considine, D. M.: *Process Instruments and Controls Handbook*, McGraw-Hill, New York, 1974.

Davis, Calvin Victor, and Kenneth E. Sorensen: *Handbook of Applied Hydraulics*, 3d ed., McGraw-Hill, New York, 1969.

Drinking Water and Health, Safe Drinking Water Committee, National Academy Press, Washington, D.C., 1980.

Environmental Quality Systems, Inc., *Earthquake Design Criteria for Water Supply and Wastewater Systems*, draft report, NSF Grant no. AEN77-22616, Rockville, Md., August 1980.

Fair, Gordon M., John C. Geyer, and Daniel A. Okun: *Water and Wastewater Engineering*, vol. 1, Wiley, New York, 1966.

Feben, D.: "Theory of Flow in Filter Media," *Journal AWWA*, vol. 52, no. 7, July 1960, p. 940.

Fenkell, George H.: "Water Works Intakes of the Great Lakes Region," *Journal AWWA*, vol. 16, no. 3, September 1926, p. 267.

Gisiger, Paul E.: "Safeguarding Hydro Plants Against the Ice Menace," *Civil Engineering*, vol. 17, no. 1, January 1947, p. 24.

Hardenbergh, W. A., and Edward B. Rodie: *Water Supply and Waste Disposal*, International Textbook, Scranton, Pa., 1963.

Hardin, Eugene A.: "Water Intakes in the Detroit River," *Journal of the Sanitary Engineering Division (ASCE)*, paper 1592, SA 2, April 1958.

Hudson, H.E.: "A Theory of the Functioning of Filters," *Journal AWWA*, vol. 40, no. 8, August 1948, p. 868.

———: "Operating Characteristics of Rapid Sand Filter," *Journal AWWA*, vol. 51, no. 1, January 1959, p. 114.

———: "Declining Rate Filtration," *Journal AWWA*, vol. 51, no. 11, November 1959, p. 1455.

———: "Functional Design of Rapid Sand Filters," *Journal of the Sanitary Engineering Division, ASCE*, vol. 89, no. 17, 1963.

———: *Water Clarification Processes*, Van Nostrand Reinhold, New York, 1981.

Hutchison, W. R., and P. D. Foley: "Operational and Experimental Results of Direct Filtration," *Journal AWWA*, vol. 66, no. 2, February 1974, p. 79.

Ives, K. J.: "Progress in Filtration," *Journal AWWA*, vol. 56, no. 9, September 1964, p. 1225.

Johnson, C. D.: *Process Control Instrumentation Technology*, Wiley, New York, 1977.

Kawamura, Susumu: "Design and Operation of High-Rate Filters," *Journal AWWA*, vol. 67, no. 10, October 1975, p. 535; vol. 67, no. 11, November 1975, p. 653; vol. 67, no. 12, December 1975, p. 705.

Kendall, Herman E.: "Cape Pond Intake, Floated and Sunk," *Willing Water (AWWA)*, vol. 17, no. 2, February 1973, p. 12.

Kirk, F. W., and N. R. Rimbui: *Instrumentation*, American Technical Society, Chicago, Ill., 1975.

Lake Michigan Intakes. Report on the Best Available Technology, Lake Michigan Cooling Water Intake Technical Committee, U.S. Environmental Protection Agency, PB-236112, August 1973. Distributed by National Technical Information Service, U.S. Department of Commerce, Springfield, Va.

Lal Arora, Maden: "Comparison of Commercial Filter Aids," *Journal AWWA*, vol. 70, no. 3, March 1978, p. 167.

Liptak, B. G., and R. Venczel: *Instrument Engineer's Handbook*, Chilton, Radnor, Pa., 1982.

Lloyd, S. A., and G. D. Anderson: *Industrial Process Control*, Fisher Controls Co., Marshalltown, Iowa, 1971.

Logsdon, G. S., and K. Fox: "Getting Your Money's Worth from Filtration," *Journal AWWA*, vol. 74, no. 5, May 1982, p. 249.

——— and E. C. Lippy: "The Role of Filtration in Preventing Waterborne Disease," *Journal AWWA*, vol. 74, no. 12, December 1982, p. 649.

McCormick, R. F., and P. H. King: "Factors that Affect Use of Direct Filtration in Treating Surface Waters," *Journal AWWA*, vol. 74, no. 5, May 1982, p. 234.

McDonald, Norman G.: "Water Works Intakes," *Journal AWWA*, vol. 32, no. 4, April 1940, p. 661.

McKee, D. M.: "Automatic Valveless Gravity Filters," *Journal AWWA*, vol. 54, no. 5, May 1962, p. 603.

Mintz, D. M.: "Modern Theory of Filtration," Special Project no. 10, International Water Supply Association, London, 1966.

James M. Montgomery, Consulting Engineers, Inc., *Water Treatment Principles and Design*, Wiley, New York, 1985.

Moseley, Harry H.: "Design Features of Cleveland's Nottingham Intake," *Journal AWWA*, vol. 42, no. 6, June 1950, p. 593.

Murray, Raymond H. N.: "Water Intakes in the Niagara River and Lake Ontario," *Journal of the Sanitary Engineering Division (ASCE)*, paper 1607, SA 2, April 1958.

Pakalnins, A., W. J. Cosgrove, and R. J. Lindsay: "Intake Design for the Reduction of Turbidity," *Journal AWWA*, vol. 59, no. 6, June 1967, p. 733.

Proceedings, 96th Annual Conference, *Water Plant Instrumentation and Automation*, American Water Works Association, New Orleans, 1976.

Proceedings, 185th Annual Public Water Supply Engineers' Conference, *Water Treatment, Part I*, University of Illinois College of Engineering, Champaign, Ill., 1976.

Qureshi, N.: "The Status of Direct Filtration," Committee Report, *Journal AWWA*, vol. 72, no. 7, July 1980, p. 405.

———: "Comparative Performance of Dual- and Mixed-Media Filters," *Journal AWWA*, vol. 73, no. 9, September 1981, p. 490.

———: "The Effect of Backwashing Rate on Filter Performance," *Journal AWWA*, vol. 74, no. 5, May 1982, p. 242.

Reh, Carl W.: "Lake Intakes," *Journal of the Sanitary Engineering Division (ASCE)*, paper 1465, SA 6, December 1957.

Rice, A. H.: "High-Rate Filtration," *Journal AWWA*, vol. 66, no. 4, April 1974, p. 258.

Robeck, G. G., K. A. Dostal, and R. L. Woodward: "Studies of Modification in Water Filtration," *Journal AWWA*, vol. 56, no. 2, February 1964, p. 198.

Roberts, S. B.: "How to Design River-Intake Pumphouses," *Engineering News-Record*, March 3, 1949, p. 52.

Shinsky, F. G.: *pH and pIon Control in Process and Waste Streams*, Wiley-Interscience, New York, 1973.

Shull, K. E.: "Experiences with Multiple-Bed Filters," *Journal AWWA*, vol. 57, no. 3, March 1965, p. 314.

Skeat, William Oswald: *Manual of British Engineering Practice*, 3d ed., Institution of Water Engineers, Heffer, Cambridge, England, 1961.

Stanley, D. R.: "Penetration of Floc into Sand Filters," doctoral dissertation, Harvard University, Cambridge, Mass., 1952.

State-of-the-Art Report on Intake Technologies, Tennessee Valley Authority and U.S. Environmental Protection Agency, PB 264 874, October 1976. Distributed by National Technical Information Service, U.S. Dept. of Commerce, Springfield, Va.

Steel, Ernest W., and Terence J. McGhee: *Water Supply and Sewerage*, 5th ed., McGraw-Hill, New York, 1979.

Tate, C. H., and R. R. Trussell: "Recent Developments in Direct Filtration," *Journal AWWA*, vol. 72, no. 3, March 1980, p. 165.

Turneaure, F. E., H. L. Russel, and M. Starr Nichols: *Public Water Supplies*, 4th ed., Wiley, New York, 1946.

Twort, A. C., R. C. Hoather, and F. M. Law: *Water Supply*, 2d ed., American Elsevier, New York, 1974.

U.S. Environmental Protection Agency, *Methods for Chemical Analysis of Water and Wastes*, EPA, Washington, D.C., 1974.

Urquhart, Leonard Church: *Civil Engineering Handbook*, 4th ed., McGraw-Hill, New York, 1959.

Valencia, J. A., and J. L. Cleasby: "Velocity Gradients in Granular Filter Backwashing," *Journal AWWA*, vol. 71, no. 12, December 1979, p. 732.

Wagner,, E. G., and H. E. Hudson: "Low-Dosage High-Rate Direct Filtration," *Journal AWWA*, vol. 74, no. 5, May 1982, p. 256.

Wastewater Treatment Plant Design, Manual of Practice no. 8, Water Pollution Control Federation, Washington, D.C., 1977.

Westerhoff, Garret P.: "Filter Loading, Filter Performance, and Water Quality," *Journal AWWA*, vol. 68, no. 6, June 1976, p. 310.

White, G. C., *Handbook of Chlorination*, Van Nostrand Reinhold, New York, 1972.

Whitmore, Howard, Jr., and James J. Matera: "Wachusett Intake and Power Station," *Journal New England Water Works Assoc.*, vol. 84, no. 1, March 1970, p. 73.

Wise, Carlton T., and D. D. Gillespie: "Novel Construction Concepts for Raw-Water Intake," *Civil Engineering*, vol. 41, no. 6, 1971, p. 43.

Index